THE BIRDWATCHER'S YEARBOOK 2012

Designed and published by
Hilary Cromack

Edited by
David Cromack

BUCKINGHAM PRESS LTD

In association with

SWAROVSKI
OPTIK

Published in 2011 by
Buckingham Press Ltd
55 Thorpe Park Road, Peterborough
Cambridgeshire PE3 6LJ
United Kingdom

(Tel/Fax) 01733 561 739
e-mail: admin@buckinghampress.com
www.buckinghampress.co.uk

© Buckingham Press Ltd 2011

ISBN 978-0-9569876-1-7
ISSN 0144-364 X

Cover image: Little Owls by Steve Cale.
Black and white images: by Steve Cale.
Steve Cale can be reached at 10 Fairview Drive, Colkirk, Norfolk NR21 7NT.
Tel: 01328 862 265; (M)07866 263 673; e-mail : steveshrike@aol.com
www.steve-cale-artist.co.uk

Printed and bound in Great Britain by
Information Press, Oxford UK.

CONTENTS

CONTENTS

PREFACE

REGIONAL variations in habitats and avifauna ensure that no matter where you might travel within the UK, there's a good chance of seeing some bird species that are absent, or infrequently seen, on your local patch.

This is particularly true for anyone crossing the border into Scotland. If you want to see Golden and White-tailed Eagles, Capercaillies, Crested Tits, breeding Dotterels and Red-necked Phalaropes then a trip to Scotland is a must. On top of that there is always an excellent prospect of seeing red squirrels, dolphins and whales, while in spring and autumn the northern isles are a magnet for wayward migrant birds.

Dramatic scenery in both the highlands and islands is another plus point for lowlanders, so it is no wonder there is such a regular traffic of English and Welsh birders across the border into Scotland. Of course Scotland has its native bird enthusiasts and for the past 75 years the Scottish Ornithologists' Club has been meeting their needs as well as documenting the changing birdlife of the country. We celebrate their achievement in one of this year's special features.

Conserving Britain's least developed areas is vitally important if we are to maintain maximum biodiversity, but how many people can understand the terms banded about so gaily by the environmental lobbyists and scientists?

Peter Cairns, one of the driving forces behind the 2020VISION project that is also featured in this edition, is convinced many of the messages sail over the heads of too many, so together with 19 other professional photographers, he's using his images to reach the widest possible audience at an emotional level.

As a professional journalist for more years than I care to confess, I share Peter's desire to create an end product that connects with its target audience, whether that be in the form of magazines, site guides, ID cards or the *Yearbook* itself.

With 31 years already under its belt, *The Birdwatcher's Yearbook* has clearly stood the test of time but I am concerned that we should continue to innovate, both in terms of content and presentation to ensure we fully meet the needs of our loyal readership. To that end, I hope you will e-mail me your thoughts about the features you'd like to see developed – or dropped – and other items that you'd like to see included in future editions. You can reach me at: **d.cromack@btinternet.com**

I look forward to hearing from you soon.
David Cromack (EDITOR)

THANKS: We are indebted to the staff members at reserves managed by RSPB, the Wildlife Trusts, Natural England and local councils for their enthusiastic support in updating reserves information. Hilary and I would also like to thank our other contacts for providing information for the County, National and International Directories and to the writers of our feature material – Richard Facey, Gordon Hamlett, David Jardine and Ken Shaw (SOC) and Peter Cairns (2020VISION). The magical Little Owl cover image is by Steve Cale and he has enhanced the inside pages with his black-and-white illustrations. To them all, our grateful thanks…. we couldn't do it without you.

A MESSAGE FROM THE SPONSORS OF THIS BOOK

AT A TIME when the country's economic fortunes are at a low ebb it is perhaps encouraging to learn that more people than ever are deciding to give their support to organisations promoting birds and wildlife.

The Royal Society for the Protection of Birds is close to recruiting its 1,100,000th member, while the 47 individual counties within the Wildlife Trusts partnership has seen membership soar past 800,000 in 2011, a remarkable performance.

For the past ten years there have been a succession of record attendances at the annual British Birdwatching Fair at Rutland Water, with thousands of pounds being raised for bird conservation around the globe.

These statistics all reinforce the view that Britain has more commited birdwatchers and nature lovers per head of population than any other country. Whether you are an 'old hand' with years of fieldwork under your belt or a newcomer to the hobby, *The Birdwatcher's Yearbook* is designed to meet all your information needs and Swarovski Optik is delighted to be celebrating its tenth year of sponsorship of this invaluable publication.

Swarovski's goal is to continually improve our binoculars, telescopes and other products through innovation and attention to detail, an ethos shared by Buckingham Press in the production of this book. I'm sure that as you look through its pages you will be astounded by the amount of information crammed into each section. Put it to the test: I feel confident that whatever you need to know – from the meeting places of local bird clubs, your nearest optics dealer or tide-tables for the next 15 months – you'll find it in the *Yearbook*. Happy birding.

Peter Antoniou
Country Manager, UK & Eire
Swarovski Optik UK

SWAROVSKI
OPTIK

FEATURES

David Cromack

Whooper Swans on Flemington Loch, near Inverness – just part of the huge influx of wildfowl into Scotland each winter. In this edition, we celebrate 75 years of the Scottish Ornithologists' Club.

BRINGING NATURE TO THE MASSES

Nature photographer Peter Cairns introduces 2020VISION, an exciting new concept in the delivery of crucial conservation messages.

IT APPEARS that 42% of UK respondents in a recent Gallup poll had never heard of biodiversity and only 27% knew what it meant. Now either I'm missing something, or these are alarming statistics. But wait, it gets worse. Not only are we already up against societal indifference, we're now proffering a fresh paradigm: Ecosystem thinking.

Instead of a fragmented sea of the traditional species-specific nature reserves, conservation science is now suggesting we need to be much bolder, more ambitious and repair whole ecosystems on a landscape-scale. It makes absolute sense of course, but how do we convey a concept measured over hundreds of square miles and spanning decades, if not centuries?

During a recent presentation to an audience of conservation scientists, I introduced a chap called Steve. Steve's a plumber from Hemel Hempstead, his wife works and their teenage children are both doing what teenage children do. Steve's busy and constantly has to juggle work with the demands of his family. His only respite is Saturday night in front of the telly with a take-away.

I asked the audience whether it's likely that Steve understood the term ecosystem services or ecological connectivity, two pieces of jargon that are presently doing the rounds in the conservation press. What about trophic cascades? And even if he understands, is he really that interested? Steve is of course fictitious, and I'm not suggesting that every plumber is nature-averse, but he's nevertheless representative of the archetypal values of modern society, a society with which the patronising finger-wagging of traditional conservation-speak, has failed to connect. It's time to reinvent how we communicate.

Conservation communication needs a fresh approach. It needs to reach beyond scientific peer groups,

The sight of a Short-eared Owl hunting will entrance even the most casual of viewers, but to capture a great images often takes some effort. Danny Green, who took this picture in Lincolnshire, explains: "With two feet of snow on the ground, I am indebted to my friend's 4WD and snow chains that got me on location where up to eight Shorties and several Barn Owls were hunting. This individual proved to be especially confiding allowing me to approach to within a few metres - a fantastic experience."

BRINGING NATURE TO THE MASSES

beyond the affluent leafy lanes of middle-class, middle-England, beyond the already converted. It needs to entertain as well as engage; it needs to not only educate but to motivate; it needs to touch what science considers the untouchable: our emotions. It needs to trade in a common currency that has been used for decades to influence consumer patterns and social perspectives. It needs to better invest in visual and creative media. OK, as a photographer, I have a vested interest here, but if you won't take it from me, take it from a scientist: "Perhaps our (conservationists) role in society is not to have all the answers nor as we may have often felt, to overburden people with technical persuasion, but to motivate people by communicating in terms that connect with their value systems." – Dr Mark Everard, *The Environmentalist*

This doesn't mean dumbing down critical societal messages, it means recognising that different audiences need different approaches based on different values. A couple of years ago I was approached by a leading conservation organisation and asked whether I had any ideas as to how 'ecosystem thinking', something that is now being promoted at a political level, could be popularised and delivered to Steve the Plumber. I got a few mates together and we hatched the embryo of a plan. Fast forward 12 months and 2020VISION is set to become the most ambitious meeting of science and visual communication Britain has ever staged. Now that's quite a claim, but rewilding Britain is a big job, so it has to be sold to a big audience.

The value of a wilder Britain, where ecosystems function as they should, has not yet been communicated on a scale such as this. 2020VISION bridges that gap using the motivational language of inspiring photography and film, a language in which everyone can find relevance.

Backed by some of Britain's most influential conservation bodies, for the first time, 2020VISION brings together 20 of the UK's top nature photographers, along with videographers, sound engineers, writers and designers. Their job? To produce the most compelling case yet for restoring Britain's battered ecosystems.

For 20 months those 20 photographers will document the story of 20 flagship projects where people and wildlife are coming back together; where ecosystems are being restored and re-connected; where the vital services we all depend upon are being secured for our long-term prosperity.

The result of this epic initiative will be a unique image bank – stills and video – of Britain's natural systems and the services they supply. Responding to the question that is often asked of nature: 'What's in it for me?' 2020VISION will inspire and motivate; it will engage and educate.

2020VISION is about far more than producing a pretty set of images, says Terry Whittaker, who shot this picture of young visitors to Rutland Water building an Osprey nest. "It aims to connect people with nature and helps communicate why it is in everyone's interest to restore habitat on a large scale, not just for the benefit of wildlife but for us all."

BRINGING NATURE TO THE MASSES

Why 2020? Well it's a snazzy media hook – 20 photographers, 20 assignments…but we're in a hurry because by 2020, a new generation of decision makers will be in place, dealing with the legacy of what we do today. The cost of the banking collapse will pale alongside that of ecosystem collapse if we don't start repairing and reconnecting the systems we've borrowed too heavily from for too long.

So what's the bottom line? We need to establish in the public mind the crucial link between our well-being and a wilder Britain – to show that healthy ecosystems are not an optional add-on, but something fundamental to every person in the land. This is not about some birds or trees, this is about us. It's about securing the

Photographers submitting work to the 2020VISION image bank provide us with images most of us would not have the patience to achieve ourselves. Mark Hamblin reports: "I'd been in the hide on the Glen Tanar Estate in Scotland for more than five hours when I heard the distant call of the male Hen Harrier, signifying he had food. The female flew up from the nest in the deep heather and within seconds returned with prey for the young chicks. The whole event lasted for less than a minute, before I settled down for another five hour wait!"

supply of things we need to keep us alive: fresh water, clean air, productive soils, and lots of other stuff. 2020VISION will deliver its message using inspirational images wrapped in a narrative that is simple, clear and motivational. No bad news. No guilt. No lecturing.

2020VISION is attracting growing support from some of Britain's most influential conservation organizations. The project has always been founded upon collaboration and the pooling of resources to achieve something more than any single organization could achieve in isolation. Moving forward to the output stage, this partnership working is even more important than ever; we simply can't deliver this on our own.

The same effort that goes in to the creation of our material will go into making it accessible and having it seen. By everyone. So that means on the web and TV, in street exhibitions and at festivals and concerts. Oh, and in good old fashioned print too. From July 2012 onwards, 2020VISION will be seen across the country in a multi-city roadshow aimed at a diverse audience. But we need to work together. None of this will be possible without true collaboration; without breaking down the barriers between different disciplines and leaving agendas, egos and politics at the door.

2020VISION can signal the dawn of a new era in conservation communication but it's a project that needs investment – financial, logistical and yes, emotional – in order to provide a return that benefits everyone. Including Steve and his family. And his mates. And the bloke that cleans his windows. And that bloke's granny. You get the idea.
To learn more visit: **www.2020V.org**

ORNITHOLOGICAL NEWS HEADLINES

Richard Facey joins Editor David Cromack to present a round-up of significant news stories from the past 12 months. Illustrations by Steve Cale.

NEW BIRD SPECIES UNCOVERED IN THE LAB

THE MOST RECENT additions to the list of world bird species demonstrate that only a proportion of the new discoveries come from the efforts of intrepid birders delving into unexplored territories.

For instancem scientists in the journal *Zootaxa* have described a completely new species of Malagasy Rail, *Mentocrex beankaensis*, a ground-dwelling bird that has made its home in Madagascar's dry forests. The bird has been well-known to locals, but it took DNA analysis by Chicago's Field Museum and the University of Antananarivo to distinguish this species from a related *Mentocrex* rail in the east of the island.

The Danum Valley Conservation Area in Sabah, Malaysia attracts many tourists and scientists, but the rainforest still has surprises left. In June an employee with a tour company came upon a bird species entirely unknown to science. Richard Webster discovered a bird he didn't recognize feeding on mistletoe berries. He took photos of the individual and later shared them with Dr David Edwards, an ornithologist from Leeds University who has been studying birds in the area for three years.

Over the next few days Webster, Edwards, and Rose Ann Rowlett found two more individuals of the unknown bird, now named Spectacled Flowerpecker, and listened to one singing. Since then there have been no more sightings of the species. The discovery was published in the Oriental Bird Club's magazine, *BirdingASIA*. The species has not yet received a scientific name.

In September 2011 it was announced that a bird rediscovered in Bolivia in 2000, after an absence of almost 100 years, is a distinct species. According to a recently published article in America's *Wilson Journal of Ornithology*, the Palkachupa Cotinga was initially thought to be a subspecies of the Swallow-tailed Cotinga, which is found in Brazil, but with further study, it became clear it deserved full species status.

The Palkachupa Cotinga is endemic to Bolivia, and is likely to be classed as Critically Endangered due to its small population (600-800 individuals) and restricted geographic range. The special forest the species requires has been devastated over the last 100 years, leaving the species struggling for survival on the remaining fragments of woodlands.

Another new species declared in August 2011 comes after work by genetic scientists at the Smithsonian National Zoological Park studying a specimen collected in 1963 on Midway Atoll, Northwestern Hawaiian Islands. The new species, Bryan's Shearwater (*Puffinus bryani*), is named after Edwin Horace Bryan Jr, curator of collections at the B.P. Bishop Museum in Honolulu from 1919 until 1968.

ORNITHOLOGICAL NEWS HEADLINES

This small shearwater is the first new species reported from the United States and Hawaiian Islands since the Po' ouli was discovered in the forests of Maui in 1974. Reports of small, unidentified shearwaters from Japan, California and the southern Gulf of Alaska may represent Bryan's Shearwater sightings.

KEEPING TRACK OF MIGRANTS IN AFRICA

DESPITE its sometimes controversial nature, ringing still provides valuable information, such as survival data, which cannot be collected by other techniques. There have been, however, great advances in the technology that can be used to track bird movements over long distances. Terms such as data loggers and geolocators are now commonplace and several high profile projects have caught the imagination of the general public.

In 2009, BTO scientists, with colleagues from the Swiss Ornithological Institute, caught and tagged 20 Nightingales with geolocators in the UK. These tiny devices weigh less than 1gm and record the time of sunrise and sunset at regular intervals which, after some clever mathematics, are converted into longitude and latitude, revealing the route taken by the bird carrying the device.

Of the 20 birds tagged, only seven returned in 2010 and just one device carried on functioning until February 2010, revealing the details of the bird's incredible journey. By late July the Nightingale had left its breeding territory and passed through France, before making it to Morroco by late August. Here it took its time, possibly refuelling, taking three weeks before it resumed its journey down the west coast of Africa.

It apparently made a brief stop-over in Western Sahara before making it to Senegal or Guinea-Bissau by the end of December where it spent its winter. By February it had started its trek north again but here its techno-cargo failed. However, the bird made it back, being re-caught 50m from where it had been ringed in 2009.

While more tracking of Nightingales is planned for 2012 (which you can help fund by donating to the BTO's Nightingale Appeal), BTO scientists spent a large part of 2011 tracking another, larger migrant, the Cuckoo, to unravel questions

Satallite transmitters attached to Cuckoos have revealed the birds are capable of travelling an average 143 miles a day on their journeys to sub-Saharan Africa.

such as the route the birds take to Africa and when they arrive in their wintering grounds.

Five gram GPS satellite tags were used to track five Cuckoos. These devices allow their carrier's journey to be followed in near real time. The tags transmit for ten hours before entering a 'sleep mode' while their battery charges via a solar panel for 48 hours.

Within weeks the tags were yielding astonishing information. One bird, nicknamed Clement, was recorded at its site of trapping, the BTO's Nunnery Lakes reserve, on June 2 but three days later was 100 miles south of Paris. Meanwhile, Martin stayed in the vicinity of his tagging location until June 25, but by June 30 he had travelled 715km.

At the time of writing, all five Cuckoos (Chris, Lyster and Kasper are the remaining names) had successfully crossed the Sahara and four were taking up residence in the Sub-Saharan savannah zone.

These tags have already shown that 'our' Cuckoos don't have neighbourly instincts when abroad; despite being trapped within 70km of each other in the UK, they are separated by more than 3,600km in their winter homes. The movements can be followed by following the links on the BTO's website **www.bto.org**

SMALL SUCCESSES LIFT RED LIST GLOOM

THE ANNUAL stock-take of the world's birds, in the form of BirdLife international's 2011 update of the IUCN Red List, shows that 1,253 species (12%) are considered threatened with extinction, though the number of species believed to be extinct in the wild remains unchanged at four.

The status of 67 species was revised in the 2011 assessment, and the good news is that the situation of 20 has improved. The descriptively-named Elusive Anitpitta and Maderia Laurel Pigeon are among those species which have been moved to the list of species of Least Concern. However, as many of the revisions result from changes in knowledge or the taxonomy, it is difficult to draw conclusions from the Red List revisions.

A quick look at the Red List Index is far more revealing, as this has the unenviable job of showing the rate at which the world's bird species are declining. Since 1988 the health of the world's birds has been steadily decreasing but looking on the bright side, category changes in 2011 included six which were improvements.

Among these increasing species is the Pale-headed Brush-finch. Although the species range is incredibly restricted (a small corner of Ecuador), its population has been increasing steadily since 2003 as a result of protecting habitat and even the control of nest parasites. However, with a population of less than 250 mature individuals, the species' future is far from secure.

SLIMBRIDGE LIFELINE FOR ENDANGERED SANDPIPER

INTENSIVE conservation efforts are often key to aiding a threatened species. One such species which made headlines in the last 12 months is the Spoon-billed Sandpiper, which was declared Critically Endangered in 2008. This distinctively billed wader is under attack from all sides. The main threat of unsustainable levels of subsistence hunting is being augmented by habitat loss in the birds' breeding and wintering grounds and along the species' 8,000km migration flyway.

ORNITHOLOGICAL NEWS HEADLINES

The numbers of Spoonbill Sandpipers able to raise chicks in the wilds of Russia continue to fall, so a captive rearing programme is thought to be the best way to stop the species becoming extinct.

Add in the effects of a changing climate and it is no wonder that the species' extremely small population (less than 200 pairs) is rapidly declining at approximately 26% per year. What population remains is aging rapidly because both fledging success and juvenile recruitment are very low. Extinction could be a matter of a decade away without intervention.

A team of conservationists, led by the Wildfowl & Wetlands Trust and Bird Russia, working alongside the RSPB, BTO, BirdLife International, ArcCona, the Spoon-billed Sandpiper Task Force and Moscow Zoo, headed to Russia's far east in 2011 to collect eggs, then hatch and rear chicks to establish a captive population.

This will form the source of birds for re-introduction once the threats in the wild have been sufficiently reduced. A captive population will also safeguard the species' existence should it go extinct in the wild in the meantime.

Spoonbill Sandpiper breeding grounds in Chukotka were scoured for nests and it proved to be a fruitful year, with the team finding enough nests to collect 20 eggs. Things began to progress more rapidly than expected – the first eggs began to hatch before the team departed and by the time the boat had docked at Anadyr they had an amazing 17 chicks and just three unhatched eggs!

Ultimately these chicks, the first of the species to hatch in captivity, will form the beginnings of a conservation breeding programme based at WWT's Slimbridge reserve. There the progeny will form the basis for releases which are unlikely to start until 2018 at the earliest.

At the time of writing at least one chick has died but this is nothing compared to the level of mortality in the wild. Only four out of every 20 chicks survives to fledge, and only one of these four returns to bolster the breeding population. If you want to know more about the efforts to secure the future of this distinctive and enigmatic species visit **www.wwt.org.uk/files/Misc-2/SBS.pdf**

ORNITHOLOGICAL NEWS HEADLINES

BLUE TITS TOP THE RINGING CHARTS

BRITISH BIRD RINGERS created a new milestone in 2010 when they ringed more than a million individual birds – it was the first time in the British Trust for Ornithology's (BTO) ringing scheme's 100-year history that the million mark has ever been topped in a single year.

In a normal year, the BTO's 2,700 ringers will ring around 800,000 birds but thanks to a bumper crop of young birds in 2010 (as revealed by the scheme's 120 Constant Effort Sites) their combined efforts saw 1,047092 birds ringed.

Two birds vive for the accolade of being the millionth bird ringed in 2010; a Coal Tit, from Raglan in Gwent and a Scottish Yellowhammer ringed near Collieston, Aberdeenshire were both fitted with a uniquely numbered ring at 2pm on December 5.

More than 260 species were ringed in Britain and Ireland and while a few rarities, such as Red-eyed Vireo, Blackpoll Warbler, and Black-throated Thrush crept into the list, the top five positions were dominated by garden birds. Unsurprisingly, the top spot was taken by the ever tenacious Blue Tit with 142,729 ringed in 2010 compared to 100,501 in 2009; CES reported a 50% increase in the species' productivity during 2010 compared to previous years! Great Tit, Chaffinch, Swallow and Blackbird were the next most commonly ringed species.

Data on bird movements using traditional metal rings, only comes from the recoveries of ringed birds, and 2010 also saw record number of ringed birds being found. Nearly 17,000 were reported to the BTO, helping to generate the important information that makes ringing one of the most important tools in bird conservation. If you find a ringed bird then please report it at **www.ring.ac** and help unravel the changes in our bird populations.

LIFE IS TOUGH FOR EUROPE'S FARM BIRDS

FARMLAND BIRD populations all over Europe are at an all-time low according to the Pan-European Common Bird Monitoring Scheme. Compiling population figures for 145 common species in 25 European countries between 1980 and 2009, it reveals farmland birds are the most threatened group, with 20 out of 36 species in decline.

Overall numbers are at an all-time low, down by

Urgent action is needed to halt the decline in farmland birds such as Grey Partridge – the European population has plummeted by more than 80 per cent in the past 30 years.

15

48% since 1980. Some of the species that have declined the most over the last three decades include Grey Partridge (minus 82%), Skylark (minus 46%), Linnet (minus 62%) and Corn Bunting (minus 66%).

Conservationists say the results prove the need for urgent reform of the Common Agricultural Policy (CAP) so that it rewards and encourages farmers who put conservation measures in place on their land.

The results of the European bird population survey suggest that after missing its 2010 biodiversity conservation target, the EU will go on to miss the 2020 biodiversity conservation target unless decisive and urgent action is taken.

MARBLED TEAL FLOCKS HERALD IRAQ MARSH RECOVERY

THE REGENERATION of Iraq's Mesopotamian Marshes, a project led by Azzad Alwash, the CEO of BirdLife Affiliate Nature Iraq, is a good news story to emerge from that troubled region.

The marshlands, one of the most extensive wetland ecosystems in western Eurasia, was home to a rich diversity of life, including a number of endemic and threatened bird species until Saddam Hussein drained the area to punish the indigenous Marsh Arab tribes who had risen against him after the first Gulf War.

Within months, the marshes, which had covered 15,000 square kilometres, were reduced to less than 10% of their original size and wildlife populations collapsed. Now large sections of the marshes have been restored, and in places the reedbeds once again stretch as far as the eye can see.

Among the highlights is a sighting of a large flock of Globally Vulnerable Marbled Teal in an area where they have not been seen for 20 years. In winter 2010, Nature Iraq counted 46,000 Marbled Teal in the marshes, around twice the previous estimate of the entire global population.

Nature Iraq's six winter and six summer surveys of the Southern Marshes since 2005 show that the endemic and Globally Endangered Basra Reed Warbler has increased in numbers, while the endemic Iraq Babbler is increasing its range in the marshes and along the Tigris and Euphrates, and spreading into neighbouring countries.

The surveys have revealed that the marshes are also very important for migrant Black-tailed Godwits, breeding Ferruginous Ducks and wintering Eastern Imperial Eagles and Greater Spotted Eagles – all globally threatened species.

WILDFIRES MAY AID SOME BIRD SPECIES

ANYONE SEEING film of the wildfires that ravaged Arizona and New Mexico in 2011 could be forgiven for thinking that they must have a devastating effect on wildlife and birds, but a new study, conducted by Baylor University, comes to a different conclusion.

ORNITHOLOGICAL NEWS HEADLINES

The researchers say that fire actually helps some bird species because of the habitat that is formed after a fire is positive for the bird's prey needs. The study found that three specific bird species in the Chihuahuan Desert – Scaled Quail, Loggerhead Shrike and Rock Wren – will be less affected by current and future wildfires because climate change will dry out the landscape, changing pine forests to uplands without trees and grasses, which provides fuel for wildfires.

The drying out of grasslands means the likelihood of widespread and intense wildfires will decrease over the next 50 years and the birds will be able to forage for prey more easily in the new environment. To conduct the study, the Baylor researchers observed birds over three years in their habitat at more than 70 locations in west Texas and eastern New Mexico. The researchers then used that data and combined it with satellite imagery and used a predictive model to calculate what will happen to the bird species over the next 50 years.

UK HARRIERS NEED MORE HELP

THE ILLEGAL persecution of Hen Harriers in parts of Britain is not only detrimental to local populations but could be preventing the expansion of the species' range. This is among the conclusions made in a report which considered scientific evidence on the species' ecology across the four home countries. The last UK survey for Hen Harrier, conducted in 2004, estimated 633 pairs in Scotland, 11 pairs in England, 43 pairs in Wales, 63 pairs in Northern Ireland, with another 50 pairs on the Isle of Man. According to the report, based on modelling, the UK's potential population could be more than 2,500 pairs.

Illegal persecution was found to be the most significant constraint on Hen Harriers in some areas but not in others. For example, in England persecution is such a problem that Hen Harrier faces extinction as a breeding bird. However, harrier populations in Wales, Northern Ireland and the Isle of Man are continuing to increase. In the Hen Harrier's UK stronghold of Scotland, persecution was a particular problem in the north-east and central Highlands, areas with managed grouse moors.

Scotland has seen an upsurge in the illegal poisoning of birds of prey: statistics published by Science and Advice for Scottish Agriculture showed that 16 birds of prey were illegally poisoned in the first half of 2010 alone. However, in March 2011, the Scottish Parliament gave its backing to the Wildlife and Natural Environment (Scotland) Bill, which updated much of the country's wildlife laws. This included the creation of a new 'vicarious liability offence' meaning those who manage or control employees involved in the illegal prosecution of wildlife are liable for prosecution themselves.
Harrier report: (http://www.jncc.gov.uk/pdf/jncc441.pdf) by the Joint Nature Conservation Committee (JNCC).

CHARTING A LONG HISTORY OF BIRDING SUCCESS IN SCOTLAND

In celebrating its 75th anniversary, the Scottish Ornithologists' Club can look back on many successes, but its plans for the future are equally important. Club president David Jardine and vice-president Ken Shaw recount the club's steady progress since 1936.

BACK IN 1936, when the decision to form the Scottish Ornithologists' Club was taken, the Crested Tit (which was to become the club emblem) had a small restricted population and its biology in Britain was relatively poorly known. Just like its emblem, which has increased in range and population size, the club it represents has grown, along with the understanding of both the Crested Tit and of Scotland's avifauna. In 2011, the SOC, Scotland's Bird Club, celebrated its 75th Anniversary.

'Early in 1936 a meeting was held in Edinburgh attended by Miss Baxter, Miss Rintoul, H F D Elder and George Waterston, where it was resolved that steps should be taken to found a national (bird) club'. This is how Ian Pennie describes the important decision made to form the SOC, which held its first meeting on January 14, 1937, in Edinburgh, and was attended by 80% of the founder members.

Formed out of the Midlothian Ornithological Club, the SOC's founding members were instrumental in the establishment of some of the most important developments in Scottish (and arguably British) ornithology.

Following the Second World War, George Waterston, along with Ian Pitman and Sir Arthur Duncan, was the driving force behind the establishment of the Fair Isle Bird Observatory, which over the years has added to much to our knowledge of migrant birds (and notably also about seabirds), not to mention its impressive number of additions to the British list.

George Waterston was also behind the decision to open up the Osprey nest at Loch Garten to visitors in the 1950s, thus helping popularise birdwatching and establishing a focus for those who take regular birding holidays (or ecotourism as it is now termed) in the Scottish Highlands to see specialities such as Dotterel, Golden Eagle, Osprey, Capercaillie, Scottish Crossbill and, of course, Crested Tit.

Waterston House, the club's headquarters, not only stages a regular programme of wildlife art exhibitions, but is conveniently located overlooking the birding hotspot of Aberlady Bay.

CHARTING A LONG HISTORY OF BIRDING SUCCESS IN SCOTLAND

In the early years the findings of the club and its members were published in the *Scottish Naturalist*, but following the publication of Scotland's first avifauna in 1953, by the good ladies (Baxter & Rintoul), it introduced its own journal *Scottish Birds* in 1958. This was followed a decade later, in 1968, by the first *Scottish Bird Report*, which annually has documented populations and important sighting in Scotland.

A. Allen

Encouraging new generations to take an interest in birds is an important part of the SOC's mission – here Dave Allen and Keith MacGregor of the Lothian branch lead a birding class for beginners.

With the growth of SOC local branches, an increasing number of bird reports are now published for the local recording areas developed by the Scottish Birds Record Committee. This body considers observations at the sub-BBRC level, but of significance in Scotland. Recently work has been taking place to move all the previous reports onto a database to provide an electronic *Scottish Bird Report* housed on the club website.

As well as providing centrally for its 2,500 members from its headquarters through publications and its website, the club has 14 branches spread between West Galloway and Orkney which organise the series of local outings and winter lectures.

So what makes birding north of the border so special for members of the SOC?

In the formative years of the club migration studies had been led by pioneering work on the east coast at the Isle of May and then shortly afterwards in the Northern Isles. Recently, greater attention has been paid to the Hebrides, off Scotland's west coast, where Northern Parula, the latest addition to the Scottish List (now 518 species), was found in September 2010.

Such work has also shown that some species as the White-billed Diver, previously considered to be a national rarity considered by BBRC, are in fact annual migrants if looked for in the correct places under suitable conditions.

However exciting migrants are, Scotland punches above its weight internationally both for its very important breeding seabirds and also for wintering waders and wildfowl. With over two and half million pairs of seabirds, it is the place to visit in summer; over half of the world's Great Skuas breed here and around a third of its Manx Shearwaters and Gannets.

On the other hand, few wildlife spectacles in Britain can match the gathering of geese at sundown at such magical places as Caerlaverock and Bridgend, Islay (Barnacle) or Aberlady, Loch Leven and the Loch of Strathbeg (Pink-footed). In a British context, Scotland's woods and forests, which represent 17% of the land cover. are also perhaps a more important refuges for red-data birds such as Song Thrush, Willow Warbler and Tree Pipit than generally recognised.

It was also not surprising that the Raptor Research Foundation held its first conference outside North America in Pitlochry in 2009, as Scotland holds internationally important populations of Golden Eagle, Hen Harrier and Peregrine, even if these birds continue to have problems from those who seek to persecute them.

The SOC has proved to be, and continues to be, a progressive club. In 2002 it moved out of its long-time home in Edinburgh, situated close to the new parliament building, to new premises next to one of Scotland's premier bird reserves at Aberlady Bay. It is now based in the eco-friendly Waterston House, opened in 2005, where a prestigious gallery exhibits works of wildlife artists throughout the year.

In 2007, a new avifauna, *The Birds of Scotland* (affectionately known as BS3 within the club, as it was the third such published) came into print. This impressive 1,700 page, two-volume tome provided the club with

Professor Maury Meiklejohn was the first editor of the SOC Journal, *Scottish Birds.*

Ian Andrews

Through the years the SOC has had many characters, who have enlivened the birdwatching scene north of the border, perhaps none more so than Professor M aury Meiklejohn, the professor of Italian at Glasgow University, who contributed regular pieces under the initial 'MFMM' to the *Glasgow Herald* for two decades. It was MFMM who, on September 20, 1949 on the Isle of May, first described a British species novum which has subsequently been found by every keen birder in the country: the Hoodwink *Dissumulatrix spuria*.

It is worth reflecting on some of the key characteristics of this elusive species:

• **Field characteristics and general habits:** Elusive, usually only a glimpse of part of the back obtained. Only perches beyond the range of strong binoculars. Polymorphic but usually unbridled. Marked power of mimicry, but when mimicking one of two similar species will always choose the rarer; eg Collared rather than Pied Flycatcher, Greenish rather than Willow Warbler.

• **Description:** General plumage buffish-tan shading to tannish-buff. Soft parts (ie the hard parts) pinkish horn shading to hornish pink.

• **Voice:** A loud explosive '*burp*', similar to that of the Murky Crosspatch *(Morosa morosa morosa)*, perhaps the same sound as that rendered by a Sledgehammer and other writers as '*twerp, twerp*'.

• **Song:** a melodious '*teww-twee-swee-swee-brrr*', also laughingly described by Sledgehammer as resembling the words 'See you outside the Odeon Saturday' uttered in a Murrayfield accent.

• **Habitat:** Varied, but always close to cover (eg cliffs, lighthouses, lunatic asylums) into which it can slip at the approach of a bird-lover.

With the growth in rarity hunting among Scottish and British birders it would be helpful to know whether there has been an increase in sightings of *D.spuria*; one suspects so, but fortunately these may have been suppressed!

CHARTING A LONG HISTORY OF BIRDING SUCCESS IN SCOTLAND

a particular impetus and a fund created from its successes will be used to further ornithological publications in Scotland.

In the last few years the SOC has worked closely with the British Trust for Ornithology (along with funding from Scottish Natural Heritage), through the Building Bird Monitoring in Scotland project to increase the numbers of contributors to regular surveys. This has been done through events which build the confidence of observers in identification and in survey techniques.

EVELYN VIDA BAXTER

LEONORA JEFFREY RINTOUL

Miss Leonora Rintoul and Dr Evelyn Baxter were elected joint founding presidents when the club was launched in 1936. Together they published the ground-breaking *Birds of Scotland* 17 years later.

Following on from this the SOC, joined the BirdTrack partnership and has helped develop this significantly, through the introduction of a validation process for records and also the introduction of the ability to record a greater levels of detail on sightings, thus providing birdwatchers with their own on-line records database.

The back issues of the club journal have recently been put on-line on the website, (**http://www.the-soc.org.uk/scottish-birds-online.htm**) to make them available to all, providing an invaluable resource on Scotland's birds. The most recent all-colour issues contain peer-reviewed papers on Scotland's birds, club news, articles on birds and conservation, along with the latest birding news. This 'broad church' publication is available only to club members.

The Crested Tit, which in the 1930s was restricted to a few woodlands that had avoided devastation by the efforts to provide timber during the First World War, has subsequently significantly expanded its range into newly created forests and now has a population of an estimated 1,000-2,000 pairs. Similarly, the Club which it represents has grown strongly during its first 75 years and it looking forward to its centennial celebrations!

David Jardine & Ken Shaw
SOC President & Vice President

BEST BIRD BOOKS OF THE YEAR

Experienced book reviewer Gordon Hamlett sifts through the releases from the past 12 months to bring you his selection of the top titles.

ROMAN PROVERB '*Tempora mutantur, nos et mutamur in illis*' translates as '*times change, and we change with them*'. Or, rather more prosaically, and to misquote Star Trek's Mr Spock, 'they're books Jim, but not as we know them.'

Three developments this year could alter the way we view our bird books. For some reason, carrying a fieldguide has always been seen as something of a badge of shame; it's something only real beginners do. The rest of us are supposed to take a full set of notes and check the mystery bird when we get back to the car or return home.

However, it seems that it is perfectly OK to use your phone as a replacement for the paper product. The advent of smart phones has brought forth a plethora of applications, known as 'apps'. In the last year, I've seen more people using the most popular of these (**www. birdguides.com/products/appneuro/**) than I've seen carrying the new *Collins Bird Guide*.

Though the illustrations are currently nowhere as good as the Collins guide, you do get far more text – the contents of the *Concise Birds of the Western Palearctic* – plus loads of photos of nests and birds in flight etc. and a full collection of songs and calls.

This last feature is open to abuse though. I've seen people playing the calls of scarce birds such as Quail, Spotted Crake, Nightjar and Golden Oriole in an attempt to lure birds out into the open, despite the fact that tape luring birds in this way is strictly illegal.

Looking a few years down the line, you can foresee an app that not only helps identify the birds (and other wildlife), but also records your sightings precisely, using satnav, and then emails them off to the BTO for their BirdTrack database.

If the future of fieldguides is changing, then what of text books? The key word here is 'Kindle', a device for reading electronic books or e-books. Originally sold by Amazon, these readers are proving so popular that Tesco has just started stocking them. Already, analysts reckon we are now downloading more books than buying hard copies.

One of the best known bird book publishers – A&C Black – has jumped on this particular bandwagon. Most of the superb Poyser series of monographs can be downloaded and if you are not sure about any title, you can download a sample chapter from each book for free. Check out the article on websites (starts on page 27) for a link.

Next year will see many more publishers rushing to compete for this new market. If you hunt around, then there are quite a few out-of-copyright natural history titles available online that can be downloaded for free.

My only gripe, and this applies to all publishers, is that the prices for downloading these titles tends to match that of a printed copy. This cannot be right. The cost of an electronic version has to be substantially less than the cost of paper, binding and printing a hard copy. In the same way as happened to recorded music, expect prices for e-books to fall over the coming years.

BEST BIRD BOOKS OF THE YEAR

A lot of this, it has to be said, has passed me by. I am sufficiently old fashioned that when I buy a compact disc or book, I prefer to have something physical to hold in my hot little hand rather than an intangible digital version.

My bookshelves groan under the weight of a multitude of titles. Nevertheless there are still many gaps in my collection, not least, all those rare Poyser and New Naturalist titles that I can't afford. Well, help is on hand, as both imprints now offer a 'print-on-demand' service, allowing you to buy a one-off copy.

How much this appeals to you depends on whether you want the book simply to read, or as part of a collection. Collectors must have first editions and these facsimiles just won't do. As for me, I'm off to the second-hand bookshop again.

Despite all this talk of second-hand books, there are still many new titles to consider. Here's the pick of last year's crop.

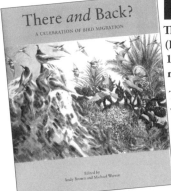

ART AND LITERATURE

The biggest book of the year is *There and Back?* (Brown and Warren, Langford Press, hb, ISBN 978-1-904078-37-1, £50), subtitled a celebration of bird migration.

The splendid assortment of pictures comes from a whole range of artists, while a multitude of authors discuss various aspects of migration.

My only cavil is that the book feels as if it was rushed out in time for an exhibition; the proof-reading falls well below the publisher's usual meticulous standards, but the ambition of this attractive book is to be applauded.

The subject of mankind's relationship with birds is endlessly fascinating. *Topics in Life with Birds* (Smith, **Whittles Publishing, pb, ISBN 978-1-84995-028-2, £18.99)** include birds in warfare and birds as food so make for an interesting read, even if the author's sarcastic tone soon begins to grate.

Vulture (van Dooren, Reaktion Books, pb, ISBN 978-1-86189-806-7, £9.99) is the latest title looking at the natural and cultural histories of a particular species or family of animals. With more than 100 illustrations, collectors of this series need not hesitate.

On Rare Birds (Albus, Saraband, hb, ISBN 978-1-188735480-6, £19.95) takes a look at a mix of extinct birds and some threatened species through contemporary accounts and illustrations, coupled with modern paintings by the author. Translated from German, it is interesting to get a non-British view of some of the folklore. The Germans have 118 dialect names for Corncrake for example.

If you are looking for something smaller and lighter to read in bed or slip into your holiday luggage, then two titles fit the bill, albeit from diametrically opposite ends of the spectrum.

Lady of the Loch (**Armitage, Constable, pb, ISBN 978-1-84901-702-2, £7.99**) is the story of one particular bird: 'Lady', Britain's oldest breeding Osprey has been returning to Loch of the Lowes every year since 1991.

Rather more birds make it into *The Biggest Twitch* (**Davies and Miller, Helm, pb, ISBN 978-1-4081-2387-4, £12.99**). This is an entertaining account of the authors' attempt to break the world record for seeing as many species of bird in a year. The previous record was 3,662 species. Look away now if you don't want to know the result…

PRACTICAL ADVICE BOOKS

The one identification guide that has divided opinion more than any other is the *Crossley ID Guide: Eastern Birds* (**Crossley, Princeton UP, pb, ISBN-13: 9780691147789, £24.95**). Digital manipulation is used to produce a montage of dozens of photos for each species, showing flocks, flight shots, different plumages, birds in close up and at distance etc. There are more than 100,000 photos in total.

Some will absolutely hate this format; to others, it will come as a real eye-opener. Its size means it is more suitable for a rucksack than the pocket. The book is far from perfect, but make no mistake, we are talking about fieldguide revolution here rather than evolution. This book covers birds found in the Eastern half of the USA and I for one can't wait to see a British version.

Two other fieldguides caught my eye. *Birds of Ghana* (**Borrow and Demey, Helm, pb, ISBN 978-1-4081-2279-2, £29.99**) is significant as it is the first book to cover Ghana and neighbouring Togo.

Though *Birds of the Middle East* (**Porter and Aspinall, Helm, pb, ISBN 978-0-7136-7602-0, £29.99**) is a new edition, it feels like a completely new book with the inclusion of 130 new species and recognisable subspecies. The plates are

BEST BIRD BOOKS OF THE YEAR

excellent. Both titles follow a similar format of map and description opposite the relevant plate, much better than having a separate section for the maps.

One common complaint is that bird books are just too expensive, so *Birdwatching on Mull and Iona* **(Sexton and Snow, Brown and Whittaker, pb, ISBN 9781904353140, £4.95)** has got to be one of the bargains of the year at under a fiver. A great mix of brand new text by the current RSPB warden and some lovely hand-drawn maps taken from a previous edition, provides everything you need to know about finding eagles and Corncrakes etc, and all in 40 pages. Every visitor to the island will find their holiday experience much enhanced.

I have a friend who monitors the rare bird news assiduously. Not because he wants to see all the latest rarities, but because he wants to find out where the crowds are going to be, before heading off elsewhere. Though not a bird book per se, I enjoyed *Britain and Ireland's Best Wild Places* **(Somerville, Penguin, pb, ISBN 978-0-141-02922-1, £19.99)** which details 500 places you might not otherwise come across.

REFERENCE WORKS

Raptor and atlases feature large this year, though not necessarily as you might imagine. *The Golden Eagle* **(Watson, Poyser, hb, ISBN 978-1-4081-1420-9, £50)** is a new edition of a classic Poyser title. Much revised and updated, by the late, lamented Jeff Watson, this is a self-recommending title.

Whittles Publishing has released a series of titles that don't sit comfortably in any existing category. They're not fully fledged monographs, but more a series of individual accounts and observations by an expert author. My favourite so far is *The Hen Harrier – In the Shadow of Slemish* **(Scott, Whittles Publishing, pb, ISBN 978-1-904445-93-7, £18.99)**, which covers a 20 year study of the birds in Northern Ireland.

The RSPB book of British Birds of Prey **(Taylor, A&C Black, hb, ISBN 978-1-4081-2849-7, £24.99)** has chapters looking at the life histories of our 15 native raptors, five species of owl and a selection or rare visitors. Stunningly illustrated by award-winning Norwegian photographer, Stig Frode Olsen, this book would make a great present for any youngster getting interested in birding. Just make sure that you read it yourself first.

Protecting endangered species is a problem that is never going to go away. Two titles, *Facing Extinction* (**Donald et al, Poyser, hb, ISBN 978-0-7136-7021-9, £45**) and *The Atlas of Rare Birds* (**Couzens, New Holland, hb, ISBN 978-1-84773-535-5, £24.99**) are published in association with BirdLife International.

The former examines some of the practical conservation steps being taken, via individual case studies. This fascinating account is both scholarly and highly readable and will make you angry and optimistic by degree. It's a title I shall be returning to time and time again. The atlas is more of a coffee table book, featuring short articles on the 50 most endangered birds. Both books are well illustrated.

Only one avifauna crossed my desk this year but it's a cracker. *The Norfolk Bird Atlas* (**Taylor and Marchant, BTO, hb, ISBN 978-1-906204-82-2, £45**) covers both summer and winter distributions over the period 1999-2007. Double page spreads on each species feature full colour maps, photos, line drawings and species accounts, together with analysis of why each bird is increasing or declining. It's good to know that Norfolk isn't just about chasing rare birds.

When I first opened the *Atlas of Birds* (**Unwin, A&C Black, pb, ISBN 978-1-4081-3470-2, £16.99**), I didn't have a clue what to expect and I think that part of this might be been the title. Perhaps *Atlas of Birds and Birding* might have been better.

A series of maps and graphs chart everything from birds in different continents, bird families, migration, culture, conservation and their value to the local economy. There's even a graph of which species are mentioned in Shakespeare's plays – doves at 60 times come out on top. A great book for trivia fans to dip into.

BEST BOOK NOMINATIONS

This is difficult as many of the books listed here are either second editions (which I've discounted from winning) or flawed in some way. Picking my favourite from each category, I've chosen:-

Art and Literature: *There and Back?*
Practical advice books: *Crossley ID Guide*
Reference works: *Facing Extinction*

KEEP UP WITH THE FAST-CHANGING WORLD OF BIRDING WEBSITES

Internet enthusiast Gordon Hamlett wonders why many people feel that information on websites is not to be trusted but concludes with a survey of 50 birding sites well worth exploring.

HOW MUCH do you trust the internet? I'm not talking about dodgy spam or assorted celebrity tittle-tattle, but the sort of information you find on the various websites I've detailed in the *Yearbook* over the past few years. I'm sure that most of you would agree that the pages that have been recommended are pretty good and that any errors – and there are bound to be some – are made in good faith.

In fact it is difficult to see how it could be otherwise. Certainly people get hot under the collar when challenging counter views on various discussion forums but that is perfectly normal in the realm of opinion. In contrast, I think that most of the 'hard facts' on birding websites are pretty reliable.

This is true for much of the internet as a whole. Take a site like Wikipedia (**http://en.wikipedia.org/**), an encyclopaedia in which anyone can edit the entries. On the face of it, this is a recipe for disaster, and certainly, there are well documented cases where articles have been altered out of malice or as a joke. But research has suggested that on the whole it is factually more accurate than *Encyclopaedia Britannica*.

The reason I raise this topic was something that occurred to me when I was wearing my other hat, that of book reviewer. Many of the reference books come with massive bibliographies, detailing research papers from all round the world. Yet very few seem to include any web addresses and I was wondering why that was.

For example, in the excellent monograph on the Golden Eagle (qv), the illustrations include maps generated by satellite-tracking various birds. The website whence they came is mentioned but no address is given, so you would have to enter the relevant information into your search engine. In the bibliography of more than 600 references, only nine websites are mentioned, mostly government documents.

So what's wrong with quoting the web? Several theories occur to me. They are all fanciful and I would love to hear from anyone who has a better theory. Is there a snob element in play here? There is the old joke that to copy your work from one source is called plagiarism; to copy from many sources is called research. Does referring to an internet site imply that you have simply cut and pasted from elsewhere?

Is the internet still considered too ephemeral? Back in 2000, I bought a book called *The Internet Guide to Birds and Birding* (Sanders, McGraw Hill) and it is true that most of the sites listed are now defunct. But things have consolidated a lot since then. All the large databases are here to stay. They just keep getting bigger and better.

Certainly as a user/reader, I would be infinitely more likely to look something up online rather than dig out copies of an obscure journal. 'Further reading' should extend far beyond books and journals. If the paper can also be found online, I'd like to be told, and then taken to some other relevant websites as well.

The net can provide a plethora of photos, sounds, maps and dynamic data far beyond the scope of a book. It can add considerably to your enjoyment and understanding. And if, somewhere down the line, I enter a web address and get a message back that the page can no longer be found, then I understand. I won't ask for my money back.

TOP TEN ESSENTIAL WEBSITES

This is my alphabetical list of the top ten websites that every British birder should have bookmarked.

http://www.birdforum.net/
With over 100,000 members discussing anything and everything bird-related, this is the number one social media site for birders.

http://www.birdguides.com/
The place to come for the latest rare bird news, photos etc. There is a basic free service, with extra content if you want to subscribe.

http://www.bto.org/
The British Trust for Ornithology's site includes the fabulous Birdtrack, for online migration recording as well as lots of other survey work.

http://www.fatbirder.com/
Whatever you are searching for, look here first; there are regularly updated links to thousands of other birding websites.

http://www.habitat.org.uk
This site searches local and national press every day for all the latest wildlife and environment stories making the news.

http://www.rspb.org.uk/
The RSPB is the number one birding charity and its site has details of British species (including sounds), reserves and conservation projects.

http://www.the-soc.org.uk/
The Scottish Ornithologists' Club covers all matter of Scottish birding, including site guides and recent sightings.

http://www.surfbirds.com/
The pick of the online magazines, Surfbirds has recent rarity photos, hundreds of blogs, trip reports, discussions etc.

http://www.wildlifetrusts.org/
An umbrella site, giving access to the 47 individual trusts as well as general information on the work of the trusts.

http://www.wwt.org.uk/
Details of all the Wildfowl and Wetland Trust's reserves can be found here, together with details of latest sightings and news etc.

WEBSITES WORTH EXPLORING

BINOCULAR TESTS

http://www.binomania.it/binocoli/megarecensione/mega_review.php
How do you test binoculars? Do you simply offer subjective views or do you present all sorts of technical details measured under laboratory condition? This Italian site has lined up seven reviewers and twelve 8X magnification models for a massive group test. You will need to click on the 'Google Translate' button to get the English version, which, though quirky, makes reasonable sense. And the winner is ...

THE FAST-CHANGING WORLD OF BIRDING WEBSITES

BIRD PHOTOGRAPHY

http://www.2020v.org/
Conservation can seem worthy but dull at times, so how do you go about making it interesting? 2020 Vision has come up with the idea of taking 20 projects, and getting them covered by 20 top photographers including the likes of David Tipling and Chris Packham. Just sit back and enjoy some simply stunning wildlife photography. See feature on page 8 for more details.

BIRD SOUNDS

http://www.bl.uk/listentonature/
specialinterestlang/langofbirdscontents.
html
This is the internet at its educational best. A paper given to the Royal Institution, by Jeffrey Boswell, on the *Language of Birds*, looks at how, why and when birds sing. It comes complete with many illustrative songs and calls, together with illustrative sonograms.

BIRD SPECIES

http://www.arctictern.info/
The Arctic Tern has one of the longest migrations in the animal kingdom, making the equivalent of three return trips to the moon during its lifetime. This slick site makes use of satellite tagging information to show the migration routes followed.

http://www.greenshank.info/index.asp
This project, based around Langstone and Chichester Harbours, is aimed at monitoring the movements of Greenshanks. There are precious few ringing recoveries showing where our birds overwinter. The organisers are delighted to welcome any sort of volunteers, whether it is simply reporting sightings, or a more hands-on approach.

http://penguins.adu.org.za/
We tend to think of penguins as birds of the Antarctic, but there are populations as far north as South Africa. Though this largely academic site has information on other species, most of the papers and stories here are devoted research into the African Penguin.

BLOGS

http://birdingblogs.com/
An eclectic collection of writers featuring top names in the birding world including Ken Kaufman from the States and our own Martin Garner and Tom McKinney. The bloggers all travel and bird widely so expect posts from all round the world.

http://birdingfrontiers.com/
As well as contributing to Birding Blogs (see above), Martin Garner also has this website on the go. It is more concerned with tricky identification problems such as unusual scoters, wagtails and redpolls.

http://pennyshotbirdingandlife.blogspot.
com/
In what is still a male-dominated hobby, this is the best blog I've seen written by a woman. Penny Clark is a keen Norfolk birder, excellent photographer and daughter of a former warden of Holme Bird Observatory. There might be too much shopping and dieting for some readers, or is that just a bloke thing?!

BRITISH BIRDING AREAS

http://beatentrackbirding.webs.com/
Considering how many people go birding in Norfolk, you would think that there isn't anywhere left to discover. Locals know that that isn't necessarily the case; you only have to go a mile inland from the coast to get away from the crowds. This site looks at some of the lesser known birding areas in the Brecks.

http://devonbirdnews.blogspot.com/
For some reason, Devon has been slow to embrace the internet when it comes to birding news. This blog, with more than 80 contributors, aims to fill the gap with news, views and photos about all the latest birds seen in the county.

http://www.natureonthemap.
naturalengland.org.uk/
Nature on the Map is Natural England's site, showing you just where all the local and national nature reserves, plus Sites of Special Scientific Interest, are in your area via a zoomable map. The design is less than user-friendly though and you might have trouble with pop-ups, something that similar sites manage to avoid.

THE FAST-CHANGING WORLD OF BIRDING WEBSITES

http://www.rspb.org.uk/community/
placestovisit/lochofstrathbeg/default.aspx
The RSPB hasn't always got it right when
it comes to information on its website but
this is what they should be aiming for on the
pages of all their reserves: a nice chatty blog,
regularly updated, with details of recent
sightings and plenty of photos. It makes you
want to visit.

http://www.sogonline.org.uk/
http://www.freewebs.com/suffolkbirding/
Whisper it quietly, especially to those
living there, but Suffolk lurks somewhat
in the shadows of its more famous
northern neighbour. These two sites – the
first mentioned is that of the Suffolk
Ornithologists' Group – aim to change all that.
Latest sightings, bang up to date, can be
found on the Suffolk Birding site, while the
SOG site takes a more measured look at what
has been happening in the county.

http://www.theurbanbirder.com/
Where do you go birding on your day out?
To the coast or your local reservoir perhaps.
David Lindo, writer and television star, aims
to convince you that there is plenty of birding
to be done within the confines of your nearest
city.

http://warwickshirebirding.blogspot.com/
Though the latest sightings were a week out
of date when I last looked, I rather suspect
that that is more due to the lack of exciting
birds in Warwickshire rather than a dilatory
approach by the author! There are links to
pages for all the major reservoirs in the
county.

http://www.worcesterbirding.co.uk/
While you can view photos and sightings from
recent years, as well as feature articles and a
few guides to sites, you will need to pay £25
per annum if you want details of all the latest
sightings. This does cover national rarities
and the rest of the counties in the Midlands
though.

E-BOOKS FOR BIRDERS

http://www.poyserbooks.com/
Poyser monographs have an enviable
reputation in the field of bird publishing,
their iconic white covers gleaming from the
bookshelves. Times are a'changin' though and

it is good to see that many of the titles are
now available as e-books, ready for download
onto your Kindle or similar. If you want to try
before you buy, you can download a sample
free chapter from each title.

GAMES AND QUIZZES

http://www.birdid.no/index.php
This Norwegian site (you can click on
an English language version) tests your
identification skills of birds and their calls,
plus mammals and tracks and signs. You can
sign up and win a certificate and tee-shirt.

http://www.birdinggame.com/
Explore the habitats of Lake Neusiedl in
Austria, Extremadura in Spain and Corpus
Christi in Texas. Click on the birds as you find
them and try to identify them. There are
three skill levels, with unusual angles or just
bits of birds as things get harder.

MULTI-MEDIA

http://www.pbase.com/mbb/
image/130429923
PBase is a massive photographic website,
with millions of pictures on every subject
imaginable. There are currently 4,000
galleries featuring the word 'bird'. The
picture I've selected here is an amazing shot
of a double strike by an Osprey, catching two
fish at once.

http://www.youtube.com/
watch?v=EBwqbqZ3L60
Nature is a perpetual struggle between the
hunter and the hunted. Here, a Gentoo
Penguin finds a novel way of avoiding the
attentions of a hunting killer whale.

http://www.youtube.com/
watch?v=eM5XNT7Jp0o
Most of us are grateful if we get one or two
Bramblings in our garden each winter. On the
continent, they occur in rather larger flocks.
So, if you have ever wondered what four
million Bramblings look like, look no further.

http://www.youtube.com/watch?v=hjxNcYT
25dY&feature=related
This footage comes from a camera set up on a
Black Stork nest. A pine marten comes looking
to steal the eggs and the clip follows the
ensuing struggle. What is notable is how good
the marten's fur is at protecting it from the

vicious attacks from the stork's massive bill.
http://www.youtube.com/watch?v=Vb4s52VQ07g
It is fair to say that not everyone liked the new logo chosen by the British Trust for Ornithology. Here, one of the trust's directors, Andy Clement, gives a presentation explaining the need for change. The clip comes in two parts and there are links to other BTO videos too.

http://www.youtube.com/watch?v=vHXQp-NhFuE
Simply the funniest thing I have seen all year and a wonderful spoof on the twitching community. After a set of 'commandments' for birders, there is a sequence of a certain Mr Lee Evans, Britain's best known twitcher, strutting his stuff. Warning, some language might offend.

OVERSEAS BIRDING

http://avis.indianbiodiversity.org/
Still in its developmental stages, this massive new project aims to provide details on every single Indian bird. For each species, there are links to photographs, sounds, bibliographic details and links to a plethora of other birding databases. Important birding areas are detailed and there is a discussion forum.

http://birdingsiteguide.com/
Though presentation of this site is functional rather than fancy, there is a lot of information here. Currently 482 sites worldwide are detailed and you are invited to submit your own favourites. Site reports range from a few paragraphs to comprehensive checklists of birds and other species. There is a good selection of links included.

http://www.chinabirdnet.org/
Birding is just beginning to take off in China. This site has a discussion forum, with plenty of photos, back issues of newsletters (in Chinese but with an English summary), a sightings database and a good assortment of links to other Chinese and Asian birding sites.

http://www.rbcu.ru/
Russia is another country where information is hard to come by and this site is not helped

by the fact that it is in Russian only! However, help is at hand. Google's translation system is fast and surprisingly good and that, coupled with a little knowledge of some scientific bird names should enable you to navigate round the pictures.

RAPTORS

http://www.africanraptors.org/
I wrote about the European equivalent of this site last year (www.europeanraptors.org), and now we have the African equivalent. There is a fine mix of articles, photos and interviews, together with a good selection of links to other raptor sites.

http://honey-buzzard.blogspot.com/
Separating Honey Buzzards from Common Buzzards is an absolute minefield for beginners and I've seen many birders erroneously ticking off the commoner cousin. This site is devoted to everything related to Honey Buzzards, with many helpful identification tips and links to other literature.

http://www.peregrinefund.org/default.asp
Despite the name, there is a lot of information here about other raptors as well. As well as data pages, you can sign up for an e-mail newsletter and watch assorted nest cameras.

http://raptorpersecutionscotland.wordpress.com/about/
This blog follows the various court cases associated with the illegal poisoning and shooting of birds of prey, mainly on large Scottish sporting estates. Sign up for the e-mail subscription and you will be notified automatically when a new story breaks. You can add your own comments to any of the entries.

http://www.raptortrack.org/
Satellite tracking of birds has provided new information for researchers, ranging from cases of suspected poisoning to where Hobbies go in winter. This site follows individual birds tagged in the Cairngorms National Park. Each bird has its own diary entries and associated maps.

THE FAST-CHANGING WORLD OF BIRDING WEBSITES

SURVEY WORK

http://www.avianknowledge.net/content
The Avian Knowledge Network ties in with eBird (qv) and allows interested parties to download the dataset. If you click on the 'About' section, you can watch a Powerpoint presentation for an overview of the system.

http://ebird.org/content/ebird/
With more than 100 million records from 100,000 locations, and growing all the time, eBird is another way of logging your sightings. Though largely American, it is expanding globally and there are already plenty of British records entered. While you can use it just to keep track of your sightings, all the data gets crunched, producing geographical and seasonal abundance charts.

http://www.norfolkwildlifetrust.org.uk/surveys.aspx
I've not always been impressed local wildlife trust websites, but this a great example of what can be done in engaging the public. You are invited to submit any records – not just birds but hedgerows, ponds, churchyards etc, in an attempt to build a better picture of Norfolk's biodiversity.

WHALE WATCHING

http://www.planetwhale.com/
Perversely, one of the best ways to see certain pelagic bird species is to go on an organised whale-watching trip. Planet Whale aims to put you in touch with reputable companies across the world. As well as showing you these magnificent creatures, the tour companies are all trying to raise the ethical standards of tour operators.

DIARY 2012

David Cromack

Birders will be hoping for crisp, bright conditions for their New Year's Day outing to get the year list off to a good start. These Mute Swans are on the River Nene at Wansford, Cambs.

EVENTS DIARY 2012

While every effort has been made to check the accuracy of these entries, the publishers advise making contact with the event organisers to ensure there are no late changes. TBA = To Be Announced (for those dates not settled before the Yearbook went to press).

JANUARY

16 -30: RSPB Big Schools Birdwatch
16-30: Little Schools Birdwatch
An expanded initiative to get children interested in wild birds - see RSPB website for local area events.

28-29: RSPB Big Garden Birdwatch
Nationwide survey of garden birds open to members of the public.
Contact: RSPB on 01767 680 551.

FEBRUARY

2: World Wetlands Day
Various events at local level to raise awareness of wetland habitats and Ramsar sites in particular. www.wwd@ramsar.org

8-9: Professional course in bird survey techniques
Stirling University, Stirling, Falkirk.
Contact: info@bto.org

24-26: BTO bird identification - residential course
Slapton Ley FSC, South Devon.
Contact: info@bto.org

MARCH

7: Berks & Oxon BTO members and bird club conference
Civic Centre, Britwell Rd, Didcot, Oxfordshire
Contact: ellen.walford@bto.org

17-20: MIGRES Foundation second bird migration and global change conference
Hotel Reina Christina, Algeciras, Spain.
Registrations on-line at:
http://www.fundacionmigres.org/congresos/globalchange/Presentation.html

25-April 1: Sixth Eilat migration festival
Bird tours, presentations and other bird-related events centred on Agamim Hotel in Eilat, southern Israel. www.eilatbirdsfestival.com or www.wildwings.co.uk

17: Scottish birdwatchers conference (BTO/SOC/Argyll Bird Club)
Corran Halls, Oban.
Contact: wendy.hicks@the-soc.org.uk

APRIL

3-5: BOU Annual Conference: Ecosystem Services: do we need birds?
University of Leicester. www.bou.org.uk

8-10: BTO bird survey techniques - residential course
Rhyd-y-Creuau FSC, North Wales
Contact: info@bto.org

13-15: RSPB members weekend
York University.

13-15 BTO bird survey techniques course
Malham Tarn FSC, Yorkshire.
Contact: info@bto.org

21: African Bird Club AGM
BTO, The Nunnery, Thetford Norfolk.
 Contact: contact@africanbirdclub.org

20-22: BTO bird identification - residential course
Dale Fort FSC, Pembrokeshire.
Contact: info@bto.org

MAY

8-10: BTO bird identification - residential course
Rhyd-y-Creuau FSC, North Wales
Contact: info@bto.org

19-20 Scottish Birdfair
Hopetoun House, Edinburgh.
Contact: Sarah McDowell on sarah.mcdowell@rspb.org uk or visit: www.scottishbirdfair.co.uk

19-21: BTO bird identification - residential course
Flatford Mill FSC, Suffolk
Contact: info@bto.org

24-26: BTO bird survey techniques - residential course
Dale Fort FSC, Pembrokeshire.
Contact: info@bto.org

30: Neoptropical Bird Club general meeting
Talks, quizzes, book and audio sales at Cley Village Hall, Norfolk.
Contact: Secretary at g7ellis@googlemail.com

EVENTS DIARY 2012

JUNE

1-4: The Ornithological Society of New Zealand Conference and AGM
Bay of Plenty, New Zealand. Topics to be confirmed.
Contact: http://osnz.org.nz/events/

2-10: Make Your Nature Count
New RSPB scheme to survey wildlife in summer.
Contact: RSPB on 01767 680 551.

3: Neotropical Bird Club AGM and Spring Meeting
Talks on various topics, plus trade stands. Cley Village Hall, Norfolk. 10.30am - 5pm.
Contact: Secretary @neotropicalbirdclub.org or visit: www.neotropicalbirdclub.org

JULY

TBA: AGM of OSME (Ornithological Society of the Middle East, the Caucasus and Central Asia)
BTO headquarters, the Nunnery, Thetford, Norfolk. Doors open 10am.
Contact: Ian Harrison on secretary@osme.org

13 to 29: NEWA (National Exhibition of Wildlife Art)
Gordale Nursey, Burton, the Wirral. Preview evening July 12.
Artist demonstrations, July 13th to 15th.
Contact: newa@mtuffrey.freeserve.co.uk or visit: www.newa-uk.com

AUGUST

12-17: Fifth International Albatross & Petrel Conference
Wellington, New Zealand.
Contact: http://osnz.org.nz/events

14-18: Fifth North American Ornithological Conference
University of British Columbia, Vancouver, Canada.
Contact:www.naoc-v2012.com

17-19: British Birdwatching Fair
Egleton Nature Reserve, Rutland Water, Rutland.
Contact: Call 01572 771 079 or e-mail: info@birdfair.org.uk

SEPTEMBER

7-10: 1st World Seabird Conference
Hosted by Pacific Seabird Group in the Victoria Conference Centre, British Columbia.
www.pacificseabirdgroup.org

22-26: Annual meeting of Raptor Research Foundation
Fort Collins, Colorado. http://raptorresearchfoundation.org/conferences.htm

OCTOBER

6: RSPB AGM & members day
Queen Elizabeth II conference centre, Westminster, London.

5-7: BTO bird identification - residential course
Kindrogan FSC, Perthshire.
Contact: info@bto.org

14-21: The 13th Pan-African Ornithological Conference: Birds in a changing environment
International Institute of Tropical Agriculture, Ibaden, Nigeria.
Contact: manushiiwua@yahoo.co.uk www. www.birdlife.org/community/2011/06/paoc13/

26-28: TBA: Scottish Ornithological Club annual conference.
Contact club for date and venue details at mail@the-soc.org

26-28: BTO Bird Survey Techniques - residential course
Flatford Mill, Suffolk.
Contact: info@bto.org

27: Feed The Birds Day
A programme of events across the UK - check local press and RSPB website for details in your area.

NOVEMBER

24-25: North-West Birdfair
WWT Martin Mere, Burscough, Lancs.
Contact: info.martinmere@wwt.org.uk

27-28-29: International Ornithological Congress of Southeast Asia
Phuket, Thailand.
Contact: Dr Chutamas Satasook (chutamas.p@psu.ac.th) http://harrison-institute.org/IOCSEA/index.html

DECEMBER

7-9: BTO Annual Conference
The Hayes Conference Centre, Swanwick, Derbyshire.
Contact: ellen.walford@bto.org

DIARY – JANUARY 2012

1	Sun	
2	Mon	New Year holiday
3	Tue	Holiday (Scotland)
4	Wed	
5	Thu	
6	Fri	
7	Sat	
8	Sun	
9	Mon	
10	Tue	
11	Wed	
12	Thu	
13	Fri	
14	Sat	
15	Sun	
16	Mon	
17	Tue	
18	Wed	
19	Thu	
20	Fri	
21	Sat	
22	Sun	
23	Mon	
24	Tue	
25	Wed	
26	Thu	
27	Fri	
28	Sat	
29	Sun	
30	Mon	
31	Tue	

DIARY – FEBRUARY 2012

1	Wed	
2	Thu	
3	Fri	
4	Sat	
5	Sun	
6	Mon	
7	Tue	
8	Wed	
9	Thu	
10	Fri	
11	Sat	
12	Sun	
13	Mon	
14	Tue	
15	Wed	
16	Thu	
17	Fri	
18	Sat	
19	Sun	
20	Mon	
21	Tue	
22	Wed	
23	Thu	
24	Fri	
25	Sat	
26	Sun	
27	Mon	
28	Tue	
29	Wed	

DIARY 2012

DIARY – MARCH 2012

1	Thu	
2	Fri	
3	Sat	
4	Sun	
5	Mon	
6	Tue	
7	Wed	
8	Thu	
9	Fri	
10	Sat	
11	Sun	
12	Mon	
13	Tue	
14	Wed	
15	Thu	
16	Fri	
17	Sat	St Patrick's Day (Bank Holiday N.Ireland)
18	Sun	Mothering Sunday
19	Mon	
20	Tue	
21	Wed	
22	Thu	
23	Fri	
24	Sat	
25	Sun	British Summertime begins
26	Mon	
27	Tue	
28	Wed	
29	Thu	
30	Fri	
31	Sat	

DIARY – APRIL 2012

1	Sun	
2	Mon	
3	Tue	
4	Wed	
5	Thu	
6	Fri	Good Friday
7	Sat	
8	Sun	Easter Day
9	Mon	Easter Monday
10	Tue	
11	Wed	
12	Thu	
13	Fri	
14	Sat	
15	Sun	
16	Mon	
17	Tue	
18	Wed	
19	Thu	
20	Fri	
21	Sat	
22	Sun	
23	Mon	
24	Tue	
25	Wed	
26	Thu	
27	Fri	
28	Sat	
29	Sun	
30	Mon	

DIARY – MAY 2012

1	Tue	
2	Wed	
3	Thu	
4	Fri	
5	Sat	
6	Sun	
7	Mon	May Day
8	Tue	
9	Wed	
10	Thu	
11	Fri	
12	Sat	
13	Sun	
14	Mon	
15	Tue	
16	Wed	
17	Thu	
18	Fri	
19	Sat	
20	Sun	
21	Mon	
22	Tue	
23	Wed	
24	Thu	
25	Fri	
26	Sat	
27	Sun	
28	Mon	
29	Tue	
30	Wed	
31	Thu	

DIARY – JUNE 2012

1	Fri	
2	Sat	
3	Sun	
4	Mon	Spring Bank Holiday
5	Tue	Diamond Jubilee Holiday
6	Wed	
7	Thu	
8	Fri	
9	Sat	
10	Sun	
11	Mon	
12	Tue	
13	Wed	
14	Thu	
15	Fri	
16	Sat	
17	Sun	
18	Mon	
19	Tue	
20	Wed	
21	Thu	
22	Fri	
23	Sat	
24	Sun	
25	Mon	
26	Tue	
27	Wed	
28	Thu	
29	Fri	
30	Sat	

DIARY – JULY 2012

1	Sun	
2	Mon	
3	Tue	
4	Wed	
5	Thu	
6	Fri	
7	Sat	
8	Sun	
9	Mon	
10	Tue	
11	Wed	
12	Thu	
13	Fri	
14	Sat	
15	Sun	
16	Mon	
17	Tue	
18	Wed	
19	Thu	
20	Fri	
21	Sat	
22	Sun	
23	Mon	
24	Tue	
25	Wed	
26	Thu	
27	Fri	Opening ceremony - London Olympics
28	Sat	
29	Sun	
30	Mon	
31	Tue	

DIARY – AUGUST 2012

1	Wed	
2	Thu	
3	Fri	
4	Sat	
5	Sun	
6	Mon	
7	Tue	
8	Wed	
9	Thu	
10	Fri	
11	Sat	
12	Sun	Closing ceremony - London Olympics
13	Mon	
14	Tue	
15	Wed	
16	Thu	
17	Fri	
18	Sat	
19	Sun	
20	Mon	
21	Tue	
22	Wed	
23	Thu	
24	Fri	
25	Sat	
26	Sun	
27	Mon	Summer Bank Holiday
28	Tue	
29	Wed	
30	Thu	
31	Fri	

DIARY – SEPTEMBER 2012

1	Sat	
2	Sun	
3	Mon	
4	Tue	
5	Wed	
6	Thu	
7	Fri	
8	Sat	
9	Sun	
10	Mon	
11	Tue	
12	Wed	
13	Thu	
14	Fri	
15	Sat	
16	Sun	
17	Mon	
18	Tue	
19	Wed	
20	Thu	
21	Fri	
22	Sat	
23	Sun	
24	Mon	
25	Tue	
26	Wed	
27	Thu	
28	Fri	
29	Sat	
30	Sun	

DIARY – OCTOBER 2012

1	Mon	
2	Tue	
3	Wed	
4	Thu	
5	Fri	
6	Sat	
7	Sun	
8	Mon	
9	Tue	
10	Wed	
11	Thu	
12	Fri	
13	Sat	
14	Sun	
15	Mon	
16	Tue	
17	Wed	
18	Thu	
19	Fri	
20	Sat	
21	Sun	
22	Mon	
23	Tue	
24	Wed	
25	Thu	
26	Fri	
27	Sat	
28	Sun	British Summertime ends
29	Mon	
30	Tue	
31	Wed	

DIARY – NOVEMBER 2012

1	Thu	
2	Fri	
3	Sat	
4	Sun	
5	Mon	
6	Tue	
7	Wed	
8	Thu	
9	Fri	
10	Sat	
11	Sun	Remembrance Sunday
12	Mon	
13	Tue	
14	Wed	
15	Thu	
16	Fri	
17	Sat	
18	Sun	
19	Mon	
20	Tue	
21	Wed	
22	Thu	
23	Fri	
24	Sat	
25	Sun	
26	Mon	
27	Tue	
28	Wed	
29	Thu	
30	Fri	

DIARY – DECEMBER 2012

1	Sat	
2	Sun	
3	Mon	
4	Tue	
5	Wed	
6	Thu	
7	Fri	
8	Sat	
9	Sun	
10	Mon	
11	Tue	
12	Wed	
13	Thu	
14	Fri	
15	Sat	
16	Sun	
17	Mon	
18	Tue	
19	Wed	
20	Thu	
21	Fri	
22	Sat	
23	Sun	
24	Mon	
25	Tue	Christmas Day
26	Wed	Boxing Day
27	Thu	
28	Fri	
29	Sat	
30	Sun	
31	Mon	

YEAR PLANNER 2013

January
February
March
April
May
June
July
August
September
October
November
December

LOG CHARTS

David Cromack

One species that birdwatchers love to add to their annual bird list is the Smew, which visits southern and eastern areas of Britain in winter – numbers will depend on how many birds are displaced by harsh weather in Denmark and Holland.

A CHECKLIST OF BIRDS

Based on the British List formulated by the British Ornithologists' Union

NEWCOMERS to birdwatching are sometimes baffled when they examine their first fieldguide as it is not immediately clear why the birds are arranged the way they are. The simple answer is that the order is meant to reflect the evolution of the included species. If one were to draw an evolutionary tree of birds, those families that branch off earliest (i.e are the most ancient) should be listed first.

Previously the British Ornithologists' Union British List was based on Voous Order (BOU 1977), the work of an eminent Dutch taxonomist and many of the popular fieldguides for British and European birds still follow this established order.

For more than 100 years, the British Ornithologists' Union Records Committee (BOURC) has maintained the official list of birds recorded in Britain — the British List. The BOURC periodically publishes up-to-date checklists incorporating changes the BOURC has announced in its reports and the Checklist published in *The Birdwatcher's Yearbook* reflects these changes.

In this edition, species in Category C (introduced species) have been sub-divided into six separate categories (see below).

SPECIES, CATEGORIES, CODES – YOUR GUIDE TO GET THE BEST USE FROM THE CHECKLIST

Species categories (column 1)

The following categories are those assigned by the British Ornithologists' Union.

A - Species that have been recorded in an apparently natural state at least once since January 1, 1950.

B - Species that were recorded in an apparently natural state at least once since January 1, 1800 and December 31,1949, but have not been recorded subsequently.

C - Species that, though introduced, now derive from the resulting self-sustaining populations.

C1 - *Naturalized introduced species* – Species that have occurred only as a result of introduction, e.g. Egyptian Goose (*Alopochen aegyptiacus*).

C2 - *Naturalized established species* - Species with established populations resulting from introduction by Man, but which also occur in an apparently natural state, e.g. Greylag Goose (*Anser anser*).

C3 - *Naturalized re-established species* - Species with populations successfully re-established by Man in areas of former occurrence, e.g. Red Kite (*Milvus milvus*).

C4 - *Naturalized feral species* - Domesticated species with populations established in the wild, e.g. Rock Pigeon (Dove)/Feral Pigeon (*Columba livia*).

C5 - *Vagrant naturalized species* - Species from established naturalized populations abroad, e.g. Sacred Ibis (*Threskiornis aethiopicu)s* from the naturalized French populations. There are currently no species in category C5.

C6 - *Former naturalized species* – Species formerly placed in C1 whose naturalized populations are either no longer self-sustaining or are considered extinct, e.g. Lady Amherst's Pheasant (*Chrysolophus amherstiae*).

D - Species that would otherwise appear in Category A except that there is reasonable doubt that they have ever occurred in a natural state. Species placed solely in Category D form no part of the British List, and are not included in the species totals.

E - Species that have been recorded as introductions, human-assisted transportees or escapees from captivity, and whose breeding populations (if any) are thought not to be self-sustaining. Species in Category E that have bred in the wild in Britain are designated as E*. Category E species form no part of the British List (unless already included within Categories A, B or C).

A species is usually placed in only one category, but some are placed in multiple categories, for example, those species occurring in Category A which now have naturalised populations (e.g. Red Kite).

The British List comprises only those species in Categories A, B and C.

LOG CHARTS

Species list (column 2)

The charts include all species from categories A, B and C on the British List, based on the latest BOU listing. Selected species included in categories D and E are listed separately at the end of the log chart.

Vagrants which are not on the British List, but which may have occurred in other parts of the British Isles, are not included. Readers who wish to record such species may use the extra rows provided on the last page. In this connection it should be noted that separate lists exist for Northern Ireland (kept by the Northern Ireland Birdwatchers' Association) and the Isle of Man (kept by the Manx Ornithological Society), and that Irish records are assessed by the Irish Rare Birds Committee.

The commoner species in the log charts are indicated by the * symbol to help make record-keeping easier.

The species names are those most widely used in the current fieldguides and each is followed by its scientific name, printed in italics.

Life list (column 3)

Ticks made in the 'Life List' column suffice for keeping a running personal total of species. However, added benefit can be obtained by replacing ticks with a note of the year of first occurrence. To take an example: one's first-ever Marsh Sandpiper, seen on April 14, 2012, would be logged with '11' in the Life List and '14' in the April column (as well as a tick in the 2012 column). As Life List entries are carried forward annually, in years to come it would be a simple matter to relocate this record.

First and last dates of migrants

Arrivals of migrants can be recorded by inserting dates instead of ticks in the relevant month columns. For example, a Common Sandpiper on March 11 would be recorded by inserting '11' against Common Sandpiper in the March column. The same applies to departures, though dates of last sightings can only be entered at the end of the year after checking one's field notebook.

Unheaded columns

The three unheaded columns on the right of the December column of each chart are for special (personal) use. This may be, for example, to cater for a second holiday, a particular county or a 'local patch'. Another use could be to indicate species on, for example, the Northern Ireland List or the Isle of Man List.

BTO species codes (column 23)

British Trust for Ornithology two-letter species codes are shown in brackets in the fourth column from the right. They exist for many species, races and hybrids recorded in recent surveys. Readers should refer to the BTO if more codes are needed.

In addition to those given in the charts, the following are available for some well-marked races or forms - Whistling Swan (WZ), European White-fronted Goose (EW), Greenland White-fronted Goose (NW), dark-bellied Brent Goose (DB), pale-bellied Brent Goose (PB), Black Brant (BB), domestic goose (ZL), Green-winged Teal (TA), domestic duck (ZF), Yellow-legged Gull (YG), Kumlien's Gull (KG), Feral Pigeon (FP), White Wagtail (WB), Black-bellied Dipper (DJ), Hooded Crow (HC), intermediate crow (HB).

Rare breeding birds (column 24)

Species monitored by the Rare Breeding Birds Panel (see National Directory) comprise all those on Schedule 1 of the Wildlife and Countryside Act 1981 (see Quick Reference) together with all escaped or introduced species breeding in small numbers. The following annotations in the charts (third column from the right) reflect the RBBP's categories:

A Rare Breeding Birds in the UK - Regular Breeders
B Rare Breeding Birds in the UK - Occasional Breeders
C Rare Breeding Birds in the UK - Potential Breeders
D Rare Non-native Breeding Birds in the UK - Regular Breeders
E Rare Non-native Breeding Birds in the UK - Occasional Breeders
F Rare Non-native Breeding Birds in the UK - Potential Breeders

Rarities (column 25)

Rarities are indicated by a capital letter 'R' in the column headed BBRC (British Birds Rarities Committee).

EURING species numbers (column 26)

EURING databanks collects copies of recovery records from ringing schemes throughout Europe and the official species numbers are given in the last column. As they are taken from the full Holarctic bird list there are many apparent gaps. It is important that these are not filled arbitrarily by observers wishing to record species not listed in the charts, as this would compromise the integrity of the scheme.

Similarly, the addition of a further digit to indicate sub-species is to be avoided, since EURING has already assigned numbers for this purpose. The numbering follows the Voous order of species so some species are now out of sequence following the re-ordering of the British List. For full details, visit: www.euring.org

SWANS, GEESE, DUCKS

BOU	Species	Scientific name	BTO	RBBP	BBRC	EU No
*AC2	Mute Swan	Cygnus olor	MS			0152
*A	Bewick's Swan	C. columbianus	BS	C		0153
*A	Whooper Swan	C. cygnus	WS	A		0154
*A	Bean Goose	Anser fabalis	BE			0157
*A	Pink-footed Goose	A. brachyrhynchus	PG	E		0158
*A	White-fronted Goose	A. albifrons	WG	E		0159
*A	Lesser White-fronted Goose	A. erythropus	LC	F	R	0160
AC2C4E	Greylag Goose	A. anser	GJ			0161
*A	Snow Goose	A. Caerulescens	SJ	D		0163
C2E	Canada Goose	Branta canadensis	CG			0166
AC2E	Barnacle Goose	B. leucopsis	BY	D		0167
*A	Brent Goose	B. bernicla	BG			0168
A	Red-breasted Goose	B. ruficollis	EB	E	R	0169
C1E	Egyptian Goose	Alopochen aegyptiaca	EG	D		0170
BDE	Ruddy Shelduck	Tadorna ferruginea	UD	D		0171
*A	Shelduck	T. tadorna	SU			0173
C1E	Mandarin Duck	Aix galericulata	MN			0178
*A	Wigeon	Anas penelope	WN	A		0179
A	American Wigeon	A. americana	AW			0180
*AC2	Gadwall	A. strepera	GA			0182
*AE	Baikal Teal	A. formosa			R	
*A	Teal	A. crecca	T			0184
A	Green-winged Teal	A. carolinensis		C		1842
AC2C4E	Mallard	A. platyrhynchos	MA			0186
	Sub total					

Column headings (across): Life list, 2012 list, 24 hr, Garden, Holiday, Jan, Feb, Mar, Apr, May, Jun, Jul, Aug, Sep, Oct, Nov, Dec

BOU	DUCKS Cont		Life list	2012 list	24 hr	Garden	Holiday	Jan	Feb	Mar	Apr	May	Jun	Jul	Aug	Sep	Oct	Nov	Dec	BTO	RBBP	BBRC	EU No
A	Black Duck	A. rubripes																		BD	B	R	0187
*A	Pintail	A. acuta																		PT	A		0189
*A	Garganey	A. querquedula																		GY	A		0191
A	Blue-winged Teal	A. discors																		TB	E	R	0192
*A	Shoveler	A. clypeata																		SV	A		0194
AC2E	Red-crested Pochard	Netta rufina																		RQ	D		0196
A	Canvasback	Aythya valisineria																				R	0197
*A	Pochard	A. ferina																		PO	A		0198
A	Redhead	A. americana																		AZ		R	0199
A	Ring-necked Duck	A. collaris																		NG	B		0200
A	Ferruginous Duck	A. nyroca																		FD	B		0202
*A	Tufted Duck	A. fuligula																		TU			0203
*A	Scaup	A. marila																		SP	B		0204
*A	Lesser Scaup	A. affinis																		AY		R	0205
*A	Eider	Somateria mollissima																		E			0206
*A	King Eider	S. spectabilis																		KE	C	R	0207
A	Steller's Eider	Polysticta stelleri																		ES		R	0209
A	Harlequin Duck	Histrionicus histrionicus																		HQ	R	R	0211
*A	Long-tailed Duck	Clangula hyemalis																		LN	C		0212
*A	Common Scoter	Melanitta nigra																		CX	A		0213
A	Black Scoter	M. americana																				R	2132
*A	Surf Scoter	M. perspicillata																		FS			0214
A	Velvet Scoter	M. fusca																		VS	C		0215
A	Bufflehead	Bucephala albeola																		VH		R	0216
	Sub total																						

65

BOU	DUCKS, GAMEBIRDS, DIVERS, ALBATROSS		Life list	2012 list	24 hr	Garden	Holiday	Jan	Feb	Mar	Apr	May	Jun	Jul	Aug	Sep	Oct	Nov	Dec	BTO	RBBP	BBRC	EU No
A	Barrow's Goldeneye	B. islandica																				R	0217
*A	Goldeneye	B. clangula																		GN	A		0218
A	Hooded Merganser	Lophodytes cucullatus																				R	2190
*A	Smew	Mergellus albellus																		SY	C		0220
*A	Red-breasted Merganser	Mergus serrator																		RM			0221
*A	Goosander	M. merganser																		GD			0223
C1E	Ruddy Duck	Oxyura jamaicensis																		BY	D		0225
*A	Red Grouse	Lagopus lagopus																		RG			0329
*A	Ptarmigan	Lagopus muta																		PM			0330
*A	Black Grouse	Tetrao tetrix																		BK			0332
*BC3	Capercaillie	T. urogallus																		CP	A		0335
C1E	Red-legged Partridge	Alectoris rufa																		RL			0358
*AC2E	Grey Partridge	Perdix perdix																		P			0367
*A	Quail	Coturnix coturnix																		Q	A		0370
C1E	Pheasant	Phasianus colchicus																		PH			0394
C1E	Golden Pheasant	Chrysolophus pictus																		GF	D		0396
C6E	Lady Amherst's Pheasant	C. amherstiae																		LM	D		0397
*A	Red-throated Diver	Gavia stellata																		RH	A		0002
*A	Black-throated Diver	G. arctica																		BV	A		0003
A	Pacific Diver	G. pacifica																					0033
*A	Great Northern Diver	G. immer																		ND	C	R	0004
A	White-billed Diver	G. adamsii																		IW	C		0005
A	Black-browed Albatross	Thalassarche melanophris																		AA	C	R	0014
A	Yellow-nosed Albatross	T. chlororhynchos																				R	0150
	Sub total																						

66

LOG CHARTS

FULMAR, PETRELS, SHEARWATERS, CORMORANTS, FRIGATEBIRDS, BITTERNS

BOU	Species		Life list	2012 list	24 hr	Garden	Holiday	Jan	Feb	Mar	Apr	May	Jun	Jul	Aug	Sep	Oct	Nov	Dec			BTO	RBBP	BBRC	EU No
*A	Fulmar	*Fulmarus glacialis*																				F			0020
A	Fea's Petrel	*Pterodroma feae*																						R	0026
A	Capped Petrel	*Pt. hasitata*																						R	0029
A	Cory's Shearwater	*Calonectris diomedea*																				CQ			0036
*A	Great Shearwater	*Puffinus gravis*																				GQ			0040
*A	Sooty Shearwater	*P. griseus*																				OT			0043
A	Manx Shearwater	*P. puffinus*																				MX			0046
A	Balearic Shearwater	*P. mauretanicus*																							0046
A	Macaronesian Shearwater	*P. baroli*																					C	R	0048
*A	Wilson's Petrel	*Oceanites oceanicus*																							0050
B	White-faced Petrel	*Pelagodroma marina*																						R	0051
*A	Storm Petrel	*Hydrobates pelagicus*																				TM			0052
*A	Leach's Petrel	*Oceanodroma leucorhoa*																				TL			0055
A	Swinhoe's Petrel	*O. monorhis*																						R	0056
A	Red-billed Tropicbird	*Phaethon aethereus*																						R	0064
*A	Gannet	*Morus bassanus*																				GX			0071
*A	Cormorant	*Phalacrocorax carbo*																				CA			0072
A	Double-crested Cormorant	*P. auritus*																						R	0078
*A	Shag	*P. aristotelis*																				SA			0080
A	Magnificent Frigatebird	*Fregata magnificens*																						R	0093
A	Ascension Frigatebird	*F. aquila*																						R	
*A	Bittern	*Botaurus stellaris*																				BI	A		0095
A	American Bittern	*B. lentiginosus*																				AM		R	0096
A	Little Bittern	*Ixobrychus minutus*																				LL	B	R	0098
	Sub total																								

67

BITTERNS, HERONS, STORKS, SPOON-BILL, GREBES, RAPTORS

BOU	Common name	Scientific name	BTO	RBBP	BBRC	EU No	Life list	2012 list	24 hr	Garden	Holiday	Jan	Feb	Mar	Apr	May	Jun	Jul	Aug	Sep	Oct	Nov	Dec
A	Night Heron	Nycticorax nycticorax	NT	E		0104																	
A	Green Heron	Butorides virescens	HR		R	0107																	
A	Squacco Heron	Ardeola ralloides	QH		R	0108																	
A	Cattle Egret	Bubulcus ibis	EC	B		0111																	
A	Snowy Egret	Egretta thula			R	0115																	
*A	Little Egret	E. garzetta	ET	A		0119																	
A	Great Egret	Ardea alba	HW	C		0121																	
A	Grey Heron	A. cinerea	H			0122																	
A	Great Blue Heron	A. herodias			R	1230																	
A	Purple Heron	A. purpurea	UR	B		0124																	
A	Black Stork	Ciconia nigra	OS		R	0131																	
A	White Stork	C. ciconia	OR	C		0134																	
A	Glossy Ibis	Plegadis falcinellus	IB		R	0136																	
*A	Spoonbill	Platalea leucorodia	NB	A		0144																	
A	Pied-billed Grebe	Podilymbus podiceps	PJ	B	R	0006																	
*A	Little Grebe	Tachybaptus ruficollis	LG			0007																	
*A	Great Crested Grebe	Podiceps cristatus	GG			0009																	
*A	Red-necked Grebe	P. grisegena	RX	B		0010																	
*A	Slavonian Grebe	P. auritus	SZ	A		0011																	
*A	Black-necked Grebe	P. nigricollis	BN	A		0012																	
*A	Honey-buzzard	Pernis apivorus	HZ	A		0231																	
A	Black Kite	Milvus migrans	KB	B		0238																	
*AC3	Red Kite	M. milvus	KT	A		0239																	
*AC3E	White-tailed Eagle	Haliaeetus albicilla	WE	A		0243																	
	Sub total																						

BOU	RAPTORS AND RAIL		Life list	2012 list	24 hr	Garden	Holiday	Jan	Feb	Mar	Apr	May	Jun	Jul	Aug	Sep	Oct	Nov	Dec		BTO	RBBP	BBRC	EU No
B	Egyptian Vulture	Neophron percnopterus																					R	0247
A	Short-toed Eagle	Circaetus gallicus																					R	0256
*A	Marsh Harrier	Circus aeruginosus																			MR			0260
*A	Hen Harrier	C. cyaneus																			HH	A		0261
A	Pallid Harrier	C. macrourus																				C	R	0262
*A	Montagu's Harrier	C. pygargus																			MO	A		0263
AC3E	Goshawk	Accipiter gentilis																			GI	A		0267
*A	Sparrowhawk	A. nisus																			SH			0269
*A	Buzzard	Buteo buteo																			BZ			0287
*A	Rough-legged Buzzard	B. lagopus																			RF	C		0290
B	Greater Spotted Eagle	Aquila clanga																					R	0293
*A	Golden Eagle	A. chrysaetos																			EA	A		0296
*A	Osprey	Pandion haliaetus																			OP	A		0301
A	Lesser Kestrel	Falco naumanni																					R	0303
*A	Kestrel	F. tinnunculus																			K			0304
A	American Kestrel	F. sparverius																					R	0305
*A	Red-footed Falcon	F. vespertinus																			FV			0307
A	Amur Falcon	F. amurensis																					R	
*A	Merlin	F. columbarius																			ML	A		0309
*A	Hobby	F. subbuteo																			HY	A		0310
A	Eleonora's Falcon	F. eleonorae																					R	0311
*A	Gyrfalcon	F. rusticolus																			YF	C	R	0318
*A	Peregrine	F. peregrinus																			PE	A		0320
*A	Water Rail	Rallus aquaticus																			WA	A		0407
	Sub total																							

LOG CHARTS

69

BOU	CRAKES, GALLINULES, CRANES, BUSTARDS AND WADERS		Life list	2012 list	24 hr	Garden	Holiday	Jan	Feb	Mar	Apr	May	Jun	Jul	Aug	Sep	Oct	Nov	Dec				BTO	RBBP	BBRC	EU No
*A	Spotted Crake	Porzana porzana																					AK	A		0408
A	Sora	P. carolina																							R	0409
A	Little Crake	P. parva																					JC		R	0410
A	Baillon's Crake	P. pusilla																					VC	C	R	0411
*A	Corncrake	Crex crex																					CE	A		0421
*A	Moorhen	Gallinula chloropus																					MH			0424
A	Allen's Gallinule	Porphyrio alleni																							R	0425
A	Purple Gallinule	P. martinica																							R	0426
*A	Coot	Fulica atra																					CO			0429
A	American Coot	F. americana																							R	0430
*A	Crane	Grus grus																					AN	A		0433
A	Sandhill Crane	G. canadensis																							R	0436
A	Little Bustard	Tetrax tetrax																							R	0442
A	Macqueen's Bustard	Chlamydotis macqueenii																							R	0444
A	Great Bustard	Otis tarda																					US	B	R	0446
*A	Oystercatcher	Haematopus ostralegus																					OC			0450
*A	Black-winged Stilt	Himantopus himantopus																					IT	B	R	0455
*A	Avocet	Recurvirostra avosetta																					AV	A		0456
*A	Stone-curlew	Burhinus oedicnemus																					TN	A		0459
A	Cream-coloured Courser	Cursorius cursor																							R	0464
A	Collared Pratincole	Glareola pratincola																							R	0465
A	Oriental Pratincole	G. maldivarum																					GM		R	0466
A	Black-winged Pratincole	G. nordmanni																					KW		R	0467
*A	Little Ringed Plover	Charadrius dubius																					LP	A		0469
	Sub total																									

BOU	WADERS Cont		Life list	2012 list	24 hr	Garden	Holiday	Jan	Feb	Mar	Apr	May	Jun	Jul	Aug	Sep	Oct	Nov	Dec				BTO	RBBP	BBRC	EU No
*A	Ringed Plover	C. hiaticula																					RP			0470
A	Semipalmated Plover	C. semipalmatus																					TV		R	0471
A	Killdeer	C. vociferus																					KL	C	R	0474
A	Kentish Plover	C. alexandrinus																					KP	B		0477
A	Lesser Sand Plover	C. mongolus																							R	0478
A	Greater Sand Plover	C. leschenaultii																							R	0479
A	Caspian Plover	C. asiaticus																							R	0480
*A	Dotterel	C. morinellus																					DO	A		0482
A	American Golden Plover	Pluvialis dominica																					ID			0484
A	Pacific Golden Plover	P. fulva																					IF		R	0484
*A	Golden Plover	P. apricaria																					GP			0485
*A	Grey Plover	P. squatarola																					GV			0486
A	Sociable Lapwing	Vanellus gregarius																					IP		R	0491
A	White-tailed Lapwing	V. leucurus																							R	0492
*A	Lapwing	V. vanellus																					L			0493
A	Great Knot	Calidris tenuirostris																					KO		R	0495
*A	Knot	C. canutus																					KN			0496
*A	Sanderling	C. alba																					SS	C		0497
A	Semipalmated Sandpiper	C. pusilla																					PZ		R	0498
A	Western Sandpiper	C. mauri																					ER		R	0499
A	Red-necked Stint	C. ruficollis																							R	0500
*A	Little Stint	C. minuta																					LX			0501
*A	Temminck's Stint	C. temminckii																					TK	B		0502
A	Long-toed Stint	C. subminuta																							R	0503
	Sub total																									

71

BOU	WADERS Cont		Life list	2012 list	24 hr	Garden	Holiday	Jan	Feb	Mar	Apr	May	Jun	Jul	Aug	Sep	Oct	Nov	Dec				BTO	RBBP	BBRC	EU No
A	Least Sandpiper	C. minutilla																					EP		R	0504
A	White-rumped Sandpiper	C. fuscicollis																					WU			0505
A	Baird's Sandpiper	C. bairdii																					BP		R	0506
A	Pectoral Sandpiper	C. melanotos																					PP	C		0507
A	Sharp-tailed Sandpiper	C. acuminata																					VV		R	0508
*A	Curlew Sandpiper	C. ferruginea																					CV			0509
A	Stilt Sandpiper	C. himantopus																							R	5150
*A	Purple Sandpiper	C. maritima																					PS	A		0510
*A	Dunlin	C. alpina																					DN			0512
A	Broad-billed Sandpiper	Limicola falcinellus																					OA	C	R	0514
A	Buff-breasted Sandpiper	Tryngites subruficollis																					BQ	C		0516
*A	Ruff	Philomachus pugnax																					RU	A		0517
*A	Jack Snipe	Lymnocryptes minimus																					JS	C		0518
*A	Snipe	Gallinago gallinago																					SN			0519
A	Wilson's Snipe	G. delicata																							R	5192
A	Great Snipe	G. media																					DS		R	0520
A	Short-billed Dowitcher	Limnodromus griseus																							R	0526
A	Long-billed Dowitcher	L. scolopaceus																					LD		R	0527
*A	Woodcock	Scolopax rusticola																					WK			0529
*A	Black-tailed Godwit	Limosa limosa																					BW	A		0532
A	Hudsonian Godwit	L. haemastica																					HU		R	0533
*A	Bar-tailed Godwit	L. lapponica																					BA	C		0534
A	Little Whimbrel	Numenius minutus																							R	0536
B	Eskimo Curlew	N. borealis																							R	0537
	Sub total																									

BOU	WADERS Cont, PHALAROPES AND SKUAS		Life list	2012 list	24 hr	Garden	Holiday	Jan	Feb	Mar	Apr	May	Jun	Jul	Aug	Sep	Oct	Nov	Dec	BTO	RBBP	BBRC	EU No
*A	Whimbrel	N. phaeopus																		WM	A		0538
A	Slender-billed Curlew	N. tenuirostris																				R	0540
*A	Curlew	N. arquata																		CU			0541
A	Upland Sandpiper	Bartramia longicauda																		UP		R	0544
A	Terek Sandpiper	Xenus cinereus																		TR		R	0555
*A	Common Sandpiper	Actitis hypoleucos																		CS			0556
A	Spotted Sandpiper	A. macularius																		PQ	B	R	0557
*A	Green Sandpiper	Tringa ochropus																		GE	A		0553
A	Solitary Sandpiper	T. solitaria																		I		R	0552
A	Grey-tailed Tattler	T. brevipes																		YT		R	0558
*A	Spotted Redshank	T. erythropus																		DR			0545
A	Greater Yellowlegs	T. melanoleuca																		LZ		R	0550
*A	Greenshank	T. nebularia																		GK	A	R	0548
A	Lesser Yellowlegs	T. flavipes																		LY		R	0551
*A	Marsh Sandpiper	T. stagnatilis																		MD		R	0547
A	Wood Sandpiper	T. glareola																		OD	A		0554
*A	Redshank	T. totanus																		RK			0546
*A	Turnstone	Arenaria interpres																		TT	C		0561
A	Wilson's Phalarope	Phalaropus tricolor																		WF		R	0563
*A	Red-necked Phalarope	P. lobatus																		NK	A		0564
*A	Grey Phalarope	Phalaropus fulicarius																		PL			0565
*A	Pomarine Skua	Stercorarius pomarinus																		PK			0566
*A	Arctic Skua	S. parasiticus																		AC	A		0567
*A	Long-tailed Skua	S. longicaudus																		OG			0568
	Sub total																						

73

BOU	GULLS		Life list	2012 list	24 hr	Garden	Holiday	Jan	Feb	Mar	Apr	May	Jun	Jul	Aug	Sep	Oct	Nov	Dec			BTO	RBBP	BBRC	EU No
*A	Great Skua	S. skua																				NX			0569
A	Ivory Gull	Pagophila eburnea																				IV		R	0604
*A	Sabine's Gull	Larus sabini																				AB			0579
*A	Kittiwake	Rissa tridactyla																				KI			0602
A	Slender-billed Gull	Chroicocephalus genei																				EI		R	0585
A	Bonaparte's Gull	C. philadelphia																				ON	C	R	0581
*A	Black-headed Gull	C. ridibundus																				BH			0582
*A	Little Gull	Hydrocoloeus minutus																				LU	B		0578
A	Ross's Gull	Rhodostethia rosea																				QG		R	0601
*A	Laughing Gull	Larus atricilla																				LF		R	0576
A	Franklin's Gull	L. pipixcan																				FG		R	0577
*A	Mediterranean Gull	L. melanocephalus																				MU	A		0575
A	Audouin's Gull	L. audouinii																							0589
B	Great Black-headed Gull	L. ichthyaetus																						R	0573
*A	Common Gull	L. canus																				CM			0590
*A	Ring-billed Gull	L. delawarensis																				IN	B		0588
*A	Lesser Black-backed Gull	L. fuscus																				LB			0591
*A	Herring Gull	L. argentatus																				HG			0592
A	Yellow-legged Gull	L. michahellis																					A		5927
A	Caspian Gull	L. cachinnans																							5927
A	American Herring Gull	L. smithsonianus																						R	26632
*A	Iceland Gull	L. glaucoides																				IG			0598
A	Glaucous-winged Gull	L. glaucescens																						R	5960
*A	Glaucous Gull	L. hyperboreus																				GZ	B		0599
	Sub total																								

GULLS Cont, TERNS, AND AUKS

BOU	Name	Scientific name	Life list	2012 list	24 hr	Garden	Holiday	Jan	Feb	Mar	Apr	May	Jun	Jul	Aug	Sep	Oct	Nov	Dec	BTO	RBBP	BBRC	EU No
*A	Great Black-backed Gull	L. marinus																		GB			0600
A	Aleutian Tern	Onychoprion aleutica																				R	0617
A	Sooty Tern	O. fuscata																				R	0623
A	Bridled Tern	O. anaethetus																				R	0622
A	Little Tern	Sternula albifrons																		AF	A		0624
*A	Gull-billed Tern	Gelochelidon nilotica																		TG	B	R	0605
A	Caspian Tern	Hydroprogne caspia																		CJ		R	0606
*A	Whiskered Tern	Chlidonias hybrida																		WD		R	0626
*A	Black Tern	C. niger																		BJ	C		0627
*A	White-winged Black Tern	C. leucopterus																		WJ			0628
*A	Sandwich Tern	Sterna sandvicensis																		TE			0611
A	Royal Tern	S. maxima																		QT		R	0607
A	Lesser Crested Tern	S. bengalensis																		TF	B	R	0609
A	Forster's Tern	S. forsteri																		FO		R	0618
*A	Common Tern	S. hirundo																		CN			0615
*A	Roseate Tern	S. dougallii																		RS	A		0614
*A	Arctic Tern	S. paradisaea																		AE			0616
*A	Guillemot	Uria aalge																		GU			0634
A	Brunnich's Guillemot	U. lomvia																		TZ		R	0635
*A	Razorbill	Alca torda																		RA			0636
B	Great Auk (extinct)	Pinguinus impennis																					
*A	Black Guillemot	Cepphus grylle																		TY			0638
A	Long-billed Murrelet	Brachyramphus perdix																				R	6412
A	Ancient Murrelet	Synthliboramphus antiquus																				R	0645
	Sub total																						

75

AUKS, DOVES, CUCKOOS AND OWLS

BOU	Name	Scientific name	Life list	2012 list	24 hr	Garden	Holiday	Jan	Feb	Mar	Apr	May	Jun	Jul	Aug	Sep	Oct	Nov	Dec	BTO	RBBP	BBRC	EU No
*A	Little Auk	Alle alle																		LK			0647
*A	Puffin	Fratercula arctica																		PU			0654
A	Tufted Puffin	F. cirrhata																					
A	Pallas's Sandgrouse	Syrrhaptes paradoxus																				R	0663
AC4E	Rock Dove / Feral Pigeon	Columba livia																		DV			0665
*A	Stock Dove	C. oenas																		SD			0668
*A	Woodpigeon	C. palumbus																		WP			0670
*A	Collared Dove	Streptopelia decaocto																		CD			0684
*A	Turtle Dove	S. turtur																		TD			0687
A	Rufous Turtle Dove	S. orientalis																				R	0689
A	Mourning Dove	Zenaida macroura																				R	0695
C1E	Ring-necked Parakeet	Psittacula krameri																		RI			0712
A	Great Spotted Cuckoo	Clamator glandarius																		UK		R	0716
*A	Cuckoo	Cuculus canorus																		CK			0724
A	Black-billed Cuckoo	Coccyzus erythrophthalmus																				R	0727
A	Yellow-billed Cuckoo	C. americanus																				R	0728
*A	Barn Owl	Tyto alba																		BO			0735
A	Scops Owl	Otus scops																			C	R	0739
*A	Snowy Owl	Bubo scandiacus																		SO	B	R	0749
A	Hawk Owl	Surnia ulula																				R	0750
*C1	Little Owl	Athene noctua																		LO			0757
*A	Tawny Owl	Strix aluco																		TO			0761
*A	Long-eared Owl	Asio otus																		LE	A		0767
*A	Short-eared Owl	A. flammeus																		SE	A		0768
	Sub total																						

NIGHTJARS, SWIFTS, KINGFISHERS, BEE-EATERS AND WOODPECKERS

BOU	Common name	Scientific name	Life list	2012 list	24 hr	Garden	Holiday	Jan	Feb	Mar	Apr	May	Jun	Jul	Aug	Sep	Oct	Nov	Dec	BTO	RBBP	BBRC	EU No
A	Tengmalm's Owl	Aegolius funereus																				R	0770
*A	Nightjar	Caprimulgus europaeus																		NJ			0778
B	Red-necked Nightjar	C. ruficollis																				R	0779
A	Egyptian Nightjar	C. aegyptius																				R	0781
A	Common Nighthawk	Chordeiles minor																				R	0786
A	Chimney Swift	Chaetura pelagica																				R	0790
A	Needle-tailed Swift	Hirundapus caudacutus																		NI		R	0792
*A	Swift	Apus apus																		SI			0795
A	Pallid Swift	A. pallidus																			C	R	0796
A	Pacific Swift	A. pacificus																				R	0797
A	Alpine Swift	A. melba																		AI			0798
A	Little Swift	A. affinis																				R	0800
*A	Kingfisher	Alcedo atthis																		KF			0831
A	Belted Kingfisher	Megaceryle alcyon																				R	0834
A	Blue-cheeked Bee-eater	Merops persicus																				R	0839
*A	Bee-eater	M. apiaster																		MZ	B		0840
A	Roller	Coracias garrulus																				R	0841
*A	Hoopoe	Upupa epops																		HP	B		0846
*A	Wryneck	Jynx torquilla																		WY	A		0848
*A	Green Woodpecker	Picus viridis																		G			0856
A	Yellow-bellied Sapsucker	Sphyrapicus varius																				R	0872
*A	Great Spotted Woodpecker	Dendrocopos major																		GS			0876
*A	Lesser Spotted Woodpecker	D. minor																		LS	A		0887
A	Eastern Phoebe	Sayornis phoebe																				R	0909
	Sub total																						

77

BOU	VIREOS, SHRIKES, CORVIDS AND 'CRESTS		Life list	2012 list	24 hr	Garden	Holiday	Jan	Feb	Mar	Apr	May	Jun	Jul	Aug	Sep	Oct	Nov	Dec			BTO	RBBP	BBRC	EU No
A	Yellow-throated Vireo	Vireo flavifrons																							1628
A	Philadelphia Vireo	V. philadelphicus																						R	1631
A	Red-eyed Vireo	V. olivaceus																				EV		R	1633
*A	Golden Oriole	Oriolus oriolus																				OL	A		1508
A	Brown Shrike	Lanius cristatus																						R	1513
A	Isabelline Shrike	L. isabellinus																				IL		R	1514
*A	Red-backed Shrike	L. collurio																				ED	A		1515
A	Long-tailed Shrike	L. schach																							1517
*A	Lesser Grey Shrike	L. minor																						R	1519
*A	Great Grey Shrike	L. excubitor																				SR	C		1520
A	Southern Grey Shrike	L. meridionalis																						R	1520
A	Woodchat Shrike	L. senator																				OO			1523
A	Masked Shrike	L. nubicus																						R	1524
*A	Chough	Pyrrhocorax pyrrhocorax																				CF	A		1559
*A	Magpie	Pica pica																				MG			1549
*A	Jay	Garrulus glandarius																				J			1539
A	Nutcracker	Nucifraga caryocatactes																				NC		R	1557
*A	Jackdaw	Corvus monedula																				JD			1560
*A	Rook	C. frugilegus																				RO			1563
*A	Carrion Crow	C. corone																				C			1567
*A	Hooded Crow	C. cornix																							1567
*A	Raven	C. corax																				RN			1572
*A	Goldcrest	Regulus regulus																				GC			1314
*A	Firecrest	R. ignicapilla																				FC	A		1315
	Sub total																							

BOU	TITS, LARKS, MARTINS AND SWALLOWS		Life list	2012 list	24 hr	Garden	Holiday	Jan	Feb	Mar	Apr	May	Jun	Jul	Aug	Sep	Oct	Nov	Dec			BTO	RBBP	BBRC	EU No
A	Penduline Tit	Remiz pendulinus																				DT	C	R	1490
*A	Blue Tit	Cyanistes caeruleus																				BT			1462
*A	Great Tit	Parus major																				GT			1464
*A	Crested Tit	Lophophanes cristatus																				CI			1454
*A	Coal Tit	Periparus ater																				CT			1461
*A	Willow Tit	Poecile montana																				WT	A		1442
*A	Marsh Tit	P. palustris																				MT			1440
*A	Bearded Tit	Panurus biarmicus																				BR	A		1364
A	Calandra Lark	Melanocorypha calandra																						R	0961
A	Bimaculated Lark	M. bimaculata																						R	0962
A	White-winged Lark	M. leucoptera																						R	0965
A	Black Lark	M. yeltoniensis																						R	0966
A	Short-toed Lark	Calandrella brachydactyla																				VL			0968
A	Lesser Short-toed Lark	C. rufescens																						R	0970
A	Crested Lark	Galerida cristata																						R	0972
*A	Woodlark	Lullula arborea																				WL	A		0974
*A	Skylark	Alauda arvensis																				S			0976
*A	Shore Lark	Eremophila alpestris																				SX	B		0978
*A	Sand Martin	Riparia riparia																				SM			0981
A	Tree Swallow	Tachycineta bicolor																						R	0983
A	Purple Martin	Progne subis																						R	0989
A	Crag Martin	Ptyonoprogne rupestris																						R	0991
*A	Swallow	Hirundo rustica																				SL			0992
*A	House Martin	Delichon urbicum																				HM			1001
	Sub total																								

79

SWALLOWS Cont, WARBLERS

BOU		Life list	2012 list	24 hr	Garden	Holiday	Jan	Feb	Mar	Apr	May	Jun	Jul	Aug	Sep	Oct	Nov	Dec	BTO	RBBP	BBRC	EU No
A	Red-rumped Swallow *Cecropis daurica*																		VR	C		0995
A	Cliff Swallow *Petrochelidon pyrrhonota*																				R	0998
*A	Cetti's Warbler *Cettia cetti*																		CW	A		1220
*A	Long-tailed Tit *Aegithalos caudatus*																		LT			1437
A	Eastern Crowned Warbler *Phylloscopus coronatus*																				R	12910
A	Green Warbler *P. nitidus*																		NP	C		1293
A	Greenish Warbler *P. trochiloides*																					1295
A	Arctic Warbler *P. borealis*																		AP		R	1295
A	Pallas's Warbler *P. proregulus*																		PA			1298
*A	Yellow-browed Warbler *P. inornatus*																		YB			1300
A	Hume's Warbler *P. humei*																				R	1300
A	Radde's Warbler *P. schwarzi*																					1301
A	Dusky Warbler *P. fuscatus*																		UY			1303
A	Western Bonelli's Warbler *P. bonelli*																		IW		R	1307
*A	Eastern Bonelli's Warbler *P. orientalis*																				R	1307
*A	Wood Warbler *P. sibilatrix*																		WO			1308
*A	Chiffchaff *P. collybita*																		CC			1311
A	Iberian Chiffchaff *P. ibericus*																			C	R	1311
*A	Willow Warbler *P. trochilus*																		WW			1312
*A	Blackcap *Sylvia atricapilla*																		BC			1277
*A	Garden Warbler *S. borin*																		GW			1276
A	Barred Warbler *S. nisoria*																		RR			1273
*A	Lesser Whitethroat *S. curruca*																		LW			1274
A	Orphean Warbler *S. hortensis*																				R	1272
	Sub total																					

WARBLERS Cont

BOU	Species	Life list	2012 list	24 hr	Garden	Holiday	Jan	Feb	Mar	Apr	May	Jun	Jul	Aug	Sep	Oct	Nov	Dec	BTO	RBBP	BBRC	EU No
A	Desert Warbler *S. nana*																			C	R	1270
*A	Whitethroat *S. communis*																		WH			1275
A	Spectacled Warbler *S. conspicillata*																			C	R	1264
*A	Dartford Warbler *S. undata*																		DW	A		1262
A	Marmora's Warbler *S. sarda*																		MM	C	R	1261
A	Rüppell's Warbler *S. rueppelli*																				R	1269
A	Subalpine Warbler *S. cantillans*																			C		1265
A	Sardinian Warbler *S. melanocephala*																			C	R	1267
A	Pallas's Grasshopper Warbler *Locustella certhiola*																				R	1233
A	Lanceolated Warbler *L. lanceolata*																				R	1235
*A	Grasshopper Warbler *L. naevia*																		GH			1236
A	River Warbler *L. fluviatilis*																		VW	C	R	1237
A	Savi's Warbler *L. luscinioides*																		VI	A	R	1238
A	Eastern Olivaceous Warbler *ippolais pallida*																				R	1255
A	Booted Warbler *H. caligata*																			C	R	1256
A	Sykes's Warbler *H. rama*																				R	12562
A	Olive-tree Warbler *H. olivetorum*																				R	12580
*A	Icterine Warbler *H. icterina*																		IC	B		1259
*A	Melodious Warbler *H. polyglotta*																		ME	C		1260
A	Aquatic Warbler *Acrocephalus paludicola*																		AQ			1242
*A	Sedge Warbler *A. schoenobaenus*																		SW			1243
A	Paddyfield Warbler *A. agricola*																		PY		R	1247
A	Blyth's Reed Warbler *A. dumetorum*																			C	R	1248
*A	Marsh Warbler *A. palustris*																		MW	A		1250
	Sub total																					

BOU	WARBLERS Cont, NUTHATCHES, TREECREEPERS, THRUSHES		Life list	2012 list	24 hr	Garden	Holiday	Jan	Feb	Mar	Apr	May	Jun	Jul	Aug	Sep	Oct	Nov	Dec	BTO	RBBP	BBRC	EU No
*A	Reed Warbler	A. scirpaceus																		RW			1251
A	Great Reed Warbler	A. arundinaceus																		QW	C	R	1253
A	Thick-billed Warbler	A. aedon																				R	1254
A	Fan-tailed Warbler	Cisticola juncidis																				R	1226
A	Cedar Waxwing	Bombycilla cedrorum																				R	1046
*A	Waxwing	B. garrulus																		WX	C		1048
A	Wallcreeper	Tichodroma muraria																				R	1482
A	Red-breasted Nuthatch	Sitta canadensis																				R	1472
*A	Nuthatch	S. europaea																		NH			1479
*A	Treecreeper	Certhia familiaris																		TC			1486
A	Short-toed Treecreeper	C. brachydactyla																		TH	C	R	1487
*A	Wren	Troglodytes troglodytes																		WR			1066
A	Northern Mockingbird	Mimus polyglottos																				R	1067
A	Brown Thrasher	Toxostoma rufum																				R	1069
A	Grey Catbird	Dumetella carolinensis																				R	1080
*A	Starling	Sturnus vulgaris																		SG			1582
A	Rose-coloured Starling	S. roseus																		OE			1594
*A	Dipper	Cinclus cinclus																		DI			1050
A	White's Thrush	Zoothera dauma																				R	1170
A	Siberian Thrush	Z. sibirica																				R	1171
A	Varied Thrush	Ixoreus naevius																		VT		R	1172
A	Wood Thrush	Hylocichla mustelina																				R	1175
A	Hermit Thrush	Catharus guttatus																				R	1176
A	Swainson's Thrush	C. ustulatus																				R	1177
	Sub total																						

LOG CHARTS

BOU	THRUSHES Cont, CHATS		Life list	2012 list	24 hr	Garden	Holiday	Jan	Feb	Mar	Apr	May	Jun	Jul	Aug	Sep	Oct	Nov	Dec			BTO	RBBP	BBRC	EU No
A	Grey-cheeked Thrush	C. minimus																						R	1178
A	Veery	C. fuscescens																						R	1179
*A	Ring Ouzel	Turdus torquatus																				RZ			1186
*A	Blackbird	T. merula																				B			1187
A	Eyebrowed Thrush	T. obscurus																						R	1195
A	Dusky Thrush	T. naumanni																						R	1196
A	Naumann's Thrush	T. naumanni																						R	11960
A	Black-throated Thrush	T. atrogularis																						R	1197
A	Red-throated Thrush	T. ruficollis																						R	11970
*A	Fieldfare	T. pilaris																				FF	A		1198
*A	Song Thrush	T. philomelos																				ST			1200
*A	Redwing	T. iliacus																				RE	A		1201
*A	Mistle Thrush	T. viscivorus																				M			1202
A	American Robin	T. migratorius																				AR		R	1203
A	Brown Flycatcher	Muscicapa dauurica																						R	
*A	Spotted Flycatcher	M. striata																							1335
A	Rufous Bush Chat	Cercotrichas galactotes																						R	1095
*A	Robin	Erithacus rubecula																				R			1099
A	Rufous-tailed Robin	Luscinia sibilans																						R	1102
A	Thrush Nightingale	L. luscinia																				FN		R	1103
*A	Nightingale	L. megarhynchos																				N	C		1104
A	Siberian Rubythroat	L. calliope																						R	1105
A	Bluethroat	L. svecica																				BU	B		1106
A	Siberian Blue Robin	L. cyane																						R	1112
	Sub total																								

CHATS, WHEATEARS, FLYCATCHERS, SPARROWS

BOU	Species	Scientific	Life list	2012 list	24 hr	Garden	Holiday	Jan	Feb	Mar	Apr	May	Jun	Jul	Aug	Sep	Oct	Nov	Dec	BTO	RBBP	BBRC	EU No
A	Red-flanked Bluetail	Tarsiger cyanurus																				R	1113
A	White-throated Robin	Irania gutturalis																				R	1117
*A	Black Redstart	Phoenicurus ochruros																		BX	A		1121
*A	Redstart	P. phoenicurus																		RT			1122
A	Moussier's Redstart	P. moussieri																				R	1127
*A	Whinchat	Saxicola rubetra																		WC			1137
*A	Stonechat	S. torquatus																		SC			1139
A	Isabelline Wheatear	Oenanthe isabellina																				R	1144
*A	Wheatear	O. oenanthe																		W			1146
A	Pied Wheatear	O. pleschanka																		PI		R	1147
A	Black-eared Wheatear	O. hispanica																				R	1148
A	Desert Wheatear	O. deserti																				R	1149
A	White-crowned Black Wheatear	O. leucopyga																				R	1157
A	Rock Thrush	Monticola saxatilis																		OH		R	1162
A	Blue Rock Thrush	M. solitarius																				R	1166
*A	Red-breasted Flycatcher	Ficedula parva																		FY			1343
A	Taiga Flycatcher	F. albicilla																				R	1343
A	Collared Flycatcher	F. albicollis																				R	1348
*A	Pied Flycatcher	F. hypoleuca																		PF			1349
*A	Dunnock	Prunella modularis																		D			1084
A	Alpine Accentor	P. collaris																				R	1094
*A	House Sparrow	Passer domesticus																		HS			1591
A	Spanish Sparrow	P. hispaniolensis																				R	1592
*A	Tree Sparrow	P. montanus																		TS			1598
	Sub total																						

BOU	WAGTAILS, PIPITS AND FINCHES		Life list	2012 list	24 hr	Garden	Holiday	Jan	Feb	Mar	Apr	May	Jun	Jul	Aug	Sep	Oct	Nov	Dec			BTO	RBBP	BBRC	EU No
A	Rock Sparrow	Petronia petronia																						R	1604
*A	Yellow Wagtail	Motacilla flava																				YW			1017
A	Citrine Wagtail	M. citreola																					C	R	1018
*A	Grey Wagtail	M. cinerea																				GL			1019
*A	Pied Wagtail	M. alba																				PW			1020
A	Richard's Pipit	Anthus richardi																				PR			1002
A	Blyth's Pipit	A. godlewskii																						R	1004
A	Tawny Pipit	A. campestris																				TI			1005
A	Olive-backed Pipit	A. hodgsoni																				OV		R	1008
*A	Tree Pipit	A. trivialis																				TP			1009
A	Pechora Pipit	A. gustavi																						R	1010
*A	Meadow Pipit	A. pratensis																				MP			1011
A	Red-throated Pipit	A. cervinus																				VP			1012
*A	Rock Pipit	A. petrosus																				RC			1014
*A	Water Pipit	A. spinoletta																				WI			1014
A	Buff-bellied Pipit	A. rubescens																						R	1014
*A	Chaffinch	Fringilla coelebs																				CH			1636
*A	Brambling	F. montifringilla																				BL	B		1638
*A	Serin	Serinus serinus																				NS	B		1640
*A	Greenfinch	Carduelis chloris																				GR			1649
A	Citril Finch	C. citrinella																						R	
*A	Goldfinch	C. carduelis																				GO			1653
*A	Siskin	C. spinus																				SK			1654
*A	Linnet	C. cannabina																				LI			1660
	Sub total																								

85

FINCHES, NEW WORLD WARBLERS

BOU	Common name	Scientific name	Life list	2012 list	24 hr	Garden	Holiday	Jan	Feb	Mar	Apr	May	Jun	Jul	Aug	Sep	Oct	Nov	Dec	BTO	RBBP	BBRC	EU No
*A	Twite	C. flavirostris																		TW			1662
*A	Lesser Redpoll	C. cabaret																		LR			1663
*A	Mealy Redpoll	C. flammea																			A		1663
A	Arctic Redpoll	C. hornemanni																		AL			1664
*A	Two-barred Crossbill	Loxia leucoptera																		PD		R	1665
*A	Common Crossbill	L. curvirostra																		CR			1666
*A	Scottish Crossbill	L. scotica																		CY			1667
*A	Parrot Crossbill	L. pytyopsittacus																		PC	A		1668
A	Trumpeter Finch	Bucanetes githagineus																				R	1676
*A	Common Rosefinch	Carpodacus erythrinus																		SQ	B		1679
A	Pine Grosbeak	Pinicola enucleator																				R	1699
*A	Bullfinch	Pyrrhula pyrrhula																		BF			1710
*A	Hawfinch	Coccothraustes coccothraustes																		HF	A		1717
A	Evening Grosbeak	Hesperiphona vespertina																				R	1718
*A	Snow Bunting	Plectrophenax nivalis																		SB	A		1850
A	Lapland Bunting	Calcarius lapponicus																		LA	B		1847
A	Summer Tanager	Piranga rubra																				R	1786
A	Scarlet Tanager	P. olivacea																				R	1788
A	Rose-breasted Grosbeak	Pheucticus ludovicianus																				R	1887
A	Indigo Bunting	Passerina cyanea																				R	1892
A	Eastern Towhee	Pipilo erythrophthalmus																				R	1798
A	Lark Sparrow	Chondestes grammacus																				R	1824
A	Savannah Sparrow	Passerculus sandwichensis																				R	1826
A	Song Sparrow	Melospiza melodia																				R	1835
	Sub total																						

BOU	NEW WORLD WARBLERS, SPARROWS, BUNTINGS		Life list	2012 list	24 hr	Garden	Holiday	Jan	Feb	Mar	Apr	May	Jun	Jul	Aug	Sep	Oct	Nov	Dec			BTO	RBBP	BBRC	EU No
A	White-crowned Sparrow	Zonotrichia leucophrys																						R	1839
A	White-throated Sparrow	Z. albicollis																						R	1840
A	Dark-eyed Junco	Junco hyemalis																				JU		R	1842
A	Black-faced Bunting	Emberiza spodocephala																						R	1853
A	Pine Bunting	E. leucocephalos																				EL		R	1856
*A	Yellowhammer	E. citrinella																				Y			1857
*A	Cirl Bunting	E. cirlus																				CL	A		1958
A	Rock Bunting	E. cia																						R	1860
A	Ortolan Bunting	E. hortulana																				OB			1866
A	Cretzschmar's Bunting	E. caesia																						R	1868
A	Yellow-browed Bunting	E. chrysophrys																						R	1871
A	Rustic Bunting	E. rustica																							1873
A	Chestnut-eared Bunting	E. fucata																						R	1869
A	Little Bunting	E. pusilla																				LJ			1874
A	Yellow-breasted Bunting	E. aureola																					C	R	1876
*A	Reed Bunting	E. schoeniclus																				RB			1877
A	Pallas's Reed Bunting	E. pallasi																						R	1878
A	Black-headed Bunting	E. melanocephala																						R	1881
*A	Corn Bunting	E. calandra																				CB			1882
A	Bobolink	Dolichonyx oryzivorus																						R	1897
A	Brown-headed Cowbird	Molothrus ater																						R	1899
A	Baltimore Oriole	Icterus galbula																						R	1918
A	Black-and-white Warbler	Mniotilta varia																						R	1720
A	Golden-winged Warbler	Vermivora chrysoptera																						R	1722
	Sub total																								

87

BOU	WARBLERS Cont		Life list	2012 list	24 hr	Garden	Holiday	Jan	Feb	Mar	Apr	May	Jun	Jul	Aug	Sep	Oct	Nov	Dec			BTO	RBBP	BBRC	EU No
A	Tennessee Warbler	*V. peregrina*																						R	1724
A	Northern Parula	*Parula americana*																						R	1732
A	Yellow Warbler	*Dendroica petechia*																						R	1733
A	Chestnut-sided Warbler	*D. pensylvanica*																						R	1734
A	Blackburnian Warbler	*D. fusca*																						R	1747
A	Cape May Warbler	*D. tigrina*																						R	1749
A	Magnolia Warbler	*D. magnolia*																						R	1750
A	Yellow-rumped Warbler	*D. coronata*																						R	1751
A	Blackpoll Warbler	*D. striata*																						R	1753
A	Bay-breasted Warbler	*D. castanea*																						R	1754
A	American Redstart	*Setophaga ruticilla*																					AD		R	1755
A	Ovenbird	*Seiurus aurocapilla*																							R	1756
A	Northern Waterthrush	*S. noveboracensis*																							R	1757
A	Common Yellowthroat	*Geothlypis trichas*																							R	1762
A	Hooded Warbler	*Wilsonia citrina*																							R	1771
A	Wilson's Warbler	*W. pusilla*																							R	1772
	Sub total																								

CATEGORY D & E SPECIES, PLUS SELECTED EUROPEAN SPECIES

BOU	Species	Scientific name	Life list	2012 list	24 hr	Garden	Holiday	Jan	Feb	Mar	Apr	May	Jun	Jul	Aug	Sep	Oct	Nov	Dec	BTO	RBBP	BBRC	EU NO
D	Ross's Goose	*Anser rossii*																				R	0181
D	Falcated Duck	*A. falcata*																		FT		R	0183
D	Baikal Teal	*A. formosa*																		IK		R	0195
D	Marbled Duck	*Marmaronetta angustirostris*																					
EU	White-headed Duck	*Oxyura leucocephala*																		WQ			0226
EU	Rock Partridge	*Alectoris graeca*																					0357
EU	Barbary Partridge	*A. barbara*																					0359
EU	Pygmy Cormorant	*P. pygmeus*																					0082
D	Great White Pelican	*Pelecanus onocrotalus*																		YP		R	0088
EU	Dalmatian Pelican	*P. crispus*																					0089
D	Greater Flamingo	*Phoenicopterus roseus*																		FL		R	0147
EU	Black-winged Kite	*Elanus caeruleus*																					0235
D	Bald Eagle	*H. leucocephalus*																				R	0244
EU	Lammergeier	*Gypaetus barbatus*																					0246
D	Black (Monk) Vulture	*Aegypius monachus*																				R	0255
EU	Levant Sparrowhawk	*A. brevipes*																					0273
EU	Long-legged Buzzard	*B. rufinus*																					0288
EU	Lesser Spotted Eagle	*Aquila pomarina*																					0292
EU	Imperial Eagle	*A. heliaca*																					0295
EU	Booted Eagle	*Hieraaetus pennatus*																					0298
EU	Bonelli's Eagle	*H. fasciatus*																					0299
EU	Lanner Falcon	*Falco biarmicus*																		FB			0314
D	Saker Falcon	*F. cherrug*																		JF		R	0316
EU	Andalusian Hemipode	*Turnix sylvatica*																					0400
	Sub total																						

89

CATEGORY D & E SPECIES, PLUS SELECTED EUROPEAN SPECIES

BOU	Common name	Scientific name	BTO	RBBP	BBRC	EU No
EU	Purple Gallinule	Porphyrio porphyrio				0427
EL	Crested Coot	F. cristata				0431
EU	Spur-winged Plover	Hoplopterus spinosus	UW			0487
EU	Black-bellied Sandgrouse	Pterocles orientalis				0661
EU	Pin-tailed Sandgrouse	P. alchata				0662
EU	Eagle Owl	Bubo bubo	EO	bD		0744
EU	Pygmy Owl	Glaucidium passerinum				0751
EU	Ural Owl	S. uralensis				0765
EU	Great Grey Owl	S. nebulosa				0766
EL	White-rumped Swift	Apus caffer				0799
EU	Grey-headed Woodpecker	Picus canus				0855
EU	Black Woodpecker	Dryocopus martius				0863
EU	Syrian Woodpecker	D. syriacus				0878
EU	Middle Spotted Woodpecker	D. medius				0883
EU	White-backed Woodpecker	D. leucotos				0884
EU	Three-toed Woodpecker	Picoides tridactylus				0898
EU	Dupont's Lark	Chersophilus duponti				0959
EU	Thekla Lark	G. theklae				0973
EU	Black Wheatear	Oenanthe leucura			R	1158
EU	Cyprus Warbler	S. melanothorax				1268
D	Mugimaki Flycatcher	F. mugimaki			R	1344
EU	Semi-collared Flycatcher	F. semitorquata				1347
EU	Sombre Tit	P. lugubris				1441
EU	Siberian Tit	P. cinctus				1448
	Sub total					

Additional column headers (blank for all rows): Life list, 2012 list, 24 hr, Garden, Holiday, Jan, Feb, Mar, Apr, May, Jun, Jul, Aug, Sep, Oct, Nov, Dec

BOU	CATEGORY D & E SPECIES, PLUS SELECTED EUROPEAN SPECIES		Life list	2012 list	24 hr	Garden	Holiday	Jan	Feb	Mar	Apr	May	Jun	Jul	Aug	Sep	Oct	Nov	Dec	BTO	RBBP	BBRC	EU No
EU	Krüper's Nuthatch	Sitta krueperi																					1469
EU	Corsican Nuthatch	S. whiteheadi																					1470
EU	Rock Nuthatch	S. neumayer																					1481
EU	Siberian Jay	Perisoreus infaustus																					1543
EU	Azure-winged Magpie	Cyanopica cyana																					1547
EU	Alpine Chough	Pyrrhocorax graculus																					1558
D	Daurian Starling	Sturnus sturninus																				R	1579
EU	Spotless Starling	S. unicolor																					1583
D	(White-winged) Snow Finch	Montifringilla nivalis																				R	1611
D	Palm Warbler	D. palmarum																				R	1752
D	Yellow-headed Blackbird	Xanthocephalus xanthocephalus																					1911
EU	Cinereous Bunting	E. cineracea																					1865
D	Chestnut Bunting	E. rutila																				R	1875
D	Red-headed Bunting	E. bruniceps																					1880
D	Blue Grosbeak	Guiraca caerulea																				R	1891
	Sub total																						

BRITISH DRAGONFLY LIST

SPECIES	2012 list	Life list	SPECIES	2012 list	Life list
DAMSELFLIES			Common Hawker		
Calopterygidae (Demoiselles)			Migrant Hawker		
Banded Demoiselle			Vagrant Emperor		
Beautiful Demoiselle			Emperor Dragonfly		
Coenagrionidae (Blue, blue-tailed & red damselflies)			Lesser Emperor		
			Hairy Dragonfly		
Dainty Damselfly			**Cordulegastridae (Golden-ringed Dragonflies)**		
Small Red Damselfly					
Northern Damselfly			Golden-ringed Dragonfly		
Irish Damselfly			**Corduliidae (Emerald dragonflies)**		
Southern Damselfly			Downy Emerald		
Azure Damselfly			Northern Emerald		
Variable Damselfly			Brilliant Emerald		
Common Blue Damselfly			**Gomphidae (Club-tailed Dragonflies)**		
Red-eyed Damselfly					
Small Red-eyed Damselfly			Common Club-tail		
Blue-tailed Damselfly			**Libellulidae (Chasers, Skimmers and Darters)**		
Scarce Blue-tailed Damselfly					
Large Red Damselfly			Scarlet Darter		
Lestidae (Emerald damselflies)			White-faced Darter		
Southern Emerald Damselfly			Broad-bodied Chaser		
Scarce Emerald Damselfly			Scarce Chaser		
Emerald Damselfly			Four-spotted Chaser		
Willow Emerald Damselfly			Black-tailed Skimmer		
Winter Damselfly			Keeled Skimmer		
Platycnemididae (White-legged damselflies)			Wandering Glider		
White-legged Damselfly			Black Darter		
DRAGONFLIES			Vagrant Darter		
Aeshnidae (Hawkers and Emperors)			Yellow-winged Darter		
Southern Migrant Hawker			Red-veined Darter		
Azure Hawker			Banded Darter		
Southern Hawker			Ruddy Darter		
Brown Hawker			Common Darter		
Norfolk Hawker					
			TOTAL		

BRITISH BUTTERFLY LIST

SPECIES	2012 list	Life list
Hesperiidae - Skippers		
Chequered Skipper		
Lulworth Skipper		
Essex Skipper		
Small Skipper		
Silver-spotted Skipper		
Large Skipper		
Grizzled Skipper		
Dingy Skipper		
Papilionidae		
Swallowtail		
Pieridae - The Whites		
Wood White		
Clouded Yellow		
Brimstone		
Large White		
Small White		
Green-veined White		
Orange Tip		
Lycaenidae - Hairstreaks, Coppers and Blues		
Green Hairstreak		
Brown Hairstreak		
Purple Hairstreak		
White-letter Hairstreak		
Black Hairstreak		
Large Copper		
Small Copper		
Small Blue		
Silver-studded Blue		
Northern Brown Argus		
Brown Argus		
Common Blue		
Chalkhill Blue		
Adonis Blue		
Holly Blue		

SPECIES	2012 list	Life list
Large Blue		
Riodinidae - Metalmarks		
Duke of Burgundy		
Nymphalidae - Vanessids, Emperors and Fritillaries		
White Admiral		
Purple Emperor		
Painted Lady		
Small Tortoiseshell		
Red Admiral		
Peacock		
Comma		
Small Pearl-bordered Fritillary		
Pearl-bordered Fritillary		
High Brown Fritillary		
Dark Green Fritillary		
Silver-washed Fritillary		
Marsh Fritillary		
Glanville Fritillary		
Heath Fritillary		
Satyridae - The Browns		
Speckled Wood		
Wall		
Scotch Argus		
Mountain Ringlet		
Gate Keeper		
Marbled White		
Grayling		
Meadow Brown		
Ringlet		
Small Heath		
Large Heath		
TOTAL		

93

Best Birdwatching Sites

The trusted name for accurate, accessible site information

Best Birdwatching Sites: Dorset
by Neil Gartshore.
Features 65 reserves and birding areas, including a full range of habitats from heathland to coastal sites.
248 pp. **Price £17.95**

Best Birdwatching Sites: The Solway
by John Miles.
Features 76 birding sites in Cumbria and 84 in Dumfries & Galloway. 260 pp. **Price £17.50**

Best Birdwatching Sites in Cornwall & Scilly
by Sara McMahon and Nigel Hudson. Features 52 mainland sites, plus seven routes around the key islands of Scilly. 208pp.
Price: £17.50 15.00

Best Birdwatching Sites in North Wales
by Alan Davies and Owen Roberts. Features 58 major sites in Gwynedd and Clwyd, plus 11 smaller birding spots around Wrexham. 192pp. **Price: £15.95**

Best Birdwatching Sites in Norfolk
(2nd Edition) by Neil Glenn. Contains 83 sites (ten more than 1st Edition) – all information updated. 256pp.
Price: £16.95.

Best Birdwatching Sites in the Scottish Highlands
by Gordon Hamlett. Features 22 birding routes from John O'Groats to Pitlochry. 164 maps, 240pp.
Price: £15.95

Best Birdwatching Sites in Sussex
by Adrian Thomas and Peter Francis. Contains 57 sites, plus innovative migration charts. 192pp.
Price: £14.50

For details of latest special offers on our books please contact Buckingham Press, 55 Thorpe Park Road, Peterborough PE3 6LJ. 01733 561 739; or visit www.buckinghampress.co.uk (see entry on page 110).

DIRECTORY OF ARTISTS, PHOTOGRAPHERS AND LECTURERS

David Cromack

The colourful birds of North America, such as this Violet-Green Swallow, feature in many of the talks on offer from speakers in the Lecturer's Directory.

ART/PHOTOGRAPHY/LECTURERS

DIRECTORY OF
WILDLIFE ART GALLERIES

BIRDSBIRDSBIRDS GALLERY

Paul and Sue Cumberland opened Birds Birds Birds in June 2001. Now it is becoming one of the nation's leading bird art galleries. A steady increase in sales has encouraged professional wildlife artists to join the roster. Prints are now being produced and published in-house, using the giclee system. The gallery exhibits at the British Birdfair and various game fairs and county shows. **Address:** 4, Limes Place, Preston St, Faversham, Kent ME13 8PQ; 01795 532 370; email: birdsbirdsbirds@birdsbirdsbirds.co.uk www.birdsbirdsbirds.co.uk

BIRDSCAPES GALLERY

Offers top quality bird art all year round, plus landscapes and other wildlife originals, sculptures, prints, wildlife art books and cards. More than 30 regular artists, including SWLA members, are represented, with new exhibitions each month. **Opening times:** Mon-Sat, (10am-5pm), Sunday, (10am-4pm). The gallery may be closed for part of the day before a new exhibition. **Address:** The BIRDscapes Gallery, Manor Farm Barns, Glandford, Holt, Norfolk. NR25 7JP. 01263 741 742; e-mail: art@birdscapes.co.uk www.birdscapesgallery.co.uk

NATURE IN ART

The world's first museum dedicated exclusively to art inspired by nature. The collection spans 1,500 years, covers 60 countries and includes work by Tunnicliffe, Harrison, Thorburn, Scott and other bird artists. See work being created by artists in residence (see website for dates), plus a vibrant exhibitions programme. Sculpture garden, coffee shop, gift shop and children's activity areas. **Opening times:** 10am-5pm (Tuesday to Sunday and bank holidays). **Address:** Wallsworth Hall, Twigworth, Gloucester GL2 9PA (two miles N of city on A38). 01452 731 422. e-mail: enquiries@nature-in-art.org.uk www.nature-in-art.org.uk

THE WILDLIFE ART GALLERY

Opened in 1988 as a specialist in 20th Century and contemporary wildlife art. It exhibits work by many of the leading European wildlife artists, both painters and sculptors, and has published several wildlife books. **Opening times:** Mon-Sat (10am-4.30pm) and Sun (2pm-4.30pm). **Address:** 97 High Street, Lavenham, Suffolk CO10 9PZ; 01787 248 562; (Fax) 01787 247 356. E-mail: wildlifeartgallery@btinternet.com www.wildlifeartgallery.com

---

DIRECTORY OF
WILDLIFE ARTISTS

BECKETT, Andrew

Worked as a freelance illustrator for 18 years represented by the agency Illustration Ltd. Exhibited as a wildlife artist at Birds in Art and NEWA (National Exhibition of Wildlife Art). **Formats:** Original artwork, prints (mounted or framed), commissions welcome. **Artwork for sale:** Contact the artist. **Address:** 7 Buckingham Road, Lytham St Annes, Lancs FY8 4EU; 01253 730 167 mobile: 07508 254 883; e-mail: andysart@freeuk.com www.illustrationweb.com/andrewbeckett

COOK, Robert A

Careful study, thoughtful composition and evocative light are the key elements in Rob's work. He has exhibited widely, including Birds in Art, NEWA and MIWAS. In 2009 his work was awarded *Wildscape* magazine 'Wildlife Artist

of The Year' prize and Rob won *BBC Wildlife* Artist of the Year 'Animals in their Environment' award. **Formats:** Oils, waterclour, pencil and charcoal. **Artwork for sale:** Original paintings, drawings and prints, commissions accepted and enquiries welcomed. **Address:** 16 Beverley Avenue, Poulton-le-Fylde, Lancashire FY6 8BN; 01253 884 849. e-mail: info@robcookart.com www.robcookart.com

CALE, Steve

Steve paints many subjects, including landscapes, but he specialises in birds. His work has been published in the *Norfolk Wildfile*, various books including *Where to Watch Birds in Northern Cyprus* and magazine articles for *Birds Illustrated*, *Bird Watching* and many others.

DIRECTORY OF WILDLIFE ARTISTS

Steve's company, Avocet Cards, specialises in greetings cards, prints and postcards featuring his artwork.
Formats: Oils, acrylics and watercolour. Pen and ink, pencil.
Exhibitions/courses for 2012: Paintings at BIRDscapes Gallery Norfolk, and British Birdwatching Fair (usually in Marquee 5). Contact Steve for details of drawing and painting courses, including January 21& 22 at Anglian Birdwatching Centre, Oakham, Rutland Water (see their website for details).
Artwork for sale: Commissions welcomed. Greetings cards, prints and postcards available direct from the artist. Trade design work undertaken for books, bookmarks, logos & greetings cards. Design work for lodges & visitor centres. Greetings card catalogue available to trade only.
Address: 10 Fairview Drive, Colkirk, Norfolk NR21 7NT. 01328 862 265 or 07866 263 673; e-mail: steveshrike@aol.com
www.steve-cale-artist.co.uk

DAVIS, John
Paintings and illustrations of many wildlife subjects and landscapes. Published work includes a new book from Langford Press, *Beyond the Plough*, illustrations for the new Buckingham Press title *Best Birdwatching Sites: Dorset*, regular illustrations for RSPB's *Birdlife Magazine*. Member of SWLA since 1987 and exhibits at their annual exhibition at the Mall Galleries.
Formats: Paints in oils, acrylics and watercolour.
Exhibitions for 2012: Paintings in BIRDscapes Gallery, Norfolk and at the Owl Barn Gallery, Helpston nr. Peterborough.
Artwork for sale: Commissions accepted.
Address: 6 Redmoor, Birdham, West Sussex PO20 7HS; 01243 512 351;
e-mail: johndavis.wildlife@tiscali.co.uk

GREENHALF, Robert
Fulltime painter and printmaker. Member of SWLA. Work features in many books including *Modern Wildlife Painting* (Pica Press 1998), Artists for Nature Foundation books on Poland and Extremadura and *Towards the Sea* (Pica Press 1999) - his first solo book.
Formats: Watercolours, oils and woodcuts, sold mainly through galleries but some commissions undertaken.
Artwork for sale: Watercolours, oils and woodcuts, available through website.
Address: Romney House, Saltbarn Lane, Playden, Rye, East Sussex TN31 7PH; 01797 222 381;
e-mail: robertgreenhalf@gmail.com
www.robertgreenhalf.co.uk

GRIFFITHS, Ian
Birds and their habitat is the main subject matter for Griff's paintings. Having lived throughout the UK and travelled widely throughout the world, he has a wealth of field experience to draw upon. In 2011 he was a winner and runner-up in the BBC Wildlife artist of the year competition.
Subjects: Mainly birds in various mediums.
Exhibitions for 2012: Working with the Lost Gardens of Heligan on a wildlife project. See web site for other exhibitions.
Artwork for sale: Commissions considered and through his web site.
Address: Griff's wildlife studio, Creftow, 6 Church Street, Helston, Cornwall TR13 8TG; 07971 678 464; e-mail: mail@artbygriff.com
www.artbygriff.com

LEAHY, Ernest
Original watercolours and drawings of Western Palearctic birds, wildlife and country scenes. Also paints British mammals and butterflies. Illustrations for many publications including Poysers. Wide range of framed and unframed originals available. Commissions accepted and enquiries welcome. See website for available artwork .
Formats: E-mail for details of current work available and for quotations on commissioned work.
Exhibitions for 2012: E-mail for details of pre-Christmas exhibitions.
Artwork for sale: See www.flickr.com/photos/ernsbirdart for latest work.
Address: 32 Ben Austins, Redbourn, Herts, AL3 7DR; 01582 793 144.
e-mail: ernest.leahy@ntlworld.com
www.flickr.com/photos/ernsbirdart

SCOTT, Dafila
Trained as a zoologist then studied art under Robin Child at the Lydgate Art Research Centre UK. Has exhibited widely in the UK. Recent work includes both figurative and abstract paintings of wildlife, people and landscape.
Formats: Media: Oil, acrylics and pastels.
Exhibitions for 2012: Antarctic paintings at the Scott Polar Research Institute, May-June, exact dates to be confirmed
Artwork for sale: Media: Oil, acrylics and pastels.
Address: White Roses, The Hythe, Reach, Cambridgeshire CB5 0JQ;
e-mail: dafilascott@yahoo.co.uk
www.dafilascott.co.uk

DIRECTORY OF WILDLIFE ARTISTS

THRELFALL, John
Member of the Society of Wildlife Artists.
Swarovski/Birdwatch Bird Artist of the Year 2007.
Award winner at the NEWA 2001, 2004, 2006
exhibitions. BIRDscapes Gallery award 2007. John
wrote and illustrated *Between The Tides*, a book
abut the landscapes and wildlife of the Solway
estuary for Langford Press.
Formats: Paintings in acrylic or pastel.
Artwork for sale: Contact artist.
Address: Saltflats Cottage, Rockcliffe,
Dalbeattie, Kirkcudbrightshire DG5 4QQ; 01556
630 262; e-mail: john@johnthrelfall.co.uk
www.johnthrelfall.co.uk

WARREN, Michael
Member of Society of Wildlife Artists (treasurer).
President of Nottinghamshire Birdwatchers.
Exhibitions for 2012: Will exhibit at Rutland
Birdfair in August and Society of Wildlife Artists
in October — See Website for more information
during year.
Artwork for sale: Original watercolour paintings
of birds, all based on field observations. Books,
calendars and cards available. Commissions
welcomed.
Address: The Laurels, The Green, Winthorpe,
Nottinghamshire, NG24 2NR; 01636 673 554.
e-mail: mike.warren@tiscali.co.uk
www.mikewarren.co.uk

DIRECTORY OF WILDLIFE PHOTOGRAPHERS

BASTON, Bill
Photographer, lecturer.
Subjects: Subjects: East Anglian rarities
and common birds, Mediterranean birds and
landscapes, UK wildlife and landscapes, Northern
Greece & Western Turkey, Spain, Goa, General
wildlife photography, The Gambia, Northern India
(birds and tigers) , Costa Rica.
Products and services: Prints, slides, digital,
mounted/unmounted.
Address: 86 George Street, Hadleigh, Ipswich,
IP7 5BU; 01473 827 062; www.billbaston.com
e-mail: billbaston@btinternet.com

BELL, Graham
Professional ornithologist, photographer, author,
cruise lecturer worldwide.
Subjects: Birds, animals, flowers, landscapes, all
seven continents, from Arctic to Antarctic.
Products and services: Original slides for sale,
£2 each. Lecture: 'Taking Better Photos'.
Address: Ros View, South Yearle, Wooler,
Northumberland, NE71 6RB; 01668 281310.
e-mail: seabirdsdgb@hotmail.com

BEJARANO, Santiago
An Ecuadorean naturalist and wildlife
photographer who worked in the Galapagos
for almost two decades, with a great depth
of knowledge and unique insight into these
remarkable islands and their wildlife.
Subjects: Flora and fauna of Galapagos Islands
and birds of Ecuador.
Products and services: Prints and posters of
the wildlife of the Galapagos Islands and birds
of Ecuador. Introductory classes to wildlife
photography, including digital and basic
Photoshop® techniques.
Address: 25 Trinity Lane, Beverley, East
Yorkshire HU17 0DY; 01482 872 716.
e-mail: info@thinkgalapagos.com
www.thinkgalapagos.com

BIRDS EYE VIEW PHOTO'S
James Bird is a photographer, lecturer and
former RSPB Local Group leader. Organiser
of East African photo safari trips as well as
South African trips into the Kruger for disabled
travellers in adapted vehicles: for more info
www.epic-enabled.com or call me.
Subjects: 12-plus slide talks and digital
presentations on wildlife and worldwide travel,
having spent 23 years living abroad.
Products for sale: Prints, postcards and mouse
mats plus free RSPB magazines and information
leaflets given out.
Address: 6 Valentine Gardens, Kimbolton,
Huntingdon, Cambridgeshire PE28 0HX;1481 861
955; (M)07941 633 355.
e-mail: photosbyjb007@gmail.com or

DIRECTORY OF WILDLIFE PHOTOGRAPHERS

jamesbird007@yahoo.co.uk
http://birdseyeviewphotos.weebly.com;
www.myfinepix.co.uk/gallery/53681;
www.flickr.com/photos/birdseyeviewphotos

BROADBENT, David
Professional photographer.
Subjects: UK birds and wild places.
Products and services: All new website features
a fully searchable picture library of UK wildlife
and landscapes to the editorial market, lectures
and photo training days, print sales and gallery
art prints.
Contact: 07771 664 973.
e-mail: info@davidbroadbent.com
www.davidbroadbent.com

BROOKS, Richard
Wildlife photographer, writer, lecturer, guide.
Subjects: Owls (Barn especially), raptors,
Kingfisher and a variety of European birds (Lesvos
especially) and landscapes. Limited edition
calendars available.
Products and services: Mounted and unmounted
computer prints (6x4 - A3+ size), framed
pictures, A5 greetings cards, surplus slides for
sale.
Address: 24 Croxton Hamlet, Fulmodeston,
Fakenham, Norfolk, NR21 0NP; 01328 878 632.
e-mail: email@richard-brooks.co.uk
www.richard-brooks.co.uk

BUCKINGHAM, John
Worldwide bird and wildlife photographer.
Subjects: Huge range of birds, botany and
wildlife in UK and Europe, plus great coverage
from Africa, Americas, Australia and worldwide.
Products and services: Original slides for
lectures and personal use.
Address: 3 Cardinal Close, Tonbridge, Kent, TN9
2EN; (Tel/fax) 01732 354 970.
e-mail: john@buckingham7836.freeserve.co.uk

COSTER, Bill
Professional wildlife photographer, writer and
photographic tour leader, author of *Creative Bird
Photography*.
Subjects: Wildlife and landscape from around
the world.
Products and services: Images for publication,
prints for sale. See my website for details.
Stunning new digital shows (see Directory of
Lecturers).
Address: 17 Elm Road, South Woodham Ferrers,
Chelmsford, Essex CM3 5QB; 01245 320 066.
e-mail: billcoster@hotmail.com
www.billcoster.com

DENNING, Paul
Wildlife photographer, lecturer.
Subjects: Birds, mammals, reptiles, butterflies,
plants and orchids from UK, Europe, Canaries,
North and Central America.
Products and services: 35mm transparencies and
digital images.
Address: 17 Maes Maelwg, Beddau, Pontypridd,
CF38 2LD; (H)01443 202607; (W)02920 673243.
e-mail: pgdenning.naturepics@virgin.net

DUGGAN, Glenn
Specialist in tropical birding.
Subjects: Tropical birds, Trogons, Tanagers,
Birds of Paradise.
Address: 25 Hampton Grove, Fareham,
Hampshire, PO15 5NL; 01329 845 976, (M)07771
605 320.
e-mail: glenn.m.duggan@ntlworld.com
www.birdlectures.com

LANE, Mike
Wildlife photographer and lecturer.
Subjects: Birds and wildlife from around the
world, also landscapes and the environment.
Products and services: Website with instantly
downloadable online pictures. Talks and
workshops.
Address: 36 Berkeley Road, Shirley, Solihull,
West Midlands B90 2HS; 0121 744 7988; (M)07766
418 013; www.nature-photography.co.uk
e-mail: mikelane@nature-photography.co.uk

LENTON, Graham
PhD Ornithology/Ecology. Former lecturer at
Oxford University and Oxford Brookes University.
Lifetime photographer of wildlife - publications
of articles and photographs of birds and wildlife.
Subjects: Worldwide birds, mammals of Africa,
wildlife, worldwide travel.
Products and services: Photos available for sale
or reproduction.
Address: The Old School, 25A Standlake Road,
Ducklington, Witney, Oxon OX29 7UR; 01993 899
033; e-mail: grahamlenton@btopenworld.com
www.gml-art.co.uk

LINGARD, David
Wildlife photographer, retired from RAF, now UK
delegate to LIPU (BirdLife in Italy).
Subjects: Birds and views of places visited
around the world.
Products and services: 35mm transparencies but
mainly digital images.
Address: Fernwood, Doddington Road, Whisby,
Lincs LN6 9BX; 01522 689 030.
e-mail: mail@lipu-uk.org - www.lipu-uk.org

NASON, Rebecca

UK, East Anglia-based bird and wildlife photographer.

Subjects: Wildlife photography. Specializing in birds, common and rare from Suffolk to the Shetland Islands and beyond.

Products and services: Large image stock library. Professionally printed images available, various sizes, mounts and frames from 6 x 4 to A1+. Acrylics, aluminium and canvases, greetings card range.

Address: 8 Angel Lane, Woodbridge, Suffolk IP12 4NG; 01394 385 030; (M)07919 256 386.

e-mail: rebecca@rebeccanason.com
www.rebeccanason.com

OFFORD, Keith

Photographer, writer, tour leader, conservationist.

Subjects: Raptors, UK wildlife and scenery, birds and other wildlife of USA, Africa, Spain, Australia, India.

Products and services: Conventional prints, greetings cards, framed pictures.

Address: Yew Tree Farmhouse, Craignant, Selattyn, Nr Oswestry, Shropshire, SY10 7NP; 01691 718 740; e-mail: keith.offord@virgin.net
www.keithofford.co.uk

READ, Mike

Photographer (wildlife and landscapes), tour leader, writer.

Subjects: Birds, mammals, plants, landscapes, and some insects. UK, France, USA, Ecuador (including Galapagos) plus many more. Behaviour, action, portraits, artistic pictures available for publication. More than 100,000 images in stock.

Products and services: Extensive stock photo library. Canvas and giclee prints, greetings cards, books.

Address: Claremont, Redwood Close, Ringwood, Hampshire, BH24 1PR; 01425 475 008.

e-mail: mike@mikeread.co.uk
www.mikeread.co.uk

SISSON, Mark

A professional nature photographer, journalist and photographic trips and workshop organiser.

Subjects: I have a large and constantly expanding library of wildlife images (principally European) available, either direct or through my representing agencies.

Products and services: High specification digital images, complete illustrated articles, talks and personalised as group photographic workshops and tours.

Address: 4 Deer Park Drive, Newport, Shropshire,TF10 7HB; 01952 411 436.

e-mail: mark@marksissonphoto.co.uk
www.marksissonphoto.co.uk and
www.natures-images.co.uk

SMART, Oliver

Photographer and lecturer.

Subjects: All wildlife subjects, mainly UK based, also Canada, Cuba, various parts of Europe, Madagascar and Seychelles.

Products and services: Bean bags, canvas prints, desk calendars, digital files, digital slideshow lectures, greeting cards, mounted prints (to A2 size) and photographic workshops.

Address: 78 Aspen Park Road, Weston-Super-Mare, Somerset BS22 8ER; 01934 628 888; (M)07802 417 810.

e-mail: oliver@smartimages.co.uk
www.smartimages.co.uk

SWASH, Andy and Gill

Professional wildlife photographers and authors.

Subjects: Birds, habitats, landscapes and general wildlife from all continents; photographic library of over 100,000 images, including more than 3,000 bird species.

Products and services: Images for publication and lectures. High resolution images on CD/DVD. Conventional and digital prints, unmounted, mounted or framed. Greetings cards.

Address: Stretton Lodge, 9 Birch Grove, West Hill, Ottery St Mary, Devon, EX11 1XP; 01404 815 383, (M)07760 188 594.

e-mail: swash@worldwildlifeimages.com
www.worldwildlifeimages.com

TYLER, John

Subjects: Plants, fungi, insects and other invertebrates.

Products and services: Images for sale.

Address: 5 Woodfield, Lacey Green, Buckinghamshire HP27 0QQ; 07814 392 335; e-mail: johnclarketyler@gmail.com
www.johntyler.co.uk

WARD, Chris

Lecturer, N Bucks RSPB Local Group Leader.

Subjects: Primarily birds (and some other wildlife) and landscapes from UK and worldwide (Spain, Mallorca, Romania, Cyprus, Oman, Americas, Africa).

Products and services: Digital images and prints on request.

Address: 41 William Smith Close, Woolstone, Milton Keynes, MK15 0AN; 01908 669 448.

e-mail: cwphotography@hotmail.com
www.cwardphotography.co.uk

WILLIAMS, Nick
Photographer, lecturer, author.
Subjects: W.Palearctic also Cape Verde Islands and Falkland Islands.
Products and services: Glossy photographs and beautiful wildlife calendars for sale.

Address: Owl Cottage, Station Street, Rippingale, Lincs, PE10 0TA; (Tel/Fax) 01778 440 500.
e-mail: birdmanandbird@hotmail.com
www.nickwilliams.eu

DIRECTORY OF LECTURERS

BASTON, Bill
Photographer, lecturer.
Subjects: East Anglian rarities and common birds, Mediterranean birds and landscapes, UK wildlife and landscapes, Northern Greece & Western Turkey, Spain, Goa, General wildlife photography, The Gambia, Northern India (birds and tigers), Costa Rica.
Fees: Negotiable.
Limits: Preferably within East Anglia.
Address: 86 George Street, Hadleigh, Ipswich, IP7 5BU; 01473 827 062.
e-mail: billbaston@btinternet.com
www.billbaston.com

BEJARANO, Santiago
An Ecuadorean naturalist and wildlife photographer who worked in the Galapagos for over a decade, with a great depth of knowledge and unique insight into these remarkable islands and their wildlife.
Subjects: 'Galapagos Islands', 'Birds of Galapagos', 'Ecuador Land of Mega Diversity', 'Hummingbirds'.
Fees: £40. **Limits:** None.
Time limitations: None.
Address: 25 Trinity Lane, Beverley, East Yorkshire HU17 0DY; 01482 872 716.
e-mail: info@thinkgalapagos.com
www.thinkgalapagos.com

BELL, Graham
Cruise lecturer worldwide, photographer, author, former BBRC member.
Subjects: Arctic, Antarctic, Siberia, Australia, Iceland, Seychelles, UK - identification, behaviour, seabirds, garden birds, entertaining bird sound imitations, birds in myth and fact,

bird names, taking better photos, etc.
Fees: £20 plus travel and B&B if required. **Limits:** None. **Time limitations:** None.
Address: Ros View, South Yearle, Wooler, Northumberland, NE71 6RB; 01668 281 310.
e-mail: seabirdsdgb@hotmail.com

BIRD, James
Photographer, lecturer and former RSPB Local Group leader. Organiser of East African photo safari trips as well as South African trips into the Kruger for disabled travellers in adapted vehicles: for more info www.epic-enabled.com or call me.
Subjects: 12 plus slide talks and digital presentations on wildlife and worldwide travel, having spent 23 years living abroad.
Fees: £70 within a 50 mile round trip from home, fuel inclusive. Over 100 miles by arrangement.
Limits: Nowhere too far. **Times:** Any time to suit.
Address: 6 Valentine Gardens, Kimbolton, Huntingdon, Cambridgeshire PE28 0HX; 01480 861 955; (M)07941 633 355.
e-mail: photosbyjb007@gmail.com or jamesbird007@yahoo.co.uk
http://birdseyeviewphotos.weebly.com;
www.myfinepix.co.uk/gallery/53681;
www.flickr.com/photos/birdseyeviewphotos

BOND, Terry
Company Cchairman, international consultant, ex-bank director, conference speaker worldwide, photographer, group field leader, lecturer on birds for more than thirty years.
Subjects: 6 talks - including Scilly Isles, Southern Europe, North America, Scandinavia, 'Birdwatching Identification - a New Approach'

ART/PHOTOGRAPHY/LECTURERS

101

DIRECTORY OF LECTURERS

(an audience participation evening).
Fees: By arrangement (usually only expenses).
Limits: Most of UK.
Time limitations: Evenings.
Address: 3 Lapwing Crescent, Chippenham, Wiltshire, SN14 6YF; 01249 462 674.
e-mail: terryebond@btopenworld.com

BOWDEN, Paul
Birdwatcher and nature photographer (HD video and photos of birds and other wildlife) for 30+ years (serious amateur). Founder member of local Wildlife Photographic Club (website: http://www.glamorganwildlifephotoclub.org.uk/). Lecture to local bird clubs and RSPB Local Groups.
Subjects: Birds of UK, Europe, USA, Canada, Hong Kong, Japan, Oman, Libya or Australia (HD-video and/or Powerpoint). Butterflies and Dragonflies of UK.
Fees: Lecture fee of £50 plus reasonable travelling expenses (also overnight accommodation where necessary for longer trips). **Limits:** None, but longer trips may require overnight stay. **Time limitations:** Lecture evenings and weekends only.
Address: 4 Patmore Close, Gwaelod-y-Garth, Cardiff, CF15 9SU; 029 2081 3044.
e-mail: bowden_pe@hotmail.com

BROADBENT, David
Gloucestershire-based photographer.
Subjects: UK birds and wild places. In praise of natural places.
Fees: £45 locally. **Limits:** 50mls without travel costs, anywhere otherwise.
Time limitations: None.
Address: 07771 664 973.
e-mail: info@davidbroadbent.com
www.davidbroadbent.com

BROOKS, Richard
Wildlife photographer, writer, lecturer, guide.
Subjects: 12 talks (including Lemnos, Lesvos, Evros Delta, Spain, Israel, Canaries, E.Anglia, Scotland, Wales, Oman).
Fees: £75 plus petrol. **Limits:** None if accom provided. **Time limitations:** None.
Address: 24 Croxton Hamlet, Fulmodeston, Fakenham, Norfolk NR21 0NP; 01328 878 632.
e-mail: email@richard-brooks.co.uk
www.richard-brooks.co.uk

BUCKINGHAM, John
Long-standing and popular lecturer, photographer, tour leader.
Subjects: 60+ titles covering birds, wildlife,

botany, ecology and habitats in UK, Europe, Africa, Australia, Indian sub-continent, North, South and Central America, including favourites such as 'How Birds Work', 'The Natural History of Birds' and 'Wonders of Bird Migration'.
Fees: £85 plus expenses. **Limits:** None. **Time limitations:** None.
Address: 3 Cardinal Close, Tonbridge, Kent TN9 2EN; (Tel/fax) 01732 354 970; e-mail: john@buckingham7836.freeserve.co.uk

CARRIER, Michael
Lifelong interest in natural history.
Subjects: 1) 'Birds in Cumbria', 2) 'The Solway and its Birds', 3)'The Isle of May', 4)'A look at Bird Migration', 5)'A Lifetime of Birds', 6)'Some Remarkable Islands'.
Fees: £20. **Limits:** None but rail connection helpful. **Time limitations:** Sept-March inc., afternoons or evenings.
Address: Lismore Cottage, 1 Front Street, Armathwaite, Carlisle, Cumbria, CA4 9PB; 01697 472 218.
e-mail: m.carrier131@btinternet.com

COSTER, Bill
Professional wildlife photographer, writer and photographic tour leader.
Subjects: Stunning new digital shows provide a unique look at subjects around the world, including: Pacific Northwest USA, Antarctica, Shetland, Birds and Landscape of USA Deserts, Florida, Britain and more. See my webite for full details (www.billcoster.com). Even if you have seen shows from the same location, my shows will be different.
Fees: £80, plus 30p per mile. **Limits:** None.
Time limitations: None.
Address: 17 Elm Road, South Woodham Ferrers, Chelmsford, Essex CM3 5QB; 01245 320 066;
e-mail: billcoster@hotmail.com
www.billcoster.com

COUZENS, Dominic
Full-time birdwatcher, tour leader (UK and overseas), writer and lecturer.
Subjects: 'The Secret Lives of Garden Birds', 'Birds Behaving Badly - the trials and tribulations of birds through the year', 'Have Wings Will Travel' - the marvel of bird migration, 'Vive la Difference' - a comparison of British birds with those across the Channel, 'My Family and 50 Other Animals' - a year spent trying to show 2 young children 50 species of mammals in Britain, 'Birding a Local Patch'.
Fees: £80 plus travel. **Limits:** London and south.

DIRECTORY OF LECTURERS

Time limitations: None.
Address: 3 Clifton Gardens, Ferndown, Dorset, BH22 9BE; 01202 874 330, (M) 07721 918 174; www.birdwords.co.uk
e-mail: dominic.couzens@btinternet.com

CROMACK, David
Editor of *Bird Art & Photography* magazine, co-publisher of Buckingham Press Ltd, president of Peterborough Bird Club.
Subjects: Subjects: 1) Bird Magazines and the Art of Bird Photography (the inside story of how publications choose and use images);
2) Wild West Birding (Arizona and California);
3) World Class Bird Images (Leading entries from International Wildbird Photographer competitions); 4) More World Class Bird Images (Outstanding entries from the 2007 IWP competition); 5) Asia's Teardrop - Birding in Sri Lanka (new talk); 6) Contemporary Bird Artists (new talk). All suitable for bird groups and photographic societies. Leaflet available on request.
Fees: £75 plus travel expenses (30p per mile). **Limits:** 150 miles from Peterborough. **Times:** All requests considered from January 2011.
Address: 55 Thorpe Park Road, Peterborough PE3 6LJ. 01733 566 815; (Fax) 01733 561 739;
e-mail: editor@buckinghampress.com

DENNING, Paul
Wildlife photographer, lecturer.
Subjects: 15 talks, (birds, mammals, reptiles, butterflies etc, UK, western and eastern Europe, north and central America, Canaries).
Fees: £40 plus petrol. **Limits:** 100 mls. **Time limitations:** Evenings, weekends.
Address: 17 Maes Maelwg, Beddau, Pontypridd, CF38 2LD; (H)01443 202 607; (W)02920 673 243.
e-mail: pgdenning.naturepics@virgin.net

DUGGAN, Glenn
Ex-Commander Royal Navy, tour leader, researcher.
Subjects: Ten talks including, The rare and extinct birds of the world, Birds of paradise and bower birds, Trogons and Tanagers, History of bird art (caveman to present day), Modern day bird art, Famous Victorian bird artists (John Gould, The Birdman and John James Audubon), Scientific voyages of discovery.
Fees: £70 plus reasonable expenses. **Limits:** none with o.n accom. **Time limitations:** None.
Address: 25 Hampton Grove, Fareham, Hampshire, PO15 5NL; 01329 845 976, (M)07771 605 320; www.birdlectures.com
e-mail: glenn.m.duggan@ntlworld.com

EYRE, John
Author, photographer, conservationist and chairman Hampshire Ornithological Society.
Subjects: Many talks covering birding around the world (Europe, Africa, Asia, Australasia and the Americas), plus special Hampshire subjects. Examples include: 'New Zealand - Seabird Feast, Land Bird Famine', 'California Birds — Sea, Sage and Spotted Owls', 'Gilbert White's Birds' and 'The Changing Fortunes of Hampshire Birds'. Please call to discuss options.
Fees: £70 plus travel. **Limits:** Any location negotiable. **Time limitations:** None.
Address: 3 Dunmow Hill, Fleet, Hampshire, GU51 3AN; 01252 677 850.
e-mail: John.Eyre@ntlworld.com

GALLOP, Brian
Speaker, photographer, tour leader.
Subjects: 35 talks covering UK, Africa, India, Galapagos, South America and Europe — All natural history subjects. Made-to-measure talks available on request. 24hr emergency service.
Fees: £50 plus travel expenses. **Limits:** None — o.n acc. if over 100 mls.
Time limitations: None.
Address: 13 Orchard Drive, Tonbridge, Kent, TN10 4LT; 01732 361892.
e-mail: brian_gallop@hotmail.co.uk

GARNER, David
Wildlife photographer.
Subjects: 20 live talks and audio-visual shows on all aspects of wildlife in UK and some parts of Europe — list available.
Fees: £40 plus 25p per ml. **Limits:** None.
Time limitations: None.
Address: 73 Needingworth Road, St Ives, Cambridgeshire, PE27 5JY; (H)01480 463194; (W)01480 463194; www.hushwings.co.uk
e-mail: david@hushwings.co.uk

GARTSHORE, Neil
23-years working in nature conservation (National Trust, South Africa, RSPB) now a freelance contractor, writer, lecturer, tour guide and natural history book seller.
Subjects: Various talks including South Africa; Sub-Antarctic Prince Edward Islands; Japan; Farne Islands; Heathlands; Poole Harbour.
Fees: Negotiable. **Limits:** Anything considered.
Time limitations: Flexible.
Address: Moor Edge, 2 Bere Road, Wareham, Dorset BH20 4DD; 01929 552 560.
e-mail: neil@onaga54.freeserve.co.uk

ART/PHOTOGRAPHY/LECTURERS

103

DIRECTORY OF LECTURERS

GLENN, Neil
Author of *Best Birdwatching Sites in Norfolk*; regular contributor to *Bird Art and Photography* and *Bird Watching* magazines; bird tour leader for Avian Adventures.
Subjects: Wildlife of the Lower Rio Grande Valley, Texas. Birding the Arctic Circle. Moroccan Spice: From The Sahara to The Atlas Mountains. More to follow!
Fees: Negotiable. **Limits:** None.
Time limitations: Any day.
Address: 13 Gladstone Avenue, Gotham, Nottingham NG11 0HN; 0115 983 0946.
e-mail: n.glenn@ntlworld.com

HAMMOND, Nicholas
Lecturer, author, former RSPB and Wildlife Trust staffer.
Subjects: More than 30 topics covering Art and Wildlife, History and Wildlife, Wildlife and Conservation. Popular topics include Modern Wildlife Painting, Hippos and Hoopoes, The Great Fen, Birds through Other People's Eyes. E-mail for full list of subjects.
Fees: From £75 plus travel expenses,
Limits: 120 miles from Sandy.
Address: 30 Ivel Road, Sandy SG19 1BA; 01767 680 504;
e-mail: n.hammond4@ntlworld.com

HASSELL, David
Birdwatcher and photographer.
Subjects: Six talks (including British Seabirds, Shetland Birds, British Birds, USA Birds, including Texas, California, Florida etc.).
Fees: £50 plus petrol. **Limits:** None.
Time limitations: None.
Address: 15 Grafton Road, Enfield, Middlesex, EN2 7EY; 020 8367 0308; www.davehassell.com
e-mail: dave@davehassell.com

LANE, Mike
Wildlife photographer and lecturer.
Subjects: Many talks from the UK and abroad.
Fees: Negotiable. **Limits:** None. **Time limitations:** None.
Address: 36 Berkeley Road, Shirley, Solihull, West Midlands B90 2HS; 0121 744 7988; (M)07766 418 013;
e-mail: mikelane@nature-photography.co.uk
www.nature-photography.co.uk

LENTON, Graham
PhD Ornithology/Ecology. Former lecturer at Oxford University and Oxford Brookes University. Lifetime photographer of wildlife - publications of articles and photographs of birds and wildlife.
Subjects: Barn Owls of Malaysia and rat control; Birds of the Seychelles; Wildlife and birds of Antarctica; Birds of New Zealand, Birds of Namibia, Two Islands (Handa & The Farnes), An Arctic Journey.
Fees: £60. **Limits:** Preferably within 60mls.
Time limitations: 1 hour to 90 minute talks.
Address: The Old School, 25A Standlake Road, Ducklington, Witney, Oxon OX29 7UR; 01993 899 033; www.gml-art.co.uk
e-mail: grahamlenton@btopenworld.com

LINGARD, David
Photographer, retired from RAF, now UK delegate to LIPU (BirdLife in Italy).
Subjects: Choice of talks on birding but primarily on Birdwatching in Italy and the work of LIPU.
Fees: Donation to LIPU, plus petrol costs.
Limits: None. **Time limitations:** None.
Address: Fernwood, Doddington Road, Whisby, Lincs LN6 9BX; 01522 689 030.
e-mail: mail@lipu-uk.org
www.lipu-uk.org

LINN, Hugh ARPS
Experienced lecturer, photographer.
Subjects: 12 talks, covering UK, Europe, Africa and bird-related subjects.
Fees: £50 plus travel expenses. **Limits:** 100 miles without o.n. accom.
Time limitations: Flexible.
Address: 4 Stonewalls, Rosemary Lane, Burton, Rossett, Wrexham, LL12 0LG; 01244 571 942;
e-mail: hugh.linn@btinternet.com

MATHER, Dr John Robert
Ornithologist, writer, tour guide, lecturer.
Subjects: Birds and other wildlife of: Kenya, Tanzania, Uganda, Ethiopia, Namibia, South Africa, Costa Rica, India, Nepal, 'Algonquin to Niagara - a tour around the Great Lakes'. 'Landscapes, Flowers and Wildlife of the American West'. 'Bird on the Bench' - a fascinating account of bird biology, 'Wildlife and Scenery of Coastal Alaska, and the Canadian Rockies'.
Fees: £75 plus 30p per mile. Overnight accommodation or £30 if over 75 miles.
Limits: Approx. 100 mls.
Time limitations: Evenings.
Address: Eagle Lodge, 44 Aspin Lane, Knaresborough, North Yorkshire, HG5 8EP; 01423 862775.

NASON, Rebecca

UK, East Anglia-based bird and wildlife photographer.
Subjects: A Fair Isle Season'. Working, birding and photography at Britain's premier birding hotspot.
Fees: Please e-mail for fee details. There is a set fee plus travel expenses depending on location.
Limits: Within 2 hours drive of Woodbridge, Suffolk. **Time limitations:** Flexible. Slideshow talks last from 1-2 hours.
Address: 8 Angel Lane, Woodbridge, Suffolk IP12 4NG; 01394 385 030; (M)07919 256 386.
e-mail: rebecca@rebeccanason.com
www.rebeccanason.com

OFFORD, Keith

Photographer, writer, tour leader, conservationist.
Subjects: 16 talks covering raptors, flight, uplands, gardens, migration, woodland wildlife, Australia, Iceland, Southern USA, Gambia, Spain, Costa Rica, Namibia, Western Cape.
Fees: £100 plus travel. **Limits:** none.
Time limitations: Sept - April.
Address: Yew Tree Farmhouse, Craignant, Selattyn, Nr Oswestry, Shropshire, SY10 7NP; 01691 718 740; e-mail: keith.offord@virgin.net
www.keithofford.co.uk

PALMER, Phil

Tour leader for Bird Holidays and undertakes conservation-based expeditions e.g. breeding surveys for Spoon-billed Sandpiper in Russia.
Subjects: Mostly birds, but includes mammals, insects, reptiles, whale watching etc. Many foreign trips including Alaska, Antarctica, Galapagos, Spitsbergen and the high Arctic. British birds; 'First for Britain' from Phil's book; The Secret Life of the Nightjar; Twitching in the UK; and bird photography.
Fees: To suit all club budgets. **Limits:** None.
Time limitations: None.
Address: 43 Grove Coach Road, Retford DN22 7HB; (Tel/fax)0113 391 0510;
e-mail: info@birdholidays.co.uk
www.birdholidays.co.uk

PICKERING, Pollyanna

Wildlife Artist, conservationist.
Subjects: 12 talks available on a variety of subjects, from running a wildlife sanctuary in Derbyshire to travelling into remote areas to paint endangered species in their natural habitat. Details of individual talks on request.
Fees: £125.00 plus travelling expenses.
Limits: None.

Time limitations: Evening talks only.
Address: Brookvale House, Oaker, Matlock, Derbyshire DE4 2JJ; 01629 55 851.
e-mail: annalouise@talktalk.net
www.pollyannapickering.co.uk

READ, Mike

Photographer, tour leader, writer.
Subjects: 12 talks featuring British and foreign subjects (list available on receipt of sae or see website).
Fees: £70 plus travel. **Limits:** 100 mls from Ringwood. **Time limitations:** Talks available 1st Sept to 31st March each winter.
Address: Claremont, Redwood Close, Ringwood, Hampshire BH24 1PR; 01425 475 008; e-mail: mike@mikeread.co.uk
www.mikeread.co.uk

REDMAN, Nigel

Tour leader, publisher and author.
Subjects: Mostly birds, including Morocco, Russia (and former Soviet Union), the Caucasus, Kenya, Ethiopia, and the Horn of Africa.
Fees: Negotiable. **Limits:** None (but overnight accommodation may be required).
Time limitations: None.
Address: Moons Hill Cottage, Moons Hill, Ninfield, East Sussex TN33 9LH; 01424 893 023; 07734 886 515; e-mail: nredman@acblack.com

SISSON, Mark

A professional nature photographer, journalist and photographic trips and workshop organiser.
Subjects: All aspects of wildlife photography, along with specific or tailormade talks on countries such as Iceland or broader topics such as Northern European birdlife — all with a photographer's eye and style.
Fees: £ 95 + travel. **Limits:** Ideally 100ml radius, but willing to be persuaded to go further! **Time limitations:** Need to fit into a busy schedule so idealy plenty of notice.
Address: 4 Deer Park Drive, Newport, Shropshire TF10 7HB; 01952 411 436.
e-mail: mark@marksissonphoto.co.uk
www.marksissonphoto.co.uk and
www.natures-images.co.uk

SMART, Oliver

Photographer and lecturer.
Subjects: 1)'Birds of Lesvos'; 2) 'Grizzly Bears of Alaska'; 3) 'Wildlife on Handa Island, NW Scotland'; 4) 'Cameras and Creatures from Cumbria to Canada'; 5) 'Cuba: A Flicker of Interest'; 6) 'RAW Nature: Images Uncovered'; 7) 'British Butterflies' (available autumn 2012).

Fees: £80 plus 25p per mile. Limits: None but o.n. accom. may be required.
Time limitations: None.
Address: 78 Aspen Park Road, Weston-Super-Mare, Somerset BS22 8ER; 01934 628 888; (M)07802 417 810; www.smartimages.co.uk
e-mail: oliver@smartimages.co.uk

SWASH, Andy
Professional wildlife photographer, lecturer and author.
Subjects: Tales from travels in search of little-known birds around the world, including the Andamans, Australia, Brazil, Ethiopia, Galápagos, Peru, Southern Africa, Sri Lanka and various birding hotspots in the USA.
Fees: £100 plus travel. Limits: None. Time limitations: Evenings preferred.
Address: Stretton Lodge, 9 Birch Grove, West Hill, Ottery St Mary, Devon, EX11 1XP; 01404 815 383, (M)07760 188 594.
e-mail: swash@worldwildlifeimages.com
www.worldwildlifeimages.com

TODD, Ralph
Lecturer & photographer, former tour leader and course tutor.
Subjects: 10 talks incl. 'Galapagos Wildlife', 'On the Trail of the Crane – parts 1 and 2', 'Polar Odyssey', 'Operation Osprey', 'Iceland & Pyrenees', 'Man & Birds-Travels through time', 'A summer in Northern Landscapes', 'Where Yeehaa meets Ole'.
Fees: £75 plus expenses. Limits: None. Time limitations: Anytime - also short notice.
Address: 9 Horsham Road, Bexleyheath, Kent DA6 7HU; (Tel/fax)01322 528335.
e-mail: rbtodd@btinternet.com

TYLER, John
Wildlife walks and talks.
Subjects: Life in a Nutshell (The world of small things); The Island of Crabs; Volcanoes and Dragons; Changing Wildlife of the Chilterns; The Ridgeway; The Glow-worm; The World of Fungi; Making Space for Wildlife.
Fees: £60 plus 50p per mile. Limits: 25 mile radius from Princes Risborough, Bucks.
Time limitations: None.
Address: 5 Woodfield, Lacey Green, Buckinghamshire HP27 0QQ; 07814 392 335; e-mail: johnclarketyler@gmail.com
www.johntyler.co.uk

WARD, Chris
Photographer, N Bucks RSPB Local Group leader.
Subjects: 20+ talks on UK and worldwide topics (Spain, Mallorca, Romania, Cyprus, Oman, Americas, Africa) - primarily birds, some other wildlife.
Fees: £50 plus petrol @30p/mile. Limits: 120 miles. Time limitations: Evenings.
Address: 41 William Smith Close, Woolstone, Milton Keynes, MK15 0AN; 01908 669 448.
e-mail: cwphotography@hotmail.com
www.cwardphotography.co.uk

WILLIAMS, Nick
Photographer, lecturer, author.
Subjects: Several audio visual shows (including Morocco, Mongolia, Spain, N.Germany, Camargue, Turkey, N.Norway, Cape Verde Islands, Falklands and Birds of Prey).
Fee: £110 - £140 depending on group size and distance. Travel costs included in the fee.
Limits: None. Time limitations: None
Address: Owl Cottage, Station Street, Rippingale, Lincs, PE10 0TA; (Tel/Fax)01778 440 500.
e-mail: birdmanandbird@hotmail.com
www.nickwilliams.eu

WREN, Graham J. ARPS
Wildlife photographer, lecturer, tour guide.
Subjects: 25 talks — birds: UK 'Breeding Birds of Southern Britain' and 'Northern Britain', including habitats, also Scandinavia. Nest-boxes (new), the environment, wildlife Kenya. Detailed information package supplied on request.
Fees: £50-80 plus petrol. Limits: None. Time limitations: None.
Address: The Kiln House, Great Doward, Whitchurch, Ross-on-Wye, Herefordshire, HR9 6DU; 01600 890 488.
e-mail: grahamjwren@aol.com

BTO SPEAKERS

This directory has been compiled to help Bird Clubs and similar organisations in finding speakers for their indoor meetings. Each entry consists of an individual speaker, a list of talks/ lectures available, details of fees and expenses required and travel distance limitations.
If you are interested in any of the speakers, please contact Ieuan Evans (ieuan.evans@bto.org) or Ellen Walford (ellen.walford@bto.org) directly. Alternatively, contact BTO: 01842 750 050.
Members of the BTO/ Bird Clubs Partnership have a 25% discount.

Appleton, Graham (Director of Communications)
Subjects: Atlas 2007 – 11; Flyway to Iceland; Time to Fly – Bird Migration.
Fees: £40 Negotiable. Distance: Dependent on expenses.

Austin, Dr Graham (Senior Research Ecologist, Wetland & Marine Research)
Subjects: Wetland Bird Survey.
Fees: £40. Distance: Travel by agreement.

Baille, Dr Stephen (Science Director Modelling & Demography)
Subjects: BirdTrack; Population Monitoring.
Fees: £40. Distance: Travel By agreement.

Baker, Jeff (Head of Marketing)
Subjects: Little Brown Jobs – Warblers & how to identify them; The Work of the BTO; Garden Birds & Feeding.
Fees: £40. Distance: Dependent on expenses.

Balmer, Dawn (Atlas Co-ordinator)
Subjects: Atlas 2007 - 11.
Fees: £40. Distance: 100 mile radius of Thetford.

Barimore, Carl (Nest Records Organiser)
Subjects: Nest Records Scheme; Barn Owl Monitoring Programme.
Fees: £40. Distance: By agreement.

Blackburn, Jez (Licensing and Sales Manager)
Subjects: Demography Team Bird Moult (suitable for ringers); Ringing for Conservation; Sule Skerry Seabirds.
Fees: £40 (£70 for private talks).
Distance: East Anglia.

Bray, James (Fieldwork & Training Coordinator BTO Scotland)
Subjects:; The Work of BTO Scotland; BTO Atlas 2007-11; BBS, Birdtrack & other BTO surveys in Scotland; Garden BirdWatch.

Clark, Jacquie (Head of Demography Team & Head of Ringing Scheme)
Subjects: Waders & Severe Weather; Ringing for Conservation; Why Ring Birds?
Fees: £40. Distance: 100 mile radius of Thetford.

Clark, Dr Nigel (Head of Projects Development Department)
Subjects: Waders, Man & Estuaries; What hope for the Spoon-billed Sandpiper?
Fees: £40. Distance: 100 mile radius of Thetford.

Cook, Mandy (Development Coordinator)
Subjects: The Work of BTO Scotland; BTO Atlas 2007-11 BBS; Birdtrack & other BTO surveys in Scotland; Garden BirdWatch.
Fees: £40. Distance: By agreement.

Conway, Greg (Research Ecologist, Land-use Research)
Subjects: Nightjars; Woodlarks; Dartford Warblers; Wintering Warblers in the UK; Firecrests.
Fees: £40. Distance: 100 mile radius of Thetford.

Dadam, Dr Daria (Reseach Ecologist Demography)
Subjects: Bird Disease.
Fees: Negotiable. Distance: By agreement.

Fuller, Prof Rob (Director of Science)
Subjects: Changing Times for Woodland Birds.
Fees: £40. Distance: Anywhere.

Gillings, Dr Simon (Senior Research Ecologist Land Use Research)
Subjects: Atlas 2007 – 11; Winter Golden Plovers & Lapwings; Waders; Knot Migration; Winter Farmland Birds.
Fees: £40. Distance: Negotiable.

DIRECTORY OF LECTURERS

Gough, Su (Editor, *BTO News* & Training Officer)
Subjects: The Work of the BTO; Urban Birds;
(private talks) Wildlife of Canada; Wildlife
of Southwestern USA; Wildlife of European
Mountains; Wildlife of Texas; Wildlife of the
Middle East.
Fees: £40. **Distance:** Negotiable.

Harrison, Dr Tim (GBW Development Officer)
Subjects: Are Gardens Good for Birds or
Birdwatchers?
Fees: £40. **Distance:** 50 mile radius of Thetford.

Henderson, Dr Ian (Senior Research Ecologist International Research)
Subjects: Arable Farming and Birds.
Fees: £40. **Distance:** By agreement.

Johnson, Dr Alison (Ecological Statistician, Population Ecology & Modelling)
Subjects: Climate Change and Birds.
Fees: £40. **Distance:** East Anglia

Lack, Dr Peter (Information Services Manager)
Subjects (private talks): Palearctic Migrants in
Africa; On Foot in Rwanda and Zambia; Ecology
in East African Savannahs; General Natural
History of Eastern Africa.
Fees: Negotiable. **Distance:** 60 miles of Bury St
Edmunds.

Marchant, John (Projects Co-ordinator Monitoring)
Subjects: Monitoring Heronries: Nine Decades
of Monitoring; Waterways Bird & Breeding Bird
Surveys.
Fees: £40. **Distance:** By agreement.

Moran, Nick (BirdTrack Organiser)
Subjects: Mapping migration with BirdTrack;
Hard weather effects on birds; Birds and birding
in Arabia (private talk).
Fees: £40. **Distance:** By agreement.

Musgrove, Dr Andy (Head of Monitoring)
Subjects: The Wetland Bird Survey; Little Egrets
in the UK.
Fees: £40. **Distance:** By agreement.

Newson, Dr Stuart (Senior Research Ecologist' Population Ecology & Modelling)
Subjects: Tree Nesting Cormorants.
Fees: £40. **Distance:** By agreement.

Noble, Dr David (Principal Ecologist, Monitoring)
Subjects: Developing Bird Indicators; Population
Trends.
Fees: £40. **Distance:** By agreement.

Pearce-Higgins, Dr James (Principal Ecologist, Climate Change)
Subjects: Birds and climate change; Upland
birds; A year in the life of a Golden Plover.
Fees: £40. **Distance:** By agreement.

Rehfisch, Dr Mark (Director of Development)
Subjects: Waterbird Alerts; Climate Change;
Habitat Loss & Waterbirds; Monitoring
Waterbirds; Introduced Species; Renewables and
Birds.
Fees: £40. **Distance:** By agreement.

Risely, Kate (Breeding Bird Survey National Organiser)
Subjects: BTO/JNCC/RSPB Breeding Birds Survey.
Fees: £40. **Distance:** By agreement.

Robinson, Dr Rob (Principal Ecologist, Modelling & Demography)
Subjects: Farming & Birds; Conservation Value
of Ringing.
Fees: £40. **Distance:** By agreement.

Siriwardena, Dr Gavin (Head of Land-Use Research)
Subjects: Research Farmland Birds (General);
Marsh & Willow Tits; Quantifying Migratory
Strategies; Winter Feeding of Farmland Birds.
Fees: £40. **Distance:** Negotiable.

Stancliffe, Paul (Press Officer)
Subjects: Atlas 2007-11; Homes to Let –
Nestboxes; Birds, Birders and the Work of the
BTO.
Fees: £40. **Distance:** Negotiable.

Toms, Mike (Head of Garden Ecology Team)
Subjects: Are Gardens Good for Birds or
Birdwatchers?
Fees: £40. **Distance:** 50 mile radius of Thetford.

Wernham, Dr Chris (Senior Research Ecologist BTO Scotland)
Subjects: The Work of BTO Scotland; Breeding
Bird Survey in Scotland; BirdTrack in Scotland.
Fees: £40. **Distance:** Travel Scotland and NE
England.

Wright, Dr Lucy (Research Ecologist, Wetland and Marine Research)
Subjects: Non-native Waterbirds in Eurasia &
Africa.
Fees: £40. **Distance:** By agreement.

TRADE DIRECTORY

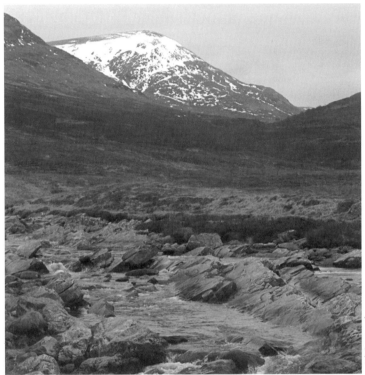

David Cromack

Spectacular scenery adds to the magic of a birding holiday in Scotland and a number of tour companies now offer trips all year round to see the special birds of the country. To see a complete list of bird tour companies turn to Page114.

BIRD GARDEN SUPPLIERS

BIRD GARDEN SUPPLIERS

CJ WILDLIFE

Company ethos: CJ Wildlife aims to make significant, recognisable contributions to the protection and welfare of wild birds and other wildlife. Our ornithologists and wildlife advisors undertake research projects to ensure we are continually producing not only high quality products, but products designed specifically for the wildlife they are intended.

Key product lines: CJ Wildlife bird feeders, bird food, nest boxes, wildlife friendly plants, bird tables and accessories, along with a broad range of wildlife care products, all available via our secure online web site or by mail order from our free catalogue.

Other services: Request a free *Handbook of Garden Wildlife* catalogue with advice, tips and products. CJ Wildlife brand products are stocked in selected supermarkets, garden centres and pet shops.

New for 2012: We are continuously adding new products to the range. Call to request a catalogue, visit the website, or follow us on Twitter and Facebook for the latest news and offers.

Opening times: Call our friendly and knowledgeable team on free-phone 0800 731 2820 Monday to Friday 9am - 5pm, Saturday 9am - 12pm or order from our website (24 hours). Next working-day delivery on orders received by 3pm, (2pm on Fridays). Delivery just £2.50 (UK only) and free on orders over £50. Goods can also be collected — 10% discount (excludes books and optics).

Address: The Rea, Upton Magna, Shrewsbury, Shropshire SY4 4UR; 0800 731 2820; (fax) 01743 709 504; e-mail: sales@birdfood.co.uk www.birdfood.co.uk

ERNEST CHARLES

Company ethos: Member of Birdcare Standards Assoc. ISO 9001 registered. Offering quality bird foods/wildlife products through a friendly mail-order service. Working in association with The British Trust for Ornithology.

Key product lines: Bird foods, feeders, nest boxes and other wildlife products.

Other services: Trade enquiries.

New for 2012: Special incentive to join BTO's Garden BirdWatch.

Opening times: Mon to Fri (8am-5pm).
Address: Copplestone Mills, Crediton, Devon EX17 2YZ; 0800 7316 770; (fax) 01363 84 147.
e-mail: sales@ernest-charles.com
www.ernest-charles.com

BOOK PUBLISHERS

BUCKINGHAM PRESS LTD

Imprints: Single imprint company — publishers of *The Birdwatcher's Yearbook* since 1981, *Who's Who in Ornithology* (1997), *Best Birdwatching Sites* series covering Norfolk, Sussex, Highlands of Scotland, Solway (Cumbria and Dumfries & Galloway), North Wales, Cornwall & Scilly. Plus sets of identification cards for British birds, garden birds, dragonflies and butterflies.

New for 2012: *Best Birdwatching Sites: Devon* and *Best Birdwatching Sites: North East England.*
Address: 55 Thorpe Park Road, Peterborough, PE3 6LJ. Tel/Fax: 01733 561 739.
e-mail: admin@buckinghampress.com
www.buckinghampress.co.uk

CHRISTOPHER HELM PUBLISHERS (an imprint of Bloomsbury Publishing)

Imprints: *Christopher Helm:* the leading publisher of ornithology books in the world; includes many fieldguides, identification guides, family guides, county and country avifaunas, and a *Where to Watch Birds* series.
T & AD Poyser: an acclaimed series of respected ornithology monographs.
Bloomsbury (formerly A&C Black Publishers): publisher of definitive natural history books.
New for 2012: *Handbook of Western Palearctic Birds* by Hadoram Shirihai and Lars Svensson, *Birds of Central Asia* by Raffael Ayé, Manuel Schweizer and Tobias Roth, *The Birds of the Malagasy Region* by Roger Safford and Frank Hawkins, *Cuckoos of the World* by Johannes Erritzoe, Clive Mann, Frederik Brammer and Richard Fuller, *Cotingas and Manakins* by Guy M. Kirwan and Graeme Green, *Extinct Birds* by Julian Hume and Michael Walters, *Field Guide to Invasive Plants and Animals* by Olaf Booy, Max Wade and Helen Roy, *Birds of Ecuador* by Juan Freile and Robin Restall, *Kenya: A Natural History* by Steve Spawls and Glenn

Matthews, *RSPB British Birdfinder* by Marianne Taylor. Also, e-books are now available for most titles and the entire Poyser monograph series is now back in print.
Address: 50 Bedford Square, London WC1B 3DP. Tel: +44 (0)20 7631 5600. Fax: +44 (0)20 7631 5800; e-mail: nigel.redman@bloomsbury.com
www.acblack.com/naturalhistory
www.bloomsbury.com

HARPERCOLLINS PUBLISHERS

Imprints: Collins Natural History — the leading publisher of fieldguides to the natural world. Collins New Naturalist Series — the encyclopaedic reference for all areas of British natural history. HarperCollins — publisher of the best illustrated books.
New for 2012: *Wonders of Life; Drawn From Paradise* by David Attenborough and Errol Fuller; Richard Mabey's *Food For Free* (40th anniversary edition); New Naturalists - *Scotland, Grasshoppers & Crickets, Partridges; A Land* by Jacquetta Hawkes, with an introduction by Robert Macfarlane; *BBC Springwatch's British Wildlife; Collins Complete British Coastal Wildlife; My Garden and Other Wildlife* by Mike Dilger.
Address: 77-85 Fulham Palace Rd, Hammersmith, London, W6 8JB; 020 8307 4998; (fax) 020 8307 4037; www.collins.co.uk
www.newnaturalists.co.uk
e-mail: Myles.Archibald@harpercollins.co.uk

THE LANGFORD PRESS

Imprints: Wildlife Art Series (WAS) — a series of lavishly illustrated books featuring the words and artworks of leading contemporary bird and wildlife artists. The company also publishes books on fruit growing and selected works by Darwin.
New for 2012: *Jewels Beyond The Plough* - A celebration of British grasslands; *New Forest Painters; A Celebration of Butterflies.* A new series of books featuring British wildlife and some of the people who have studied it for a long time!
Address: 10 New Road, Langtoft, Peterborough PE6 9LE; e-mail: sales@langford-press.co.uk
www.langford-press.co.uk

NEW HOLLAND PUBLISHERS (UK) LTD

Imprints: New Holland: field guides, photographic guides, garden wildlife books and other illustrated titles on birds and general wildlife, plus personality-led natural history. Recent bestsellers include *New Holland Concise Bird Guide, Advanced Bird ID Guide, Tales of a Tabloid Twitcher, Atlas of Rare Birds, A Field Guide to the Birds of Borneo, A Field Guide to the Birds of South-East Asia* and *Creative Bird*

Photography. Struik: the world's leading natural history publisher on African wildlife.
New for 2012: *The Urban Birder, Advanced Bird ID Handbook* and *The Birdman Abroad.*
Address: Garfield House, 86-88 Edgware Road, London W2 2EA; 020 7724 7773; (fax) 020 7258 1293; e-mail: simon.papps@nhpub.co.uk
www.newhollandpublishers.com

WILDGuides LTD

Imprints: *WILDGuides:* natural history fieldguides covering Britain's wildlife: butterflies, dragonflies, reptiles and amphibians, orchids, arable plants and plant galls.
OCEANGuides: identification guides to marine wildlife covering Antarctic, Atlantic and Pacific oceans.
Destination Guides: lavishly illustrated visitor guides to Galapagos, Seychelles, South Georgia, Falklands.
Crossbill Guides: regional guides to the top wildlife destinations in Europe covering Spain, France, Poland, Hungary and Finland.
Recently published: *Britain's Plant Galls; Orchids and Wildflowers of the Kitulo Plateau (Tanzania); Antarctic Wildlife; Natural History Guides to Extremadura (2nd Edition) and the Loire Valley; Nightjars of the World; The Jewel Hunter; Britain's Butterflies* (2nd Edition); *Britain's Dragonflies* (2nd Edition).
New for 2012: *Wildlife of South Georgia; Britain's Hoverflies; Britain's Day-flying Moths; The World's Rarest Birds.* Please visit our website for latest information.
Address: PO Box 680, Maidenhead, Berkshire SL6 9ST; 01628 529 297; (fax) 01628 525 314.
e-mail: info@wildguides.co.uk
www.wildguides.co.uk

BOOK SELLERS

CALLUNA BOOKS

Company ethos: We specialise in buying and selling out-of-print natural history titles, with an emphasis on quality stock at competitive prices.
Key subjects: Birds, mammals, flora, invertebrates in the UK and worldwide, including the Poyser and New Naturalist series, general natural history, conservation and countryside titles including some reports and journals. Stock of 2000+ titles maintained.
Other services: Catalogues issued (usually 3 p.a). We exhibit at some

bird fairs including Rutland Water. Wants lists welcomed — no obligation to buy.
Opening times: Mail order but viewing by appointment possible.
Address: Moor Edge, 2 Bere Road, Wareham, Dorset BH20 4DD; 01929 552 560.
e-mail: enquiries@callunabooks.co.uk
www.callunabooks.co.uk

NHBS - EVERYTHING FOR WILDLIFE, SCIENCE & ENVIRONMENT

Company ethos: A unique natural history, conservation and environmental supplier offering the world's largest range of wildlife books and field equipment.
Key subjects: Natural history, birding, conservation, environmental science, zoology, habitats, botany, marine biology, bat detecting, entomology, GPS.

Other services: Search and browse our full online catalogue of more than 110,000 titles (www.nhbs.com). Rapidly growing range of field equipment and essential travel kit for safari and expeditions.
Opening times: Mon-Fri (9am-5pm), for mail-order service. Browse or order anytime at www.nhbs.com
Address: 2-3 Wills Road, Totnes, Devon TQ9 5XN; 01803 865 913.
e-mail: customer.services@nhbs.co.uk
www.nhbs.com

PICTURE BOOK

Company ethos: Picture Book is a general bookshop specialising in bird books and local history.
Key subjects: Birdwatching, natural history, local history. Churnet Valley publish local history and Arnold Bennett titles in paperback and hardback with introductions by the Arnold Bennett Society.
Other services: Amazon mail order, new and secondhand books.
Opening times: The shop is open to the public Tuesday to Saturday 9.30am - 4.00pm Best to phone to check if travelling any distance.
Address: Picture Book, 6 Stanley Street, Leek, ST13 5HG; 01538 399 033 & 384 337; (fax) 01538 399 696; e-mail: info@leekbooks.co.uk
www.leekbooks.co.uk or
www.picturebookleek.co.uk

SECOND NATURE

Company ethos: Buying and selling out-of-print/secondhand/antiquarian books on natural history, topography and travel.
Key subjects: Birds, mammals, flowers and all other aspects of natural history.
Other services; Exhibits at bird/wildlife fairs.
New for 2012: A comprehensive website - www.secondnaturebooks.com
Opening times: Mail order only.
Address: Knapton Book Barn, Back Lane, Knapton, York YO26 6QJ; (Tel/fax) 01904 795 489; e-mail: SecondnatureYork@aol.com
www.secondnaturebooks.com

SUBBUTEO NATURAL HISTORY BOOKS

Company ethos: Specialisation and careful selection have allowed us to develop a fine reputation for supplying & publishing natural history books, DVDs, travel and fieldguides for those who enjoy birdwatching and the natural world, while providing a fast, friendly and efficient service.
Key subjects: Natural History - Ornithology; UK, Europe & worldwide, mammals,

reptiles & amphibians, aquatic fauna, butterflies & moths, plants & fungi, ecology & environmental science, wildlife art & photography.
Other services: Comprehensive online bookstore, gift wrap service, booklist service, worldwide book sourcing. Online ordering, with free delivery on orders over £50 (in-print titles & UK titles only), free catalogue, updates & monthly e-newsletter. Subbuteo Natural History Books is a division of CJ WildBird Foods Ltd.
New for 2012: Continuously adding new titles to the range, call for a brochure, visit the website or alternatively visit us in Shropshire. You can now find us on Twitter and Facebook.
Opening times: Book shop: Monday to Friday (9am-5pm). Saturday (9am-12pm). Online ordering 24 hrs.
Address: The Rea, Upton Magna, Shrewsbury, Shropshire SY4 4UR; 01743 709 420; (fax) 01743 709 504; e-mail: info@wildlifebooks.com
www.wildlifebooks.com

WILDSOUNDS

Company ethos: Donates a significant portion of profit to bird conservation, committed to sound environmental practices, official bookseller to African Bird Club. Operates the *Bird Watching* magazine bookshop.
Key product lines: Mail order, post-free books,

CLOTHING AND EQUIPMENT SUPPLIERS

CDs, DVDs and multi-media guides at discounted prices. Publisher of *Birding in Eastern Europe* by Gerard Gorman. Distributor of many best-selling DVDs i.e. *British Butterflies, North Norfolk Coast - Birder's Guide, Rare Birds 2010* etc. Field recording equipment stockist. Attends all major Bird Fairs and many local events.
New for 2012: See www.wildsounds.com
Opening times: Weekdays (9.30am-5pm).
Address: Cross Street, Salthouse, Norfolk NR25 7XH; 020 7724 7773; (fax) 020 7258 1293.
e-mail: sales@wildsounds.com
www.wildsounds.com

CLOTHING SUPPLIERS

COUNTRY INNOVATION
Company ethos: Specialists in clothing, footwear and accessories specifically for the birdwatching market. Offering friendly advice by well trained staff.
Key product lines: Full range of outdoor wear: Jackets, fleeces, trousers, travel clothing, Ventile garments, Brasher footwear, Tilley hats, bags and accessories, Ladies fit available. Mail order and website. Check website for appearances at shows and events
New for 2012: Osprey Jacket - a fully featured Ventile jacket. Traveller Jacket - a unique multi-pocketed waterproof jacket. New range of ladies lightweight shirts and trousers.
Opening times; Mon-Fri (9am-5pm).
Address: 1 Broad Street, Congresbury, North Somerset BS49 5DG; 01934 877 333;
e-mail: sales@countryinnovation.com
www.countryinnovation.com

PARÁMO DIRECTIONAL CLOTHING SYSTEMS
Company ethos: Innovators of technical mountain, birding and travel clothing using revolutionary Nikwax fabrics and functional design to provide performance and comfort for all outdoor enthusiasts and professionals, whatever their activity. Ethical manufacture.
Key product lines: Waterproof jackets and trousers, technical base layers, insulating overlayers & ultra cooling travel wear. Of especial note: Halcon & Pájaro birdwatching jackets & Pájaro waterproof trousers and Andy Rouse Limited Edition range of Aspira smock, Cascada trousers and Mountain Vent.
Other services: Repair and service of Páramo garments; online sales at www.naturallyparamo.co.uk
New for 2012: New Halcon Waistcoat with 14

pockets, plus new base layers.
Opening times; For independent retailers, consult our website or ring 01892 786 444 for stockist list and catalogue pack. Páramo London Store, 29 Henrietta Street, WC2E 8NA open 10.30am – 7pm Mon – Sat, 11am- 4pm on Sunday.
Address: Unit F, Durgates Industrial Estates, Wadhurst, East Sussex TN5 6DF; 01892 786 444; e-mail: info@paramo.co.uk
www.paramo.co.uk

EQUIPMENT SUPPLIERS

ALWYCH BOOKS
Company ethos: The Bird Watcher's All-Weather Flexible Pocket Note Book.
Key product lines: Alwych Notebooks with all-weather flexible covers.
Opening times: Order online 24 hours a day.
Address: 84 Stewarton Street, Wishaw, Lanarkshire ML2 8AG. Sales: 0845 270 2828; Admin: 01698 357 223; www.alwych.co.uk

BIRD IMAGES
Company ethos: High quality products at affordable prices.
Key product lines: Bird DVDs. A range of titles including identification guides and innovative guides to birdwatching places.
New for 2012: *Birdwatching In Europe.*
Opening times: Telephone first.
Address: 28 Carousel Walk, Sherburn in Elmet, North Yorkshinre LS25 6LP; 01977 684 666.
e-mail: paul@birdvideodvd.com
www.birdvideodvd.com

BIRDGUIDES LTD
Company ethos: Better birding through technology. The number one birder's website.
Key product lines: Software and video guides to British, European and American birds. Rare bird news services via e-mail, website and SMS. Books and an expanding range of natural history products for mobile phones.
New for 2012: New apps, search for BirdGuides on the iTunes store.
Address: BirdGuides Ltd, 3 Warple Mews, Warple Way, London W3 0RF; 020 8141 3272; order line (freephone) 0800 919 391; www.birdguides.com
e-mail: contact@birdguides.com

BLUEBIRD TECHNOLOGY
Company ethos: Bluebird Technology focuses on creating quality wildlife recording software products for all birders to enjoy. All of our

TRADE DIRECTORY

113

software is really easy to use; you don't have to be a computer or database geek to use it.

Key product lines: Bird Journal for the Desktop, Bird Journal for the iPhone.

Opening times: Lines are open 9am-5pm (UK time), Monday to Friday, except national holidays. Calls charged at local rate.

Address: Bluebird Technology Limited, 28 Grebe Court, Cambridge, CB5 8FR; 0845 094 6012.

E-mail: mail@bluebirdtechnology.com

Website: www.bluebirdtechnology.com

Follow us on Twitter: http://twitter.com/Bluebird_Tech/

FaceBook: www.facebook.com/BluebirdTechnology/

WILDLIFE WATCHING SUPPLIES

Company ethos: To bring together a comprehensive range of materials, clothing and equipment to make it easier and more comfortable for you to blend in with the environment. Quick and friendly service.

Key product lines: Hides, camouflage, bean bags, lens and camera covers, clothing etc.

New for 2012: Some new designs and more outdoor products.

Opening times: Mon to Fri (9am-5pm), mail order. Visitors by appointment.

Address: Wildlife Watching Supplies, Tiverton Way, Tiverton Business Park, Tiverton, Devon EX16 6TG; +44 (0)1884 254 191; Fax: +44 (0)1884 250 460; www.wildlifewatchingsupplies.co.uk

e-mail: enquiries@wildlifewatchingsupplies.co.uk

WILDSOUNDS

Company ethos: Donates a significant portion of profit to bird conservation, committed to sound environmental practices, official bookseller to African Bird Club. Operates the *Bird Watching* magazine bookshop.

Key product lines: Mail order, post-free books, CDs, DVDs and multi-media guides at discounted prices. Publisher of *Birding in Eastern Europe* by Gerard Gorman. Distributor of many best-selling DVDs i.e. *British Butterflies, North Norfolk Coast - Birder's Guide, Rare Birds 2010* etc. Field recording equipment stockist. Attends all major Bird Fairs and many local events.

New for 2012: See www.wildsounds.com

Opening times: Weekdays (9.30am-5pm).

Address: Cross Street, Salthouse, Norfolk NR25 7XH; 020 7724 7773; (fax) 020 7258 1293.

e-mail: sales@wildsounds.com

www.wildsounds.com

HOLIDAY COMPANIES

AVIAN ADVENTURES

Company ethos: First class value-for-money tours, escorted by friendly, experienced leaders at a fairly relaxed pace. Financial protection - ATOL 3367.

Types of tours: Birdwatching, birds and wildlife photography and wildlife safaris, all suitable for both the first-time and the more experienced traveller.

Destinations: 50 tours worldwide.

New for 2012: Belarus, Croatia; Ethiopia; Nile Cruise; Ohio (Magee Marsh); Colombia. New photographic tours to Varanger Fjord, Botswana, Kenya, Tanzania & Brazil's Pantanal.

Brochure from: 49 Sandy Road, Norton, Stourbridge, DY8 3AJ; 01384 372 013; (Fax)01384 441 340; e-mail: info@avianadventures.co.uk www.avianadventures.co.uk

BIRDFINDERS

Company ethos: Top-value birding tours to see all specialities/endemics of a country/area, using leading UK and local guides. ATOL 5406.

Types of tours: Birdwatching holidays for all abilities.

Destinations: Nearly 80 tours in UK, Europe, Africa, Asia, Australasia, North, Central and South America and Antarctica.

New for 2012: Australia south-east and Tasmania, Belarus, China (Sichuan), Colombia, France (Corsica), India (South), Turkey (Brown Fish-owls), Colorado (US grouse tour) and Western Sahara.

Brochure from: Vaughan Ashby, Westbank, Cheselbourne, Dorset DT2 7NW. 01258 839 066; e-mail: info@birdfinders.co.uk www.birdfinders.co.uk Our office is open seven days a week (8am-8pm).

Birdfinders

BRITISH-BULGARIAN FRIENDSHIP SOCIETY

Company ethos: To introduce people to the beauty of Bulgarian wildlife at exceptional value prices with expert leaders. ATOL 4465.

Types of tours: Birdwatching tours in winter, spring and autumn, also early summer and midsummer butterfly tours. Group size 12-14 persons.

Destinations: Specialists to Bulgaria, over 35 years experience.

New for 2012: Spring birdwatching; Spring natural history; Bulgarian mountains and Greek wetlands.

Brochure from: Balkania Travel Ltd, Office 3.08 Avanta Harrow, 79 College Road, Harrow, Middlesex, HA1 1BD. (Tel) 020 7536 9400. e-mail: ognian@balkaniatravel.com or annie.kay@btinternet.com - www.bbfs.org.uk

CLASSIC JOURNEYS

Company ethos: Professional and friendly company, providing well organised and enjoyable wildlife and photography holidays.

Types of tours: General wildlife and photography holidays on the Indian sub-continent and beyond.

Destinations: Nepal, India, Bhutan, Sri Lanka, Tibet, Indonesia, Ecuador, Galapagos, Peru, Brazil, Tanzania, Svalbard, Antarctica.

New for 2012: Brazil for jaguars and amazing wildlife.

Opening times: Mon-Fri (9:30am-4pm).

Further information: www.classicjourneys.co.uk Tel: 01773 873 497; e-mail: info@classicjourneys.co.uk

DORSET BIRDING

Company ethos: To provide local knowledge and an expertise of Dorset's birds and wildlife catering for all levels of experience and tailor-made to your requirements.

Types of tours: A guiding service for individuals and groups aimed at providing an experience of Dorset's birds, wildlife and landscapes. Although there is a particular emphasis on birds, all species groups are covered. Half-day, full day, weekends or longer breaks are available.

Destinations: Dorset.

Brochure from: Moor Edge, 2 Bere Road, Wareham, Dorset BH20 4DD; 01929 552 560. e-mail: enquiries@dorsetbirdingandwildlife.co.uk www.dorsetbirdingandwildlife.co.uk

GLENLOY WILDLIFE

Company ethos: We offer guided exploration of the stunning West Coast of Scotland, based from beautiful Glen Loy near Fort William in a former hunting lodge with views over the Nevis Range. The glen contains Red Deer, Golden Eagle, Otter and Chequered Skippers with Pine Martens visiting the Lodge each evening. Other birds we might hope to see include White-tailed Eagle, Divers, Twite, Black Grouse and Ring Ouzel.

Types of tours: We visit a variety of habitats by minibus and by foot. Suitable for anyone who can walk 3-4 miles over uneven ground.

Destinations: We explore the region of Lochaber, including the Great Glen, Ardnamurchan peninsula and the Small Isles.

Further information from: Jon Mercer, Glenloy Lodge Guest House, Banavie, Nr Fort William PH33 7PD; 01397 712 700 or 07817 443 370. e-mail: info@glenloylodge.co.uk www.glenloylodge.co.uk; www.glenloy-wildlife.org.uk

NATURETREK

Company ethos: Friendly, gentle-paced, birdwatching holidays with broad-brush approach. Sympathetic to other wildlife interests, history and local culture. Also operate faster-paced bargain birdwatching selection. ATOL no 2692

Types of tours: Escorted birdwatching, botanical and natural history holidays worldwide.

Destinations: Worldwide – see brochure.

New for 2012: 30+ exciting new European tours, plus several new long-haul destinations.

Brochure from: Cheriton Mill, Cheriton, Alresford, Hampshire SO24 0NG; 01962 733 051; (fax) 01962 736 426; www.naturetrek.co.uk e-mail: info@naturetrek.co.uk

NORTH WEST BIRDS

Company ethos: Friendly, relaxed and unhurried but targetted to scarce local birds.

Types of tours: Very small groups (up to four) based on large family home in South Lakes with good home cooking. Short breaks with birding in local area. Butterflies in season.

Destinations: Local to Northwest England. Lancashire, Morecambe Bay and Lake District.

Brochure from: Mike Robinson, Barn Close, Beetham, Cumbria LA7 7AL; (Tel/fax) 01539 563 191; e-mail: mike@nwbirds.co.uk www.nwbirds.co.uk

ORNITHOLIDAYS

Company ethos: Oldest bird tour company in the world (established 1965). Friendly and fun holidays led by full-time tour leaders. ATOL no 0743.

Types of tours: Escorted birdwatching, photographic and natural history tours.

Destinations: Worldwide including Trinidad and Tobago, Costa Rica, Chile, Bhutan, Taiwan, Sri Lanka, South Africa, Uganda, Iceland and Antarctica.

New for 2012: Papua New Guinea, China & Tibet, India Brahmaputra Cruise, Chile (puma tour), Belarus and Macedonia.
Brochure from: 29 Straight Mile, Romsey, Hampshire SO51 9BB; 01794 519 445; (fax) 01794 523 544; e-mail: info@ornitholidays.co.uk
www.ornitholidays.co.uk

ROMNEY MARSH BIRDWATCHING BREAKS
Company ethos: To pass on an appreciation of the wildlife of Romney Marsh in a family-friendly atmosphere.
Types of tours: Fully inclusive 3 or 5-day Birdwatching Breaks based at our cottage in Lydd-on-Sea. Also, one day birdwatching and historical tours around Romney Marsh.
Destinations: Romney Marsh, including Dungeness and Rye Harbour, and elsewhere across Kent and Sussex.
New for 2012: Day trips to northern France.
Brochure from: Paul Trodd, Plovers, 1 Toby Road, Lydd-on-Sea, Romney Marsh, Kent TN29 9PG; 01797 366 935 & 07920 197 535; e-mail: troddy@plovers.co.uk; www.plovers.co.uk

SPEYSIDE WILDLIFE
Company ethos: Fun-filled wildlife experiences with expert guides, where you are always treated as an individual, not one of a crowd.
Types of tours: Fully inclusive bird and mammal watching holidays in Scotland and overseas (ATOL no 4259). Also tailor-made trips, day guiding and dusk watches.
Destinations: Speyside in the Cairngorms National Park and around Scotland, Europe; Scandinavia and the Arctic; North, Central and South America; Africa.
New for 2012: Solway Firth; Northumberland; Belarus; New York City; Florida; California.
Brochure from: Garden Office, Inverdruie House, Inverdruie, Aviemore, Inverness-shire PH22 1QH; (Tel/fax) +44 (0) 1479 812 498; e-mail: enquiries@speysidewildlife.co.uk
www.speysidewildlife.co.uk,
www.facebook.com/speysidewildlife

SUNBIRD
Company ethos: Enjoyable birdwatching tours led by full-time professional leaders. ATOL no 3003.
Types of tours: Birdwatching, Birds & Music, Birds & History.
Destinations: Worldwide.

New for 2012: British Columbia, Cuba, Ecuador, Manitoba, Oregon, Portugal.
Brochure from: 26B The Market Square, Potton, Sandy, Bedfordshire SG19 2NP; 01767 262 522; (fax) 01767 262 916.
e-mail: sunbird@sunbirdtours.co.uk
www.sunbirdtours.co.ukcheck new destinations

THE TRAVELLING NATURALIST
Company ethos: Friendly, easy-going, expertly-led birdwatching and wildlife tours. ATOL no.3435. AITO 1124.
Types of tours: Birds and Butterflies, Butterflies and Flowers, Tigers, Whales, also Wild Ambitions - wildlife holidays for independent travellers.
Destinations: Worldwide.
New for 2012: Edible fungi in Latvia; Volcanoes and Northern Lights in Iceland.
Brochure from: PO Box 3141, Dorchester, Dorset DT1 2XD; 01305 267 994; (fax) 01305 265 506.
e-mail: info@naturalist.co.uk
www.naturalist.co.uk; www.wildambitions.co.uk

THINKGALAPAGOS
Company ethos: Specialists in the Galapagos Islands, great value, expert guides and personal attention to ensure a once-in-a-lifetime adventure travel experience.

Types of tours: Friendly and relaxed holidays that are educationally orientated for people with a keen interest in wildlife and photography. Suitable for both the first-time and more experienced traveller.
Destinations: Galapagos and mainland Ecuador.
New for 2012: Birding Special trip to Ecuador and Galapagos in May, led by top birding guides.
Brochure from: Rachel Dex, 25 Trinity Lane, Beverley, East Yorkshire HU17 0DY; 01482 872 716; e-mail: info@thinkgalapagos.com
www.thinkgalapagos.com

WILD INSIGHTS
Company ethos: Friendly, no-rush tours designed to savour, understand and enjoy birds and wildlife fully, rather than simply build large tick lists. Emphasis on quality. ATOL no 5429 (in association with Wildwings).
Types of tours: Skills-building UK courses, UK identification workshops plus a range of overseas tours.

OPTICAL DEALERS

Destinations: Various UK locations, plus selected destinations throughout USA, Central America, Africa, Northern India and Europe.
Calendar brochure from: Yew Tree Farmhouse, Craignant, Selattyn, Oswestry, Salop SY10 7NP. (Tel/fax) 01691 718 740; www.wildinsights.co.uk
e-mail: keith.offord@virgin.net

OPTICAL DEALERS

To assist readers in locating optics dealers in their own area more easily, this section is devoted into five regions, listed alphabetically as follows: Eastern England, Northern England, South East England, South West England and Western England.

CENTRAL & EASTERN ENGLAND

IN-FOCUS
Company ethos: The binocular and telescope specialists, offering customers informed advice at birdwatching venues throughout the country. Leading sponsor of the British Birdwatchng Fair.
Viewing facilities: Available at all shops (contact your local outlet), or at field events (10am-4pm) at bird reserves (see *Bird Watching* magazine or website www.at-infocus.co.uk for calendar)
Optical stock: Many leading makes of binoculars and telescopes, plus own-brand Delta range of binoculars and tripods.
Non-optical stock: Wide range of tripods, clamps and other accessories. Repair service available.
Opening times: These can vary, so please contact local shop or website before travelling.

LEAMINGTON
Address: Clarendon Avenue, Leamington, Warwickshire, CV32 5PP; 01926 886 166; (Fax)01926 887 611;
e-mail: leamington@lcegroup.co.uk

NORFOLK
Address: Main Street, Titchwell, Nr King's Lynn, Norfolk, PE31 8BB; 01485 210 101.

RUTLAND
Address: Anglian Water Birdwatching Centre, Egleton Reserve, Rutland Water, Rutland, LE15 8BT; 01572 770 656.

LONDON CAMERA EXCHANGE
Company ethos: To supply good quality optical equipment at a competitive price, helped by knowlegeable staff.
Viewing facilities: In shop and at local shows. Contact local branch for details of local events.

Optical stock: All leading makes of binoculars and scopes.
Non-optical stock: All main brands of photo, digital and video equipment.
Opening times: Most branches open 9am to 5.30pm.

CHESTERFIELD
Address: 1A South Street, Chesterfield, Derbyshire, S40 1QZ; 01246 211 891; (Fax) 01246 211 563;
e-mail: chesterfield@lcegroup.co.uk

COLCHESTER
Address: 12 Led Lane, Colchester, Essex CO1 1LS; 01206 573 444.

DERBY
Address: 17 Sadler Gate, Derby, Derbyshire, DE1 3NH; 01332 348 644; (Fax) 01332 369 136;
e-mail: derby@lcegroup.co.uk

LINCOLN
Address: 6 Silver Street, Lincoln, LN2 1DY; 01522 514 131; (Fax) 01522 537 480;
e-mail: lincoln@lcegroup.co.uk

NORWICH
Address: 12 Timber Hill, Norwich, Norfolk NR1 3LB; 01603 612 537.

NOTTINGHAM
Address: 7 Pelham Street, Nottingham, NG1 2EH; 0115 941 7486; (Fax) 0115 952 0547;
e-mail: nottingham@lcegroup.co.uk

NORTHERN ENGLAND

IN-FOCUS
LANCASHIRE
Address: WWT Martin Mere, Burscough, Ormskirk, Lancs, L40 0TA: 01704 897 020.

WEST YORKSHIRE
Address: Westleigh House Office Est. Wakefield Road, Denby Dale, West Yorks, HD8 8QJ: 01484

LONDON CAMERA EXCHANGE
CHESTER
Address: 9 Bridge Street Row, CH1 1NW; 01244 326 531.

MANCHESTER
Address: 37 Parker Street, Picadilly, M1 4AJ; 0161 236 5819.

WILKINSON CAMERAS
Company ethos: The widest range of photographic and birdwatching equipment

available at competitive prices at all times.
Viewing facilities: Optical field days at selected nature reserves in northern England. See website for details of photographic courses and other events.
Optical stock: Binoculars from Bushnell, Canon, Hawke, Leica, Nikon, RSPB, Steiner, Swarovski, Vanguard and Viking. Spotting scopes from Bushnell, Hawke, Leica, Nikon, Summit, Swarovski and Vanguard. Wide range of bags, digital cameras, lenses and video equipment.
Opening times: Branches open 9am to 5:30pm Monday to Saturday. Sunday 11am to 4pm (Preston only). e-mail: sales@wilkinson.co.uk
www.wilkinson.co.uk

BLACKBURN
42 Northgate, Blackburn, Lancs BB2 1JL: 01254 581 272; (Fax) 01254 695 867.

BURNLEY
95 James Street, Burnley, Lancs BB11 1PY; 01282 424 524; (Fax) 01282 831 722.

BURY
61 The Rock, Bury, Greater Manchester BL9 0NB; 01617 643 402; (Fax) 01617 615 086.

CARLISLE
13 Grapes Lane, Carlisle, Cumbria CA3 8NQ; 01228 538 583; (Fax) 01228 514 699.

KENDAL
19A The Westmorland Centre, Kendal, Cumbria LA9 4AB; 01539 735 055; (Fax) 01539 734 929.

LANCASTER
6 James Street, Lancaster, Lancs LA1 1UP; 01524 380 510; (Fax) 01524 380 512.

PRESTON
27 Friargate, Preston, Lancs PR1 2NQ; 01772 556 250; (Fax) 01772 259 435.

SOUTHPORT
38 Eastbank Street, Southport, Merseyside, PR8 1ET. 01704 534 534; (Fax) 01704 501 546; e-mail: southport@wilkinson.co.uk

SOUTH EAST ENGLAND

IN-FOCUS
(see introductory text in Eastern England).

ST ALBANS
Address: Bowmans Farm, London Colney, St Albans, Herts, AL2 1BB: 01727 827 799.

SOUTH WEST LONDON
Address: WWT The Wetland Centre, Queen Elizabeth Walk, Barnes, SW13 9WT: 020 8409 4433.

LONDON CAMERA EXCHANGE
(see introductory text in Eastern England).

FAREHAM
Address: 135 West Street, Fareham, Hampshire, PO16 0DU; 01329 236 441; (Fax) 01329 823 294; e-mail: fareham@lcegroup.co.uk

GUILDFORD
Address: 8/9 Tu nsgate, Guildford, Surrey, GU1 2DH; 01483 504 040; (Fax) 01483 538 216; e-mail: guildford@lcegroup.co.uk

PORTSMOUTH
Address: 40 Kingswell Path, Cascados, Portsmouth, PO1 4RR; 023 9283 9933; (Fax) 023 9283 9955; e-mail: portsmouth@lcegroup.co.uk

READING
Address: 7 Station Road, Reading, Berkshire, RG1 1LG; 0118 959 2149; (Fax) 0118 959 2197; e-mail: reading@lcegroup.co.uk

SOUTHAMPTON
Address: 10 High Street, Southampton, Hampshire, SO14 2DH; 023 8022 1597; (Fax) 023 8023 3838; e-mail: southampton@lcegroup.co.uk

STRAND, LONDON
Address: 98 The Strand, London, WC2R 0AG; 020 7379 0200; (Fax) 020 7379 6991; e-mail: strand@lcegroup.co.uk

WINCHESTER
Address: 15 The Square, Winchester, Hampshire, SO23 9ES; 01962 866 203; (Fax)01962 840 978; e-mail: winchester@lcegroup.co.uk

SOUTH WEST ENGLAND

LONDON CAMERA EXCHANGE
(see introductory text in Eastern England).

BATH
Address: 13 Cheap Street, Bath, Avon, BA1 1NB; 01225 462 234; (Fax) 01225 480 334. e-mail: bath@lcegroup,co.uk

BRISTOL
Address: 53 The Horsefair, Bristol, BS1 3JP; 0117 927 6185; (Fax) 0117 925 8716; e-mail: bristol.horsefair@lcegroup.co.uk

EXETER
Address: 174 Fore Street, Exeter, Devon, EX4 3AX; 01392 279 024/438 167; (Fax) 01392 426 988. e-mail: exeter@lcegroup.co.uk

PAIGNTON
Address: 71 Hyde Road, Paington, Devon, TQ4 5BP;01803 553 077; (Fax) 01803 664 081. e-mail: paignton@lcegroup.co.uk

PLYMOUTH
Address: 10 Frankfort Gate, Plymouth, Devon, PL1 1QD; 01752 668 894; (Fax) 01752 604248.
e-mail: plymouth@lcegroup.co.uk

SALISBURY
Address: 6 Queen Street, Salisbury, Wiltshire, SP1 1EY; 01722 335 436; (Fax) 01722 411 670;
e-mail: salisbury@lcegroup.co.uk

TAUNTON
Address: 6 North Street, Taunton, Somerset, TA1 1LH; 01823 259955; (Fax) 01823 338 001.
e-mail: taunton@lcegroup.co.uk

WESTERN ENGLAND

CLIFTON CAMERAS

Company ethos: Optical specialists for binoculars and spotting scopes based near Slimbridge Wetland Centre in Gloucestershire. Main sponsors of the Dursley birdwatching society.
Optical stock: All top brands stocked. Nikon Premier Dealer, Swarovski Premier Dealer, Zeiss Centre Partner and Leica Premier Dealer.
Non-optical stock: Professional camera supplier, Canon, Nikon, Pentax, Sigma and Gitzo Tripods to name a few.
New products to try: Nikon EDG spotting scopes, Swarovski CL Companion binoculars and Leica M9-P camera.
Opening times: Mon-Sat (9am-5.30pm).
Address: 28 Parsonage Street, Dursley, Gloucestershire GL11 4AA; 01453 548 128.
e-mail: sales@cliftoncameras.co.uk
www.cliftoncameras.co.uk

cliftoncameras.co.uk

FOCUS OPTICS

Company ethos: Friendly, expert service. Top quality instruments. No 'grey imports'.
Viewing facilities: Our own pool and nature reserve with feeding stations.
Optical stock: Full range of leading makes of binoculars and telescopes.
Non-optical stock: Waterproof clothing, fleeces, walking boots and shoes, bird food and feeders.

Books, videos, walking poles.
Opening times: Mon-Sat (9am-5pm). Some Bank-holidays.
Address: Church Lane, Corley, Coventry, CV7 8BA;

01676 540 501/542 476; (fax) 01676 540 930;
e mail: enquiries@focusoptics.eu
www.focusoptics.eu

IN-FOCUS

GLOUCESTERSHIRE
Address: WWT Slimbridge, Gloucestershire, GL2 7BT: 01453 890 978. 22314; (Fax) 01905 724 585;
e-mail: worcester@lcegroup.co.uk

LONDON CAMERA EXCHANGE

(see introductory text in Eastern England).

CHELTENHAM
Address: 10-12 The Promenade, Cheltenham, Gloucestershire, GL50 1LR; 01242 519 851; (Fax) 01242 576 771;
e-mail: cheltenham@lcegroup.co.uk

GLOUCESTER
Address: 12 Southgate Street, Gloucester, GL1 2DH; 01452 304 513; (Fax) 01452 387 309;
e-mail: gloucester@lcegroup.co.uk

WORCESTER
Address: 8 Pump Street, Worcester, WR1 2QT; 01905 22314; (Fax) 01905 724 585;
e-mail: worcester@lcegroup.co.uk

OPTICAL IMPORTERS AND MANUFACTURERS

CARL ZEISS LTD

Company ethos: World renowned, high quality performance and innovative optical products.

ZEISS

Product lines: Victory FL, Conquest, Stabilised, Victory and Classic compacts, PhotoScope 85T* FL and DiaScope FL telescopes.
Address: PO Box 78, Woodfield Road, Welwyn Garden City, Hertfordshire AL7 1LU; 01707 871 350; (fax) 01707 871 426;
e-mail: c.karn@zeiss.co.uk
www.zeiss.co.uk/sportsoptics

DEBEN GROUP INDUSTRIES

Company ethos: We design Hawke Sport Optics as a quantity range of binoculars and spotting scopes, which in turn offer excellent value for money. We have two market leaders within the range and will continue to create a simple but very popular range.
Product lines: Hawke Sport Optics consists of the following families: New Sapphire ED, New Frontier ED, New Endurance PC and the much-loved Nature-Trek range. The full range offers compacts, mid-size and full size binoculars from

TRADE DIRECTORY

OPTICAL IMPORTERS AND MANUFACTURERS

£50 - £550, plus spotting scopes (from £100 - £600) which also include models with ED glass. A range of trap cameras for filming wildlife now has an 8M HD model with colour screen.

New for 2012: We will be launching a new Sapphire range which offers both open hinge and top-hinge designs, compact binoculars in both the Endurance PC and Sapphire ED families, plus completing the range of spotting scopes with new ED ranges in the Sapphire family, with a choice of eyepieces.

Address: Avocet House, Wilford Bridge Road, Melton, Woodbridge, Suffolk IP12 1RB; 01394 387 762; e-mail: salesl@deben.com
www.deben.com

INTRO 2020 LTD

Company ethos: Experienced importer of photo and optical products.

Product lines: Steiner Binoculars, Tamron Lenses, Crumpler Bags, Tamrac Bags, Velbon Tripods, Slik Tripods, Hoya and Cokin filters. Plus many other photographic accessories.

New for 2012: Phottix photographic accessories.

Address: Unit 1, Priors Way, Maidenhead, Berkshire SL6 2HP; 01628 674 411; (fax) 01628 771 055; e-mail: sales@intro2020.co.uk
www.intro2020.co.uk, www.cokin.co.uk, www.metzflash.co.uk, www.sliktripod.co.uk, www.velbon.co.uk, www.tamrac.co.uk, www.steiner-binoculars.co.uk, www.tamron.co.uk

NEWPRO UK LTD

Company ethos: Some very well-established and respected brand names with new company technology and attitude.

Product lines: Vortex binoculars, scopes and monoculars – all with an unlimited lifetime warranty. Op/tech straps, pouches and harnesses, Cullman tripods and monopods. ROR (Residual Oil Remover) optics cleaner.

New for 2012: Vortex Viper HD binoculars and Viper HD scopes.

Opening times: Mon-Fri (8.30am-5pm) plus many outdoor events.

Address: Old Sawmills Road, Faringdon, Oxon SN7 7DS. 01367 242 411; www.newprouk.co.uk
e-mail: sales@newprouk.co.uk

opticron

Company ethos: To continuously develop high quality binoculars, telescopes and accessories that are useful, ergonomically sound and exceptional value for money.

Product lines: Opticron binoculars, monoculars, telescopes, tripods, telephotography/digi-scoping equipment and accessories.

Address: Unit 21, Titan Court, Laporte Way, Luton LU4 8EF; 01582 726 522; (fax) 01582 273 559; e-mail: sales@opticron.co.uk
www.opticron.co.uk

SWAROVSKI OPTIK

Company ethos: Constantly improving on what is good in terms of products and committed to conservation world-wide.

Product lines: CL – Companion 8x30 and 10 x30 and EL 10 x 50 and EL 12 x 50 binoculars are the latest additions to a market-leading range of binoculars.

SWAROVSKI OPTIK

Swarovski tripods AT101, CT101 and CT Travel are also new.

Address: Perrywood Business Park, Salfords, Surrey RH1 5JQ; 01737 856 812; (fax) 01737 856 885; e-mail: info@swarovski.com
www.swarovskioptik.com

OPTICAL REPAIRS AND SERVICING

OPTREP OPTICAL REPAIRS

Company ethos: To give a speedy, economical and effective repair service.

Key services: Servicing and repair of binoculars, telescopes etc. Conversant with the special needs of birdwatchers.

Opening times: Mon-Thu (9am-5pm), Fri (9am-3pm).

Address: 16 Wheatfield Road, Selsey, West Sussex PO20 0NY; 01243 601 365.
e-mail: info@opticalrepairs.com
www.opticalrepairs.com

BIRD RESERVES AND OBSERVATORIES

Boardwalks take visitors around the extended reserve areas of the Hawk & Owl Trust's Sculthorpe nature reserve in Norfolk.

ALL ENTRIES in the Reserves Directory are listed on a regional basis. This has been the standard practice for Scotland and Wales in recent editions, whereas the English counties have been listed alphabetically, but it is felt that grouping counties into regions will be more helpful to our readers.

We hope this proves helpful but welcome reader feedback on any way we can improve this section of the *Yearbook*. Please e-mail your comments to the Editor David Cromack at: editor@buckinghampress.com

Central England

Derbyshire, Gloucestershire, Leicestershire & Rutland, Lincolnshire, Northamptonshire, Nottinghamshire, Oxfordshire, Shropshire, Staffordshire, Warwickshire, West Midlands, Worcestershire

Derbyshire

1. CARR VALE NATURE RESERVE

Derbyshire Wildlife Trust.
Location: SK 45 70. 1km W of Bolsover on A632 to Chesterfield. Turn L at roundabout (follow brown tourist signs) into Riverside Way. Car park at end of road. Follow footpath (waymarked) around Peter Fidler reserve.
Access: Open all year.
Facilities: Car park, coach parking on approach road, good disabled access, paths, viewing platforms.
Public transport: Various Stagecoach services from Chesterfield (Stephenson Place) all pass close to the reserve: Mon to Sat - 83 serves Villas Road, 81, 82, 82A and 83 serve the roundabout on the A632. Sun - 81A, 82A serve the roundabout on the A632.
Habitat: Lakes, wader flashes, reedbed, sewage farm, scrub, arable fields.
Key birds: Up to 150 species seen annually at this productive site. *Winter:* Large numbers of wildfowl including flocks of Wigeon and Teal, also wintering flocks of finches and buntings, Water Rail. Large skeins of geese fly over in early and late winter. *Spring/autumn:* Birds on migration including pipits and thrushes. In September Swallows gather in the marsh, in a gigantic roost of between 10-12,000 birds. They usually attract Hobbies. *Early summer:* Breeding birds, including Reed and Sedge Warblers, Whitethroat, Yellowhammer, Moorhen and Gadwall, plus Skylark. Long list of rarities.
Other notable flora and fauna: Dragonflies, mammals (hare, water vole, harvest mouse, water shrew).
Contact: Derbyshire Wildlife Trust, East Mill, Bridgefoot, Belper, Derbyshire, DE56 1XH. 01773 881 188; e-mail: enquiries@derbyshirewt.co.uk www.derbyshirewildlifetrust.org.uk

2. CARSINGTON WATER

Severn Trent Water.
Location: SK 24 51 (for visitor centre and main facilities). Off the B5035 Ashbourne to Cromford road.
Access: Open all year except Christmas Day. The car parks are open from 7am to sunset (Apr - end Oct) and 7.30am to sunset in winter. There are various access points. New lower track opened in spring 09 to improve access.
Facilities: Visitor centre with exhibition, restaurant, four bird hides (inc RSPB), play area and toilets. RSPB 'Aren't Birds Brilliant' project operates here twice a week. Four bird hides and three car parks (two

chargeable, one free).
Public transport: TM Travel operates service 411 from Matlock and Ashbourne. The nearest train station is at Cromford. Call TM on 01142 633 890.
Habitat: Open water, islands, mixed woodland, scrub and grasslands, small reedbed.
Key birds: *Winter:* Wildfowl and a large gull roost plus possibility of divers and rare grebes. *Spring:* Good passage including Yellow and White Wagtails, Whimbrel, Black and Arctic Terns. *Summer:* Warblers and breeding waders. *All year:* Tree Sparrows and Willow Tits.
Other notable flora and fauna: Species-rich hay meadows, ancient woodlands with bluebells, three species of orchid, five species of bat, 21 species of butterfly, water vole.
Contact: Carsington Water, The Visitor Centre, Ashbourne, Derbyshire DE6 1ST. 01629 540 696. e-mail: customer.relations@severntrent.co.uk

NATURE RESERVES - CENTRAL ENGLAND

www.moretoexperience.co.uk and www.
carsingtonbirdclub.co.uk

3. DRAKELOW NATURE RESERVE

E-ON, leased to Derbyshire Wildlife Trust.
Location: SK 223 204 (Landranger 128). Drakelow
Power Station, one mile NE of Walton-on-Trent, off
A38.
Access: Dawn to dusk for permit-holders only (plus up
to two guests). Annual permit can be obtained from
Derbyshire Wildlife Trust.
Facilities: Seven hides, no other facilities.
Public transport: None.
Habitat: Disused flooded gravel pits with wooded
islands and reedbeds.
Key birds: *Summer:* Breeding Reed and Sedge
Warblers. Water Rail, Hobby. *Winter:* Wildfowl
(Goldeneye, Gadwall, Smew), Merlin, Peregrine.
Recent rarities include Great White and Little Egret,
Bittern and Spotted Crake, Ring-necked Duck and
American Wigeon.
Other notable flora and fauna: Good for common
species of dragonflies and butterflies.
Contact: Trust HQ, 01773 881 188.
e-mail: enquiries@derbyshirewt.co.uk
www.derbyshirewildlifetrust.org.uk

4. EREWASH MEADOWS

Derbyshire & Notts Wildlife Trusts
Location: SK 441 517. In three parts: Aldercar Flash,
Brinsley Meadows and part of Cromford Canal. Ripley
is nearest large town.
Access: Open all year — please keep to paths.
Facilities: None.
Public transport: Local bus services.
Habitat: The sites are now part of the largest
floodplain grassland and wetlands in Erewash Valley.
Key birds: *Spring/summer:* Breeding Lapwing, Snipe,
Reed Bunting and warblers. Raptors, waders and
wildfowl seen on passage. *Winter:* Wildfowl species.
Other notable flora and fauna: Grass snake,
amphibians, dragonflies, butterflies.
Contact: Trust HQ, 01773 881 188.
e-mail: enquiries@derbyshirewt.co.uk
www.derbyshirewildlifetrust.org.uk

5. HILTON GRAVEL PITS

Derbyshire Wildlife Trust.
Location: SK 249 315 (OS Langranger 128). From
Derby, take A516 from Mickleover W past Etwall onto
A50 junction at Hilton. Turn R at first island onto
Willow Pit Lane. Turn L next to a large white house
and park next to the gate. Follow track along S side
of the pools.
Access: Open all year.
Facilities: Tracks and boardwalks, viewing screens.
Public transport: Local bus services from Derby.
Habitat: Ponds, scrub, wood, fen.
Key birds: *Spring/summer:* Great Crested Grebe,
Common Tern, warblers. *Winter:* Wildfowl, Siskin,
Goldcrest. *All year:* All three woodpeckers,

Kingfisher, tits inc possible Willow Tit, Tawny Owl,
Bullfinch.
Other notable flora and fauna: Dragonflies (15
species inc emperor, ruddy darter and red-eyed
damselfly), Great crested newt, orchids, black
poplar, fungi.
Contact: Trust HQ, 01773 881 188.
e-mail: enquiries@derbyshirewt.co.uk
www.derbyshirewildlifetrust.org.uk

6. OGSTON RESERVOIR

Severn Trent Water Plc.
Location: SK 37 60 (Landranger map 119). From
Matlock, take A615 E to B6014, just after Tansley.
From Chesterfield take A61 S of Clay Cross onto
B6014, towards Tansley. Cross railway, the reservoir
is on L after the hill.
Access: View from roads, car parks or hides. Suitable
for coaches. Heronry in nearby Ogston Carr Wood
(Derbyshire Wildlife Trust) viewable from road, W of
reservoir.
Facilities: Three car parks (no charges), with toilets
at N and W locations. Ogston BC members-only
hide and public hide both wheelchair-accessible.
Information pack on request.
Public transport: Hulleys 63 bus service (Chesterfield
to Clay Cross) and 64 service (Clay Cross to Matlock)
both serves N end of reservoir (not Sundays).
Habitat: Open water, pasture, mixed woodland.
Key birds: All three woodpeckers, Little and Tawny
Owls, Kingfisher, Grey Wagtail, warblers. Passage
raptors (inc. Osprey), terns and waders. *Winter:* Gull
roost attracts thousands of birds, inc regular Glaucous
and Iceland Gulls. Top inland site for Bonaparte's
Gull and also attracts Caspian/ Herring Gull complex.
Good numbers of wildfowl, tit and finch flocks.
Contact: Malcolm Hill, Treasurer, Ogston Bird Club,
c/o 2 Sycamore Avenue, Glapwell, Chesterfield, S44
5LH. 01623 812 159; www.ogstonbirdclub.co.uk

7. PADLEY GORGE

The National Trust (East Midlands).
Location: From Sheffield, take A625. After eight
miles, turn L on B6521 to Nether Padley. Grindleford
Station is just off B6521 (NW of Nether Padley) and
one mile NE of Grindleford village.
Access: All year. Not suitable for disabled people or
those unused to steep climbs. Some of the paths are
rocky. No dogs allowed.
Facilities: Café and toilets at Longshaw lodge.
Public transport: Bus: from Sheffield to Bakewell
stops at Grindleford/Nether Padley. Tel: 01709 566
000. Train: from Sheffield to Manchester Piccadilly
stops at Grindleford Station. Tel: 0161 228 2141.
Habitat: Steep-sided valley containing largest area of
sessile oak woodland in south Pennines.
Key birds: *Summer:* Pied Flycatcher, Spotted
Flycatcher, Redstart, Wheatear, Whinchat, Wood
Warbler, Tree Pipit.
Contact: National Trust, High Peak Estate Office,
Edale End, Edale Road, Hope S33 2RF. 01433 670 368.
www.nationaltrust.org.uk

123

8. WILLINGTON GRAVEL PITS

Derbyshire Wildlife Trust.
Location: SK 285 274. From A50 'Toyota Island' turn onto Repton Road towards Willington and Repton. Go through village towards Repton. Just before bridge over River Trent, turn R onto un-made track (Meadow Lane). Park on track and walk along lane.
Access: Access along Meadow Lane to viewing platforms all year. No access on site.
Facilities: Viewing platforms. Limited parking in lane.
Public transport: Local trains stop at Willington, local bus service from Derby.
Habitat: Reedbed, shingle island, grassland.

Key birds: *Summer:* Breeding Lapwing, other waders, Common Tern, raptors (including Peregrine, Kestrel, Hobby and Sparrowhawk), Sand Martin, wildfowl. *Winter:* Waders and large flocks of wildfowl including Wigeon, Teal, Pochard and Shoveler. *Passage:* Large numbers of Curlew in spring, up to 20 species of waders in spring/autumn.
Other notable flora and fauna: Short-leaved water starwort. Several species of dragonfly, plus occasional otter signs, fox and other mammals.
Contact: Trust HQ, 01773 881 188.
e-mail: enquiries@derbyshirewt.co.uk
www.derbyshirewildlifetrust.org.uk

Gloucestershire

1. ASHLEWORTH HAM NATURE RESERVE

Gloucestershire Wildlife Trust.
Location: SO 830 265. Leave Gloucester N on A417; R at Hartpury and follow minor road through Ashleworth towards Hasfield.
Access: Access prohibited at all times but birds may be viewed from new hide in Meerend Thicket.
Facilities: Bird viewing hide and screen, interpretation panels.
Habitat: Low-lying grassland flood plain.
Key birds: *Winter:* Wildfowl (inc. 4,000 Wigeon, 1,500 Teal, Pintail, Goldeneye, Bewick's Swan), passage waders, Peregrine. *Summer:* Hobby.
Contact: Trust HQ, 01452 383 333.
e-mail: info@gloucestershirewildlifetrust.co.uk
www.gloucestershirewildlifetrust.co.uk

2. COTSWOLD WATER PARK

Cotswold Water Park Society.
Location: The CWP comprises 163 lakes in the Upper Thames Valley, between Cirencester and Swindon. Many lakes are accessible via public rights of way. Start from Cotswold Water Park Gateway Visitor Centre (SU 072 971), immediately on L after A419. For Millenium Visitor Centre at Keynes Country Park (SU 026 957) from A419, take B4696 towards Ashton Keynes. At staggered crossroads, go straight over, heading towards Somerford Keynes. Take next R turn to Circencester. Entrance to Keynes Country Park is second entrance on R.
Access: Cotswold Water Park is open all year round. The visitor centres are open every day except Christmas Day.
Facilities: Paths are flat but with stiles and footbridges. Many are wheelchair accessible. Toilets, refreshments, car parking and information available from the visitor centres. Hides available at Cleveland Lakes/Waterhay (lakes 68a and 68c), Shorncote Reed Bed (lakes 84/85), Cokes Pit (Lake 34) and Whelford Pools (Lake 111). Free copies of the CWP Leisure Guide are available from the visitor centres, also the guidebook *Wildlife in the Cotswold Water Park: Where to go and what to see.*

Public transport: Bus: from Kemble, Cheltenham, Cirencester and Swindon. 08457 090 899. Train: nearest station is four miles away at Kemble. 08457 484 950.
Habitat: Gravel extraction has created more than 1,000ha of standing open water, plus other associated wetland habitats, creating one of the largest man-made wetlands in Europe.
Key birds: *Winter:* Common wildfowl, Smew, Red-crested Pochard, Merlin, Peregrine. *Summer:* Breeding ducks, warblers, Nightingale, Hobby, Common Tern, Black-headed Gull colony, Reed Bunting, hirundines.
Contact: Cotswold Water Park Society, Cotswold House, Down Ampney Estate, Cirencester, Glos GL7 5QF. 01793 752 413. e-mail: info@waterpark.org
www.waterpark.org

3. HIGHNAM WOODS

RSPB (South West England Office).
Location: SO 778 190. Signed on A40 three miles W of Gloucester.
Access: Open at all times, no permit required. The nature trails can be very muddy. Some limited wheelchair access. Dogs allowed on leads.
Facilities: One nature trail (approx 1.5 miles).
Public transport: Contact Traveline (public transport information) on 0871 2002 233 between 7am-10pm each day.
Habitat: Ancient woodland in the Severn Vale with areas of coppice and scrub.
Key birds: *Spring/summer:* The reserve has about 12 pairs of breeding Nightingales. Resident birds include all three woodpeckers, Buzzard and Sparrowhawk. Ravens are frequently seen. *Winter:* Feeding site near car park good for woodland birds.
Other notable flora and fauna: Tintern spurge in late June-early July. White-letter hairstreak and white admiral butterflies seen annually.
Contact: Barry Embling, Site Manager, The Puffins, Parkend, Lydney, Glos, GL15 4JA. 01594 562 852.
e-mail: barry.embling@rspb.org.uk www.rspb.org.uk

4. LOWER WOODS NATURE RESERVE

Gloucestershire Wildlife Trust.
Location: ST 749 885. Reserve is about one mile E

NATURE RESERVES - CENTRAL ENGLAND

Key birds: *Spring*: Pied Flycatcher, Wood Warbler, Redstart, warblers. *Summer*: Nightjar. *Winter*: Siskin, Crossbill in some years. *All year*: Buzzard, Raven, Hawfinch, all three woodpeckers.

Other notable flora and fauna: Golden-ringed dragonfly seen annually. Silver-washed and small pearl-bordered fritillaries and white admiral butterflies present.

Contact: Barry Embling, Site Manager, 01594 562 852.

e-mail: barry.embling@rspb.org.uk www.rspb.org.uk

6. SHORNCOTE REEDBED (LAKES 84/85)

Cotswold Water Park Society.

Location: Lakes 84 and 85, Cotswold Water Park. From A419 Cirencester to Swindon road, take B4696 towards Cotswold Water Park West. Turn R at crossroads towards South Cerney. Follow road through village and park in playing fields car park after sharp R bend (SU 044 970). Take footpath through playing fields, cross road and continue on path through reedbeds to small lakes and hides.

Access: Open at all times, most paths firm and flat so suitable for wheelchairs.

Facilities: Toilets, refreshments, car parking and information available from nearby Keynes Country Park adjacent. Two hides.

Public transport: Bus: from Kemble, Cheltenham, Cirencester and Swindon. Tel: 08457 090 899. Train: nearest station is four miles away at Kemble. Tel: 08457 484 950.

Habitat: Lakes with reedbed, marsh, ditches, islands and loafing areas.

Key birds: *Winter*: Common wildfowl, Smew, Peregrine, Merlin, Bittern, Stonechat. *Summer*: Breeding ducks, warblers, Hobby, Sand Martin, Reed Bunting.

Other notable flora and fauna: Several species of dragonfly.

Contact: Cotswold Water Park Society, 01793 752 413.

7. SLIMBRIDGE

The Wildfowl & Wetlands Trust.

Location: SO 723 048. S of Gloucester. Signposted from M5 (exit 13 or 14).

Access: Open daily (9am-5.30pm or 5pm in winter) except Dec 25. Last entry 30 mins before closing. Wheelchair hire (book beforehand) — all paths wheelchair accessible. Free parking for cars and coaches.

Facilities: Restaurant, gift shop, gallery, cinema, discovery centre. Outdoor facilities inc 15 hides, tropical house, worldwide collection of wildfowl species, observatory and observation tower. Plenty of family attractions including a pond zone, wader aviary, commentated swan feeds in the winter, Land Rover safaris and a canoe safari trail.

Public transport: Request bus service - contact www.

---

of Wickwar. Main parking is at Lower Woods Lodge, via a track off the Wickwar-Hawkesbury road. Public footpaths and bridleways cross the reserve.

Access: Open all year.

Facilities: Well-marked footpaths and bridleways. Walk leaflet available.

Habitat: Mixed woodland, mildly acidic or slightly calcareous clay, grassland, river, springs.

Key birds: *Spring/summer*: Nightingale. *All year*: Usual woodland species including Tawny Owl, Jay, Nuthatch and Sparrowhawk. Kingfisher on river.

Other notable flora and fauna: 71 species of ancient woodland plants.

Contact: Trust HQ. 01452 383 333,
 e-mail: info@gloucestershirewildlifetrust.co.uk
www.gloucestershirewildlifetrust.co.uk

5. NAGSHEAD

RSPB (South West England Office).

Location: SO 097 085. In Forest of Dean, N of Lydney. Signed immediately W of Parkend village on the road to Coleford.

Access: Open at all times, no permit required. The reserve is hilly but there is limited wheelchair access. Dogs must be kept on leads during bird nesting season and under close control at all other times.

Facilities: There are two nature trails (one mile and 2.25 miles). Information centre, with toilet facilities (including disabled), open at weekends mid-Apr to end Aug. Schools education programme available.

Public transport: Contact Traveline (public transport information) on 0871 2002 233 (7am to 10pm each day).

Habitat: Much of the reserve is 200-year-old oak plantations, grazed in some areas by sheep. The rest of the reserve is a mixture of open areas and conifer/mixed woodland.

stroud.gov.uk. Nearest train station at Cam and Dursley (4 miles).
Habitat: Reedbed, saltmarsh, freshwater pools, mudflats and wet grassland.
Key birds: *Winter:* Between 30,000 to 40,000 wildfowl esp. Bewick's Swan, White-fronted Goose, Wigeon, Teal, Pintail. Waders inc Lapwing, Golden Plover, Spotted Redshank and Little Stint. Often there are large roosts of Starlings and gulls. *Breeding:* Kingfisher, Lapwing, Redshank, Oystercatcher, Common Tern, Reed Bunting and a good range of warblers. *Passage:* Waders, terns and gulls, inc Mediterranean and Yellow-legged Gulls. Yellow Wagtail and large passerine movements. Hobbies now reach double figures and there is an impressive list of rarities.
Other notable flora and fauna: Brown hare, otter, polecat and water vole. Scarce chaser and hairy dragonfly among 22 recorded species.
Contact: Marketing Manager, WWT, Slimbridge,

Gloucester, GL2 7BT. 01453 891 900; e-mail: info.slimbridge@wwt.org.uk

8. SYMOND'S YAT
RSPB/Forestry Commission England.
Location: SO 563 160. Hill-top site on the edge of Forest of Dean, three miles N of Coleford on B4432, signposted from Forest Enterprise car park. Also signposted from A40, S of Ross-on-Wye.
Access: Open at all times. RSPB Information Officer on site daily, April to August.
Facilities: Car park, toilets with adapted facilities for disabled visitors, picnic area, drinks and light snacks. Environmental education programmes available.
Public transport: Very limited.
Habitat: Cliff above the River Wye and woodland.
Key birds: *Summer:* Peregrine, Buzzard, Goshawk, Raven and woodland species. Telescope is set up daily to watch the Peregrines on the nest.
Contact: RSPB, 01594 562 852.

Leicestershire and Rutland

1. BEACON HILL COUNTRY PARK
Leicestershire County Council.
Location: SK 522 149. From Loughborough, take A512 SW for 2.5 miles. Turn L onto Woodhouse Lane and follow it for 2.5 miles through Nanpantan. The Lower car park is on the right. For the Upper car park, continue past the Lower car park, turn right onto Beacon Road, car park is at top of the hill.
Access: Open all year from 7am. Closing times are clearly displayed. A permissive path from Deans Lane to Woodhouse Lane is occasionally closed during the year. Please check first.
Facilities: Two pay-on-entry car parks, easy-to-follow waymarked tracks and woodland paths. Several climbs to hill tops. Rocky outcrops slippery after rain. Information boards. Toilets at both car parks. Wheelchair access along park paths but no access to summit. Refreshments at Bull's Head, Woodhouse Eaves.
Public transport: Bus: Nos 54, 121 and 123 from Loughborough call at Woodhouse Eaves. Tel: 0870 608 2608.
Habitat: Forest, one of the oldest geological outcrops in England and the second highest point in Leicestershire.
Key birds: *All year:* Treecreeper, Nuthatch, Lesser Spotted, Greater Spotted and Green Woodpeckers, Great and Coal Tits, Little Owl, wagtails. *Summer:* Pied Flycatcher, Whitethroat, Blackcap, Whinchat, Garden Warbler, Stonechat, Tree Pipit.
Contact: Beacon Hill Estate Office, Broombriggs Farm, Beacon Road, Woodhouse Eaves, Loughborough LE12 8SR. 0116 305 8790.

2. EYEBROOK RESERVOIR
Corby & District Water Co.
Location: SP 853 964. Reservoir built 1940. S of

Uppingham, from unclassified road W of A6003 at Stoke Dry.
Access: Access to 150 acres private grounds granted to members of Leics and Rutland OS and Rutland NHS. All visitors should sign in at fishing lodge. Organised groups should contact Andy Miller on 01536 772 930.
Facilities: SSSI since 1956. Three bird hides. Fishing season March - Nov. Toilets and visitor centre at fishing lodge.
Habitat: Open water, plantations and pasture.
Key birds: *Summer:* Good populations of breeding birds, sightings of Ospreys and Red Kite. Passage waders and Black Tern. *Winter:* Wildfowl (inc. Goldeneye, Goosander, Smew) and waders. Tree Sparrow and Yellowhammer at feeding station. During winter months, Barn and Short-eared Owl may be seen hunting at dusk near Great Easton village (close to recycling centre).
Other notable flora and fauna: Otter, muntjac deer, red darter, demoiselles and blue damselfly.
Contact: Andy Miller, Fishery Estate Manager, 01536 772 930. www.eyebrook.com

3. NARBOROUGH BOG
Leics and Rutland Wildlife Trust.
Location: SP 549 979. Reserve lies between River Soar and M1, 8km S of Leicester. From city, turn L off B4114 just before going under motorway, follow track to sports club. Park near club house and walk across recreation ground to reserve entrance.
Access: Open at all times, please keep to paths. Not suitable for wheelchairs. Dogs on short leads only.
Facilities: None. Use the small bus/coach could park in sports field car park
Public transport: Narborough train station. Buses X5, 140 to Narborough then 1km walk.
Habitat: Peat bog SSSI (the only substantial deposit in Leicestershire), wet woodland, reedbed, dense scrub and fen meadow.
Key birds: More than 130 species of birds have been

recorded including all three species of woodpeckers, six species of tit, Tawny Owl, Sparrowhawk and Kingfisher.

Other notable flora and fauna: Good variety of butterflies including large and small skippers, small heath and gatekeeper. Banded demoiselles, also good for moths and beetles. Harvest mice and water voles recorded, also breeding grass snakes. Meadow saxifrage, common meadow-rue and marsh thistle.
Contact: Trust HQ. 0116 272 0444.

4. RUTLAND WATER

Leics and Rutland Wildlife Trust.
Location: Two nature reserves 1. Egleton Reserve SK 878 075: from Egleton village off A6003 or A606 S of Oakham. Hosts British Birdwatching Fair every August. 2. Lyndon Reserve SK 894 058: south shore E of Manton village off A6003 S of Oakham. Follow 'nature reserve' signs to car park.
Access: 1. Open daily 9am-5pm, (4pm Nov to Jan). 2. Open winter (Sat, Sun 10am-4pm), Summer daily (9am-5pm). Day permits available for both. Reduced admission for disabled and carers. Closed Dec 25 and 26. Badger-watching hide can be booked from mid-April to July.
Facilities: 1: Anglian Water Birdwatching Centre has toilets and disabled access, mobility scooter to hire, conference facilities. Disabled access possible to most of 25 hides. Three new hides overlook Heron Bay. More lagoons to be created. 2: Interpretive centre now upgraded with new toilets, including disabled, new paths, use of a mobility scooter. Seven hides include four accessible to wheelchairs. Marked nature trail leaflet.
Habitat: Ramsar designated reservoir, lagoons, scrapes, woods, meadows, plantations, reedbeds.
Key birds: *Spring/autumn:* Outstanding wader passage, with up to 28 species recorded. Also wide range of harriers, owls, passerine flocks, terns (Black, Arctic, breeding Common, occasional Little and Sandwich). *Winter:* Up to 28 species of wildfowl

(inc international important numbers of Gadwall and Shoveler). Also Goldeneye, Smew, Goosander, rare grebes, all divers, Ruff. *Summer:* Ospreys among 70 breeding species.
Other notable flora and fauna: Otter, badger, fox, weasel, stoat. Up to 20 species of dragon and damselflies and 24 butterfly species.
Contact: Tim Appleton, 01572 770 651; e-mail awbc@rutlandwater.org.uk; www.rutlandwater.org.uk www.ospreys.org.uk

5. SENCE VALLEY FOREST PARK

Forestry Commission
Location: SK 400 115. Within The National Forest. Ten miles NW of Leicester and two miles SW of Coalville, between Ibstock and Ravenstone. The car park is signed from A447 N of Ibstock.
Access: Open all year. Car park open 8.30am-dusk (precise times on noticeboard). Lower car park (2.2m height barrier) gives easy access to wheelchair-friendly surfaced paths. Week's notice required for coach or minibus visits.
Facilities: Two car parks, toilets (including disabled and baby-changing facilities), information and recent sightings boards, hide, surfaced trails.
Public transport: None.
Habitat: New forest (native broadleaf, mixed and pine), rough grassland, wildflower meadow, pools, wader scrape, river.
Key birds: *Spring/summer:* Artificial Sand Martin nesting wall, Wheatear, Whinchat, Redstart, Common and Green Sandpipers, Ringed and Little Ringed Plovers, Redshank. Dunlin and Greenshank frequent, possible Wood Sandpiper. Reed Bunting, Meadow Pipit, Skylark, Linnet, Yellow Wagtail. Possible Quail. Kestrel and Barn Owl seen occasionally. *Winter:* Stonechat, Redpoll, Short-eared Owl, Goosander and Wigeon possible.
Contact: Forestry Commission, 01889 586 593. www.forestry.gov.uk

Lincolnshire

1. DONNA NOOK

Lincolnshire Wildlife Trust.
Location: TF 422 998. Near North Somercotes, off A1031 coast road, S of Grimsby.
Access: Donna Nook beach is closed on weekdays as this is an active bombing range, but dunes remain open. Dogs on leads. Some disabled access.
Facilities: No toilets or visitor centre.
Habitat: Dunes, slacks and intertidal areas, seashore, mudflats, sandflats.
Key birds: *Summer:* Little Tern, Ringed Plover, Oystercatcher. *Winter:* Brent Goose, Shelduck, Twite, Lapland Bunting, Shore Lark, Linnet.
Other notable flora and fauna: The reserve has one of the largest and most accessible breeding colonies of grey seals in the UK. Other mammals include fox,

badger, stoat and weasel and three species of shrew have been identified. Common lizard.
Contact: Lincolnshire Wildlife Trust, Banavallum House, Manor House Street, Horncastle, Lincs, LN9 5HF. 01507 526 667. e-mail: lincstrust@cix.co.uk www.lincstrust.co.uk

2. EPWORTH TURBERY

Lincolnshire Wildlife Trust.
Location: SE 758 036. SW of Scunthorpe. Take A18 W from Scunthorpe then A161 S to Epworth. Turn R on High Street, continue onto Tottermire Lane then bear left onto Battle Green. Turn L onto Fieldside, R onto Carrside then L onto Turbary Road. The entrance is near bridge over Skyer's Drain. Parking available through gate, which should be kept closed, or on verge adjoining reserve. Park well away from corner.
Access: Open at all times. Keep to waymarked paths and use hides when viewing open area. In order to

avoid disturbing birds on the ponds, please do not climb on the banks.

Facilities: Car park, way-marked trail, two hides.

Public transport: None.

Habitat: One of the few relicts of raised bog in Lincolnshire. Although extensively dug for peat in the past, areas of active sphagnum bog still exist. Areas of reed swamp and mixed fen vegetation, also fen and wet heath conditions and a considerable area of birch woodland of varying ages.

Key birds: Breeding birds include Tree Pipit, warblers, finches, Green and Great Spotted Woodpeckers and Woodcock. Greenshank, Green Sandpiper and Little Grebe on wet area. Around Steve's Pond, occasional Hobby and Marsh Harrier, plus Teal, Little Grebe, Tree Pipit, Sparrowhawk and Buzzard. Willow and Long-tailed Tits, Reed Bunting and Willow Warbler in the woodland areas. Occasionally Corn Buntings on adjoining farmland. In the autumn and winter large flocks of Rooks, Carrion Crows and Jackdaws fly into reserve to roost. At Pantry's Pond in winter occasional Hen Harrier. Other birds include Yellowhammer and Linnet. Sometimes in winter Long-eared Owls can be observed roosting close to the path.

Other notable flora and fauna: 11 species of breeding dragonflies and damselflies have been recorded. Wood tiger moth is well established. Plants include sneezewort, yellow and purple-loosestrife, meadow-rue, and devil's-bit scabious.

Contact: Trust HQ, 01507 526 667, e-mail: lincstrust@cix.co.uk www.lincstrust.co.uk

3. FRAMPTON MARSH

RSPB (Eastern England Office).

Location: TR 364 385. Four miles SE of Boston. From A16 follow signs to Frampton then Frampton Marsh.

Access: Visitor Centre open 10am-4pm each day except Dec 25. Footpaths and hides open at all times, free. Visitor Centre (including toilets), footpaths and hides all suitable for wheelchairs.

Facilities: Visitor centre with hot drinks and snacks, three hides, footpaths, benches, viewpoints, 50-space car park (three for disabled visitors), bicycle rack, free information leaflets and events programmes. Childrens activities.

Public transport: None.

Habitat: Saltmarsh, wet grassland, freshwater scrapes and developing reedbed.

Key birds: *Summer*: Breeding Redshank, Avocet, Lapwing, Skylark, Little Ringed Plover, Ringed Plover, Sand Martin and several species of ducks plus passage waders (inc Greenshank, Curlew Sandpiper, Wood Sandpiper, Little and Temminck's Stints, Ruff and Black-tailed Godwit), Marsh Harrier and Hobby. *Winter*: Hen Harrier, Short-eared Owl, Merlin, dark-bellied Brent Goose, Twite, Golden Plover, Lapland Bunting.

Other notable flora and fauna: Water vole, muntjac and roe deer, stoat. Dragonflies inc emperor, hawkers, chasers and darters. Common butterflies plus wall brown, painted lady and speckled wood.

Scarce pug, star wort and crescent striped moths on saltmarsh. Important brackish water flora and fauna includes nationally scarce spiral tassleweed and several rare beetles.

Contact: John Badley, Site Manager, Roads Farmhouse, Frampton Roads, Frampton, Boston, Lincs PE20 1AY. 01205 724 678. www.rspb.org.uk e-mail: johnbadley@rspb.org.uk

4. FREISTON SHORE

RSPB (Eastern England Office).

Location: TF 397 424. Four miles E of Boston. From A52 at Haltoft End follow signs to Freiston Shore.

Access: Open at all times, free.

Facilities: Footpaths, two car parks, bird hide. Free information leaflets on site, guided walks programme. Bicycle rack, benches, viewpoints, seawatching shelter, reservoir viewing screen, wet grassland viewing platform.

Public transport: None.

Habitat: Saltmarsh, saline lagoon, mudflats, wet grassland.

Key birds: *Summer*: Breeding waders including Avocet, Ringed Plover and Oystercatcher, Common Tern, Corn Bunting and Tree Sparrow. *Winter*: Twite, dark-bellied Brent Goose, wildfowl, waders, Short-eared Owl and Hen Harrier. *Passage*: Waders, including Greenshank, Curlew Sandpiper and Little Stint. *Autumn*: Occasional seabirds including Arctic and Great Skuas.

Other notable flora and fauna: Water vole, muntjac and roe deer, stoat. Dragonflies inc emperor, hawkers, chasers and darters. Common butterflies plus wall brown, painted lady and speckled wood. Scarce pug, star wort and crescent striped moths on saltmarsh. Important lagoon invertebrates and plants.

Contact: John Badley, Site Manager, 01205 724 678, e-mail: john.badley@rspb.org.uk www.rspb.org.uk

5. GIBRALTAR POINT NNR & BIRD OBSERVATORY

Lincolnshire Wildlife Trust.

Location: TF 556 580. Three miles S of Skegness on the N edge of The Wash. Signposted from Skegness town centre.

Access: Reserve open dawn-dusk all year. Charges for car parking. Free admission to reserve, visitor centre and toilets. Some access restrictions to sensitive sites at S end, open access to N. Dogs on leads at all times — no dogs on beach during summer. Visitor centre and toilets suitable for wheelchairs, as well as network of surfaced foot paths. Bird observatory and four hides suitable for wheelchairs. Groups must book day visits in advance - contact The Wash Study Centre for residential or day visits. Access for coaches.

Facilities: Site also location of Wash Study Centre and Bird Observatory. Field centre is an ideal base for birdwatching/natural history groups in spring, summer and autumn. Visitor centre, gift shop and cafe. Toilets open daily. Network of footpaths bisect all major habitats. Public hides overlook freshwater and brackish lagoons. Wash viewpoint overlooks saltmarsh and mudflats.

NATURE RESERVES - CENTRAL ENGLAND

Public transport: Bus service from Skegness runs occasionally but summer service only. Otherwise taxi/car from Skegness. Cycle route from Skegness.
Habitat: Sand dune grassland and scrub, saltmarshes and mudflats, freshwater marsh and lagoons.
Key birds: Large scale visible migration during spring and autumn passage. Internationally important populations of non-breeding waders Jul-Mar (peak Sep/Oct). Winter flocks of Brent Geese, Shelduck and Wigeon on flats and marshes with Hen Harrier, Merlin and Short-eared Owl often present. Red-throated Divers offshore, peak Feb. Little Tern and Ringed Plover colonies in summer. More than 100 species can be seen in a day during May and Sept. Good passage of autumn seabirds in northerly winds.
Other notable flora and fauna: Pyramidal orchids occur in patches. Grey and common seal colonies, with porpoises offshore in most months. Butterflies include brown argus and green hairstreak.
Contact: Reserve and wildlife: Kev Wilson. Visit bookings: Jill Hardy, Sykes Farm, Gibraltar Point Nature Reserve, Gibraltar Road, Skegness, Lincs PE24 4SU. 01754 898 057; e-mail: kwilson@linwtrust.co.uk or gibadmin@lincstrust.co.uk
www.lincstrust.org.uk and
GibraltarPointBIrdObservatory.blogspot.com

6. KILLINGHOLME HAVEN PITS

Lincolnshire Wildlife Trust.
Location: TA 165199 NW of Grimsby. Take A180 W, turn R on A1173 towards Immingham. Turn L at roundabout and continue to A160. Turn L then R onto Eastfield road. Turn R onto Chase Hill road then L onto Haven road. The reserve is situated to the S of Haven Road on the approach to North Killingholme Haven. Park carefully on the road.
Access: No general access to the reserve, but adequate viewing points are available from the public road and bank-top footpath.
Facilities: None.
Habitat: Marsh/wetland.
Key birds: A good site for water birds. Diving ducks, such as Pochard, Tufted Duck and, occasionally, Scaup. Breeding species include Little Grebe, plus Reed, Sedge, Willow and Grasshopper Warblers. Ruddy Duck has also been known to breed here.
The two large shallow pits, are of the greatest importance for birds, particularly for migrant waders in spring and autumn. Spotted Redshank, Dunlin, Greenshank, Common Sandpiper, Little Ringed Plover, Ruff and Black-tailed Godwit, the latter often in large numbers, are regular visitors.
The list of scarce and rare species is long and includes Spoonbill, Avocet, Little Egret, Little and Temminck's Stints, Red-necked Phalarope, and Curlew, Pectoral, Baird's And White-rumped Sandpipers.
Contact: Trust HQ, 01507 526 667,
e-mail: lincstrust@cix.co.uk
www.lincstrust.co.uk

7. SALTFLEETBY-THEDDLETHORPE DUNES NNR

Natural England.
Location: TF 465 924 - TF 490 883. Approx two miles N of Mablethorpe. All the following car parks may be accessed from the A1031: Crook Bank, Brickyard Lane, Churchill Lane, Rimac, Sea View.
Access: Open all year at all times. Keep dogs under close control. Easy access half mile trail suitable for wheelchair users starts adjacent to Rimac car park. Includes pond and saltmarsh viewing platforms.
Facilities: Toilets, including wheelchair suitability at Rimac car park. Events programme (April to end of October). Easy access trail at Rimac with a panorama viewing platform that has wheelchair access.
Public transport: Grayscroft coaches (01507 473 236) and Lincolnshire Roadcar (01522 532 424) run services past Rimac entrance (Louth to Mablethorpe service). Lincs Roadcar can connect with trains at Lincoln. Applebys Coaches (01507 357 900) Grimsby to Saltfleet bus connects with Grimsby train service.
Habitat: 13th Century dunes, freshwater marsh, new dune ridge with large areas of sea buckthorn, saltmarsh, remnants of a shingle ridge and foreshore.
Key birds: *Summer:* Breeding birds in scrub include Grasshopper Warbler, Whitethroat, Lesser Whitethroat. *Winter:* Large flocks of Brent Goose, Shelduck, Teal and Wigeon. Wintering Short-eared

Owl, Hen Harrier. Area good for autumn and spring passage particularly at Paradise Ponds.
Other notable flora and fauna: Impressive show of sea lavender in late summer, orchids in marsh and dunes including pyramidal, marsh and bee. 16 species

of dragonfly including emperor. Water vole, roe and muntjac deer, foxes and badgers are common.
Contact: Peter Roworth, Natural England Workshops, Seaview, Saltfleetby St Clement, Louth, Lincs LN11 7TR. 01507 338 611. www.naturalengland.org.uk

Northamptonshire

1. DITCHFORD LAKES

Beds, Cambs, Northants & Peterborough Wildlife Trust.
Location: SP 931 678. From Wellingborough, take A45 towards Rushden and Higham Ferrers. Take exit marked A5001 to Rushden. Turn left at roundabout onto Ditchford Road towards Irthlingborough/ Ditchford. 500 m on right is small car park with height restriction. Entrance is off car park.
Access: Rough grass paths, flat overall. Some areas soft and muddy especially in winter. Grazing animals at certain times of the year.
Facilities: None.
Public transport: Northampton/Wellingborough-Irthlingborough bus, then walk 1.5 miles.
Habitat: Part of the upper Nene valley floodplain – a complex of old gravel pits, grassland, lakes surrounded by mature scrub.
Key birds: *Winter:* Common Sandpiper, Snipe, Teal, Wigeon, Gadwall, Tufted Duck. *Spring:* Redshank, Oystercatcher, Cetti's Warbler, Little Grebe, Grey Heron. *Summer:* Reed Warbler, Sedge Warbler, Swift, House Martin. *Autumn:* Snipe, Great Crested Grebe, Moorhen, Coot, Grey Heron.
Other notable flora and fauna: Hairy dragonfly, grass snake. Otter. Plants include marsh woundwort, dropwort, great burnet.
Contact: Trust HQ, 01954 713 500; e-mail: cambridgeshire@wildlifebcnp.org www.wildlifebcnp.org

2. OLD SULEHAY

Beds, Cambs, Northants & Peterborough Wildlife Trust.
Location: TL 060 985 Stamford seven miles. From A1 take exit to Wansford. In Wansford take minor road past church towards Fotheringhay, Nassington and Yarwell. After one mile turn right at crossroads in Yarwell onto Sulehay Road. From here access can be gained to nature reserve by various public rights of way. Limited parking in lay-bys along Sulehay Road.
Access: Main ride is surfaced in woodland although other paths can get muddy. Quarry has uneven paths and steep slopes. Grazing animals at certain times of the year
Facilities: Ring Haw section has surfaced track and grassed paths.
Public transport: Bus Oundle to Peterborough stops at Yarwell (Stagecoach).
Habitat: Mosaic of limestone quarries, grassland, woodland and wetland.
Key birds: *Winter:* Snipe, Woodcock. *Spring:* Nuthatch, migrant warblers. *Summer:* Buzzard, Red Kite. *Autumn:* Fieldfare, Redwing. *All year:* Green

Woodpecker, Jay, Bullfinch.
Other notable flora and fauna: Butterflies, green tiger beetle, long horn beetle. Common lizard, grass snake. Badger, fox. Plants include stinking hellebore, spurge laurel, toothwort, ramsons, nettle-leaved bellflower, ploughman's spikenard, yellow-wort, clustered bellflower, common spotted-orchid, woodland and limestone grassland fungi.
Contact: Trust HQ, 01954 713 500; e-mail: cambridgeshire@wildlifebcnp.org www.wildlifebcnp.org

3. PITSFORD WATER

Anglian Water, managed by Beds, Cambs, Northants & Peterborough Wildlife Trust.
Location: SP 787 702. Five miles N of Northampton. On A43 take turn to Holcot and Brixworth. On A508 take turn to Brixworth and Holcot.
Access: Lodge open mid-Mar to mid-Nov from 8am-dusk. Winter opening times variable, check in advance. Permits for reserve available from Lodge on daily or annual basis. Reserve open to permit holders 365 days a year. No dogs. Disabled access from Lodge to first hide.
Facilities: Toilets available in Lodge, 15 miles of paths, bird hides, car parking.
Public transport: None.
Habitat: Open water (up to 120 ha), marginal vegetation and reed grasses, wet woodland, grassland and mixed woodland (40 ha).
Key birds: Typically 165-170 species per year with a total list of 253 species. *Summer:* Breeding warblers, terns, grebes, herons. *Autumn:* Waders if water levels suitable. *Winter:* Up to 10,000 wildfowl, feeding station with Tree Sparrow and occasional Corn Bunting.
Other notable flora and fauna: 32 butterfly species, 392 macro moths, 21 dragonfly species (including damselflies), 377 species of flora and 105 bryophytes, 404 fungi species.
Contact: Dave Francis, Pitsford Water Lodge, Brixworth Road, Holcot, Northampton, NN6 9SJ. 01604 780 148; e-mail: dave.francis@wildlifebcnp.org

4. STORTON'S PITS LNR

Beds, Cambs, Northants & Peterborough Wildlife Trust.
Location: SP 732 600. In Northampton. From junction of A45 with A43 west of town centre take A45 north to first roundabout and turn right. At next roundabout turn right and immediately left into Fisherman's car park. The two sites are either side of the track.
Access: Flat overall. Section of surfaced path to viewing platform, other paths soft and uneven in places with many steps on peninsula. The two reserves are adjoining.

NATURE RESERVES - CENTRAL ENGLAND

Facilities: Viewing platform, paths, some surfaced.
Public transport: Train to Northampton then walk
1 mile or bus to St Giles and get off at Sixfields
roundabout.
Habitat: One of a number of old gravel pits along the
Nene valley.
Key birds: *Winter*: Water Rail, Snipe, Teal, Tufted
Duck, Starling. *Spring*: Cuckoo, Green Woodpecker,
Reed Bunting, Bullfinch, tits, Whitethroat,
Blackcap. *Summer*: Reed Warbler, Sedge
Warbler, Common Tern, Swift, House Martin.
Autumn: Snipe, Great Crested Grebe,
Moorhen, Coot, Grey Heron.
Other notable flora and fauna:
Holly blue and green-veined white
butterflies, water beetles. Grass snake.
Bats. Cuckooflower, reed sweet-grass,
marsh woundwort, purple loosestrife,
water mint.
Contact: Trust HQ, 01954 713
500; e-mail: cambridgeshire@
wildlifebcnp.org
www.wildlifebcnp.org

5. SUMMER LEYS LNR

Northamptonshire County Council.
Location: SP 886 634. Three miles
from Wellingborough, accessible
from A45 and A509, situated on
Great Doddington to Wollaston Road.
Access: Open 24 hours a day, 365 days a year, no
permits required. Dogs welcome but must be kept on
leads at all times. 40 space car park, small tarmaced
circular route suitable for wheelchairs.
Facilities: Three hides, one feeding station. No
toilets, nearest are at Irchester Country Park on A509
towards Wellingborough.
Public transport: Nearest main station is
Wellingborough. No direct bus service, though buses
run regularly to Great Doddington and Wollaston,
both about a mile away. Tel: 01604 670 060 (24 hrs)
for copies of timetables.
Habitat: Scrape, two ponds, lake, scrub, grassland,
hedgerow.
Key birds: Hobby, Lapwing, Golden Plover, Ruff,
Gadwall, Garganey, Pintail, Shelduck, Shoveler,
Little Ringed Plover, Tree Sparrow, Redshank, Green
Sandpiper, Oystercatcher, Black-headed Gull colony,
terns.
Contact: Chris Haines, Countryside Service,
Northamptonshire Council, PO Box 163, County Hall,
Northampton, NN1 1AX. 01604 237 227.
e-mail: countryside@northamptonshire.gov.uk

6. THRAPSTON GRAVEL PITS & TITCHMARSH LNR

Beds, Cambs, Northants and Peterborough Wildlife
Trust/Natural England.
Location: TL 008 804. Seven miles E of Kettering.
From A14 take A605 N. For Titchmarsh turn L at
Thorpe Waterville, continue towards Aldwincle. Take
first L after church and continue to small car park
on L. Take footpath to reserve.

Access:
As well as
the Aldwincle
access point, there
is a public footpath
from layby on A605 N of
Thrapston.
Facilities: Six hides.
Public transport: Bus service to
Thrapston.
Habitat: Alder/birch/willow wood; old duck decoy,
series of water-filled gravel pits.
Key birds: *Summer*: Breeding Grey Heron (no access
to Heronry), Common Tern, Little Ringed Plover;
warblers. Migrants, inc. Red-necked and Slavonian
Grebes, Bittern and Marsh Harrier recorded. *Winter*:
Good range of wildfowl inc Goosander and gulls.
Contact: Northants Wildlife Trust, 01604 405 285,
e-mail: northamptonshire@wildlifebcnp.org

7. TOP LODGE FINESHADE WOOD

Forestry Commission
Location: SP 978 983. Off the A43 between Stamford
and Corby. Follow brown tourist signs to Top Lodge
Fineshade Woods.
Access: Visitor Centre (10am – 5pm), Car parking
(7am – 7pm) always open except Christmas Day.
Caravan Club site open Mar-Nov — please see CC
website for details. Visitor Centre is fully accessible
— Smelter's Walk is an all-ability trail leading to the
hide.
Facilities: Visitor centre, toilets, Top Lodge Café,
RSPB shop, with live footage of Red Kite nests in
season. Guided walks and events throughout the year.
Wildlife hide in wood. Three waymarked walking
trails (one is for all abilities, two are surfaced), 1
horse trail, 1 family cycle trail, dedicated coach and
horse box parking.
Public transport: None.
Habitat: Ancient woodland, coniferous woodland,
beech woodland, open areas, small pond.
Key birds: Centre of Northants' Red Kite
reintroduction scheme. A wide range of birds of

mixed woodlands. *All year*: Red Kite, Great Spotted Woodpecker, Goshawk, Nuthatch, Crossbill, Marsh Tit, Willow Tit. *Summer*: Turtle Dove, warblers. *Winter*: Hawfinch.
Other notable flora and fauna: Adder, grass snake, slow worm, common lizard. Fallow deer, badger. Orchids including greater butterfly, early purple and common spotted, other flora of ancient woodland.
Contact: Sarah Walker, Visitor and Community Services Manager, Forestry Commission Northants, Top Lodge, Fineshade, Nr. Corby, Northamptonshire NN17 3BB. 01780 444 920.
e-mail: sarah.walker@forestry.gsi.gov.uk
www.forestry.gov.uk/toplodge

Nottinghamshire

1. ATTENBOROUGH NATURE RESERVE

Nottinghamshire Wildlife Trust.
Location: SK 523 343. On A6005, seven miles SW of Nottingham alongside River Trent. Signposted from main road.
Access: Open at all times. Dogs on leads (guide dogs only in visitor centre). Paths suitable for disabled access. Coaches welcome by prior appointment.
Facilities: Education and visitor centre with café and shop, all accessible to wheelchair users. Nature trail (leaflet from Notts WT), one hide.
Public transport: Railway station at Attenborough - reserve is five mins walk away, visitor centre a further 10 minutes. Rainbow 5 bus service between Nottingham Broadmarsh and Derby bus station runs regularly throughout day. Alight at Chilwell Retail Park and walk 500m along Barton Lane.
Habitat: Disused, flooded gravel workings with associated marginal and wetland vegetation.
Key birds: *Spring/summer*: Breeding Common Tern (40-plus pairs), Reed Warbler, Black Tern regular (bred once). *Winter*: Wildfowl (including Bittern), Grey Heron colony, adjacent Cormorant roost.
Other notable flora and fauna: Smooth newt, dragonflies including four-spotted chaser and migrant hawker.
Contact: Attenborough Nature Centre, Barton Lane, Attenborough, Nottingham, NG9 6DY. 01159 721 777.
e-mail: enquiries@attenboroughnaturecentre.co.uk
www.attenboroughnaturecentre.co.uk

2. BESTHORPE NATURE RESERVE

Nottinghamshire Wildlife Trust.
Location: SK 817 640 and SK813 646 (access points). Take A1133 N of Newark. Turn into Trent Lane S of Besthorpe village, reserve entrances second turn on L and R turn at end of lane (at River Trent).
Access: Open access to two hides (one with disabled access from car park at present). No access to SSSI meadows. Limited access to areas grazed with sheep. Dogs on leads.
Facilities: No toilets (pubs etc in Besthorpe village), two hides, paths, nature trail (northern part).
Public transport: Buses (numbers 22, 67, 68, 6, S7L) run by Marshalls, Lincs, Road Car and Travel Wright along A1133 to Besthorpe village (0.75 mile away). Tel: 0115 924 0000 or 01777 710 550 for information.
Habitat: Gravel pit with islands, SSSI neutral grasslands, hedges, reedbed, etc.
Key birds: *Spring/summer*: Breeding Grey Heron,

Cormorant, Little Ringed Plover, Kingfisher, Grasshopper Warbler. *Winter*: Large numbers of ducks (Pochard, Tufted Duck, Pintail, Wigeon) and Peregrine.
Contact: Trust HQ, 01159 588 242;
e-mail:
info@nottswt.co.uk
www.wildlifetrust.org.uk/nottinghamshire

3. BUNNY OLD WOOD WEST

Nottinghamshire Wildlife Trust.
Location: Limited parking off the A60 at Bunny Hill (SK 579 283). Please do not obstruct access. Further footpath access is at SK 584 293 off Wysall Lane.
Access: Open all year. No coach parking available.
Facilities: None. **Public transport:** None.
Habitat: Ancient coppiced woodland.
Key birds: *All year*: Usual woodland species, all three woodpeckers, Tawny and Little Owls. *Spring/summer*: Usual visitors, including Blackcap, Spotted Flycatcher

and Tree Pipit.
Other notable flora and fauna: Bluebells, plus good selection of common woodland plants. Butterflies including white-letter hairstreak.
Contact: Trust HQ, 01159 588 242;
e-mail: info@nottswt.co.uk
www.wildlifetrust.org.uk/nottinghamshire

4. COLWICK COUNTRY PARK

Nottingham City Council.
Location: SK 610 395. Off A612 between Sneinton and Colwick, three miles E of Nottingham city centre.
Access: Open at all times, but no vehicle access after dusk or before 7am. Park in Colwick Hall access road from racecourse entrance.
Facilities: Nature trails. Sightings log book in Fishing Lodge.
Habitat: Lakes, pools, woodlands, grasslands, new plantations, River Trent.
Key birds: *Summer:* Warblers, Hobby, Common Tern (15+ pairs). *Winter:* Wildfowl and gulls. Passage migrants.
Other notable flora and fauna: Purple and white letter hairstreak butterflies, 16 species of dragonfly.
Contact: Head Ranger, The Fishing Lodge, Colwick, Country Park, River Road, Colwick, Nottingham NG4 2DW. 01159 870 785. www.nottinghamcity.gov.uk

5. LOUND GRAVEL PITS

Tarmac Ltd/ Hanson/ Nottinghamshire Wildlife Trust.
Location: SK 690 856. Two miles N of Retford off A638 adjacent to Sutton and Lound villages.
Access: Open at all times. Use public rights of way only (use OS Map Sheet No 120 Landranger Series).
Facilities: Two public viewing screens off Chainbridge Lane (overlooking Chainbridge Nature Reserve Scrape) and two more overlooking Neatholme Scrape.
Public transport: Buses from Bawtry (Church Street), Retford bus station and Worksop (Hardy Street) on services 27/27A/83/83A/84 to Lound Village crossroads (Chainbridge Lane).

Habitat: Working sand and gravel quarries, restored gravel workings, woodland, reedbeds, fishing ponds, river valley, in-filled and disused fly ash tanks, farmland, scrub, willow plantations, open water. Wildlife Trust has received a large lottery grant to transform site into a wetland reserve.
Key birds: 250 bird species recorded.
Summer: Gulls, terns, wildfowl and waders. Passage waders, terns, passerines and raptors. *Winter:* Wildfowl, gulls, raptors.
Rarities have inc. Ring-billed Gull, Caspian, White-winged Black, Gull-billed and Whiskered Terns, Richard's Pipit, Baird's, Pectoral and Buff-breasted Sandpipers.
Contact: Lound Bird Club, Gary Hobson (Secretary), 18 Barnes Avenue, Wrenthorpe, Wakefield WF1 2BH. 01924 384 419; e-mail: gary.lbc1@tiscali.co.uk
www.loundbirdclub.piczo.com

6. WOLLATON PARK

Wollaton Hall.
Location: 500 acre deer park situated approx 3 miles W of Nottingham City Centre. Follow brown signs from A52 or A6514.
Access: Open all year from 8am-dusk.
Facilities: Pay/display car parks. Some restricted access (deer), leaflets.
Public transport: Trent Buses: no 22 and Nottingham City Transport: no's 31, and 28 running at about every 15 mins.
Habitat: Lake, small reedbed, woodland.
Key birds: *All year:* Main woodland species present, with good numbers of Nuthatch, Treecreeper and all three woodpeckers. *Summer:* Commoner warblers, incl Reed Warbler, all four hirundine species, Spotted Flycatcher. *Winter:* Pochard, Gadwall, Wigeon, Goosander, occasional Smew and Goldeneye. Flocks of Siskin and Redpoll, often feeding by the lake.
Contact: Wollaton Hall & Park, Wollaton, Nottingham, NG8 2AE. 01159 153 900.
e-mail: wollaton@ncmg.org.uk

Oxfordshire

1. ASTON ROWANT NNR

Natural England.
Location: SU 731 966. From the M40 Lewknor interchange at J6, travel NE for a short distance and turn R onto A40. After 1.5 miles at the top of the hill, turn R and R again into a narrow, metalled lane. Drive to car park, which is signposted from the A40.
Access: Open all year. Some wheelchair access, please contact site manager for more information.
Facilities: On-site parking, easy access path to viewpoint, seats, interpretation panels.
Public transport: Regular bus services to Stokenchurch, 2km S of reserve. Red Rose Travel bus goes to Aston Rowant village (call 01296 747 926).

Habitat: Chalk grassland, chalk scrub, beech woodland.
Key birds: *Spring/summer:* Blackcap, other warblers, Turtle Dove. Passage birds inc Ring Ouzel, Wheatear and Stonechat. *Winter:* Brambling, Siskin, winter thrushes. *All year:* Red Kite, Buzzard, Sparrowhawk, Woodcock, Tawny Owl, Green and Great Spotted Woodpeckers, Skylark, Meadow Pipit, Marsh Tit.
Other notable flora and fauna: Rich chalk grassland flora, including Chiltern gentian clustered bellflower, frog, bee, pyramidal and fragrant orchids. Good range of less common butterflies, inc silver-spotted, dingy and grizzled skippers, chalkhill blue, green hairstreak and green fritillary.
Contact: Natural England, 01844 351 833.
e-mail: thames.chilterns@naturalengland.org.uk
www.naturalengland.org.uk

2. FOXHOLES RESERVE

Berks, Bucks & Oxon Wildlife Trust.
Location: SP 254 206. Head N out of Burford on the A424 towards Stow-on-the-Wold. Take third turning on R. Head NE on unclassified road to Bruern for 3.5km. Just before reaching Bruern, turn L along track following Cocksmoor Copse. After 750m, park in car park on R just before some farm buildings.
Access: Open all year. Please keep to the paths.
Facilities: Car park, footpaths. Can be very muddy in winter.
Habitat: Broad-leaved Woodland, and grassland.
Key birds: *Spring/summer:* Spotted Flycatcher, Marsh Tit and warblers. *Winter:* Redwing, Fieldfare, Woodcock. *All year:* Raven, little Owl, all three woodpeckers.
Other notable flora and fauna: Fantastic show of bluebells in May. Autumn fungi. Silver-washed fritillary butterfly.
Contact: Trust HQ, 01865 77 5476.
www.bbowt.org.uk

3. OTMOOR NATURE RESERVE

RSPB (Central England Office).
Location: SP 570 126. Car park seven miles NE of Oxford city centre. Take B4027, to Islip and on to Horton-cum-Studley, then first L to Beckley. After 0.67 miles at the bottom of a short hill turn R (before the Abingdon Arms public house). After 200 yards, turn L into Otmoor Lane. Reserve car park is at the end of the lane (approx one mile).
Access: Open dawn-dusk. No permits or fees. No dogs allowed except on public rights of way. In wet conditions, the visitor route can be muddy and wellingtons are essential.
Facilities: Limited. Small car park with cycle racks, visitor trail (3 mile round trip) and two screened viewpoints. The reserve is not accessible by coach and is unsuitable for large groups.
Public transport: None.
Habitat: Wet grassland, reedbed and open water.
Key birds: *Summer:* Breeding birds include Cetti's and Grasshopper Warblers, Lapwing, Redshank, Curlew, Snipe, Yellow Wagtail, Shoveler, Gadwall, Pochard, Tufted Duck, Little and Great Crested Grebes. Hobby breeds locally. *Winter:* Wigeon, Teal, Shoveler, Pintail, Gadwall, Pochard, Tufted Duck, Lapwing, Golden Plover, Hen Harrier, Peregrine, Merlin. *Autumn and spring passage:* Marsh Harrier, Short-eared Owl, Greenshank, Green Sandpiper, Common Sandpiper, Spotted Redshank and occasional Black Tern.
Contact: RSPB, c/o Folly Farm, Common Road, Bexley, OX3 9YR. 01865 351 163. www.rspb.org.uk

4. SHOTOVER COUNTRY PARK

Oxford City Council.
Location: SP 565 055. Lies E of Oxford. From A420 in Headington, turn onto B4495 (Windmill Road) and Old Road.
Access: Open all year, best early morning or late in the evening.
Facilities: Car park, toilets, nature trails, booklets.
Public transport: None.
Habitat: Woodland, farmland, heathland, grassland, scrub.
Key birds: *Spring/summer:* Willow Warbler, Blackcap, Garden Warbler, Spotted Flycatcher, Whitethroat, Lesser Whitethroat, Pied Flycatcher, Redstart, Tree Pipit. *Autumn:* Crossbill, Redpoll, Siskin, thrushes. *All year:* Sparrowhawk, Jay, tits, finches, woodpeckers, Corn Bunting.
Contact: Oxford City Council, 01865 249 811. www.oxford.gov.uk
e-mail: countryside@oxford.gov.uk

5. SYDLINGS COPSE

Berks, Bucks & Oxon Wildlife Trust.
Location: SP 559 096. 3.5 miles north-east of Oxford. From Headington roundabout, take Bayswater Road N through Barton; turn L on B4027; after 500 m, park opposite Royal Oak Farm and tea room; take bridleway for 600m, passing two small woods; reserve on R 100m from bridleway. Parking on soft verge.
Access: Open daily.
Facilities: Public footpath. Public hide.
Habitat: Reedbed, fen, a stream, ancient woodland, heath, limestone grassland in steep valley.
Key birds: Summer warblers including grasshopper warbler, Marsh Tit, woodpeckers and occasional Stonechat.

Other notable flora and fauna: Mammals such as badgers, deer, foxes and bats. More than 400 species of chalk grassland, woodland and heath plants. Common lizard, grass snake, slow worm. Brown and purple hairstreak butterflies.
Contact: Trust HQ, 01865 77 5476.

6. WARBURG RESERVE

Berks, Bucks & Oxon Wildlife Trust.
Location: SU 720 879. Leave Henley-on-Thames NW on A4130. Turn R at the end of the Fair Mile onto B480. L fork in Middle Assendon. After 1 mile, follow road round to R at grassy triangle, then on for 1 mile. Car park is on R.
Access: Open all year – visitor centre opens 9am-5pm. Please keep dogs on a lead. In some areas, only guide dogs allowed.

Facilities: Visitor centre, toilets, car park, two hides, one with disabled access, nature trail, leaflets. Visitors with disabilities and groups should contact the warden before visits. Car park not suitable for coaches, only mini-buses.
Public transport: None.
Habitat: Scrub, mixed woodland, grassland, ponds.
Key birds: Spring/summer: Whitethroat, Lesser Whitethroat. All year: Sparrowhawk, Red Kite, Treecreeper, Nuthatch, Tawny Owl and Lesser Spotted Woodpecker. Winter: Redpoll, Siskin, sometimes Crossbill, Woodcock.
Other notable flora and fauna: Good for orchids, butterflies, roe, fallow and muntjac deer.
Contact: Warburg Reserve, 01491 642 001.
e-mail: bbowtwarburg@cix.co.uk

Shropshire

1. BUSHMOOR COPPICE

Shropshire Wildlife Trust
Location: SO 430 880. Head S from Church Stretton and take first R off A49 signed Bushmoor.
Access: Park in Bushmoor village and follow track leading from right-angled bend. Follow green lane to gate and carry onto wood along field margin. Appox half mile from road.
Facilities: None.
Public transport: Buses stop at Bushmoor village.
Habitat: Small mixed woodland and scrub.
Key birds: Spring/summer: Migrant warblers and flycatchers, plus common woodland species.
Other notable flora and fauna: Golden saxifrage, bluebells and yellow archangel. Dormouse.
Contact: Shropshire Wildlife Trust, 01743 284 280; www.shropshirewildlifetrust.org.uk

2. CLUNTON COPPICE

Shropshire Wildlife Trust.
Location: SO 343 806. From Craven Arms, take B4368 to Clunton village, go straight over bridge and up the hill to small car park just before reserve sign.
Access: Open at all times. Access along road and public rights of way only.
Facilities: Limited parking in small quarry entrance on R, or opposite The Crown pub.
Public transport: Buses between Craven Arms and Clun stop at Clunton. One mile walk to reserve is steep.
Habitat: Sessile oak coppice. Good for ferns, mosses and fungi.
Key birds: Buzzard and Raven regular. Spring/summer: Wide range of woodland birds, inc. Redstart, Wood Warbler and Pied Flycatcher, Woodcock.
Other notable flora and fauna: Hairy woodrush and hairy bromerape, sessile oak woodland plants, bluebell, bilberry.
Contact: Trust HQ, 01743 284 280; www. shropshirewildlifetrust.org.uk

3. EARL'S HILL

Shropshire Wildlife Trust
Location: SJ 409 048. Near Minsterley, SW of Shrewsbury. Turn off A488 at Pontesford along lane by Rea Valley Tractors. Car park 700 yards further on.
Access: Follow green route for easier walking. Purple route leads to summit. Car park at entrance.
Facilities: None.
Public transport: Buses to Bishops Castle and Minsterley stop at Pontesford.
Habitat: Steep-sided volcanic hill, scree slopes and crags, topped by Iron Age fort. Ancient woodland on eastern slopes.
Key birds: Spring: Migrants species such as Redstart, Pied Flycatcher and warblers. Dipper and Grey

Wagtail on stream. Green Woodpecker common on open grassland.

Other notable flora and fauna: Dormouse. More than 30 species of butterfly recorded, plus bluebells and ash woodland plants. Yellow meadow ant. Spring ephemerals on anthills.

Contact: Trust HQ, 01743 284 280; www.shropshirewildlifetrust.org.uk

4. FENN'S WHIXALL AND BETTISFIELD MOSSES NNR

Natural England (North Mercia Team).

Location: The reserve is located four miles SE of Whitchurch, ten miles SW of Wrexham. It is to the S of the A495 between Fenn's bank, Whixall and Bettisfield. There is roadside parking at entrances, car parks at Morris's Bridge, Roundthorn Bridge, World's End and a large car park at Manor House. Disabled access by prior arrangement along the railway line.

Access: Permit required except on Mosses Trail routes.

Facilities: There are panels at all of the main entrances to the site, and leaflets are available when permits are applied for. Three interlinking Mosses Trails explore the NNR and canal from Morris's and Roundthorn bridges.

Public transport: Bus passes nearby. Railway two miles away.

Habitat: 2,000 acres of raised peatland meres and mosses.

Key birds: *Spring/summer:* Nightjar, Hobby, Curlew, Tree Sparrow. *All year:* Skylark, Linnet. *Winter:* Short-eared Owl.

Other notable flora and fauna: Water vole, brown hare, polecat, adder, 2,000 species of moth, 27 species of butterfly, nationally important for dragonflies, inc white-faced darter.

Contact: Natural England, Attingham Park, 01743 282 000; e-mail: north.mercia@natural-england.org.uk

5. LLYNCLYS COMMON

Shropshire Wildlife Trust.

Location: SJ 273 237. Five miles SW of Oswestry. Park in layby on A495 at SJ 277 242, opposite Dolgoch and walk up Turner's Lane or follow footpaths.

Access: Open at all times.

Facilities: None.

Public transport: Buses stop at Pont and Dolgoch.

Habitat: Old mixed limestone sward with some woodland and scrub, small pond.

Key birds: Sparrowhawk, Green Woodpecker, Goldcrest, large warbler population. Occasional Peregrine, Buzzard.

Other notable flora and fauna: Common and palmated newts in Oliver's Pond. More than 300 species of plant, including 12 species of orchid and limestone flowers. Bluebells and ramsons in woods. Good site for skippers and pearl-bordered fritillary butterflies, horned dung beetle and hairy-footed flower bee.

Contact: Trust HQ, 01743 284 280; www.shropshirewildlifetrust.org.uk

6. VENUS POOL

Shropshire Ornithological Society.

Location: SJ 5478 0607. Site located 6 miles SE of Shrewsbury in angle formed by A458 Shrewsbury to Much Wenlock road and minor road leading S to Pitchford. Entrance is half a mile along minor road which leaves A458 half a mile (0.8 km) SE of Cross Houses.

Access: Public access to much of site, including four hides. Please keep to footpaths shown on notice boards at both entrances. Wheelchair-friendly paths to two public hides and Lena's Hide overlooking feeding station. Dogs not allowed anywhere.

Facilities: Car park with height restricting barrier. Five hides (one for SOS members only). Information boards.

Public transport: Shrewsbury-Bridgnorth buses stop at Cross Houses, which is one mile walk from Venus Pool, partly along busy main road.

Habitat: Site extends to almost 27 hectares (66 acres) and incorporates the pool itself, several islands and areas of open shoreline, fringing tall vegetation, marshy grassland, hedgerows, and areas of scrub and woodland. Species-rich meadows surround the pool, with an arable field growing bird-friendly crops.

Key birds: Venus Pool is noted for wintering wildfowl and passage waders, plus a sprinkling of county rarities, which have included Black-necked Grebe, Purple Heron, Spoonbill, Red Kite, Hen Harrier, Pectoral Sandpiper, Long-eared Owl, Black Redstart, and Woodlark. *All year:* Common ducks and waterfowl, many resident passerines, including Tree Sparrow. *April-June:* Passage waders include Curlew, Ringed Plover, Dunlin, Redshank, Green and Common Sandpipers, and both godwits. Passage Black Tern. Breeding Oystercatcher, Little Ringed Plover, Lapwing, warblers, hirundines. *July-September:* Return wader passage from late July can include Little Stint, Greenshank, Green, Wood, Curlew and Common Sandpipers, and possible unusual species such as Pectoral Sandpiper. *October-March:* Occasional wintering Bittern, Tundra and Whooper Swans (both scarce). Geese include occasional White-fronted. Ducks include Wigeon, Teal, Pintail, Shoveler, Pochard, Goosander (up to 50 in evening roosts) and occasional Goldeneye. Water Rail, vagrant raptors and owls, winter thrushes and large passerine flocks including Lesser Redpoll, Linnet, Tree Sparrow, Reed Bunting and Yellowhammer.

Contact: For full details about Venus Pool, visit www.shropshirebirds.com

7. WOOD LANE

Shropshire Wildlife Trust.

Location: SJ 421 331. Turn off A528 at Spurnhill, 1 mile SE of Ellesmere. Car park is three quarter miles down on R.

Access: Open at all times. Apply to Trust for permit to use hides. Reserve accessible to people of all abilities.

Facilities: Car parks signposted. Hides (permit only).

Habitat: Gravel pit restored by Tudor Griffiths.

Key birds: *Summer*: 168 species recorded since 1999. Breeding Sand Martin, Lapwing, Little Ringed Plover and Tree Sparrow. Osprey platforms erected to tempt over-flying birds. Popular staging post for waders (inc. Redshank, Greenshank, Ruff, Dunlin, Little Stint, Green and Wood Sandpiper). *Winter*: Large flocks of Lapwing, plus Curlew and common wildfowl.
Other notable flora and fauna: Good range of dragonflies.
Contact: Trust HQ, 01743 284 280; www.shropshirewildlifetrust.org.uk

Staffordshire

1. BELVIDE RESERVOIR

British Waterways Board and West Midland Bird Club.
Location: SJ865102. Near Brewood, 7 miles NW of Wolverhampton.
Access: Access only by permit from the West Midland Bird Club.
Facilities: Hides.
Public transport: Bus to Kiddermore Green (eight minute walk to reserve). Traveline – 0870 6082608.
Habitat: Canal feeder reservoir with marshy margins and gravel islands.
Key birds: Important breeding, moulting and wintering ground for wildfowl), including Ruddy Duck, Goldeneye and Goosander) and waders. Night roost for gulls.
Contact: Barbara Oakley (permit sec), 147 Worlds End Lane, Quinton, Birmingham B32 1JX. e-mail: permits@westmidlandbirdclub.com
www.westmidlandbirdclub.com/belvide

2. BLITHFIELD RESERVOIR

South Staffs Waterworks Co.
Location: SK 058 237. View from causeway on B5013 (Rugeley/Uttoxeter).
Access: Access to reservoir and hides by permit from West Midland Bird Club.
Facilities: None.
Public transport: None.
Habitat: Large reservoir.
Key birds: *Winter*: Good populations of wildfowl (inc. Bewick's Swan, Goosander, Goldeneye, Ruddy Duck), large gull roost (can inc. Glaucous, Iceland). Passage terns (Common, Arctic, Black) and waders, esp. in autumn (Little Stint, Curlew Sandpiper, Spotted Redshank regular).
Contact: Barbara Oakley (permit sec), 147 Worlds End Lane, Quinton, Birmingham B32 1JX. e-mail: permits@westmidlandbirdclub.com

3. BRANSTON WATER PARK

East Staffordshire Borough Council.
Location: SK 217 207. Follow brown tourist sign from A38 N. No access from A38 S – head to the Barton-under-Needwood exit and return N. The park is 0.5 miles S of A5121 Burton-upon-Trent exit.
Access: Open all year, flat, wheelchair-accessible stone path all round the lake.
Facilities: Green Flag award-winning park. Parking, public toilets including a RADAR key-operated disabled toilet, picnic area (some wheelchair accessible tables), modern children's play area, dog dip area, fishing through Burton Mutual Angling Club.
Public transport: Contact Arriva bus services.
Habitat: Reedbed, willow carr woodland, scrub, meadow area.
Key birds: *Spring/summer*: Reed Warbler, Cuckoo, Reed Bunting. Important roost for Swallow and Sand Martin. *Winter*: Waders, Little Ringed Plover occasionally, Pied Wagtail roost.
Other notable flora and fauna: Wide range of butterflies and dragonflies.
Contact: East Staffordshire Borough Council, 01283 508 000; e-mail: greenspaces@eaststaffsbc.gov.uk
www.eaststaffsbc.gov.uk/Services/GreenSpaces/Pages/GreenSpacesBranstonWaterpark.aspx

4. COOMBES VALLEY

RSPB (Midlands Regional Office).
Location: SK 005 530. Four miles from Leek along A523 between Leek and Ashbourne and 0.5 miles down unclassified road – signposted.

Access: Open daily — no charge. Free parking. Coach groups welcome by prior arrangement. No dogs allowed. Most trails unsuitable for disabled visitors.
Facilities: Visitor centre, toilets, two miles of nature trail, one hide.
Public transport: Contact local bus company First Potteries on 01782 207 999.
Habitat: Sessile oak woodland, unimproved pasture and meadow.
Key birds: *Spring*: Pied Flycatcher, Redstart, Wood Warbler. Jan-Mar: Displaying birds of prey.
Other notable flora and fauna: Bluebells, various butterflies.
Contact: Jarrod Sneyd, Six Oaks Farm, Bradnop, Leek ST13 7EU. 01538 384 017. www.rspb.org.uk

5. COTTON DELL

Staffordshire Wildlife Trust.
Location: SK 055 450. From Cheadle take B5417 E to Oakamoor. Entering village, turn R before the river bridge, following brown tourist signs for the Staffs CC parking area. Walk back and cross bridge. Take second turning on L up a gravel track next to the black and white house. Continue to reserve entrance.
Access: Park on council car park next to river and follow track north into woodland.
Facilities: None
Public transport: Infrequent bus service from nearby towns and villages.
Habitat: Ancient woodland in steep-sided valley and flower-rich grassland pasture.
Key birds: Dipper, Grey Wagtail, Wood Warbler, all three woodpeckers, Spotted Flycatcher and common woodland birds.
Other notable flora and fauna: Diverse flower-rich grasslands at northern end.
Contact: Staffordshire Wildlife Trust. 01889 880 100; e-mail: info@staffs-wildlife.org.uk www.staffs-wildlife.org.uk/page/cotton-dell

6. DOXEY MARSHES

Staffordshire Wildlife Trust.
Location: SJ 903 250. On western side of Stafford town centre. Parking at end of Wootton Drive ST16 1PU.

Access: Open at all times. Most of site accessible by wheelchair. Dogs on leads.
Facilities: One hide, three viewing platforms.
Public transport: Buses and trains to Stafford town centre, walk upstream from Sainsbury's supermarket along River Sow to reserve entrance.
Habitat: Designated SSSI for wet meadow habitats. Marsh, pools, reedbeds, hedgerows, reed sweet-grass swamp
Key birds: *Spring/summer*: Breeding Lapwing, Redshank, Little Ringed Plover, Oystercatcher, Shelduck, warblers, Skylark, Water Rail. *Autumn/winter*: Snipe, Jack Snipe, Goosander, wildfowl, Passage waders, vagrants.
Other notable flora and fauna: Otter, harvest mouse, water shrew, noctule bat, musk beetle.
Contact: Staffordshire Wildlife Trust. 01889 880 100; e-mail: info@staffs-wildlife.org.uk www.staffs-wildlife.org.uk/page/doxey-marshes

7. HIGHGATE COMMON

Staffordshire Wildlife Trust.
Location: SO 836 895. Near Wombourne, South Staffordshire. From A449 at Himley take B4176 towards Bridgnorth. After approx 1 mile, turn left at traffic lights onto Wombourne Rd, signposted towards Swindon. Continue through village of Swindon, along Chasepool Rd. At the T Junction turn R onto Camp Hill Road. About 1 mile after Camp Farm, take 1st L then R at the T junction onto Highgate Rd. Take 1st entrance on R.
Access: Several car parks, network of paths.
Facilities: Public toilets at Warden's Office (restricted opening hours).
Public transport: None.
Habitat: Lowland heath with broadleaf woodland and glades.
Key birds: Cuckoo, Stonechat, Tree Pipit, Skylark
Other notable flora and fauna: More than 5,000 species of insect recorded, including several red data book species of bee and wasp, also glow worm and common lizard.
Contact: Trust HQ, 01889 880 100; www.staffs-wildlife.org.uk/page/highgate-common

Warwickshire

1. BRANDON MARSH

Warwickshire Wildlife Trust.
Location: SP 386 762. Three miles SE of Coventry, 200 yards SE of A45/A46 junction (Tollbar End). Turn E off A45 into Brandon Lane. Reserve entrance 1.25 miles in R.
Access: Open weekdays (9am-4.30pm), weekends (10am-4pm). Entrance charge currently £2.50 (free to Wildlife Trust members). Wheelchair access to nature trail and Wright hide. No dogs. Parking for 2 coaches.

Facilities: Visitor centre, toilets, tea-room (open daily 10am-3pm weekdays, 10am-4pm weekends), nature trail, seven hides.
Public transport: Bus service from Coventry to Tollbar End then 1.25 mile walk. Tel Travel West Midlands 02476 817 032 for bus times.
Habitat: Ten pools, together with marsh, reedbeds, willow carr, scrub and small mixed woodland in 260 acres, designated SSSI in 1972.
Key birds: *Spring/summer*: Garden and Grasshopper Warblers, Whitethroat, Lesser Whitethroat, Hobby, Little Ringed Plover, Whinchat, Wheatear. *Autumn/winter*: Bittern (last few winters), Dunlin, Ruff, Snipe, Greenshank, Green and Common Sandpipers,

Wigeon, Shoveler, Pochard, Goldeneye, Siskin, Redpoll. *All year*: Cetti's Warbler, Kingfisher, Water Rail, Gadwall, Little Grebe, Buzzard.
Other notable flora and fauna: More than 20 species of butterfly and 18 species of dragonfly recorded. Almost 500 plants species listed on www. brandonbirding.co.uk
Contact: Ken Bond, Hon. Sec. Brandon Marsh Voluntary Conservation Team, 54 Wiclif Way, Stockingford, Nuneaton CV10 8NF. 02476 328 785.

2. COOMBE COUNTRY PARK

Coventry City Council
Location: CV3 2AB. SP 402 795. Five miles East of Coventry city centre, on B4027 Coventry to Brinklow road.
Access: Park opens everyday, 7.30am to dusk. Entry by foot is free with pay and display parking for vehicles. Paths mainly hard surfaces accessible for wheelchairs. Manual wheelchairs can be hired for a £5 returnable deposit.
Facilities: Information centre, toilets, including disabled, café, bird hide, gift shop, picnic benches and wildflower meadow (March to September).
Public transport: By rail: To Coventry City Centre, 20 minute bus journey to park. By bus: No-585 Mike de Courcey Travel (for timetable ring 024 7630 2656).
Habitat: Parkland, lake, woodland, formal gardens.
Key birds: Large heronry, plus many Cormorants. Lesser Spotted Woodpecker and Marsh Tit top the list of woodland species.
Other notable flora and fauna: More than 250 species of plant, including lesser celandine, foxglove, bluebell, red campion and herb robert. Mammals include wood mouse and muntjac deer.
Contact: Coombe Country Park, 024 7645 3720.
e-mail: Coombe.countrypark@coventry.gov.uk

3. HARTSHILL HAYES COUNTRY PARK

Warwickshire County Council.
Location: SP 317 943. Signposted Country Park from B4114 W of Nuneaton.
Access: Open all year. Closed Christmas Day. Pay and display car park.
Facilities: Three waymarked walks (one easy-going). Visitor centre, play area, toilets with facilities for disabled.
Public transport: None.
Habitat: Mixed woodland, grassland hillside.
Key birds: Warblers, woodpeckers, tits, Goldcrest, Sparrowhawk, Tawny Owl.
Other notable flora and fauna: Bluebells and numerous variety of birds. More detailed information on the wildlife can be found in the Visitor Centre.
Contact: Kingsbury Water Park, Bodymoor Heath Lane, Sutton Coldfield, West Midlands B76 0DY. 01827 872 660. e-mail: parks@warwickshire.gov.uk
www.warwickshire.gov.uk/parks

4. KINGSBURY WATER PARK

Warwickshire County Council.
Location: SP 203 960. Signposted `Water Park' from J9 M42, A4097 NE of Birmingham.
Access: Open all year except Christmas Day. Pay on entry car park.
Facilities: Four hides, two with wheelchair access. Miles of flat surfaced footpaths, loan scheme for mobility scooters. Cafes, Information Centre with gift shop.
Public transport: Call for advice.
Habitat: Open water; numerous small pools, some with gravel islands; gravel pits; silt beds with reedmace, reed, willow and alder; rough areas and grassland.
Key birds: *Summer:* Breeding warblers (nine species), Little Ringed Plover, Great Crested and Little Grebes. Shoveler, Shelduck and a thriving Common Tern colony. Passage waders (esp. spring). *Winter:* Wildfowl, Short-eared Owl.
Other notable flora and fauna: Orchids.
Contact: Kingsbury Water Park, Bodymoor Heath

Lane, Sutton Coldfield, West Midlands B76 0DY. 01827 872 660. e-mail: parks@warwickshire.gov.uk www.warwickshire.gov.uk/parks

5. MARSH LANE NATURE RESERVE

Packington Estate Enterprises Limited.
Location: SP 217 804. Equidistant between Birmingham and Coventry, both approx 7-8 miles away. Off A452 between A45 and Balsall Common, S of B4102/A452 junction. Turn R into Marsh Lane and immediately R onto Old Kenilworth Road (now a public footpath), to locked gate. Two other entrances; gateway off B4102 east of Hampton in Arden (SP 212 814), also off Marsh Lane, Hampton in Arden, via bridge under railway (SP 211 805).
Access: Only guide dogs allowed. Site suitable for disabled on east side of river only. Access by day or year permit. Contact reserve for membership rates. Day permits: adult £4, OAP £3.50, children (under 16) £3 obtained from the Somers Fishery (top end of car park to Stonebridge Golf Centre), Somers Road, Meriden, CV7 7PL.
Facilities: No toilets or visitor centre. Six hides and hard tracks between hides. Three car parks behind locked gates.
Public transport: Hampton-in-Arden railway station within walking distance on footpath loop. Bus no 194 stops at N end of Old Kenilworth Road, one mile from reserve gate.
Habitat: Two large pools with islands, three small and one large (Siden Hill) areas of woodland and crop field for finches and buntings as winter feed.
Key birds: 190 species. *Summer*: Breeding birds include Little Ringed Plover, Common Tern, most species of warbler including Grasshopper. Good passage of waders in Apr, May, Aug and Sept. Hobby and Buzzard breed locally.
Other notable flora and fauna: Attractive display in spring/summer of wild flowers in woodlands,

including lesser celandine, foxglove, bluebell, red campion, herb robert and many more.
Contact: Nicholas P Barlow or Kay Gleeson, Packington Hall, Packington Park, CV7 7HF. 01676 522 020; e-mail: kay@packingtonestate.co.uk www.packingtonestate.net

6. MIDDLETON LAKES

RSPB (Midlands Regional Office)
Location: SP 192 967. Reserve lies in the Tame Valley, S of Tamworth, next to Middleton Hall (site of Spring Birdwatchers' Fair). Leave M42 at J9 onto A446, then A4091 and finally into Bodymoor Heath Road.
Access: Open dawn till dusk every day. Surfaced path from car park to Middleton Hall and heronry. Other paths are unsurfaced but generally flat. Playmeadow Trail has wheelchair access for part of the route. Car parking for 30 and bike racks on site. Dogs allowed on leads in parts of the site.
Facilities: Three viewing platforms and a viewing screen. A hide will be constructed soon. Four trails, ranging from 500m to 3km in length.
Public transport: No local bus service. Wilnecote train station is 2.5 miles from the reserve.
Habitat: This former quarry now boasts lakes, reedbeds, meadows and woodland areas.
Key birds: *All year*: Barn Owls are regularly seen and Cetti's Warbler frequently heard. *Spring/summer*: 100-strong heronry, plus common migrant warblers, Lapwing, hirundines and woodland species. *Winter*: Lesser Spotted and Great Spotted Woodpeckers and Willow Tit on the feeders, plus peak numbers of wildfowl and waders. Raptors include Hen and Marsh Harriers, Merlin, Peregrine and Short-eared Owl.
Other notable wildlife: Bluebells and spring flowers, grass snake, common butterflies and moths.
Contact: Call reserve on 01827 259 454 or e-mail: middletonlakes@rspb.org.uk

West Midlands

1. LICKEY HILLS COUNTRY PARK

Birmingham County Council.
Location: Eleven miles SW of Birmingham City Centre.
Access: Open all year, (10am-7pm in summer; 10am-4.30pm in winter). Land-Rover tours can be arranged for less able visitors.
Facilities: Car park, visitor centre with wheelchair pathway with viewing gallery, picnic site, toilets, café, shop.
Public transport: Bus: West Midlands 62 Rednal (20 mins walk to visitor centre). Rail: Barnt Green (25 mins walk through woods to the centre).
Habitat: Hills covered with mixed deciduous woodland, conifer plantations and heathland.
Key birds: *Spring/summer*: Warblers, Tree Pipit,

Redstart. *Winter*: Redwing, Fieldfare. *All year*: Common woodland species.
Contact: The Visitor Centre, Lickey Hills CP, Warren Lane, Rednal, Birmingham, B45 8ER. 01214 477 106. e-mail: lickey.hills@birmingham.gov.uk

2. ROUGH WOOD CHASE LNR

Walsall Metropolitan Borough Council
Location: SJ 987 012. From M6 (Jt 10) head for Willenhall and A462. Turn R into Bloxwich Road North and R again into Hunts Lane. Car park on bend.
Access: Open all year.
Facilities: Circular nature trail.
Public transport: WMT bus 341 from Walsall.
Habitat: 70 acres of oakwood, significant for West Midlands. Also meadows, ponds, pools, marsh and scrubland.
Key birds: Great Crested and Little Grebes on pools in the north end of Chase. Breeding Jay and

NATURE RESERVES - CENTRAL ENGLAND

Sparrowhawk. Common woodland species all year and warblers in summer.
Other notable flora and fauna: Great crested and smooth newts, water vole, various dragonfly species, purple hairstreak, brimstone and small heath butterflies.
Contact: Walsall Countryside Services, Walsall Metropolitan Borough Council, Top Hangar, Bosty Lane, Aldridge, Walsall WS9 0QQ. 01922 458 328, e-mail: countrysideservices@walsall.gov.uk www.walsall.gov.uk

3. SANDWELL VALLEY COUNTRY PARK

Sandwell Metropolitan Borough Council.
Location: Entrances at SP 012 918 & SP 028 992. Located approx. 1 mile NE of West Bromwich town centre. Main entrance off Salters Lane or Forge Lane.
Access: Car parks open 8am to sunset. Wheelchair access to Priory Woods LNR, Forge Mill Lake LNR and other parts of the country park.
Facilities: Café on site. Visitor centre, toilets, café at Sandwell Park Farm (10am-4.30pm). Good footpaths around LNRs and much of the country park. Coach parking by appointment. Also 20 acre RSPB reserve (see below).
Public transport: West Bromwich bus station and central metro stop a ten minute walk from park (Traveline 0871 200 2233).
Habitat: Pools, woodlands, grasslands, including three local nature reserves.
Key birds: Wintering wildfowl including regular flock of Goosander, small heronry. *All year:* Grey Heron, Great Crested Grebe, Lapwing, Reed Bunting, Great Spotted and Green Woodpecker, Sparrowhawk, Kestrel. *Spring:* Little Ringed Plover, Oystercatcher, up to eight species of warbler breeding, plus passage migrants. *Autumn:* Passage migrants. *Winter:* Goosander, Shoveler, Teal, Wigeon, Snipe.
Other notable flora and fauna: Common spotted and

southern marsh orchid. Ringlet butterfly. Water vole, weasel.
Contact: Senior Countryside Ranger, Sandwell Park Farm, Salters Lane, West Bromwich, W Midlands B71 4BG. 01215 530 220 or 2147.

4. SANDWELL VALLEY

RSPB (Midlands Regional Office).
Location: SP 035 928. Great Barr, Birmingham. Follow signs S from M6 J7 via A34. Take R at 1st junction onto A4041. Take 4th L onto Hamstead Road (B4167), then R at 1st mini roundabout onto Tanhouse Avenue.
Access: 800 metres of paths accessible to assisted and powered wheelchairs with some gradients (please ring centre for further information). No parking on Mondays but reserve can be accessed on foot.
Facilities: Car park (Tue-Fri 9am-5pm, Sat-Sun 10am-5pm. Closes at dusk in winter), four viewing screens, one hide. Phone centre for details on coach parking. The hide is open from 10.30 am - 1 pm Tue-Fri, 10.30-3.30pm Sat-Sun. **PLEASE NOTE** - While operating from the temporary building, we cannot offer full visitor facilities and opening times may vary so please check before making a special journey.
Public transport: Bus: 16 from Corporation Street (Stand CJ), Birmingham City Centre (ask for Tanhouse Avenue). Train: Hamstead Station, then 16 bus for one mile towards West Bromwich from Hamstead (ask for Tanhouse Avenue).
Habitat: Open water, wet grassland, reedbed, dry grassland and scrub.
Key birds: *Summer:* Lapwing, Little Ringed Plover, Reed Warbler, Whitethroat, Sedge Warbler, Willow Tit. Passage: Sandpipers, Yellow Wagtail, chats, Common Tern. *Winter:* Water Rail, Snipe, Jack Snipe, Goosander, Bullfinch, woodpeckers and wildfowl.
Contact: Lee Copplestone, 20 Tanhouse Avenue, Great Barr, Birmingham, B43 5AG. 0121 3577 395.

Worcestershire

1. BEACONWOOD/THE WINSEL

Worcestershire Wildlife Trust.
Location: SO 974 759. N of Bromsgrove. Entrance near Lydiate Ash, three miles north of Bromsgrove, at end of cul-de-sac of Old Birmingham Road. Take public footpath along metalled track going N and enter reserve through a metal gate on L after about 20 yards.
Access: The reserve is open throughout the year but please keep to the footpaths.
Facilities: None.
Public transport: Nearest station – Longbridge (three miles). Nearest bus stops in Rubery (1 mile).
Habitat: Mixed woodlands.
Key birds: Buzzard, Kestrel, Sparrowhawk, Tawny Owl, Little Owl, Great Spotted Woodpecker, Spotted Flycatcher, Nuthatch, Treecreeper and many other

woodland birds are resident. *Summer:* Pied and Spotted Flycatcher, warblers.
Other notable flora and fauna: In May there is an unbroken sea of bluebells over five acres. Good variety of trees including the Great Oak, probably 250 years old.
Contact: Worcestershire Wildlife Trust, Lower Smite Farm, Smite Hill, Hindlip WR3 8SZ. 01905 754 919. e-mail: enquiries@worcestershirewildlifetrust.org www.worcswildlifetrust.co.uk

2. BROADWAY GRAVEL PIT

Worcestershire Wildlife Trust.
Location: SP 087 379. Approx. half mile NW of Broadway on the N side of Broadway to Childswickham road and E of old disused railway line.
Access: Open access at all times. Disabled access to hide only. Parts of circular path sometimes flooded but hide is usually clear.
Facilities: 1 hide. Cafes and toilets in Broadway. Very

141

NATURE RESERVES - CENTRAL ENGLAND

limited car parking (2-3 cars), no room for a coach. Large car park within half mile in Broadway.
Public transport: No rail connection. Buses to Broadway from Evesham etc. Check the timetable.
Habitat: Open water, wet woodland, dry scrub.
Key birds: As this is a very small site (1.6ha), it does not hold great numbers of bird species. Wintering Chiffchaff with tit and crest flocks, finches and buntings. Whitethroat, Blackcap, Chiffchaff, Cuckoo in spring/summer.
Other notable flora and fauna: A good dragonfly site for commoner species. Butterflies in drier, grassy areas. Mare's tail (unusual in Worcestershire wetland sites) found in abundance in June and August.
Contact: Trust HQ, 01905 754 919; e-mail: enquiries@worcestershirewildlifetrust.org www.worcswildlifetrust.co.uk

3. GWEN FINCH WETLAND

Worcestershire Wildlife Trust.
Location: SO 937 421. W of Evesham. Take B4080 S off A4104. Turn L at Eckington. Park where available and view reserve from road.
Access: Due to its sensitive nature, access to this reserve is restricted to special open days or guided walks. The whole site can be viewed from the minor road between Nafford and Eckington at grid reference SO 937 417, where you can park. A footpath leads down to Nafford Lock and on to Birlingham village, the first part of which passes alongside part of the Gwen Finch reserve.
Facilities: None.
Habitat: Recently created wetland with pools and marshes.
Key birds: Redshank, Water Rail and Reed Warbler breed and, Green Sandpiper and other waders are regular passage visitors. The pools attract hundreds of House Martins and Swallows, which feed on insects over the reeds and pools before heading south on migration.
Other notable flora and fauna: Dragonflies and damselflies are abundant along the margins of the river and the pools. Regular haunt for otters.
Contact: Trust HQ, 01905 754 919; e-mail: enquiries@worcestershirewildlifetrust.org www.worcswildlifetrust.co.uk

4. KNAPP AND PAPERMILL

Worcestershire Wildlife Trust.
Location: SO 749 522. Take A4103 SW from Worcester; R at Bransford roundabout then L towards Suckley and reserve is approx three miles (do not turn off for Alfrick). Park at Bridges Stone layby (SO 751 522), cross road and follow path to the Knapp House.
Access: Open daily. Large parties should contact Warden

Facilities:
Nature trail, small information centre, wildlife garden, Kingfisher viewing screen.
Public transport: None.
Habitat: Broadleaved woodland, unimproved grassland, fast stream, old orchard in Leigh Brook Valley.
Key birds: *Summer:* Breeding Grey Wagtail, Kingfisher, Spotted Flycatcher nests in warden's garden, all three woodpeckers. Buzzard, Sparrowhawk and Redstart also occur.
Other notable flora and fauna: Otters have returned recently. Good numbers of dragonflies and butterflies on all three meadows include holly blue, purple hairstreak and white admiral. Bluebells, green-winged and spotted orchids.
Contact: The Warden, Knapp and Papermill reserve, The Knapp, Alfrick WR6 5HR. 01886 832 065.

5. TIDDESLEY WOOD NATURE RESERVE

Worcestershire Wildlife Trust.
Location: SO 929 462. Take B4084 from Pershore to Worcester. Turn L towards Besford and Croome near town boundary just before the summit of the hill. Entrance is on L after about 0.75 miles.
Access: Open all year except Christmas Day. Cycles and horses only allowed on the bridleway. Please keep dogs fully under control. Military firing range at the SW corner of wood, so do not enter the area marked by red flags. The NE plot is private property and visitors should not enter the area. Main ride stoney, with some potholes. Small pathways difficult if wet. Coach parking by appointment.

Facilities: Information board. May find numbered posts around the reserve which were described in an old leaflet. Circular trail around small pathways.
Public transport: First Midland Red services (see above).
Habitat: Ancient woodland, conifers.
Key birds: *All year:* Coal Tit, Goldcrest, Sparrowhawk, Willow Tit, Marsh Tit. *Spring:* Chiffchaff, Blackcap, Cuckoo. *Winter:* Redwing, Fieldfare.
Other notable flora and fauna: Dragonflies including club-tailed and white-legged damselflies. Good for butterflies, including white admiral, peacock and gatekeeper. Important invertebrates, include nationally rare noble chafer beetle which has been recorded here for many years.
Contact: Worcestershire Wildlife Trust, 01905 754 919. e-mail:enquiries@worcestershirewildlifetrust.org www.worcswildlifetrust.co.uk

6. UPTON WARREN

Worcestershire Wildlife Trust.
Location: SO 936 675. Two miles S of Bromsgrove on A38. Leave M5 at junction 5.
Access: Christopher Cadbury Wetland Reserve divided into two parts — Moors Pools and Flashes Pools. Always open except Christmas Day. Trust membership gives access, or day permit from sailing centre. Disabled access to hides at Moors Pools only. No dogs.
Facilities: Seven hides, maps at entrances, paths can be very muddy. Coach parking at sailing centre by previous booking.
Public transport: Birmingham/Worcester bus passes reserve entrance.
Habitat: Fresh and saline pools with muddy islands, some woodland and scrub.
Key birds: *Winter:* Wildfowl. *Spring/autumn:* Passage waders. *Summer:* Breeding Avocet, Redshank, Little Ringed Plover, Oystercatcher, Common Tern, Sedge, Reed, Grasshopper and Cetti's Warblers. Hobby nearby.
Other notable flora and fauna: Saltmarsh plants, dragonflies.
Contact: A F Jacobs, 3 The Beeches, Upton Warren, Bromsgrove, Worcs B61 7EL. 01527 861 370.

7. WILDEN MARSH

Worcestershire Wildlife Trust.
Location: SO 825 730 and SO 829 735. S of Kidderminster. Take A449 S from Kidderminster. At junction with A442 go straight across roundabout into Wilden Lane. This is a very busy road with few parking spaces so park carefully. There are gated entrances off Wilden Lane.
Access: Parts of reserve accessed by gated entrances are open at all times. Visitors to the more northerly part of the reserve should obtain a permit from the Trust's office.
This reserve is complex and new visitors should consult a map. Cattle will be on the reserve at all times so ensure that all gates are secured after use. Parts of this reserve are dangerous with boggy areas, steep banks by the River Stour and deep ditches.
Public transport: Nearest bus stop at Wilden, half mile from reserve.
Habitat: Dry and marshy fields with small alder and willow woods, reed beds and many drainage ditches.
Key birds: 192 bird species have been recorded since 1968 and about 70 breed, including Yellow Wagtail, nine species of warblers and Redshank. It is one of the few wintering places for Water Pipits in county, though numbers have declined recently.
Other notable flora and fauna: Plants include southern marsh orchids, marsh cinquefoil, marsh arrow-grass, marsh pennywort and lesser water parsnip.
Contact: Trust HQ, 01905 754 919; e-mail: enquiries@worcestershirewildlifetrust.org

8. WYRE FOREST

Natural England/Worcs Wildlife Trust.
Location: SO 750 760. Half a mile NW of Bewdley (on the A456) and four and a half miles W of Kidderminster.
Access: Observe reserve signs and keep to paths. Forestry Commission visitor centre at Callow Hill. Fred Dale Reserve is reached by footpath W of B4194 (parking at SO 776 763).
Facilities: Toilet and refreshment facilities at Wyre Forest Visitor Centre (near the Discovery Centre) at Callow Hill.
Several waymarked trails in the Forest (some suitable for wheelchair users) as well as regular guided walks, also family cycle routes through the reserve. The Visitor Centre and Discovery Centre provide facilities for disabled visitors.
Public transport: The nearest train station is in Bewdley, served by the Severn Valley Railway (01299 403 816) although service is seasonal and sometimes infrequent. Also Central Trains to Kidderminster (0121 634 2040) and local bus services between Bewdley and Kidderminster.
Habitat: Oak forest, conifer areas, birch heath, lowland grassland, stream.
Key birds: Breeding birds include Redstart, Pied Flycatcher, Wood Warbler, Buzzard and Raven, with Dipper, Grey Wagtail and Kingfisher found on the larger streams.
Other notable flora and fauna: Mammals include, fallow, roe and muntjac deer, polecat, otter and mink, yellow neck mouse, dormouse, voles and water shrew. Several bat species including pipistrelle and Daubenton's. Important site for invertebrates including England's largest colony of pearl-bordered fritillary butterflies.
Contact: Tim Dixon, Natural England, Block B, Government Buildings, Whittington Road, Worcester WR5 2LQ. 01905 763 355; (fax) 01905 764 973; e-mail: herefordshire.worcestershire@ www.naturalengland.org.uk

Eastern England

Bedfordshire

1. BEGWARY BROOK

Beds, Cambs, Northants and Peterborough Wildlife Trust.
Location: TL 169 564. 2 miles S of St Neots. From A1 S take A428 E and continue to Wyboston Lakes complex. Pass through complex and follow nature reserve signs to car park.
Access: Open all year. Partially suitable for wheelchairs.
Facilities: None.
Public transport: Bus, St Neots to Sandy, some stop in Wyboston (Saffords Coaches - 01767 677 395).
Habitat: Former gravel pit. Marsh and open pools next to Great Ouse.
Key birds: Wildfowl and wader species. *Spring*: Sedge, Reed and Willow Warblers, Blackcap. *All year*: Reed Bunting, Kingfisher, Goldcrest.
Other notable flora and fauna: Orange-tip and speckled wood butterflies, dragonflies and grass snakes. Plants include great burnet, common fleabane and marsh woundwort.
Contact: Beds, Cambs, Northants & Peterborough Wildlife Trust, The Manor House, Broad Street, Great Cambourne, Cambridgeshire CB23 6DH. 01954 713 500; e-mail: cambridgeshire@wildlifebcnp.org www.wildlifebcnp.org

2. BLOW'S DOWNS

Beds, Cambs, Northants and Peterborough Wildlife Trust.
Location: TL 033 216. On the outskirts of Dunstable. Take A5065 from W of Luton, cross M1, take first exit at roundabout, park with care on verge. Alternatively, walk half mile from Dunstable centre to W entrance at Half Moon Lane off A5.
Access: Open all year, not suitable for wheelchairs.
Facilities: None.
Public transport: None.
Habitat: SSSI, chalk downland, scrub and grassland, that is a traditional resting place for incoming spring migrants.
Key birds: *Winter*: Lapwing, Meadow Pipit, Skylark, Stonechat. *Spring/autumn*: Ring Ouzel, Wheatear, Whinchat, Black Redstart, Willow Warbler.
Other notable flora and fauna: Chalkhill blue, brown argus and marbled white butterflies. Plants include small scabious, burnet-saxifrage, squinancywort, great pignut, common spotted and bee orchids.
Contact: Trust HQ, 01954 713 500; e-mail: bedfordshire@wildlifebcnp.org www.wildlifebcnp.org

3. FLITWICK MOOR

Beds, Cambs, Northants and Peterborough Wildlife Trust.

Location: TL 046 354. E of Flitwick. From Flitwick town centre (Tesco roundabout) on A5120, cross railway bridge, R at roundabout, immediately L into King's Road. After 500m, L into Moulden Road towards A507. After quarter mile R at Folly Farm, follow track to small car park. Also footpath to reserve from Moor Lane.
Access: Open all year.
Facilities: Car park. Please stick to public paths.
Public transport: Frequent buses (United Counties) from Bedford and Luton to Flitwick, or take train to Flitwick and then three-quarter mile walk.
Habitat: SSSI. Important wetland for the area, blend of fen, meadow, wet woodland and fragile peaty soil. Supports mosses ferns and flowers.
Key birds: *Winter*: Siskin, Water Rail, Great Spotted Woodpecker. *Spring*: Lesser Spotted Woodpecker, Willow Warbler, Blackcap. *Summer*: Water Rail, Grasshopper and Garden Warblers, Cuckoo. *Autumn*: Brambling.
Other notable flora and fauna: Good variety of butterflies and dragonflies, plus chimney sweeper moth and conehead bush cricket. Plants include nine species of sphagnum moss, marsh pennywort, black

knapweed, water figwort plus fly agaric and yellow brain fungus in autumn.
Contact: Trust HQ, 01954 713 500;
e-mail: bedfordshire@wildlifebcnp.org
www.wildlifebcnp.org

4. LODGE (THE)

RSPB (Central England Office).
Location: TL 191 485. Reserve lies 1 mile/1.6km E of Sandy on the B1042 to Potton.
Access: Reserve is open daily 9am-9pm (or sunset when earlier); shop 9am-5pm weekdays, 10am-5pm weekends. Non-members: £4 per motor vehicle. Dogs only allowed on bridleway.
Facilities: Nature trails being extended to five miles. One bridleway (half mile) and gardens are wheelchair/pushchair accessible. One hide (wheelchair accessible), 50 yards from car park. Coach parking at weekends by arrangement. Refreshments at shop.
Public transport: Buses to Sandy Market Square from Bedford, infrequent service. One mile walk from centre of Sandy or half mile from Sandy railway station, in part along trail through heathland restoration.
Habitat: This 180-hectare reserve is a mixture of woodland, heathland and acid grassland and includes the formal gardens of the RSPB's UK headquarters. New land being restored to heathland.
Key birds: Spring/summer: Hobby, Spotted Flycatcher. All year: Woodpeckers, woodland birds. Winter: Winter thrushes, woodland birds.
Other notable flora and fauna: Natterjack toad, common lizard, grass snake, rare heathland insects, dragonflies and butterflies. Particularly good site for fungi, and lichens. Garden pools are good for dragonflies.
Contact: RSPB, The Lodge Shop, Sandy, Beds SG19 2DL. 01767 680 541. www.rspb.org.uk/reserves/ e-mail: thelodgereserve@rspb.org.uk

5. MARSTON VALE MILLENNIUM COUNTRY PARK

Marston Vale Trust (Regd Charity No 1069229).
Location: SW of Bedford off A421 at Marston Moretaine. Only five mins from J13 of M1.
Access: Park and forest centre open seven days a week. Summer 10am-6pm, winter 10am-4pm. No dogs in wetlands reserve, rest of site OK for dogs and horses. Entry charge for wetland reserve (£2.50 for adults and £1.75 for Concessions). Main 8km trail surfaced for wheelchair and pushchair access. All-terrain wheelchair available for free loan. Coach parking available.
Facilities: Cafe bar, gift shop, art gallery, exhibition. Free parking.
Public transport: Bedford to Bletchley line — trains to Millbrook and Stewartby station, 20 minute walk to Forest Centre.
Habitat: Lake - 610 acres/freshwater marsh (man-made), reedbed, woodland, hawthorn scrub and grassland.

Key birds: Winter: Iceland and Glaucous Gulls (regular), gull roost, wildfowl, Great Crested Grebe. Spring: Passage waders and terns (Black Tern, Arctic Tern), Garganey. Summer: Nine species of breeding warblers, Hobby, Turtle Dove, Nightingale, Bearded Tit. Autumn: Passage waders and terns. Rarities: White-winged Black Tern, Laughing Gull, divers, Manx Shearwater, Bittern.
Other notable flora and fauna: Dingy and grizzled skipper butterflies, excellent for dragonflies, red-veined darter in 2008. Also otter and brown hare, plus bee and pyramidal orchids and stoneworts.
Contact: Forest Centre, Station Road, Marston Moretaine, Beds, MK43 0PR. 01234 767 037.
e-mail: info@marstonvale.org
www.marstonvale.org

6. PEGSDON HILL RESERVE

Beds, Cambs, Northants and Peterborough Wildlife Trust.
Location: TL 120 295. 5 miles W of Hitchin. Take B655 from Hitchin towards Barton-le-Clay. Turn R at Pegsdon then immediately L and park in lay-by. Reserve entrance across B655 via footpath.
Access: Open all year. Dropping off point for coaches only.
Facilities: None.
Public transport: Luton to Henlow buses (United Counties) stop at Pegsdon.
Habitat: Chalk grassland, scrub and woodland.
Key birds: Winter: Brambling, Stonechat, winter thrushes, raptors including Buzzard. Spring: Wheatear, Ring Ouzel, Tree Pipit, Yellowhammer. Summer: Turtle Dove, Grey Partridge, Lapwing, Skylark.
Other notable flora and fauna: Dragonflies, dark green fritillary, dingy and grizzled skippers, chalkhill blue, brown argus and small heath butterflies. Glow worms. Plants include pasqueflower in spring, fly, spotted and pyramidal orchids.
Contact Trust HQ, 01954 713 500;
e-mail: bedfordshire@wildlifebcnp.org
www.wildlifebcnp.org

7. PRIORY COUNTRY PARK AND MARINA

Bedford Borough Council.
Location: TL 071 495. 1.5 miles SE from Bedford town centre. Signposted from A428 & A421. Entry point to new 'River Valley Park'
Access: Park and hides open at all times. No access to fenced/gated plantations.
Facilities: Toilets and visitor centre open daytime, all-year-round disabled access on new path around lake. Hides, nature trails, labyrinth, cycle hire, Premier Inn for meals, accomodation.
Public transport: Stagecoach (01604 676 060) 'Blue Solo 4' every 20 mins. Mon-Sat. Alight 1st stop Riverfield Drive (200 m). Rail station at Bedford (approx 2.5 miles)
Habitat: Lakes, reedbeds, scrub and woodland, meadows adjoining Great Ouse.

Key birds: Good numbers/variety of winter wildfowl, varied mix of spring passage species, with breeding warblers and woodpeckers, augmented by feeding terns, hirundines and raptors. *Winter:* Grebes, Pochard, Shoveler, Gadwall, Merlin, Water Rail, gulls, thrushes, Chiffchaff, corvids, buntings. *Passage:* Raptors, waders, terns, pipits. *Summer:* Hobby, Turtle Dove, Swift, hirundines, *acrocephalus* and *sylvia* warblers. *All year:* Cormorant, Little Egret, Heron, Stock Dove, woodpeckers, Kingfisher, Grey Wagtail, Treecreeper, Goldfinch, Bullfinch.
Other notable flora and fauna: 23 species of dragonfly, incl small red-eyed damsel & hairy hawker. 20 species of butterfly. Large plant list. Fox, muntjac and otter.
Contact: Jon Bishop, Wardens Office, Visitor Centre, Priory CP, Barkers Lane, Bedford, MK41 9SH. 01234 211 182.

Cambridgeshire

1. BRAMPTON WOOD

Beds, Cambs, Northants & Peterborough Wildlife Trust.
Location: TL 184 698. 4 miles W of Huntingdon. Access via A1 (Buckden roundabout) through Grafham village and Brampton Road. Access also via A14 through Brampton village.
Access: Open daily. Coaches able to drop passengers off but unfortunately not sufficient space available to park.
Facilities: Car park, interpretative shelter. The wood has wide grass rides and small mud paths. Suitable for disabled access when dry on grassy rides, but may be muddy even in summer.
Public transport: Bus from Huntingdon to Brampton (H&D) then two mile walk.
Habitat: Ancient woodland, primarily oak, ash and field maple with hazel coppice. Areas of planted conifer and species rich grassland rides and glades.
Key birds: Autumn/*Winter:* Marsh Tit, Woodcock, winter thrushes. *Spring/summer:* Common woodland birds, Green Woodpecker, Spotted Flycatcher.
Other notable flora and fauna: Brown argus, white admiral and black hairstreak butterflies, pine beauty and pine hawk moths. Dormouse, glow worms, smooth and great crested newts, plus various dragonfly species. Plants include meadow grasses, cowslip, yellow rattle, devil's-bit scabious.
Contact: Beds, Cambs, Northants & Peterborough Wildlife Trust, The Manor House, Broad Street, Great Cambourne, Cambridgeshire CB23 6DH. 01954 713 500; e-mail: cambridgeshire@wildlifebcnp.org www.wildlifebcnp.org

2. FEN DRAYTON

RSPB (Eastern England Office).
Location: TL 352 680. NW of Cambridge. Leave A14 at Junction 28; follow signs to Swavesey. Turn L in Boxworth End (signed to Fen Drayton). Turn R onto minor road (signed to Swavesey), then L into entrance to Fen Drayton Lakes. Follow signs to car park.
Access: Open at all times. Dogs allowed on public footpaths and bridleways. Disabled birders can get car access to one viewing screen.
Facilities: There are a number of public and permissive rights of way around the lakes and two open access fields. Information boards give access details. Free trail guides and events leaflets are available from the Elney car park.
Public transport: Huntingdon: Stagecoach service 553 (with change to service 15 at St Ives), alight at Fen Drayton High Street. Cambridge: Stagecoach service 15 to Swavesey Middle Watch or Whippet No 15 to Fenstanton, alight in Fen Drayton High Street. Walk north (600 m) from Fen Drayton High Street onto Holywell Ferry Road, past recreation ground on left. Cambridgeshire Guided Bus service has a request stop in reserve.
Habitat: A complex of lakes and traditional riverside meadows next to the River Great Ouse that used to be gravel workings.
Key birds: At least 213 species have been recorded in the area with some 65 species being regular breeders including Common Tern. Hobby, waders on passage. Rarities include Great White Egret, Purple Heron, Glossy Ibis, Common Crane, Red-Footed Falcon, Honey Buzzard and Whiskered Tern. Bitterns are now a regular sight, with Holywell Lake and Elney Lake being the favoured sites. *Winter:* Nationally important numbers of Gadwall and Coot.
Other notable flora and fauna: Good site for butterflies, dragonflies and mammals.
Contact: The Warden, RSPB Fens area office, The Grange, Market Street, Swavesey, Cambridge, CB24 4QG. 01603 661 662. www.rspb.org.uk/reserves/

3. FERRY MEADOWS COUNTRY PARK

Nene Park Trust.
Location: TL 145 975. Three miles W of Peterborough town centre, signed off A605.
Access: Open all year, 7am to dusk (summer, 8am until sunset in winter. Electric scooters and wheelchair available for loan — call to book in advance. Coach parking free at all times. Car parking charges apply at weekends and Bank Holidays between April - Oct.
Facilities: Car park, visitor centre, toilets (inc disabled), café, two wheelchair-accessible hides in nature reserve area. Hard surface paths in park's central areas, but steep slopes in Bluebell Wood.
Public transport: Stagecoach X14 stops on A605 by Notcutts Nursey. Half mile walk to park entrance. Tel. Traveline 0870 6082 608 or www.traveline.org.uk
Habitat: Lakes, meadows, scrub, broadleaved woodland and small wetland nature reserve.
Key birds: *Spring:* Terns, waders, Yellow Wagtail. *Winter:* Grebes, Siskin, Redpoll, Water Rail, occasional Hawfinch. *All year:* Good selection of woodland and water birds, Kingfisher.
Other notable flora and fauna: Bluebell, wood anenome, wild garlic in woodland.
Contact: Visitor Services Officer, Nene Park Trust,

NATURE RESERVES - EASTERN ENGLAND

Ham Farm House, Orton, Peterborough, PE2 5UU.
01733 234 443; www.nene-park-trust.org.uk
e-mail: visitor.services@nene-park-trust.org.uk

4. FOWLMERE

RSPB (Eastern England Office).
Location: TL 407 461. 7 miles S of
Cambridge. Turn off A10 Cambridge to
Royston road by Shepreth and follow sign.
Access: Access at all times along marked
trail.
Facilities: One and a half miles of trails.
Three hides, toilets. Space for one coach, prior
booking essential. Wheelchair access to one
hide, toilet and some of the trails.
Public transport: Shepreth railway station
2 miles.
Habitat: Reedbeds, meres, woodland,
scrub.
Key birds: *Summer*: Ten breeding warblers.
All year: Water Rail, Kingfisher. *Winter*:
Snipe, raptors.
Other notable flora and fauna: Healthy
population of water shrews and otters. 18 species
of dragonfly recorded.
Contact: The Warden, RSPB, Manor Farm, High
Street, Fowlmere, Royston, Herts SG8 7SH. Tel/Fax
01763 208 978.

5. GRAFHAM WATER

Beds, Cambs, Northants & Peterborough Wildlife Trust.
Location: TL 143 671. Follow signs for Grafham
Water from A1 at Buckden or A14 at Ellington. Nature
Reserve entrance is from Mander car park, W of Perry
village.
Access: Open all year. Dogs barred in wildlife garden
only, on leads elsewhere. Car parking £2 for day
ticket.
Facilities: Five bird hides in nature reserve, two
in the bird sanctuary area. Two in wildlife garden
accessible to wheelchairs. Cycle track through
reserve also accessible to wheelchairs. Visitor centre
with restaurant, shop and toilets. Disabled parking.
Use Plummer car park for lagoons and Marlow car
park for dam area (good for waders and vagrants).
Public transport: Bus, St Neots to Bedford. Get off at
Great Staughton then two mile walk.
Habitat: Open water, settlement lagoons ranging
from reedbeds, open water, wet mud and willow
carr, ancient and plantation woodland, scrub, species
rich grassland.
Key birds: *Resident*: Common woodland birds,
wildfowl. *Winter*: Waders including Common
Sandpiper and Dunlin, Great Crested Grebe, wildfowl
including large flocks of Tufted Duck and Coot,
Pochard, Shoveler, Shelduck, Goldeneye, Goosander
and Smew, gulls (can be up to 30,000 roosting in
mid-winter). *Spring/summer*: Breeding Nightingale,
Reed, Willow and Sedge Warblers, Common and
Black Terns. *Autumn*: Passage waders. *Rarities*: Have
included Wilson's Phalarope (2007), Ring-necked

Duck, Great Northern Diver, Glaucous, Iceland and
Mediterranean Gulls.
Other notable flora and fauna: Bee and common
spotted orchids, early purple orchid, common
twayblade (in woods), cowslip. Common blue and
marbled white butterflies, dragonflies including
broad-bodied chaser, voles, grass snakes.
Contact: The Warden, Grafham Water Nature
Reserve, c/o The Lodge, West Perry, Huntingdon,
Cambs, PE28 0BX. 01480 811 075.
e-mail: matt.hamilton@wildlifebcnp.org
www.wildlifetrust.org.uk/bcnp

6. NENE WASHES

RSPB (Eastern England Office).
Location: TL 317 992. N of Whittlesey and six miles E
of Peterborough.
Access: Open at all times along South Barrier Bank,
accessed at Eldernell, one mile NE of Coates, off
A605. Group visits inside reserve by arrangement. No
access to fields. No access for wheelchairs.
Facilities: Small car park - one coach max.
Information board. No toilets or hide.
Public transport: Bus and trains to Whittlesey, bus to
Coates - Stagecoach 01733 554 575.
Habitat: Wet grassland with ditches. Frequently
flooded.
Key birds: *Spring/early summer*: Corncrake release
scheme. Breeding waders (inc Black-tailed Godwit),
duck (inc Garganey), Marsh Harrier and Hobby.

147

Winter: Waterfowl in large numbers (inc Bewick's Swan, Pintail, Shoveler), Barn and Short-eared Owls, Hen Harrier.
Other notable flora and fauna: Water vole, otter, water violet, flowering rush and fringe water lily.
Contact: Charlie Kitchin, RSPB Nene Washes, 21a East Delph, Whittlesey, Cambs PE7 1RH. 01733 205 140.

7. OUSE WASHES

RSPB (Eastern England Office).
Location: TL 471 860. Between Chatteris and March on A141, take B1093 to Manea. Reserve signposted from Manea. Reserve office and visitor centre located off Welches Dam. Approximately ten miles from March or Chatteris.
Access: Access at all times from visitor centre (open 9am - 5pm every day except Dec 25/26). Welches Dam to public hides approached by marked paths behind boundary bank. No charge. Dogs to be kept on leads at all times. Disabled access to Welches Dam hide, 350 yards from car park. Track between Kingfisher and Stevens Hides very muddy following maintenance work.
Groups welcome, but note that large coaches (36+ seats) cannot traverse final bend to reserve.
Facilities: Car park (inc 2 disabled bays) and toilets. Space for up to two small coaches. Visitor centre - unmanned but next to reserve office. Ten hides overlooking the reserve: nearest 350 yards from visitor centre (with disabled access) up to 1.8 miles from visitor centre. Boardwalk over pond — good for dragonflies in summer.
Public transport: No public transport to reserve entrance. Buses and trains stop at Manea — three miles from reserve.
Habitat: Lowland wet grassland — seasonally flooded. Open pool systems in front of some hides.
Key birds: *Summer:* Around 70 species breed including Black-tailed Godwit, Lapwing, Redshank, Snipe, Shoveler, Gadwall, Garganey and Spotted Crake. Also Hobby and Marsh Harrier.
Autumn: Passage waders including Wood and Green Sandpipers, Spotted Redshank, Greenshank, Little Stint, plus terns and Marsh and Hen Harriers.
Winter: Large number of wildfowl (up to 100,000 birds) including Bewick's and Whooper Swans, Wigeon, Teal, Shoveler, Pintail, Pochard.
Other notable flora and fauna: Good range of dragonflies, butterflies and fenland flora.
Contact: Jon Reeves, (Site Manager), Ouse Washes Reserve, Welches Dam, Manea, March, Cambs, PE15 0NF. 01354 680 212; e-mail: jon.reeves@rspb.org.uk www.rspb.org.uk

8. PAXTON PITS NATURE RESERVE

Huntingdonshire District Council.
Location: TL 197 629. Access from A1 at Little Paxton, two miles N of St Neots.
Access: Free entry. Open 24 hours. Visitors' centre open seven days a week. Dogs allowed under control. Heron trail suitable for wheelchairs during summer.

Facilities: Visitors' centre provides information about the surrounding area, books, bird feeders and seed etc are on sale and light refreshments are available. Leaflets for the Nature Reserve can also be purchased. Toilets (including disabled) are available when the visitor centre is open. Two bird hides (always open), marked nature trails.
Public transport: Buses run from St Neots and Huntingdon to Little Paxton (enquiries 0845 045 5200). The nearest train station is St Neots (enquiries 08457 48 49 50).
Habitat: Grassland, scrub, lakes. Site being expanded over the next nine years, to include extensive reedbed.
Key birds: *Spring/summer:* Nightingale, Kingfisher, Common Tern, Sparrowhawk, Hobby, Grasshopper, Sedge and Reed Warblers, Lesser Whitethroat. Large Cormorant nesting colony.
Winter: Smew, Goldeneye, Goosander, Gadwall, Pochard.
Other notable flora and fauna: Wildflowers, butterflies and dragonflies are in abundance. Along the meadow trail there are common spotted orchids. Bee orchids are found around the car park. Otters are known to use the reserve.
Contact: The Rangers, Paxton Pits Nature Reserve,, High Street, Little Paxton, St Neots, Cambs, PE19 6ET. 01480 406 795. e-mail: paxtonpits@btconnect.com www.paxton-pits.org.uk

9. WICKEN FEN

The National Trust.
Location: TL 563 705. Lies 17 miles NE of Cambridge and ten miles S of Ely. From A10 drive E along A1123.
Access: Reserve is open daily except Christmas Day. Visitor centre is open daily all year round. Cafe open daily March - Oct, Weds - Sun Nov - Feb. Boardwalk suitable for wheelchairs, with 2 hides. Disabled toilet
Facilities: Toilets, visitor centre, café, hides, boardwalk, footpaths, cycle route (NCN Route 11 passes through the reserve), coach and disabled parking. Dragonfly Centre open weekends during the summer months.
Public transport: Nearest rail link either Cambridge or Ely. Buses only on Thu and Sun. No buses to Wicken.
Habitat: Open fen, cut hay fields, sedge beds, grazing marsh, partially flooded wet grassland, reedbed, scrub, woodland.
Key birds: *Spring:* Passage waders and passerines. *Summer:* Marsh Harriers, waders and warblers. *Winter:* Wildfowl, Hen Harrier, Bittern.
Other notable flora and fauna: More than 8,000 species recorded: 22 species of dragonfly/damselfly, 27 species of butterfly and 1,000-plus species of moth. Water vole, otter.
Contact: Isobel Sedgwick, Wicken Fen, Lode Lane, Wicken, Cambs, CB7 5XP. 01353 720 274; e-mail: isabel.sedgwick@nationaltrust.org.uk or wickenfen@nationaltrust.org.uk www.wicken.org.uk

Essex

1. ABBERTON RESERVOIR

Essex Wildlife Trust.
Location: TL 963 185. Five miles SW of Colchester on B1026. Follow signs from Layer-de-la-Haye.
Access: Open Tue-Sun and Bank Holiday Mondays (9am-5pm). Closed Christmas Day and Boxing Day.
Facilities: Essex & Suffolk Water's reservoir enhancement scheme has seen concrete edges replaced. Work on the visitor centre continues, but toilets and other facilities (gift shop and light refreshments) still available. Nature trails with panoramic views. Ample parking, including coaches. Also good viewing where roads cross reservoir.
Public transport: Phone Trust for advice.
Habitat: 100 acres on edge of 1,200-acre reservoir.
Key birds: *Winter*: Nationally important for Mallard, Teal, Wigeon, Shoveler, Gadwall, Pochard, Tufted Duck, Goldeneye (most important inland site in Britain). Smew, Bittern and Goosander regular. Passage waders, terns, birds of prey. Tree-nesting Cormorant colony; raft-nesting Common Tern. *Summer*: Hobby, Yellow Wagtail, warblers, Nightingale, Corn Bunting; *Autumn*: Red-crested Pochard, Water Rail.
Other notable flora and fauna: Dragonflies including broad-bodied chaser, small red-eyed damselfly, butterflies including green and purple hairstreak, roesel's bush-cricket. Brown hare.
Contact: Abberton Reservoir Visitor Centre, 01206 738 172. e-mail: abberton@essexwt.org.uk

2. ABBOTTS HALL FARM

Essex Wildlife Trust.
Location: TL 963 145. Seven miles SW from Colchester. Turn E off B1026 (Colchester-Maldon road) towards Peldon. Entrance is 0.5 mile on R.
Access: Weekdays (9am-5pm). Two hides with wheelchair ramps. No dogs please. Working farm so please take care. HQ of wildlife trust.
Facilities: Toilets, hides, guided walks, fact-sheets, information boards.
Public transport: None.
Habitat: Saltmarsh, saline lagoons, grazing marsh, farmland, woodland, freshwater lakes and ponds.
Key birds: *Winter*: Waders and wildfowl. Passage migrants and summer warblers. Large roost of ducks and Little Egrets on lake.
Other notable flora and fauna: Range of butterflies, reptiles, newts and water vole.
Contact: Trust HQ, 01621 862 960;
e-mail: admin@essexwt.org.uk

3. BRADWELL BIRD OBSERVATORY

Essex Birdwatching Society
Location: 100 yards S of St Peter's Chapel, Bradwell-on-Sea. Mouth of Blackwater estuary, between Maldon and Foulness.
Access: Open all year.
Facilities: Accommodation for eight in hut; two rooms each with four bunks; blankets, cutlery, etc. supplied.
Habitat: Mudflats, saltmarsh.
Key birds: *Winter*: Wildfowl (inc. Brent Geese, Red-throated Diver, Red-breasted Merganser), large numbers of waders; small numbers of Twite, Snow Bunting and occasional Shorelark on beaches, also Hen Harrier, Merlin and Peregrine. Good passage of migrants usual in spring and autumn. *Summer*: Small breeding population of terns and other estuarine species.
Other notable flora and fauna: A variety of dragonflies inc hairy dragonfly and scarce emerald damselfly.
Contact: Graham Smith, 48 The Meads, Ingatestone, Essex CM4 0AE. 01277 354 034.

4. FINGRINGHOE WICK

Essex Wildlife Trust.
Location: TM 046 197. Colchester five miles. The reserve is signposted from B1025 to Mersea Island, S of Colchester.
Access: Open 7 days a week. Winter Opening: November 1 – March 31 (9am – 4pm Tuesday to Sunday). Closed Christmas Day & Boxing Day. Summer Opening: April 1– October 31 (9am – 5pm). Entry by donation: Adult £2, Child £1 and Family £5. Dogs limited to Dog Trail only and must be kept on a lead.
Facilities: Visitor centre: toilets Inc: baby changing facilities, easy access toilet and one wheelchair is available, Gift shop, light

refreshments, optics, observation room with displays, sea and sky observatory, car park, Reserve: seven bird hides, nature trails.

Habitat: Old gravel pit, large lake, many ponds, sallow/birch thickets, young scrub, reedbeds, saltmarsh, gorse heathland.

Key birds: *Autumn/winter:* Brent Goose, waders, Hen Harrier, Little Egret. *Spring:* Approx 30 male Nightingales. Good variety of warblers in scrub, thickets, reedbeds and Turtle Dove, Green/Great Spotted Woodpeckers. *Winter:* Little Grebe, Mute Swan, Teal, Wigeon, Shoveler, Gadwall on lake.

Contact: Fingringhoe Wick Visitor Centre, 01206 729 678; e-mail: louised@essexwt.org.uk - Follow us on Facebook: www.facebook.com/EWTFingringhoe

5. HANNINGFIELD RESERVOIR

Essex Wildlife Trust.

Location: TQ 725 972. Three miles N of Wickford. Exit off Southend Road (Old A130) at Rettendon onto South Hanningfield Road. Follow this for two miles until reaching the T-junction with Hawkswood Road. Turn R and the entrance to the visitor centre and reserve is one mile on the R.

Access: Open daily (9am-5pm) all year. Closed Christmas Day and Boxing Day. Disabled parking, toilets, and adapted birdwatching hide. No dogs. No cycling.

Facilities: Visitor centre, gift shop, optics, refreshments, toilets, four bird hides, nature trails, picnic area, coach parking, education room.

Public transport: Chelmsford to Wickford bus no 14 to Downham village and walk half mile down Crowsheath Lane.

Habitat: Mixed woodland (110 acres) with grassy glades and rides, adjoining 870-acre Hanningfield Reservoir, designated an SSSI due to its high numbers of wildfowl.

Key birds: *Spring:* Good numbers and mix of woodland warblers. *Summer:* Vast numbers of Swifts, Swallows and martins feeding over the water. Hobby and Osprey. *Winter:* Good numbers and mix of waterfowl. Large gull roost.

Other notable flora and fauna: Spectacular displays of bluebells in spring. Damselflies and dragonflies around the ponds. Grass snakes and common lizards sometimes bask in rides.

Contact: Hanningfield Reservoir Visitor Centre, 01268 711 001; www.essexwt.org.uk

6. OLD HALL MARSHES

RSPB (Eastern England Office).

Location: TL 975 125. Approx 10 miles S of Colchester. From A12 take B1023, via Tiptree, to Tolleshunt D'Arcy. Then take Chapel Road (back road to Tollesbury), after one mile turn L into Old Hall Lane. Continue up Old Hall Lane, over speed ramps and through iron gates, over cattle grid and straight ahead to car park.

Access: By permit only (free in advance from Warden. Write to address below). Open 9am-9pm or dusk. No wheelchair access or facilities. No coaches.

Facilities: Two trails — one of three miles and one of 6.5 miles. Viewing screens overlooking saline lagoon area at E end of reserve. No visitor centre or toilets.

Public transport: Limited bus service to Tollesbury (one mile from reserve).

Habitat: Coastal grazing marsh, reedbed, open water saline lagoon, saltmarsh and mudflat.

Key birds: *Summer:* Breeding Avocet, Redshank, Lapwing, Pochard, Shoveler, Gadwall, Marsh Harrier and Barn Owl. *Winter:* Large assemblies of wintering wildfowl: Brent Goose, Wigeon, Teal, Shoveler, Goldeneye, Red-breasted Merganser, all the expected waders, Hen Harrier, Merlin, Short-eared Owl and Twite. *Passage:* All expected waders inc Spotted Redshank, Green Sandpiper and Whimbrel. Yellow Wagtail, Whinchat and Wheatear.

Other notable flora and fauna: Brown hare, water vole, hairy dragonfly, scarce emerald damselfly, ground lackey and cream spot tiger moths, white letter hairstreak.

Contact: Paul Charlton, Site Manager, c/o 1 Old Hall Lane, Tolleshunt D'Arcy, Maldon, Essex CM9 8TP. 01621 869 015. e-mail: paul.charlton@rspb.org.uk

7. RAINHAM MARSHES

RSPB (South Eastern Regional Office).

Location: On N bank of River Thames, SE of Dagenham. From London take A13 to A1306 turn-off and head towards Purfleet for half a mile. At traffic lights, turn right, signposted A1090 and reserve entrance is 300 metres along this road.

Access: Open all year. Extensive programme of guided walks — check RSPB website for details. Approx 2.5 miles of boardwalks suitable for wheelchairs and pushchairs.

Facilities: Visitor centre, disabled toilets, car park on site, picnic area, shop, refreshments available. Two bird hides and another on the way.

Public transport: Route 44 (Ensignbus - 01708 865 656) runs daily between Grays and Lakeside via Purfleet. Arriva service (0870 120 1088) hourly Sundays and most public holidays.

Habitat: Former MoD shooting range, largest remaining area of lowland wetland along the Thames.

Key birds: *Spring:* Marsh Harrier, Hobby, Wheatear, hirundines and other migrants. *Summer/autumn:* Many waders, including Black-tailed Godwit, Whimbrel, Greenshank, Snipe, Lapwing, Avocet. Yellow-legged Gull. Merlin and Peregrine hunt among the gathering flocks. *Winter:* Waders, wildfowl, Water Pipit, Short-eared Owl, Little Egret and Penduline Tit most winters.

Other notable flora and fauna: 21 species of dragonfly, including hairy hawker, scarce emerald and small red-eyed damselfly. Marsh frogs, water vole, water shrew, fox, stoat, weasel, 30 species of butterfly, and 13 species of grasshoppers and crickets. Deadly nightshade.

Contact: The Warden, The Visitor Centre, 01708 899 840; www.rspb.org.uk/rainham

8. RIVER LEE COUNTRY PARK

Lee Valley Regional Park
Location: The Country Park spreads from Waltham Abbey in Essex to Broxbourne in Hertfordshire. Car parks at Waltham Abbey Gardens (EN9 1XD), Fishers Green (EN9 2EF), Cheshunt (EN9 1XQ) and Broxbourne (EN10 6LX).
Access: All hides open to public daily (excepting Christmas Day). Hides and paths are suitable for wheelchair users.
Facilities: There is a café, toilet and shop at Lee Valley Park Farms and toilet facilities are also available at Fishers Green, Cheshunt and Broxbourne car parks.
Public transport: All sites served by buses — call Arriva on 0871 200 2233.
Habitat: Former gravel pits now flooded, with wooded islands, reedbeds and marshy corners.
Key birds: *Winter:* Bittern at Fishers Green. Wide variety of wildfowl incl. Smew, Goosander, Shoveler and Gadwall. *Summer:* Breeding warblers, Nightingale, Little Ringed Plover, Turtle Dove and various birds of prey. Wide variety of species on spring/autumn passage.
Other notable flora and fauna: Two orchid meadows within the Country Park, and a dragonfly sanctuary in the south of the Country Park.
Contact: Lee Valley Regional Park Authority, 08546 770 600; e-mail: info@leevalleypark.org.uk www.leevalleypark.org.uk

9. STOUR ESTUARY

RSPB (Eastern England Office).
Location: Between Manningtree and Harwich. From Manningtree, stay on B1352 past Strangers Home pub in Bradfield, then look for brown sign to reserve just past Wrabness village.
Access: Open all year. Stour wood walk (1 mile) OK for wheelchairs in dry conditions. Walks to estuary and furthest hide not suitable, due to terrain and kissing gates. Dogs only allowed in Stour Wood and on public footpaths.
Facilities: Two hides, one viewing screen. Two picnic tables.
Public transport: Nearest train station (One Railway) at Wrabness is 1 mile away. Hourly buses (Mon - Sat) running between Colchester and Harwich will stop at entrance to woods on request or at new bus stop at SW corner of Stour Wood.

Habitat: Extensive woodland leading down to the River Stour estuary, saltmarsh at Deep Fleet and mudflats at Copperas Bay.
Key birds: *Spring/autumn:* Black-tailed Godwit, Dunlin, Pintail. *Summer:* Nightingale and warblers. *Winter:* Brent Goose, plus nationally important numbers of wildfowl and waders.
Other notable flora and fauna: Woodland wildflowers in spring.
Contact: RSPB Eastern England Office, 01473 328 006. www.rspb.org.uk/reserves/

10. TOLLESBURY WICK MARSHES

Essex Wildlife Trust.
Location: TL 969 104. On Blackwater Estuary eight miles E of Maldon. Follow B1023 to Tollesbury via Tiptree, leaving A12 at Kelvedon. Then follow Woodrolfe Road S towards the marina. Use small public car park at Woodrolfe Green (TL 964 107), 500m before reserve entrance on sea wall. Car park suitable for mini-buses and small coaches.
Access: Open all times along public footpath on top of sea wall. The route is exposed to the elements so be prepared with adequate clothing. Motorised wheelchair access possible to Block House Bay.
Facilities: Public toilets at Woodrolfe Green car park.
Public transport: Hedingham bus services run to Tollesbury from Maldon, Colchester and Witham — call 01621 869 214 for information.
Habitat: Estuary with fringing saltmarsh and mudflats with some shingle. Extensive freshwater grazing marsh, brackish borrowdyke and small reedbeds.
Key birds: *Winter:* Large numbers of wintering wildfowl and waders, particularly Brent Geese and Wigeon, Lapwing and Golden Plover. Short-eared Owl, Hen Harrier and, increasingly, Marsh Harrier. *Summer:* Breeding Avocet, Redshank, Lapwing, Little Tern, Reed and Sedge Warblers, Reed Bunting, Barn Owl. *Passage:* Whimbrel, Spotted Redshank, Green Sandpiper.
Other notable flora and fauna: Plants include spiny restharrow, grass vetchling, yellow horned-poppy, slender hare's-ear. Hairy dragonfly, Roesel's and great green bush-crickets. Hares and occasional common seals can be seen from the footpath on top of the sea wall.
Contact: Jonathan Smith, Tollesbury, Maldon, Essex, CM9 8RJ. 01621 868 628.
e-mail: jonathans@essexwt.org.uk

Hertfordshire

1. AMWELL NATURE RESERVE

Herts Wildlife Trust.
Location: TL 375 128. SE of Ware, on the back road to Stanstead Abbotts near Great Amwell village. Park in Amwell Lane, St Margarets.
Access: Open all year. Dragonfly trail open May to September.

Facilities: Public hide and viewing area.
Public transport: Nearest station is St Margarets.
Habitat: Disused gravel pit with reedbeds and woodland.
Key birds: *Spring/summer:* Breeding Little and Great Crested Grebes, Kingfisher, Ringed Plover, Little Ringed Plover and warblers. *Winter:* Smew, other ducks, Bittern seen regularly. Of international importance for wintering Gadwall and Shoveler.
Other notable flora and fauna: Otter, 19 species

of dragonfly recorded, inc ruddy darter and hsairy dragonfly. Marsh dock.

Contact: Trust HQ, 01727 858 901;
e-mail: info@hmwt.org
www.hertswildlifetrust.org.uk

2. CASSIOBURY PARK

Welwyn & Hatfield Council.
Location: TL 090 970. 190 acres of green space close to Watford town centre.
Access: Open all year.
Facilities: Car park, footpaths.
Public transport: Watford Metropolitan Underground station.
Habitat: Municipal park, wetland, river, alder/willow wood.
Key birds: *Spring/summer*: Hobby, Kingfisher, Grey Wagtail. *Winter*: Wildfowl, Snipe, Water Rail, occasional Bearded Tit.
Contact: Welwyn & Hatfield Council, 01707 357 000.
e-mail: council.services@welhat.gov.uk

3. KINGS MEADS

Herts & Middlesex Wildlife Trust /various owners.
Location: Between Hertford and Ware, lying alongside A119 Ware Road. Park in Priory Street and Broadmeads (Ware) and streets in Hertford.
Access: Open all year.
Facilities: None.
Public transport: Bus stops on Hertford Road (A119). Trains to Ware (5 mins walk) station and Hertford East Station (10 mins walk).
Habitat: Largest remaining area of grazed riverside flood meadow in Hertfordshire.
Key birds: *Summer*: Skylark, Reed Warbler, Reed Bunting, Sedge Warbler, Yellow Wagtail. *Winter/ spring*: Gadwall, Shoveler, Wigeon, Teal, Snipe, gulls, Stonechat, waders.
Other notable flora and fauna: 265 species of wildflower. Best site in county for dragonflies, with 18 species recorded.
Contact: Herts & Middlesex Wildlife Trust, 01727 858 901. e-mail: info@hmwt.org
www.hertswildlifetrust.org.uk

4. LEMSFORD SPRINGS NATURE RESERVE

Herts & Middlesex Wildlife Trust.
Location: TL 223 123. Lies 1.5 miles W of Welwyn Garden City town centre, off roundabout leading to Lemsford village on B197, W of A1(M).
Access: Access, via key, by arrangement with warden. Open at all times, unless work parties or group visits in progress. Keep to paths. Dogs on leads. 150m earth path to hide. Wheelchair access ramp to hide. Coaches welcome and room to park on road, but limit of 30 persons.

Facilities: Two hides, classroom, chemical toilet, paths and bridges. Circular walk.
Public transport: Bus service to Valley Road, WGC & Lemsford Village No 366 (Arriva, Traveline 0871 200 2233). Nearest railway station Welwyn Garden City.
Habitat: Former water-cress beds, open shallow lagoons. River Lea, marsh, hedgerows. Nine acres.
Key birds: *Spring/summer*: Breeding warblers, Grey Wagtail, Kestrel, Green Woodpecker. *Autumn/ winter*: Green Sandpiper, Water Rail, Snipe, Siskin, Little Egret, occasional Jack Snipe. *All year*: Mandarin Duck, Kingfisher, Grey Heron, Sparrowhawk.
Other notable flora and fauna: Muntjac, fox and stoat. Common butterflies and damselflies in summer.
Contact: Barry Trevis, Warden, 11 Lemsford Village, Welwyn Garden City, Herts, AL8 7TN. 01707 335 517.
e-mail: info@hmwt.org www.hertswildlifetrust.org.uk

5. MAPLE LODGE NATURE RESERVE

Thames Water/Maple Lodge Conservation Society
Location: TQ 036 925. South of Ricksmansworth, close to village of Maple Cross. From M25 (Jt 17) turn left at traffic lights. Drive down Maple Lodge Close and park in social club car park.
Access: Restricted to members of MLCS. Visits by non-members and groups can be arranged in advance. Site can be boggy – please keep to designated paths.
Facilities: Information centre, toilets. Eight bird hides – two wheelchair-friendly. Winter feeding station.
Habitat: A man-made wetland habitat formed from two gravel pits and a sludge settlement area. Mixed broadleaf plantation on eastern side.
Key birds: Wildfowl throughout year, numbers building in winter. All three woodpeckers, plus variety of finches, thrushes and woodland species. Nesting species

include Kingfisher, Tawny Owl, migrant warblers. Green, Common and Wood Sandpipers on passage. **Other notable flora and fauna:** 170 species of moth recorded, plus many butterflies and aquatic insects. 125 species of wildflower recorded.
Contact: For membership of MLCS or to arrange visits, contact chairman Miss Gwyneth Bellis on 01923 230 277. www.maplelodge.org

6. RYE MEADS

RSPB/Hertfordshire & Middlesex Wildlife Trust.
Location: TL 387 099. Take Hoddesdon turn off A10 and follow brown duck signs. Near Rye House railway station.
Access: Open every day 10am-5pm (or dusk if earlier), except Christmas Day and Boxing Day.
Facilities: Disabled access and toilets. Drinks machine, staffed reception, classrooms, picnic area, car park, bird feeding area. Nature trails, hides. RSPB reserve has close-circuit TV on Kingfisher and Common Tern nests in summer.
Public transport: Rail (Rye House) 55 metres, bus (310) stops 600 metres from entrance.
Habitat: Marsh, willow scrub, pools, scrapes, lagoons and reedbed.
Key birds: *Summer:* Breeding Tufted Duck, Gadwall, Common Tern, Kestrel, Kingfisher, nine species of warblers. *Winter:* Bittern, Shoveler, Water Rail, Teal, Snipe, Jack Snipe, Redpoll and Siskin.
Other notable flora and fauna: Fen vegetation, invertebrates and reptiles.
Contact: RSPB Rye Meads Visitor Centre, Rye Road, Stanstead Abbotts, Herts, SG12 8JS. 01992 708 383;

7. TRING RESERVOIRS

All four reservoirs - British Waterways / Herts & Middlesex Wildlife Trust / Friends of Tring Res. WTW lagoon - Thames Water/FoTR.
Location: Wilstone Res. SP 905 134. Other reservoirs SP 920 135. WTW Lagoon SP 923 134 adjacent to Marsworth Res. Reservoirs 1.5 miles due N of Tring, all accessible from B489 which crosses A41 Aston Clinton by-pass. NB: exit from by-pass only southbound
Access: Reservoirs open at all times. Events need to be cleared with British Waterways. WTW Lagoon & Hide — open at all times by permit from FoTR. Coaches can only drop off and pick up, for advice contact FoTR. Wilstone Res. has restricted height access of 2.1 metres Disabled access available for Startops & Marsworth Reservoirs from Car park, as well as FoTR Lagoon Hide.
Facilities: Café and Pubs adjacent to Startops Res. car park, safe parking for cycles. Wilstone Res.: Pub 0.5 mile away in village. Cafe and farm shop 0.25 mile from car park. Hides on all reservoirs.
Public transport: Buses from Aylesbury & Tring including a weekend service, tel. 0871 200 2233. Tring station is 2.5 miles away via canal towpath.
Habitat: Four reservoirs with surrounding woodland, scrub and meadows. Two of the reservoirs have extensive reedbeds. WTW Lagoon with islands and dragonfly scrape, surrounding hedgerows and scrub.
Key birds: *Spring/summer:* Breeding water birds, Common Terns and heronry. Regular Hobby, Black Terns and Red Kite, warblers including Cetti's. Occasional Marsh Harrier, Osprey.
Autumn/winter passage: Waders, occasional White-winged Black Tern. *Winter:* Gull roost, large wildfowl flocks, bunting roosts, Bittern.
Other notable flora and fauna: Black poplar trees seen from banks, some locally rare plants in damp areas. 18 species of dragonfly include black-tailed skimmer, ruddy darter and emerald damselfly. Holly blue and specked wood butterflies. Chinese water deer, Daubenton's, Natterer's and both pipistrelle bats.
Contact: Herts & Middsx Wildlife Trust: see Directory entry, FoTR: see Directory entry, www.fotr.org.uk, British Waterways, 510-524 Elder House, Eldergate, Milton Keynes MK9 1BW. 01908 302500, e-mail: enquiries.southeast@britishwaterways.co.uk www.waterscape.com

Norfolk

1. CLEY MARSHES NNR

Norfolk Wildlife Trust.
Location: TG 054 441. NWT Cley Marshes is situated four miles N of Holt on A149 coast road, half a mile E of Cley-next-the-Sea. Visitor centre and car park on inland side of road.
Access: Open all year round, except Christmas Day. Visitor centre open Apr-Oct (10am-5pm daily), Nov-early Dec (10am-4pm Wed-Sun). Cost: adults £3.75, children under 16 free. NWT members free. Out of season, obtain permit from Watcher's Cottage, 400m along coast road towards Cley village. No dogs.
Facilities: Environmentally-friendly visitor centre incorporates an observation area, interactive interpretation including a remote controllable wildlife camera, a café, and sales area. Five hides (with excellent wheelchair access) provide birdwatching within metres of the pools where the birds congregate. Audio trail. Wildlife Detective Bumbags for children are free to hire. Boardwalk and information boards. Reserve leaflet.
Public transport: Coasthopper bus service stops outside, every two hours. Connections for train and bus services at Sheringham. Special discounts to visitors arriving by bus. Call Norfolk County Bus Information Line on 01603 223 800 for info.
Habitat: Reedbeds, salt and freshwater marshes, scrapes and shingle ridge with international reputation as one of the finest birdwatching sites in Britain.
Key birds: Bittern, Avocet, Marsh Harrier, Spoonbill, Bearded Tit and large numbers of wildfowl, including

NATURE RESERVES - EASTERN ENGLAND

Wigeon, Teal, Pintail and Brent Goose. Migrating waders such as Ruff and Temminck's Stint. Many rarities.
Contact: NWT, Bewick House, 22 Thorpe Road, Norwich, Norfolk NR1 1RY. 01263 740 008.
e-mail: admin@norfolkwildlifetrust.org.uk
www.wildlifetrust.org.uk.Norfolk

2. HICKLING BROAD NNR

Norfolk Wildlife Trust.
Location: TG 428 222. Approx four miles SE of Stalham, just off A149 Yarmouth Road. From Hickling village, follow the brown badger tourist signs into Stubb Road at the Greyhound Inn. Take first turning L to follow Stubb Road for another mile. Turn R at the end for the nature reserve. Car park is ahead of you.
Access: Open all year. Visitor centre open Apr-Sep (10am-5pm daily). Admission charge for non-NWT members. No dogs.
Facilities: Visitor centre, boardwalk trail through reedbeds, birdwatching hides, wildlife gift shop, refreshments, picnic site, toilets, coach parking, car parking, disabled access to broad, boardwalk and toilets. Groups welcome. Water trail mid-May to mid-Sept (extra charge — booking essential).
Public transport: Morning bus service only Mon-Fri from Norwich (Neaves Coaches) Cromer to North Walsham (Sanders). Buses stop in Hickling village, a 25 minute walk away.
Habitat: Hickling is the largest and wildest of the Norfolk Broads with reedbeds, grazing marshes and wide open skies.
Key birds: Marsh Harriers, Bittern, warblers. From October to March Stubb Mill provides excellent views of raptors flying in to roost. Likely birds include Marsh Harriers, Hen Harriers, Merlins, Cranes and Pink-footed Geese.
Other notable flora and fauna: Swallowtail butterfly, Norfolk hawker (rare dragonfly)

Contact: John Blackburn, Hickling Broad Visitor Centre, Stubb Road, Hickling, NR12 0BW.
e-mail: johnb@norfolkwildlifetrust.co.uk
www.norfolkwildlifetrust.org.uk

3. HOLKHAM NNR

Natural England (Norfolk and Suffolk Team).
Location: TF 890 450. From Holkham village turn N off A149 down Lady Anne's Drive to park.
Access: Unrestricted, but keep to paths and avoid grazing marshes and farmland. Car parks at Burnham Overy (free), Lady Anne's Drive and Wells Beach Road.
Facilities: Two hides. Disabled access.
Public transport: Bus Norbic Norfolk bus information line 0845 3006 116.
Habitat: Sandflats, dunes, marshes, pinewoods.
Key birds: *Passage:* Migrants. *Winter:* Wildfowl, inc. Brent, Pink-footed and White-fronted Geese. *Summer:* Breeding Little Tern.
Other notable flora and fauna: Seablite bushes, attractive to incoming migrant birds, sea aster and sea lavender.
Contact: M. Rooney, Hill Farm Offices, Main Road, Holkham, Wells-next-the-Sea, Norfolk NR23 1AB. 01328 711 183; Fax 01328 711 893.

4. HOLME BIRD OBSERVATORY

Norfolk Ornithologists' Association (NOA).
Location: TF 717 450. E of Hunstanton, signposted from A149. Access from Broadwater Road, Holme. The reserve and visitors centre are beyond the White House at the end of the track.
Access: Reserve open daily to members dawn to dusk; non-members (9am-5pm) by permit from the Observatory. Please keep dogs on leads in the reserve. Parties by prior arrangement.
Facilities: Accredited Bird Observatory operating

all year for bird ringing (new Heligoland trap), MV moth trapping and other scientific monitoring. Visitor centre, car park and five hides (seawatch hide reserved for NOA members), together with access to beach and coastal path.

Public transport: Coastal bus service runs from Hunstanton to Sheringham roughly every 30 mins but is seasonal and times may vary. Phone Norfolk Green Bus, 01553 776 980.

Habitat: In ten acres of diverse habitat: sand dunes, Corsican pines, scrub and reed-fringed lagoon make this a migration hotspot.

Key birds: Species list over 320. Ringed species over 150. Recent rarities have included Red Kite, Common Crane, Red-backed Shrike, Osprey, Yellow-browed, Pallas's, Greenish and Barred Warblers.

Contact: The warden, Holme Bird Observatory, Broadwater Road, Holme, Hunstanton, Norfolk PE36 6LQ. 01485 525 406. e-mail: info@noa.org.uk www.noa.org.uk

5. NUNNERY LAKES

British Trust for Ornithology.

Location: TL 873 815. On the S edge of Thetford, adjacent to the BTO's headquarters at The Nunnery. Main access point is via Nun's Bridges car park, across pedestrian bridge at TL 874 821.

Access: Open dawn to dusk. Public access along permissive paths. Keep dogs on leads at all times. Call reception in advance to arrange wheelchair access to the lakes and hide.

Facilities: Waymarked paths, information panels, bird hide, boardwalk through wet woodland. Pre-booked coaches can park in grounds.

Public transport: Thetford railway station approx 1 mile (0845 7484 950). Thetford bus terminal approx half a mile (0870 6082 608).

Habitat: Flood meadows, scrape, flooded gravel pits, scrub and woodland.

Key birds: Wide range of species present throughout the year including Grey Heron, Egyptian Goose, Kingfisher, Green Woodpecker. *Spring:* Passage waders, hirundines, Swift, passerines. *Summer:* Warblers, Cuckoo, Oystercatcher, Lapwing, Hobby. *Winter:* Goosander, Teal, Water Rail, Snipe, Siskin.

Other notable flora and fauna: Otter, brown hare, muntjac, grass snake, common lizard. Emperor dragonfly, red-eyed damselfly. Speckled wood and orange tip butterflies. Mossy stonecrop.

Contact: Chris Gregory, The British Trust for Ornithology, 01842 750 050. e-mail: chris.gregory@bto.org - www.bto.org

6. PENSTHORPE NATURE RESERVE AND GARDENS

Private ownership /Pensthorpe Conservation Trust.

Location: TG 950 295. Take A1067 Norwich road E from Fakenham. After 1 mile look for signs for Pensthorpe Nature Reserve & Gardens. Look for Brown Tourist signs from all major roads.

Access: Designated route for wheelchair users to both hides overlooking wader scrape. Paths are firm, but

those S of River Wensum can be muddy. Toilets for disabled at cafe and main toilet block. Designated Blue Badge parking. Admission charges (see website).

Facilities: Cafe. Shop sells bird food, nest boxes, natural history books and optical equipment.

Public transport: Bus stops at top of drive; Norfolk Green's X29 is an hourly service between Norwich and Fakenham. The X10 connects to King's Lynn; the 'Coast Hopper' service links Fakenham to the north Norfolk coast.

Habitat: Woodland, farmland, the River Wensum, eight large lakes, gardens and wildflower meadows.

Key birds: *Spring/summer:* Little Ringed Plover, Lapwing, Oystercatcher and Redshank breed, with Green Sandpipers and other waders on migration. Warblers include Reed and Sedge Warblers, Blackcap, Chiffchaff, Willow Warbler, Whitethroat and smaller numbers of Garden Warbler. Linnets nest in the gorse. Hobbies are over wader scrape and wildflower meadow, while Buzzards, Kestrels, Sparrowhawks and Barn Owls all breed. Marsh Harriers breed nearby. *Winter:* Large flocks of Wigeon and Teal, plus Shoveler and Gadwall. Birds of prey inc. Buzzard, Marsh Harrier and Peregrine. Bittern is regularly seen. The woodland and its feeders attract finches in winter including Brambling, Nuthatch and Treecreeper.

Other notable flora and fauna: 21 species of butterfly and 19 species of dragonfly. Southern marsh and common spotted orchid. Regular sightings updates on www.pensthorpe.com/wildlife/ sightings-board.htm

Contact: Pensthorpe Nature Reserve and Gardens, Fakenham Norfolk NR21 0LN. 01328 851 465. e-mail: info@pensthorpe.com www.pensthorpe.com

7. SCULTHORPE MOOR COMMUNITY NATURE RESERVE

Hawk and Owl Trust.

Location: TF 900 305. In Wensum Valley, just W of Fakenham, on A148 to King's Lynn, brown sign signposted 'Nature Reserve' opposite village of Sculthorpe. Follow Turf Moor Road to the Visitor and Education Centre.

Access: Open Tue-Sun plus Bank Holiday Mondays (except Christmas Day). April to September: Tues-Wed (8am-6pm), Thur-Sun (8am-dusk). October to March: Tues-Sun (8am-4pm). £3 suggested donation for adult visitors. A car park at visitor and education centre. Guide dogs only.

Facilities: Visitor and education centre open 9am-5pm Tuesday - Sunday, with adapted toilets, hot drinks dispenser, interpretive displays and live CCTV coverage from around the reserve. Base for specialist courses, school visits and other events. Reserve and 2 hides accessible to wheelchairs and buggies via a mile of boardwalk. Additional hide accessed by bark chipping path. Coach parking available.

Public transport: Norfolk Green (tel: 01553 776 980 website: www.norfolkgreen.co.uk) bus X8 Fakenham to King's Lynn stops at the end of Turf Moor Road. Sustrans no.1 cycle route from Harwich to Hull runs within 200 metres of the end of Turf Moor Road.

Habitat: Wetland reserve, with fen containing saw sedge (a European priority habitat), reedbed, wet woodland, pools, ditches and riverbank.

Key birds: More than 80 species recorded, including breeding Marsh Harrier, Barn Owl and Tawny Owl, visiting Buzzard, Goshawk, Hobby, Kestrel, Osprey, Sparrowhawk, also Water Rail, Kingfisher, Marsh Tit, Willow Tit and Golden Pheasant.

Other notable flora and fauna: Mammals include otter, water vole and roe deer, 19 species of dragonfly/damselfly, butterflies including white admiral, glow-worms, fungi including scarlet elf cup and a host of plants including marsh fern and saw sedge.

Contact: The Hawk and Owl Trust, Sculthorpe Moor Community Nature Reserve, Turf Moor Road, Sculthorpe, Fakenham, Norfolk NR21 9GN. 01328 856 788. e-mail: leanne.thomas@hawkandowl.org

8. SNETTISHAM

RSPB (Eastern England Office).

Location: TF 651 330. Car park two miles along Beach Road, signposted off A149 King's Lynn to Hunstanton, opposite Snettisham village.

Access: Open at all times. Dogs to be kept on leads. Two hides are suitable for wheelchairs. Disabled access is across a private road. Please phone office number for permit and directions. Coaches welcome, but please book in advance as a height barrier needs to be removed.

Facilities: Four birdwatching hides, connected by 3.5 mile reserve footpath. No toilets on site. Furthest hide c1.5 miles from car park.

Public transport: Nearest bus stop over two miles away.

Habitat: Intertidal mudflats, saltmarsh, shingle beach, brackish lagoons, and unimproved grassland/scrub. Highest tides best for good views of waders.

Key birds: *Autumn/winter/spring*: Waders (particularly Knot, Bar and Black-tailed Godwits, Dunlin, Grey Plover), wildfowl (particularly Pink-footed and Brent Geese, Wigeon, Gadwall, Goldeneye), Peregrine, Hen Harrier, Merlin, owls. Migrants in season.

Summer: Breeding Mediterranean Gull, Ringed Plover, Redshank, Avocet, Common Tern. Marsh Harrier regular.

Other notable flora and fauna: Yellow horned poppies and other shingle flora along the beach.

Contact: Jim Scott, RSPB, Barn A, Home Farm Barns, Common Road, Snettisham, King's Lynn, Norfolk PE31 7PD. 01485 542 689. e-mail: snettisham@rspb.org.uk www.rspb.org.uk

9. STRUMPSHAW FEN

RSPB (Eastern England Office).

Location: TG 33 06. Seven miles ESE of Norwich. Follow signposts. Entrance across level-crossing from car park, reached by turning sharp R and R again into Low Road from Brundall, off A47 to Great Yarmouth.

Access: Open dawn-dusk. RSPB members free, adults £2.50, children 50p, family £5. Guide dogs only.

Limited wheelchair access — please phone for advice.

Facilities: Toilets, reception hide and two other hides, five miles of trails.

Public transport: Brundall train station about one mile from reserve. Bus stops half a mile from reserve - contact NORBIC (0845 300 6116).

Habitat: Reedbed and reedfen, wet grassland and woodland.

Key birds: *Summer:* Bittern, Little Egret, Bearded Tit, Marsh Harrier, Hobby, Kingfisher, Cetti's Warbler and other reedbed birds. *Winter:* Bittern, wildfowl, Marsh and Hen Harrier.

Other notable flora and fauna: Rich fen flora inc marsh pea, milk parsley, marsh sowthistle, six species of orchid, inc marsh helleborine and narrow-leaved marsh orchid. Otter, Chinese water deer and water vole. Norfolk hawker, scarce chaser and variable damselfly among 20 dragonfly species. Swallowtail, white admiral and small heath butterflies.

Contact: Tim Strudwick, Staithe Cottage, Low Road, Strumpshaw, Norwich NR13 4HS. 01603 715 191. e-mail: strumpshaw@rspb.org.uk www.rspb.org.uk

10. TITCHWELL MARSH

RSPB (Eastern England Office).

Location: TF 749 436. E of Hunstanton, off A149.

Access: Wheelchairs available free of charge. All paths and trails suitable for wheelchairs. Reserve and hides open at all times. Coach parking — pre-booking essential. Coastal project work has caused restrictions to visitors - for latest info, call 01485 210 779 before visiting.

Facilities: New hides. Visitor centre and shop open every day 9.30am to 5pm (closes at 4pm between Nov 5 - Feb 10). Same opening times for tearoom. Visitor centre and tearoom closed on Christmas Day and Boxing Day.

Public transport: Phone Traveline East Anglia on 0871 200 22 33.

Habitat: Freshwater reedbed, brackish and fresh water lagoons, extensive salt marsh, dunes, sandy beach with associated exposed peat beds.

Key birds: Diverse range of breeding reedbed and wetland birds with good numbers of passage waders during late summer/autumn.

Spring/summer: Breeding Avocet, Bearded Tit, Bittern, Marsh Harrier, Reed Sedge and Cetti's Warbler, Redshank, Ringed Plover and Common Tern. *Summer/autumn*: Passage waders including Knot, Wood and Green Sandpiper, Little Stint, Spotted Redshank, Curlew Sandpiper and many more. *Winter*: Brent Goose, Hen/Marsh Harrier roost, Snow Bunting. Offshore Common and Velvet Scoter, Long-tailed Duck, Great Northern and Red-throated Divers.

Other notable flora and fauna: 25 species of butterfly, including all the common species plus Essex skipper and annual clouded yellow.
21 species of dragonfly, including small red-eyed damselfly. Good diversity of salt marsh plants including shrubby sea-blite (*suaeda vera*) and three species of sea lavender.

Contact: Centre Manager, Titchwell Marsh Reserve, King's Lynn PE31 8BB. Tel/Fax 01485 210 779. e-mail: titchwell@rspb.org.uk www.rspb.org.uk

11. WEETING HEATH

Norfolk Wildlife Trust.
Location: TL 756 881. Weeting Heath is signposted from the Weeting-Hockwold road, two miles W of Weeting near to Brandon in Suffolk. Nature reserve can be reached via B1112 at Hockwold or B1106 at Weeting.
Access: Open daily from Apr-Sep. Cost: adults £2.50, children free. NWT members free. Disabled access to visitor centre and hides.
Facilities: Visitor centre open daily Apr-Aug, birdwatching hides, wildlife gift shop, refreshments, toilets, coach parking, car park, groups welcome (book first).
Public transport: Train services to Brandon and bus connections (limited) from Brandon High Street.
Habitat: Breckland, grass heath.
Key birds: Stone Curlew, migrant passerines, Woodlark.
Contact: Bev Nichols, Norfolk Wildlife Trust, Bewick house, 22 Thorpe Road, Norwich NR1 1RY. 01603 625 540. e-mail: BevN@norfolkwildlifetrust.org.uk www.wildlifetrust.org.uk/Norfolk

12. WELNEY

The Wildfowl & Wetlands Trust.
Location: TL 546 944. Ten miles N of Ely, signposted from A10 and A1101.
Access: Open daily except Christmas Day. (Nov - Feb) Mon-Wed 10am - 5pm, Thurs-Sun 10am - 8pm; (Mar - Oct) Mon-Sun 9.30am - 5pm. Free admission

to WWT members, otherwise £7.30 (Adult), £5.50 (Concession), £3.60 (Child), £19.50 (Family). Wheelchair accessible. During wet winter, paths to remote hides may be flooded.
Facilities: Visitor centre (wheelchair-friendly), café open daily (Nov - Feb) Mon-Wed 10am - 4.30pm, Thurs-Sun 10am - 6.15pm; (Mar - Oct) Mon-Sun 9.30am - 4.30pm. Large, heated observatory, additional 5 hides. Free parking and coach parking. Provision for disabled visitors, e.g. reserved parking, wheelchairs for hire (1 electric scooter and 2 manual chairs), lifts, disabled toilets, ramps, all access windows in hides.
Public Transport: Poor. Train to Littleport (6 miles away), but from there, taxi is only option or cycling – Welney is on the National Cycle route.
Habitat: 1,000 acres of washland reserve, spring damp meadows, winter wildfowl marsh (SPA, RAMSAR site, SSSI, SAC). Additional 200 acres of recently created wetland habitat next to visitor centre.
Key birds: Large numbers of wintering wildfowl are replaced by breeding waders, terns and warblers. *Winter:* Bewick and Whooper Swans, wintering wildfowl e.g. Wigeon. *Spring/summer:* Common Tern, Avocets, Lapwing, Black-Tailed Godwit, House Martin, occasional rarities.
Other notable flora and fauna: Key flora includes: purple loosestrife, meadow rue, mixed grasses. Dragonflies include scarce chaser, emperor, banded demoiselle, small red-eyed damselfly. Approx. 400 species of moth including goat moth. Butterflies include brown argus.
Contact: Emma Brand, Events & Marketing Officer, WWT, Hundred Foot Bank, Welney, Nr Wisbech, PE14 9TN. 01353 860 711. e-mail: info.welney@wwt.org.uk www.wwt.org.uk

Suffolk

1. BOYTON MARSHES

RSPB (Eastern England Office).
Location: TM 387 475. Approx. seven miles E of Woodbridge. Follow B1084 to village of Butley. Turn R and follow road through to Capel St. Andrew. Turn L and follow road towards Boyton village. Approximately quarter mile before village, bear L down concrete track on sharp right-hand turn.
Access: Open at all times. Entrance free but donations welcome. Public footpath on site not suited to wheelchair use.
Facilities: Car park too small for coaches. No toilets or hides.
Public transport: None.
Habitat: 57 ha of coastal grazing marsh. Also saltmarsh.
Key birds: *Spring:* Breeding waders and wildfowl, such as Lapwing, Redshank, Shoveler and Gadwall. Spring migrants inc Yellow Wagtail and Whitethroat.

Barn and Little Owls. *Autumn:* Wintering wildfowl such as Teal and Wigeon. Migrating waders inc Whimbrel, Black-tailed Godwit and Greenshank. *Winter:* Wintering wildfowl and wading birds, including Pintail, Curlew, Dunlin and Redshank. Fieldfare, Redwing and Mistle Thrush.
Other notable flora and fauna: Grassland butterflies such as skippers, wall and meadow browns and dragonflies.
Contact: RSPB Havergate, Unit 3, Richmond Old Dairy, Gedgrave, Woodbridge, Suffolk IP12 2BU. 01394 450 732. www.rspb.org.uk/reserves/

2. BRADFIELD WOODS NNR

Suffolk Wildlife Trust.
Location: TL 935 581. W of Stowmarket. From J46 on A14 take road through Beyton and Hessett towards Felsham. Turn R on Felsham road towards Cargate. Wood and parking is on L.
Access: Often wet and muddy, Wheelchair/pushchair accessible in parts, please phone 01449 737 996 for advice. Dogs on leads only.

NATURE RESERVES - EASTERN ENGLAND

Facilities: Visitor centre (open at weekends, no toilets), local pubs. Three coloured trails of different lengths, trail guide available.
Habitat: Broadleaved woodland.
Key birds: Good range of woodland birds and migrant warblers.
Contact: Suffolk Wildlife Trust, Brooke House, The Green, Ashbocking, Ipswich, IP6 9JY. 01473 890 089.
e-mail: info@suffolkwildlife.cix.co.uk
www.wildlifetrust.org.uk/suffolk

3. CASTLE MARSHES

Suffolk Wildlife Trust.
Location: TM 471 904. Head E on the A146 from Beccles to Lowestoft. Take the first L turn after Three Horseshoes pub. Continue on the minor road which bends round to the R. Carry straight on – the road bends to the R again. The car park is on the L just after White Gables house.
Access: Public right of way. Unsuitable for wheelchairs. Stiles where path leaves the reserve. Unmanned level crossing is gated.
Facilities: None.
Public transport: Bus: nearest bus route is on the A146 Lowestoft to Beccles road. Tel: 0845 958 3358. Train: Beccles and Oulton Broad South on the Ipswich to Lowestoft line.
Habitat: Grazing marshes, riverbank.
Key birds: *Spring/summer:* Marsh Harrier, Cetti's Warbler, occasional Grasshopper Warbler. *Winter:* Hen Harrier, wildfowl, Snipe.
Contact: Trust HQ, 01473 890 089.
e-mail: info@suffolkwildlifetrust.org
www.suffolkwildlifetrust.org

4. DINGLE MARSHES NNR

Suffolk Wildlife Trust/RSPB.
Location: TM 48 07 20. Eight miles from Saxmundham. Follow brown signs from A12 to Minsmere and continue to Dunwich. Forest car park (hide) TM 467 710. Beach car park TM 479 707. The reserve forms part of the Suffolk Coast NNR.
Access: Open at all times. Access via public rights of way and permissive path along beach. Dogs on lead please. Coaches can park on beach car park.
Facilities: Toilets at beach car park, Dunwich. Hide in Dunwich Forest overlooking reedbed, accessed via Forest car park. Circular trail waymarked from car park.

Public transport: Via Coastlink, Dial-a-ride service to Dingle (01728 833 546) links to buses and trains.
Habitat: Grazing marsh, reedbed, shingle beach and saline lagoons
Key birds: *All year:* In reedbed, Bittern, Marsh Harrier, Bearded Tit. *Winter:* Hen Harrier, White-fronted Goose, Wigeon, Snipe, Teal on grazing marsh. *Summer:* Lapwing, Avocet, Snipe, Black-tailed Godwit, Hobby. Good for passage waders.
Other notable flora and fauna: Internationally important site for starlet sea anemone – the rarest sea anemone in Britain. Otter and water vole.
Contact: Alan Miller, Suffolk Wildlife Trust, Moonrakers, Back Road, Wenhaston, Halesworth Suffolk IP16 4AP. www.suffolkwildlife.co.uk
e-mail: alan.miller@suffolkwildlifetrust.org

5. HAVERGATE ISLAND

RSPB (Eastern England Office).
Location: TM 425 496. Part of the Orfordness-Havergate Island NNR on the Alde/Ore estuary. Orford is 17km NE of Woodbridge, signposted off the A12.
Access: Open Apr-Aug (1st & 3rd weekends and every Thu), Sep-Mar (normally 1st Sat every month, but no boat trips till March 2012 due to habitat management work). Book in advance through Minsmere RSPB visitor centre, tel 01728 648 281. Park in Orford at the large pay and display car park next to the quay.
Facilities: Toilets, picnic area, five birdwatching hides, viewing platform, visitor trail (approx 2km).
Public transport: Orford served by local buses (route 160). For timetable info, 0870 608 2608. Bus stop is 0.25 miles from quay.
Habitat: Shallow brackish water, lagoons with islands, saltmarsh, shingle beaches.
Key birds: *Summer:* Breeding gulls, terns, Avocet, Redshank and Oystercatcher. *Winter:* Wildfowl and waders.
Contact: RSPB Havergate Reserves, Unit 3, Richmond Old Dairy, Cedgrave, Woodbridge Suffolk IP12 2BU. 01394 450 732.

158

NATURE RESERVES - EASTERN ENGLAND

6. HEN REEDBED NNR

Suffolk Wildlife Trust.
Location: TM 470 770. Three miles from Southwold. Turn off A12 at Blythburgh and follow along A1095 for two miles where brown signs guide you to the car park. Not suitable for coaches. The reserve forms part of the Suffolk Coast NNR.
Access: Open at all times.
Facilities: Two hides and two viewing platforms on waymarked trails.
Public transport: Bus service between Halesworth and Southwold.
Habitat: Reedbed, grazing marsh, scrape and estuary.
Key birds: *Spring/summer*: Marsh Harrier, Bittern, Bearded Tit, Hobby, Lapwing, Snipe, Avocet, Black-tailed and Bar-tailed Godwits. *Passage*: Wood and Green Sandpipers. *Winter*: Large flocks of waders on estuary, inc Golden and Grey Plovers, Bar and Black-tailed Godwits, Avocet and Dunlin.
Other notable flora and fauna: Otters and water voles frequently seen. Hairy dragonfly, occasional Norfolk hawker. Brown argus butterfly colony close to car park.
Contact: Alan Miller, www.suffolkwildlife.co.uk
e-mail: alan.miller@suffolkwildlifetrust.org

7. LACKFORD LAKES NATURE RESERVE

Suffolk Wildlife Trust.
Location: TL 803 708. Via track off N side of A1101 (Bury St Edmunds to Mildenhall road), between Lackford and Flempton. Five miles from Bury.
Access: Visitor centre open winter (10am-4pm), summer (10am-5pm) Wed to Sun (closed Mon and Tues). Tea and coffee facilities, toilets. Visitor centre and 4 hides with wheelchair access.
Facilities: Visitor centre with viewing area upstairs. Tea and coffee facilities, toilets. Eight hides. Coaches should pre-book.
Public transport: Bus to Lackford village (Bury St Edmunds to Mildenhall service) — walk from church.
Habitat: Restored gravel pit with open water, lagoons, islands, willow scrub, reedbeds.
Key birds: *Winter*: Bittern, Water Rail, Bearded Tit. Large gull roost. Wide range of waders and wildfowl (inc. Goosander, Pochard, Tufted Duck, Shoveler). *Spring/autumn*: Migrants, inc. raptors. Breeding Shelduck, Little Ringed Plover and reedbed warblers.
Other notable flora and fauna: 17 species of dragonfly including hairy dragonfly and emperor. Early marsh and southern orchid.
Contact: Lackford Lakes Visitor Centre, Lackford, Bury St Edmunds IP28 6HX. 01284 728 706. www.suffolkwildlifetrust.org
e-mail: lackford@suffolkwildlifetrust.org

8. LAKENHEATH FEN

RSPB (Eastern England Office).
Location: TL722 864. W of Thetford, straddling the Norfolk/Suffolk border. From A11, head N on B1112 to Lakenheath and then two miles further. Entrance is 200 metres after level crossing.

Access: Dawn to dusk, year round. Group bookings welcome. Wheelchair users can access visitor centre and a few points on the reserve.
Facilities: Visitor centre, toilets (inc disabled). Coach parking (must book). Hard and grass paths. Viewpoints. Picnic area with tables. Events programme.
Public transport: Limited weekend stops at Lakenheath train station.
Habitat: Reedbed, riverside pools, poplar woods.
Key birds: Principally a site for nesting migrants but ducks and some wild swans in winter. *Spring*: Marsh Harrier, Crane. *Summer*: Bittern, Golden Oriole, Hobby, Reed and Sedge Warblers. *Autumn*: Harriers, Bearded Tit. *Winter*: Ducks, swans, Peregrine.
Other notable flora and fauna: More than 15 species of dragonflies and damselflies, inc hairy dragonfly and scarce chaser. Range of fenland plants e.g. water violet, common meadow rue and fen ragwort. Roe deer, otter and water vole.
Contact: Becky Pitman (Information Officer), Visitor Centre, RSPB Lakenheath Fen, Lakenheath, Norfolk IP27 9AD. 01842 863 400. www.rspb.org.uk/reserves/ e-mail: lakenheath@rspb.org.uk

9. LANDGUARD BIRD OBSERVATORY

Landguard Conservation Trust
Location: TM 283 317. Road S of Felixstowe to Landguard Nature Reserve and Fort.
Access: Visiting by appointment.
Facilities: Migration watch point and ringing station.
Public transport: Call for advice.
Habitat: Close grazed turf, raised banks with holm oak, tamarisk, etc.
Key birds: Unusual species and common migrants.
Other notable flora and fauna: 18 species of dragonfly and 29 species of butterfly have been recorded on the site. Several small mammal species plus sightings of cetaceans and seals off-shore.
Contact: Landguard Bird Observatory, View Point Road, Felixstowe, Suffolk IP11 3TW. 01394 673 782. e.mail: landguardbo@yahoo.co.uk www.lbo.co.uk

10. MINSMERE

RSPB (Eastern England Regional Office)
Location: TM 452 680. Six miles NE of Saxmundham. From A12 at Yoxford or Blythburgh. Follow brown tourist signs via Westleton village. Car park is two miles from the village.
Access: Open every day except Dec 25/26. Visitor centre open 9am-5pm (9am-4pm Nov-Jan). Shop and tea-room open from 10am. Free entry to visitor centre. Nature trails free to RSPB/Wildlife Explorer members, otherwise £5 adults, £1.50 children, £3 concession, family £10. Site partially accessible to wheelchairs.
Facilities: Car park, hides, toilets (inc disabled and nappy changing), visitor centre with RSPB shop and tearoom. Family activity packs. Volunteer guides. Guided walks and family events (see website for details). Educational programme. Coaches by

appointment only (max two per day, not bank holidays).
Public transport: Train to Saxmundham or Darsham (6 miles) then Coastlink (book in advance on 01728 833 526).
Habitat: Coastal lagoons, 'the scrape', freshwater reedbed, grazing marsh, vegetated dunes, heathland, arable reversion and woodland.
Key birds: *All year:* Marsh Harrier, Bearded Tit, Bittern, Cetti's and Dartford Warblers, Little Egret, Green and Great Spotted Woodpeckers. *Summer:* Breeding Hobby, Avocet, Lapwing, Redshank, Common, Sandwich and Little Terns, Mediterranean Gull, Sand Martin, warblers, Nightingale, Nightjar, Woodlark, Redstart (scarce).
Winter: Wildfowl inc White-fronted Goose, Bewick's Swan, Smew, Hen Harrier (scarce), Water Pipit, Siskin.
Autumn/spring: Passage waders inc Black-tailed Godwit, Spotted Redshank, Ruff. Regular Wryneck, Red-backed Shrike, Yellow-browed Warbler.
Other notable flora and fauna: Red and muntjac deer, otter, water vole, badger. Dragonflies inc emperor, Norfolk hawker and small red-eyed damselfly. Butterflies inc purple and green hairstreaks, brown argus, silver-studded blue. Adder. Antlion. Marsh mallow, southern marsh orchid. Shingle flora.
Contact: RSPB Minsmere, Westleton, Saxmundham, Suffolk, IP17 3BY. 01728 648 281.
e-mail: minsmere@rspb.org.uk
www.rspb.org.uk/minsmere

11. NORTH WARREN & ALDRINGHAM WALKS

RSPB (Eastern England Office).
Location: TM 468 575. Directly N of Aldeburgh on Suffolk coast. Use signposted main car park on beach.
Access: Open at all times. Please keep dogs under close control. Beach area suitable for disabled.
Facilities: Three nature trails, leaflet available from Minsmere RSPB. Toilets in Aldeburgh and Thorpeness. Three spaces for coaches at Thorpeness beach car park.
Public transport: Bus service to Aldeburgh. First Eastern Counties (08456 020 121). Nearest train station is Saxmundham.
Habitat: Grazing marsh, lowland heath, reedbed, woodland.
Key birds: *Winter:* White-fronted Goose, Tundra Bean Goose, Wigeon, Shoveler, Teal, Gadwall, Pintail, Snow Bunting.
Spring/summer: Breeding Bittern, Marsh Harrier, Hobby, Nightjar, Woodlark, Nightingale, Dartford Warbler.
Other notable flora and fauna: Hairy dragonfly, Norfolk hawker and red-eyed damselfly, green and purple hairstreak butterflies and southern marsh orchid.
Contact: Dave Thurlow, RSPB Minsmere, Westleton, Saxmundham, Suffolk IP17 3BY. 01728 648 082; (M)07980 278 586. e-mail: dave.thurlow@rspb.org.uk

12. REDGRAVE AND LOPHAM FENS

Suffolk Wildlife Trust.
Location: TM 05 07 97. Five miles from Diss, signposted and easily accessed from A1066 and A143 roads.
Access: Open all year (10am - 5pm summer, 10am - 4pm winter), dogs strictly on short leads only. Visitor centre open all year at weekends and bank holidays: call for details on 01379 688 333. Circular trails can be muddy after rain (not wheelchair accessible).
Facilities: Visitor centre with café, gift shop, toilets, including disabled toilet, car park with coach space. Bike parking area, wheelchair access to visitor centre and viewing platform/short boardwalk. Regular events and activities — call for details or look on website.
Public transport: Buses and trains to Diss — Coaches to local villages of Redgrave and South Lopham from Diss. Simonds Coaches 01379 647 300 and Galloway Coaches 01449 766 323.
Habitat: Calcareous fen, wet acid heath, river corridor, scrub and woodland
Key birds: *All year:* Water Rail, Snipe, Teal, Shelduck, Gadwall, Woodcock, Sparrowhawk, Kestrel, Great Spotted and Green Woodpeckers, Tawny, Little and Barn Owls, Kingfisher, Reed Bunting, Bearded Tit, Willow and Marsh Tits, Linnet.
Summer: Reed, Sedge, Grasshopper and Willow Warblers, Whitethroat, Hobby plus large Swallow and Starling roosts. *Winter/ occasionals on passage:* Marsh Harrier, Greenshank, Green Sandpiper, Shoveler, Pintail, Garganey, Jack Snipe, Bittern, Little Ringed Plover, Oystercatcher, Wheatear, Stonechat.
Other notable flora and fauna: Otter, water vole, roe, muntjac and Chinese water deer, stoat, pipistrelle and natterer's bats. Great crested newt, grass snake, adder, slow worm, common lizard. More than 270 flowering plants inc water violet, saw sedge, black bog-rush and bladderwort. 19 species of dragonfly inc emperor, hairy dragonfly, black-tailed skimmer and emerald damselfly. Visit website for more species information.
Contact: Bev Blackburn (visitor centre co-ordinator), Redgrave and Lopham Fens, Low Common Road, South Lopham, Diss, Norfolk IP22 2HX. 01379 688 333. e-mail: redgrave.centre@suffolkwildlifetrust.org
www.suffolkwildlife.co.uk

13. SNAPE

RSPB (Eastern England Regional Office)
Location: TM393574. Five miles S of Saxmundham. From A12 take A1094 towards Aldeburgh. At Snape crossroads, turn right on B1069. Car park is at Snape Maltings, half a mile after passing through Snape village.
Access: Snape Warren and riverside walks open at all times. No access to Snape Wetlands. RSPB Information Centre open Thursday to Tuesday 10am to 4pm. (Check website for winter opening times). Free entry to Information centre and Snape Warren. Shops and cafes at Snape Maltings open daily 10am to

5.30pm (to 6pm in August or 5pm in winter)
Facilities: Car park, toilets, shops, cafes, pub, art galleries and concert hall at Snape Maltings. RSPB Information Centre at Snape Maltings. Guided walks and family activities.
Public transport: Train to Saxmundham (5 miles distant), then taxi or bus. Anglia Buses 165 from Aldeburgh and Leiston to Woodbridge and Ipswich. Some routes via Saxmundham.
Habitat: Estuary, heathland, grazing marsh, tidal reedbed, freshwater reedbed creation.
Key birds: *All year*: Little Egret, Shelduck, Marsh Harrier, Avocet, Barn Owl, Kingfisher, Woodlark, Cetti's and Dartford Warblers. *Breeding*: Hobby, Cuckoo, Hirundines, Warblers, including Grasshopper Warbler and Lesser Whitethroat. *Winter*: Wigeon, Hen Harrier (rare), Water Rail, Black-tailed Godwit, Curlew, Bearded Tit, Starling Roost. *Autumn/spring*: Waders, especially Black-tailed Godwit, Whimbrel, Common Sandpiper.
Other notable flora and fauna: Otter, common seal, adder, slow worm. Dragonflies, including banded demoiselle, emperor. Butterflies. Saltmarsh flora.

Contact: RSPB Snape nature reserve, c/o RSPB Minsmere, Westleton, Saxmundham, Suffolk, IP17 3BY. 01728 687 192. e-mail: snape@rspb.org.uk www.rspb.org.uk/snape

14. WALBERSWICK
Natural England (Suffolk Team).
Location: TM 475 733. Good views from B1387 and from lane running W from Walberswick towards Westwood Lodge; elsewhere keep to public footpaths or shingle beach.
Access: Parties and coach parking by prior arrangement.
Facilities: Hide on S side of Blyth estuary, E of A12.
Public transport: Call for advice.
Habitat: Tidal estuary, fen, freshwater marsh and reedbeds, heath, mixed woodland, carr.
Key birds: *Spring/summer*: Marsh Harrier, Bearded Tit, Water Rail, Bittern, Nightjar. *Passage/winter*: Wildfowl, waders and raptors.
Contact: The Warden, Natural England, Regent House, 110 Northgate Street, Bury St Edmunds IP33 1HP. 01502 676 171.

Northern England

Cheshire, Cleveland, Cumbria, Co Durham, Lancashire, Manchester (Greater), Merseyside, Northumberland, Tyne & Wear, East Yorkshire, North Yorkshire, South Yorkshire, West Yorkshire

Cheshire

1. DEE ESTUARY (BURTON MERE WETLANDS)
RSPB Dee Estuary Office, (formerly known as Inner Marsh Farm).
Location: SJ 31927 73914 Located on the Wirral. From Chester High Road (A540) follow signs for Burton Mere Wetlands, turning down Puddington Lane the reserve's entrance is just outside Burton Village.
Access: Open between 9am and 9pm (or dusk if earlier) each day. £4 admission for non-RSPB members. Guide dogs only.
Facilities: 97-berth car park, three hides overlooking a series of pools and wetland area. Wheelchair access to much of footpath network and two of the hides. Toilets including disabled facilities. Picnic tables. Guided walks available.
Public Transport: Trains stop at Neston and Hooton. Buses between Neston and Hooton stop at Burton post office, from where it is a 600m walk to reserve entrance. Contact Traveline on 0871 200 2233.
Habitat: Former farm and fishery now converted to wetland and meadow habitats.
Key birds: *All year*: Little Egret. Great Spotted and Green Woodpecker *Spring/summer*: Avocet, Grasshopper, Lesser Whitethroat and other commoner warblers, passage Black-tailed Godwit, Spotted Redshank and regular Mediterranean Gulls. Hobby, Marsh Harrier, Spoonbill. *Autumn*: Passage waders (inc Little Stint, Ruff, Spotted Redshank, Green, Curlew and Wood Sandpipers). *Winter*: Linnet, Brambling, Fieldfare, Redwing, Whooper and Bewick's Swans, Teal, Water Rail, Hen Harrier.
Other notable flora and fauna: Extensive butterfly list. Pipistrelle, noctule, Daubenton's bats, water vole, wide array of orchids. Red-eyed damselfly.
Contact: Colin E Wells, Burton Point Farm, 0151 3367 681. e-mail:colin.wells@rspb.org.uk

2. DEE ESTUARY (PARKGATE)
RSPB Dee Estuary Office.
Location: SJ 27370 78952. On W side of Wirral, S of Birkenhead. View high tide activity from Old Baths car park near Boathouse pub, Parkgate off B5135.
Access: Open at all times. Viewing from public

footpaths and car parks. Please do not walk on the saltmarsh, the tides are dangerous and to avoid disturbance of nesting birds.
Facilities: Car park, picnic area, group bookings, guided walks, special events, wheelchair access. Toilets at Parkgate village opposite the Square.
Public transport: Bus to Parkgate every hour. Rail station at Neston, two miles from reserve.
Habitat: Estuary, saltmarsh, pools, mud, sand.
Key birds: *Spring/summer/autumn:* Little Egret, Greenshank, Spotted Redshank, Curlew Sandpiper, Skylark, Reed Bunting. *Winter:* Pink-footed Goose, Shelduck, Teal, Wigeon, Pintail, Oystercatcher, Black-tailed Godwit, Curlew, Redshank, Merlin, Peregrine, Water Rail, Short-eared Owl, Hen Harrier.
Other notable flora and fauna: On very high tides, the incoming water displaces several mammal species inc pygmy shrew, water shrew, harvest mouse, weasel and stoat.
Contact: Colin E Wells, Burton Point Farm, 0151 3367 681; e-mail:colin.wells@rspb.org.uk

3. GOWY MEADOWS

Shell UK/Cheshire Wildlife Trust.
Location: SJ 435 740. Lies alongside River Gowy at Thornton-le-Moors, N of Chester, between A5117 and M56.
Access: Park next to church in Thornton-le-Moors and take footpath opposite into reserve. Open all year.
Facilities: None.
Public transport: The Arriva bus service stops on the Thornton Green Lane opposite the church.
Habitat: 410 acres of lowland grazing marsh, rich in flora.
Key birds: Approx 100 species recorded, inc Barn Owl, Buzzard, Peregrine, Merlin, Hobby. *Spring/summer:* Wildfowl, warblers, Whinchat, Green Sandpiper, Lapwing, Jack Snipe, Snipe. *Winter:* Pintail, Shoveler, Reed Bunting. *Passage:* Stonechat, Wheatear.
Other notable flora and fauna: Stronghold of endangered silver

water beetle. 14 species of dragonfly; 17 species of butterfly.
Contact: Trust HQ, 01948 820 728; e-mail: info@cheshirewt.org.uk
www.cheshirewildlifetrust.co.uk

4. MOORE NATURE RESERVE

Waste Recycling Group.
Location: SJ 577 854. SW of Warrington, via A56 Warrington-to-Chester road. At traffic lights at Higher Walton, follow signs for Moore. Take Moore Lane over swing bridge to reserve. Sat Nav users follow WA4 6XE.
Access: Open all year. One hide suitable for wheelchairs, other parts of site unsurfaced or gravel paths.
Facilities: Car park, coaches by prior arrangement. Paths, ten bird hides, bird feeding area. Guided walks available on request. See website for wildlife events throughout the year.
Public transport: 62 and 66 buses from Warrington and Runcorn stop in Moore village, less than 1km from reserve. Call 0870 608 2608 for times.
Habitat: Wetland, woodland, grasslands, five pools.
Key birds: More than 130 species every year, inc. occasional rarities. *Spring/summer:* Breeding wildfowl and waders, warblers. *Autumn/winter:* Wide variety of wildfowl, Bittern. Also good for gulls, woodpeckers, owls and raptors. See website for list and latest sightings.
Other notable flora and fauna: Wildfowers including some rarities. Great crested newts.
Contact: Paul Cassidy/Brian Webber, c/o Waste Recycling Centre, 01925 444 689.
e-mail: paul.cassidy@wrg.co.uk
www.wrg.co.uk/moorenaturereserve

5. RUDHEATH WOODS NATURE RESERVE

Cheshire Wildlife Trust.
Location: SJ 740 700. Located five miles S of Knutsford, at Allostock. From A50, turn W on to Wash Lane. Park in an unmade track which heads S after 0.25 miles. The track continues as a bridle path along the reserve, which is accessed over stiles and along various paths.
Access: Open all year.
Facilities: None.
Public transport: None.
Habitat: Heathland, wet woodland.
Key birds: *Spring/summer:* Chiffchaff, other warblers, possible Hobby. *Autumn:* Waders, possible Greenshank, Green Sandpiper. *Winter:* Siskin, Redpoll, Snipe. *All year:* All three woodpeckers, Willow Tit.
Contact: Cheshire Wildlife Trust, 01948 820 728; e-mail:info@cheshirewt.org.uk
www.cheshirewildlifetrust.co.uk

6. SANDBACH FLASHES

Privately owned.
Location: SJ 720 590. Series of flashes S and W of Sandbach. Leave M6 at junction 17 for Sandbach.
Access: No public access - view from roadside. Elton Hall Flash from new road at SJ 716 595; The Moat (also known as Foden's Flash) from road at SJ 730 614; Watch Lane Flash from car park at SJ 728 608.
Facilities: None. **Public transport:** None.
Habitat: Fresh and brackish water, reedbed, carr woodland, inland saltmarsh.
Key birds: Wildfowl including Mallard, Teal, Shoveler, Wigeon, Gadwall, Barnacle Goose, Shelduck, occasional Garganey, Mandarin. Waders inc Black-tailed Godwit, Lapwing, Common Sandpiper, Dunlin, Green Sandpiper, Curlew, Snipe, Ringed and Little Ringed Plovers, Little Stint, Ruff, Oystercatcher, Greenshank, Spotted Redshank. Raptors inc Sparrowhawk, Kestrel, Buzzard, Hobby. Warblers: Lesser Whitethroat, Blackcap, Garden Warbler. Ravens, Water Rail, Kingfisher, Wheatear, Stonechat, Turtle Dove, Swift, Yellow Wagtail. Many rarities.

7. WOOLSTON EYES

Woolston Eyes Conservation Group.
Location: SJ 654 888. E of Warrington between the River Mersey and Manchester Ship Canal. Off Manchester Road down Weir Lane or from Latchford to end of Thelwall Lane. Do not park at the bottom end of Weir Lane.
Access: Open all year. Permits required from Chairman, £10 each, £20 per family (see below).
Facilities: Toilets are available on No 3 bed.
Public transport: Buses along A57 nearest stop to Weir Lane, or Thelwall Lane, Latchford. The bus to Weir Lane, Martinscroft (to access reserve from the N) along A57 is No3 from Central Station and Terminus. To access reserve from S take either No1 or No2 to Westy, Whitley Avenue and walk to the East end of Thelwall Lane. For further info go to www.warringtonboroughtransport.co.uk
Habitat: Wetland, marsh, scrubland, wildflower meadow areas.
Key birds: Breeding Black-necked Grebe, warblers (including Grasshopper Warbler), all raptors (Merlin, Peregrine, Marsh Harrier). SSSI for wintering wildfowl, many duck species breed.
Other notable flora and fauna: 19 mammal species recorded, plus 241 species of lepidoptera, four species of bat. Wide variety of butterflies and 22 species of dragonfly. Notable plants include marsh and bee orchids, helleborine, snakeshead fritillary and cowslip.
Contact: BR Ankers, Chairman, 9 Lynton Gardens, Appleton, Cheshire, WA4 1PD. 01925 267 355. Please enclose A5 S.A.E. for reply; www.woolstoneyes.co.uk

Cumbria

1. CAMPFIELD MARSH

RSPB (Northern England).
Location: NY 197 615. At North Plain Farm, on S shore of Solway estuary, W of Bowness-on-Solway. Signposted on unclassified coast road from B5307 from Carlisle.
Access: Open at all times, no charge. Disabled visitors can drive to wheelchair-friendly hide to view high-tide roosts.
Facilities: Hide overlooking wetland areas, along nature trail (1.5 miles). No toilets or visitor centre.
Public transport: Bus No 93 from Carlisle terminates at reserve's eastern end — 1.5 mile walk to North Plain Farm.
Habitat: Saltmarsh/intertidal areas, open water, peat bog, wet grassland.
Key birds: *Winter:* Waders and wildfowl include Barnacle and Pinkfooted Geese, Shoveler, Scaup, Grey Plover. *Spring/summer:* Breeding Lapwing, Curlew, Redshank, Snipe, Tree Sparrow and warblers. *Spring/autumn:* Passage waders such as Black-tailed Godwit, Whimbrel. Look for Pomarine, Arctic, Great and Long-tailed Skuas over the Solway. *Autumn/winter:* Up to 10,000 Oystercatchers among large roosting wader flocks. Hen Harrier.
Other notable flora and fauna: Roe deer, brown hare. Bog rosemary, bog asphodel, sundews and cotton grass. Large numbers of dragonflies (inc azure and emerald damselflies and four-spotted chaser).
Contact: RSPB Office, North Plain Farm, Bowness-on-Solway, Wigton, Cumbria, CA7 5AG.
e-mail: dave.blackledge@rspb.org.uk

2. DRUMBURGH MOSS NNR

Cumbria Wildlife Trust.
Location: NY 255 586 (OS Landranger 85). From Carlisle city centre, head W on B5307 to Kirkbride. After about one mile, turn R to Burgh by Sands. Follow road for 7.5 miles to Drumburgh village. Turn L by post office, continue down track and park on R past Moss Cottage.
Access: Open all year. Difficult terrain, so it is best to walk on bunds built to re-wet the site.
Facilities: None.
Public transport: Bus service between Carlisle and Bowness-on-Solway stops in Drumburgh.
Habitat: Raised bog, woodland, grassland.
Key birds: *Summer:* Red Grouse, Curlew, Grasshopper Warbler. *Autumn:* Short-eared Owl. *Winter:* Geese from the Solway.
Other notable flora and fauna: Large heath butterfly, emperor moth, adder and lizards, roe deer, brown hare. Specialist plants include 13 species of sphagnum moss, sundews, cotton grass and bog rosemary.
Contact: Trust HQ, 01539 816 300;
e-mail: mail@cumbriawildlifetrust.org.uk
www.cumbriawildlifetrust.org.uk

NATURE RESERVES - NORTHERN ENGLAND

3. FOULNEY ISLAND

Cumbria Wildlife Trust.
Location: SD 246 640. Three miles SE of Barrow town centre on the A5087 from Barrow or Ulverston. At a roundabout 2.5 miles S of Barrow take a minor road through Rampside to Roa Island. Turn L into reserve car park. Walk to main island along stone causeway.
Access: Open all year. Access restricted to designated paths during bird breeding season. Slitch Ridge is closed at this time. No dogs allowed during bird breeding season. The island may be cut off for several hours around high-tide, so please consult tide tables.
Facilities: None.
Public transport: Bus: regular service from Barrow to Roa Island.
Habitat: Shingle, sand, grassland.
Key birds: *Summer*: Arctic and Little Terns, Oystercatcher, Ringed Plover, Eider Duck. *Winter*: Brent Goose, Redshank, Dunlin, Sanderling.
Other notable flora and fauna: Sea campion, yellow horned poppy. Six spot burnet and common blue butterfly.
Contact: Trust HQ, 01539 816 300;
e-mail: mail@cumbriawildlifetrust.org.uk
www.cumbriawildlifetrust.org.uk

4. HAWESWATER

RSPB and United Utilities.
Location: NY 470 108. Golden Eagle viewpoint, near Bampton, 5 miles NW of Shap, off A6. Turn L in Bampton to car park at S of reservoir.
Access: The viewpoint is always open but only manned as below. Visitors are asked not to go beyond the viewpoint. There is no wheelchair access.
Facilities: Golden Eagle viewpoint, open Saturday and Sunday, plus bank holidays, Apr to end Aug (11am-4pm), telescopes available. No coach parking.
Public transport: None.
Habitat: Fells with rocky streams, steep oak and birch woodlands.
Key birds: *Upland breeders*: Golden Eagle, Peregrine, Raven, Ring Ouzel, Curlew, Redshank, Snipe. *Woodlands*: Pied Flycatcher, Wood Warbler, Tree Pipit, Redstart, Buzzard, Sparrowhawk.
Contact: RSPB Office, 01931 713 376;
e-mail: haweswater@rspb.org.uk

5. ST BEES HEAD

RSPB (Northern England).
Location: NX 962 118. S of Whitehaven via the B5345 road to St Bees village.
Access: Open at all times, no charge. Access via coast-to-coast footpath. The walk to the viewpoints is long and steep in parts.
Facilities: Three viewpoints overlooking seabird colony. Public toilets in St Bees beach car park at entrance to reserve.
Public transport: Nearest trains at St Bees (0.5 mile).
Habitat: Three miles of sandstone cliffs up to 300 ft high.
Key birds: *Summer*: Largest seabird colony on

W coast of England: Guillemot, Razorbill, Puffin, Kittiwake, Fulmar and England's only breeding pairs of Black Guillemot.
Contact: North Plain Farm, 01697 351 330;
e-mail: dave.blackledge@rspb.org.uk
www.rspb.org.uk

6. SMARDALE GILL NNR

Cumbria Wildlife Trust.
Location: NY 727 070. NNR occupies a 6km stretch of the disused railway between Tebay and Darlington. Approx 2.5 miles NE of Ravenstonedale on A685 or 0.5 miles S of Kirkby Stephen station, take turning signed to Smardale. Cross over railway and turn L to junction, ignoring turn to Waitby. Cross over railway and turn L at junction ignoring sign for Smardale. Cross disused railway, turn L immediately and L again to car park.
Access: Railway line is open to all but non-members should obtain a permit before visiting other parts of the reserve.
Facilities: None.
Public transport: Train: nearest station Kirkby Stephen. Buses from here to Kendal, Brough and Sedburgh.
Habitat: Limestone grassland, river, ancient semi-natural woodland, quarry.
Key birds: *Summer*: Redstart, Pied Flycatcher, Wood Warbler and commoner woodland species. *All year*: Usual woodland birds, Buzzard, Sparrowhawk.
Other notable flora and fauna:
Scotch argus, northern brown argus, common blue and dark

164

green fritillary butterflies. Fragrant orchid, common rockrose, bluebell and bloody cranesbill. Red squirrel.
Contact: Trust HQ, 01539 816 300;
e-mail: mail@cumbriawildlifetrust.org.uk

7. SOUTH WALNEY

Cumbria Wildlife Trust.
Location: SD 215 620. Six miles S of Barrow-in-Furness. From Barrow, cross Jubilee Bridge onto Walney Island, turn L at lights. Continue through Biggar village to South End Caravan Park. Follow road for 1 mile to reserve.
Access: Open daily (10am-5pm) plus Bank Holidays. No dogs except assistance dogs. Day permits: £2 adults, 50p children. Cumbria Wildlife Trust members free.
Facilities: Toilets, nature trails, eight hides (two are wheelchair accessible), 200m boardwalk, cottage (sleeps 10) available to rent. Electric wheelchair for hire. Coach parking available.
Public transport: Bus service as far as Biggar.
Habitat: Shingle, lagoon, sand dune, saltmarsh.
Key birds: *Spring/autumn*: Passage migrants. *Summer*: 14,000 breeding pairs of Herring, Greater and Lesser Black-backed Gulls, Shelduck, Eider. *Winter*: Teal, Wigeon, Goldeneye, Redshank, Greenshank, Curlew, Oystercatcher, Knot, Dunlin, Merlin, Short-eared Owl, Twite.
Other notable flora and fauna: 450 species of flowering plants. Natterjack toad at North Walney.
Contact: The Warden, No 1 Coastguard Cottages, South Walney Nature Reserve, Walney Island, Barrow-in-Furness, Cumbria LA14 3YQ. 01229 471 066.
e-mail: mail@cumbriawildlifetrust.org.uk
www.cumbriawildlifetrust.org.uk

8. TALKIN TARN COUNTRY PARK

Location: NY544 591. Twelve miles E of Carlisle. From A69 E at Brampton, head S on B6413 for two miles. Talkin Tarn is on E just after level crossing.
Access: All year. Wheelchair access around tarn, two kissing gates accessible. Tearoom has lift. Coaches welcome.
Facilities: Tearoom open all year (10.30am-4pm). Monday to Wednesday, takeaway only, during winter. Dogs allowed around Tarn. Rowing boat hire at weekends and school holidays. Angling by day permit

(with closed season).
Public transport: Bus: infrequent. Tel: 0870 608 2608. Train: nearest station is Brampton Junction. Tel: 0845 748 4950. One mile away by footpath.
Habitat: Natural glacial tarn, mature oak/beech woodland, orchid meadow (traditionally managed), wet mire and farmland.
Key birds: *Spring/summer*: Pied Flycatcher, Spotted Flycatcher, Redstart, Chiffchaff, Wood Warbler. *Winter*: Grebes, Smew, Long-tailed Duck, Goosander, Gadwall, Wigeon, Brambling, swans.
Other notable flora and fauna: Common blue damselfly, common darter, small copper butterfly, otter, red squirrel.
Contact: Countryside Ranger, Talking Tarn Country Park, Tarn Road, Brampton CA8 1HN. 01697 73129.

9. WALNEY BIRD OBSERVATORY

Location: Walney Island, Barrow-in-Furness, Cumbria.
Access: Several areas, notably the golf course and airfield, are restricted but the island's narrow width means most sites are viewable from the road or footpaths. Access to South Walney Nature Reserve (10am-5pm) is along permitted trails.
Facilities: Monitoring and ringing of breeding and migrant birds occurs across the island, with ringing opportunities for qualified ringers. For availability write to Walney Bird Observatory (address below).
Public transport: Barrow-in-Furness connects to the rail network and local bus routes serve Walney Island. Routes 1 and 1A cover the central area while 6 and 6A cover the north end of the island. No bus route is available for the southern end.
Habitat: Estuarine, maritime, dunes, freshwater and brackish pools, scrub and farmland.
Key birds: Renowned Eider and gull colonies at south end. The winter months provide a wildfowl and wader spectacular across the island. Migrants aplenty appear during both passage periods — the island has a proven pedigree for attracting rare and unusual species.
Other notable flora and fauna: Famed for Walney geranium, but also important for coastal shingle species such as sea holly, sea rocket and sea kale. More than 500 species of moth recorded, inc sand dune specialities such as coast dart and sand dart.
Contact: Walney Bird Observatory, Coastguard Cottages, Walney Island, Barrow-in-Furness, Cumbria LA14 3YQ.

Co Durham

1. BEACON HILL AND HAWTHORN DENE MEADOW

Durham Wildlife Trust and National Trust
Location: NZ 427 458. Hawthorn Dene and Meadow located between Easington and Seaham on Durham coast. Leave A19 at Easington or Seaham and join B1432, turn into Hawthorn village. From N end of village, follow minor road E, signposted 'Quarry Traffic'. After quarter mile, road ends at two metal

gates, with a cottage and farmhouse on the right. Park on grass verge on opposite side to cottage, taking care not to obstruct gateways. Access is by foot taking the right-hand path. Access to Beacon Hill (NZ 440 455) is along coastal footpath or through southern end of Hawthorn Dene.
Access: Open all year, dogs on leads in spring.
Facilities: Information point. Footpaths.
Public transport: Regular bus services from Durham to Hawthorn.
Habitat: Extensive area of semi-natural habitat situated on magnesian limestone escarpment.

NATURE RESERVES - NORTHERN ENGLAND

Steep- sided ravine woodland and limeston(
grassland.
Key birds: *Summer*: Skylark (important conservation site), Twite, Linnet, Yellowhammer, Goldfinch, Whitethroat, Blackcap, Wren, Long-tailed Tit, Grasshopper Warbler, Reed Bunting, Green Woodpecker, Kestrel, Sparrowhawk. *Winter*: Wide variety of waders inc Turnstone, Purple Sandpiper, Redshank, Curlew, Oystercatcher. Seabirds inc Red-throated Diver, Common Scoter, Guillemot, Cormorant and Great Crested Grebe. *Passage*: Wheatear, Fieldfare, Redw Waxwing, Buzzard, Ringed Plover, Dunlin, I Lapwing.
Other notable flora and fauna: Good varie butterflies. Snowdrops, bluebells and numerous species of orchid grow here, including early purple, bird's nest, lesser butterfly and bee orchids. Grassland plants include field scabious, greater knapweed, wild carrot, cowslip and bee, fragrant, common spotted and northern marsh orchids. Roe deer, badger and brown hare.
Contact: Durham Wildlife Trust, 0191 584 3112.
e-mail: mail@durhamwt.co.uk www.durhamwt.co.uk

2. BISHOP MIDDLEHAM QUARRY

Durham Wildlife Trust.
Location: NZ 331 326. Half mile N of Bishop Middleham Village, to W of A177. Car parking restricted to two lay-bys on the west side of the road adjacent to the reserve entrances.
Access: Open all year. Car parking restricted to two lay-bys. Keep to footpaths, dogs on leads in spring.
Public transport: Regular bus service from Durham and Darlington to Coxhoe and Sedgefield.
Habitat: A large magnesian limestone quarry.
Key birds: Good range of farmland birds inc. Corn Bunting, Tree Sparrow, Willow Tit and Yellow Wagtail. Rare breeding record of Bee-eater.
Other notable flora and fauna: Butterflies including northern brown argus, dingy skipper, common blue, small heath, ringlet and small and large skippers. Internationally rare habitat, rich in orchid species such as pyramidal, common spotted, fragrant and bee plus large numbers of dark red helleborines. Other plants include blue moor grass, moonwort, autumn gentian and fairy flax.
Contact: Trust HQ, 0191 584 3112.
e-mail: mail@durhamwt.co.uk www.durhamwt.co.uk

3. HAMSTERLEY FOREST

Forestry Commission
Location: NZ 091 312. Eight miles W of Bishop Auckland. Main entrance is five miles from A68, S of Witton-le-Wear and signposted through Hamsterley village and Bedburn.
Access: Open all year. Toll charge (£3). Forest drive and car park close 8pm (dusk in winter). Visitor centre open weekdays (10am-4pm) and weekends (11am-5pm).

Facilities: Visitor Centre, tearoom, toilets, shop, access for disabled. Visitors should not enter fenced farmland.
Public transport: None.
Habitat: Commercial woodland, mixed and broadleaved trees.
Key birds: *Spring/summer*: Nightjar, Willow Warbler, Chiffchaff, Wood Warbler, Redstart, Pied Flycatcher. *Winter*: Redwing, Fieldfare. *All year*: Crossbill, Jay, Dipper, Green Woodpecker, Goshawk, Peregrine.
Other notable flora and fauna: Hay meadows have wide variety of plants including globe flower.
Contact: Forestry Commission, Eals Burn, Bellingham, Hexham, Northumberland, NE48 2HP. 01434 220 242.
e-mail: richard.gilchrist@forestry.gsi.gov.uk

4. MAZE PARK AND PORTRACK MARSH

Tees Valley Wildlife Trust.
Location: Maze Park: NZ 467 191, Portrack Marsh: NZ 465 194. Located midway between Middlesbrough and Stockton. Access from A66 at Tees Barrage. Sites are located on opposite banks of the River Tees, E of the barrage.
Access: No permits required. National cycle route passes through Maze Park. Surfaced paths at both sites. Suitable for disabled users at Portrack Marsh. Please keep to public rights of way.
Facilities: Hide at Portrack Marsh. No toilets or visitor centre.
Public transport: Regular buses between Middlesbrough and Stockton stop at the Tees Barrage (Arriva, tel 0870 608 2608). Thornaby Station one mile. Frequent trains from Darlington and Middlesbrough.
Habitat: Freshwater marsh, scrub, post-industrial grassland, riverside.
Key birds: *Winter*: Ducks, passage waders, Redshank, Snipe and Jack Snipe, Lapwing, Grey Heron, Skylark, Grey Partridge, Sand Martin, occasional Kingfisher and Grasshopper Warbler.
Contact: Steve Ashton, Tees Valley Wildlife Trust, 01287 636 382; e-mail: teesvalleywt@cix.co.uk www.wildlifetrust.org.uk/teesvalley

5. SALTHOLME, THE WILDLIFE RESERVE AND DISCOVERY PARK

RSPB.
Location: NZ 506 231. From A19, take A689 north of Stockton and then A1185. After four miles join A178 at mini roundabout. Take third exit and reserve is 250 yards on right.
Access: Open April 1 to Sept 30 (10am-5pm), Oct 1 to March 31 (10am-4pm). £3 per car, RSPB members, users of public transport and cyclists free. Open every day except Christmas Day.
Facilities: Award-winning visitor centre with cafe and shop, large car park, including wheelchair-friendly and coach parking, toilets (inc disabled), picnic area. Crushed stone paths ¬ wheelchair users may need assistance to reach bird hides. Walled garden designed by TV gardener Chris Beardshaw
Public transport: Stagecoach No1 bus from Hartlepool stops at reserve entrance. Cycle track across reserve from Port Clarence; cycle storage in car park.
Habitat: Wet grasslands, reedbeds, pools with tern islands, wader scrapes.
Key birds: *All year:* Lapwing, Peregrine, Water Rail. *Spring/summer:* Snipe, Common Tern, Yellow Wagtail. *Autumn:* Varied waders inc Black-tailed Godwit and Green Sandpiper, occasional rarer species. *Winter:* Large numbers of wildfowl and waders.
Other notable flora and fauna: Hares, orchids, butterflies and dragonflies.
Contact: The Warden, Saltholme, Seaton Carew Road, Port Clarence, Middlesbrough TS2 1TU. 01642 546 625; e-mail: saltholme@rspb.org.uk
www.rspb.org.uk/reserves

6. TEESMOUTH NNR

Natural England (North East Region).
Location: Two components, centred on NZ 535 276 and NZ 530 260, three and five miles S of Hartlepool, E of A178. Access to northern component from car park at North Gate (NZ 534 282), 0.5 miles E of A178. Access to southern part from A178 bridge over Greatham Creek at Cowpen Marsh (NZ 510 254). Car park adjacent to A178 at NZ 508 251. Both car parks can accommodate coaches.
Access: Open at all times. In northern component, no restrictions over most of dunes and North Gare Sands (avoid golf course, dogs must be kept under close control). In southern component, disabled access path to public hides at NZ 516 255 and NZ 516 252 (no other access).
Fa ilities: Nearest toilets at Seaton Carew, one mile to the N. Disabled access path and hides (see above), interpretive panels and leaflet. Teesmouth Field Centre (Tel: 01429 264 912).
Public transport: Half-hourly bus service (service 1) operates Mon-Sat between Middlesbrough and Hartlepool (hourly on Sundays), along A178, Stagecoach Hartlepool, Tel: 01429 267 082.
Habitat: Grazing marsh, dunes, intertidal flats.
Key birds: Passage and winter wildfowl and waders. Passage terns and skuas in late summer. Scarce passerine migrants and rarities. *Winter:* Merlin, Peregrine, Snow Bunting, Twite, divers, grebes.
Other notable flora and fauna: Northern component has large marsh orchid populations in damp dune grassland. Seal Sands supports a colony of 70 common seals.
Contact: Mike Leakey, Natural England, c/o British Energy, Tees Road, Hartlepool, TS25 2BZ. 01429 853 325; e-mail: northumbria@naturalengland.org.uk
www.naturalengland.org.uk

Lancashire

1. CUERDEN VALLEY PARK

Cuerden Valley Park Trust.
Location: SD 565 238. S of Preston on A49. Easy access from J28 and J29 of the M6, J8 and J9 on M61 and the end of M65.
Access: 650-acre site open all year.
Facilities: Visitor centre at Berkeley Drive, Bamber Bridge with toilets available between 9am and 5pm on weekdays. Sunday afternoon opening dependent on volunteer help. Track from Town Brow to lake is wheelchair friendly.
Public transport: None.
Habitat: 650 acres of mixed woodland, river, pond, lake, wildflower meadow, agricultural grassland.
Key birds: *All year:* Great Crested Grebe, Little Grebe, Kingfisher, Dipper, Great Spotted Woodpecker, Goldcrest, Little Owl and usual woodland and river birds.
Other notable flora and fauna: Dragonflies including emperor, emerald, black darter and migrant hawker.

Butterflies including large and small skipper, holly blue, small copper, comma and gatekeeper. Roe deer and seven species of bat. Common spotted and marsh orchid, moschatel.
Contact: Cuerden Valley Park Trust, 01772 324 436.
e-mail: rangers@cuerdenvalleypark.org

2. HEYSHAM NATURE RESERVE AND BIRD OBSERVATORY

The Wildlife Trust for Lancashire, Manchester and North Merseyside in conjunction with British Energy Estates.
Location: Main reserve is at SD 404 596 W of Lancaster. Take A683 to Heysham port. Turn L at traffic lights by Duke of Rothesay pub, then first R after 300m.
Access: Gate to reserve car park usually open 9.30am-6pm (longer in summer and shorter in winter). Pedestrian access at all times. Dogs on lead. Limited disabled access.
Facilities: Hide overlooking power station outfalls. Map giving access details at the reserve car park.

NATURE RESERVES - NORTHERN ENGLAND

only. Groups and coaches welcome (advance booking required).
Facilities: Visitor centre, shop, cafe and toilets. Nature trails and five hides (four have wheelchair access), plus two hides at saltmarsh pools.
Public transport: Silverdale train station 250 metres from reserve.
Habitat: Reedbed, shallow meres and woodland. Saltmarsh pools approx 1 mile.
Key birds: *All year:* Bittern, Bearded Tit, Water Rail, Shoveler, Gadwall, Marsh Tit, Little Egrets *Summer:* Marsh Harrier, Reed and Sedge Warblers. Avocets at saltmarsh pools. *Winter:* Large flocks of Starlings roosting.
Other notable flora and fauna: Common reed, otter, red deer.
Contact: RSPB Leighton Moss Nature Reserve, Myers Farm, Silverdale, Carnforth, LA5 0SW. 01524 701601. e-mail: leighton.moss@rspb.org.uk www.rspb.org.uk/leightonmoss

4. MARTIN MERE

The Wildfowl & Wetlands Trust.
Location: SD 428 145. Six miles N of Ormskirk via Burscough Bridge (A59), 20 miles from Liverpool and Preston.
Access: Opening times: 9.30am-5.00pm (Nov-Feb), 9.30am-5.30pm (rest of year). Special dawn and evening events. Guide dogs only allowed. Admission charge except for WWT members. Fully accessible to disabled, all hides suitable for wheelchairs. Coach park available. Site of North-West Bird Fair.
Facilities: Visitor centre with toilets, gift shop, restaurant, education centre, play area, nature reserve and nature trails, hides, waterfowl collection and sustainable garden. Provision for disabled visitors.
Public transport: Bus service to WWT Martin Mere from Ormskirk. Train to Burscough Bridge or New Lane Stations (both 1.5 miles from reserve). For bus times contact Traveline 0870 608 2608.
Habitat: Open water, wet grassland, moss, copses, reedbed, parkland.
Key birds: *Winter:* Whooper and Bewick's Swans, Pink-footed Goose, various ducks, Ruff, Black-tailed Godwit, Peregrine, Hen Harrier, Tree Sparrow. *Spring:* Ruff, Shelduck, Little Ringed and Ringed Plovers, Lapwing, Redshank. *Summer:* Marsh Harrier, Garganey, hirundines, Tree Sparrow. Breeding Avocet, Lapwing, Redshank, Shelduck. *Autumn:* Pink-footed Goose, waders on passage.
Other notable flora and fauna: Whorled caraway, golden dock, tubular dropwort, 300 species of moth.
Contact: WWT Martin Mere Wetland Centre, 01704 895 181; e-mail: info.martinmere@wwt.org.uk

5. MERE SANDS WOOD

The Wildlife Trust for Lancashire, Manchester and North Merseyside.
Location: SD 44 71 57. 12 miles by road from Southport, 0.5 miles off A59 Preston - Liverpool road, in Rufford along B5246 (Holmeswood Road).

No manned visitor centre or toilet access, but someone usually in reserve office, next to the main car park, in the morning. Latest sightings board can be viewed through the window if office is closed.
Public transport: Train services connect with nearby Isle of Man ferry. Plenty of buses to Lancaster from various Heysham sites within walking distance (ask for nearest stop to the harbour).
Habitat: Varied: wetland, acid grassland, alkaline grassland, foreshore.
Key birds: Passerine migrants in the correct conditions. Good passage of seabirds in spring, especially Arctic Tern. Storm Petrel and Leach's Petrel during strong onshore (SW-WNW) winds in midsummer and autumn respectively. Breeding birds inc. eight species of warbler. Scarce land-birds each year, most frequent being Yellow-browed Warbler.
Other notable flora and fauna: Notable area for dragonflies, red-veined darter breeds at nearby Middleton Community Woodland main pond (SD 418 592) between mid June - mid July. Bee orchid.
Contact: Reuben Neville, Reserve Warden, 01524 855 030; 07979 652 138. www.lancswt.org.uk http://heyshamobservatory.blogspot.com; Annual report from Leighton Moss RSPB reserve shop.

3. LEIGHTON MOSS

RSPB (Northern England).
Location: SD 478 750. Four miles NW of Carnforth. Signposted from A6 N of Carnforth.
Access: Reserve open daily dawn-dusk. Visitor centre open daily 9.30am-5pm (9.30am-4.30pm Nov-Jan inclusive), except Christmas Day. No charge to RSPB members or those who arrive by public transport or bike (you also get 10% off in our cafe if you come by bus, train or bike). Dogs allowed on causeway

Access: Visitor centre open 9.30am-4.30pm — closed Fridays and Christmas Day. Car park open until 8pm in summer. Three miles of wheelchair-accessible footpaths. All hides accessible to wheelchairs.
Facilities: Visitor centre with toilets (disabled), six viewing hides, three trails, exhibition room, latest sightings board. Feeding stations. Booking essential for two motorised buggies.
Public transport: Bus: Southport-Chorley 347 and Preston-Ormskirk 2B stop in Rufford, 0.5 mile walk. Train: Preston-Ormskirk train stops at Rufford station, one mile walk.
Habitat: 40h inc freshwater lakes, mixed woodland, sandy grassland/heath.
Key birds: *Winter*: Regionally important for Teal and Gadwall, good range of waterfowl, Kingfisher. Feeding stations attract Tree Sparrow, Bullfinch, Reed Bunting, Water Rail. *Woodland*: Treecreeper, Nuthatch. *Summer*: Kingfisher. *Passage*: Most years, Osprey, Crossbill, Green Sandpiper, Greenshank.
Other notable flora and fauna: 18 species of dragonfly recorded annually.
Contact: Lindsay Beaton, Reserve Manager, Mere Sands Wood Nature Reserve, 01704 821 809.
e-mail: meresandswood@lancswt.org.uk
www.lancswt.org.uk

6. MORECAMBE BAY (HEST BANK)

RSPB (Northern England).
Location: SD 468 667. Two miles N of Morecambe at Hest Bank.
Access: Open at all times. Do not venture onto saltmarsh or intertidal area, as there are dangerous channels and quicksands.

Facilities: Viewpoint at local council car park.
Public transport: No 5 bus runs between Carnforth and Morecambe. Tel: 0870 608 2608.
Habitat: Saltmarsh, estuary.
Key birds: *Winter*: Wildfowl (Pintail, Shelduck, Wigeon) and waders. This is an important high tide roost for Oystercatcher, Curlew, Redshank, Dunlin and Bar-tailed Godwit.
Contact: RSPB Leighton Moss & Morecambe Bay Nature Reserves, 01524 701601;
e-mail:leighton.moss@rspb.org.uk
www.rspb.org.uk/morecambebay

7. RIBBLE ESTUARY

Natural England (Cheshire to Lancashire team).
Location: SD 380 240. W of Preston.
Access: Open at all times.
Facilities: No formal visiting facilities.
Public transport: None.
Habitat: Saltmarsh, mudflats.
Key birds: High water wader roosts (of Knot, Dunlin, Black-tailed Godwit, Oystercatcher and Grey Plover) are best viewed from Southport, Marshside, Lytham St Annes. Pink-footed Geese and wintering swans are present in large numbers from Oct-Feb on Banks Marsh and along River Douglas respectively. The large flocks of Wigeon, for which the site is renowned, can be seen on high tides from Marshside but feed on saltmarsh areas at night. Good numbers of raptors also present in winter.
Contact: Site Manager, English Nature, Ribble Estuary NNR, Old Hollow, Marsh Road, Banks, Southport PR9 8DU. 01704 225 624.

Manchester, Greater

1. ASTLEY MOSS

The Wildlife Trust for Lancashire, Manchester and North Merseyside.
Location: Lies 7km S of Leigh at SJ 692 975. S of A580 at Astley; follow Higher Green Lane to Rindle Farm.
Access: Permit required — apply to Trust office.
Facilities: None.
Habitat: Remnant peat bog, scrub, oak/birch woodland.
Key birds: *Spring/summer*: Breeding Tree Pipit, Willow Tit, Whinchat and Curlew. *Winter*: Raptors (inc. Merlin, Hen Harrier), finch flocks, thrush flocks; Long-eared and Short-eared Owls.
Other notable flora and fauna: Sphagnum mosses, ten species of dragonfly recorded.
Contact: Trust HQ, 01772 324 129.
e-mail: info@lancswt.org.uk www.lancswt.org.uk

2. ETHEROW COUNTRY PARK

Stockport Metropolitan Borough Council.
Location: SJ 965 908. In Compstall on the B6104 between Romiley and Marple Bridge.

Site is well signposted.
Access: Open at all times; permit required for conservation area. Keep to paths.
Facilities: Reserve area has SSSI status. Hide, nature trail, visitor centre, motorised scooters for disabled, (best to book at weekends).
Public transport: None.
Habitat: River Etherow, woodlands, marshy area (240 acres in total).
Key birds: Sparrowhawk, Buzzard, Dipper, all three woodpeckers, Pied Flycatcher, warblers. *Winter*: Brambling, Siskin, Water Rail. Frequent sightings of Merlin and Raven over hills.
Other notable flora and fauna: 200 species of plant.
Contact: John Rowland, Etherow Country Park, Compstall, Stockport, Cheshire SK6 5JD. 01614 276 937; e-mail: parks@stockport.gov.uk

3. HOLLINGWORTH LAKE

Rochdale MBC.
Location: SD 939 153 (visitor centre). Four miles NE of Rochdale, signed from A58 Halifax Road and J21 of M62. Take B6225 to Littleborough.
Access: Access open to lake and surroundings at all times.

Facilities: Cafes, hide, trails and education service, pay-and-display car parks, coach park by prior arrangement. Free wheelchair hire, disabled toilets and baby changing facilities. Visitor centre open 10.30am-6pm in summer, 11am-4pm (Mon-Fri), 10.30am-5pm (Sat & Sun) in winter.
Public transport: Bus Nos 452, 450. Train to Littleborough or Smithy Bridge.
Habitat: Lake (116 acres, includes 20 acre nature reserve), woodland, streams, marsh, willow scrub.
Key birds: *All year*: Great Crested Grebe, Kingfisher, Lapwing, Little Owl, Bullfinch, Cormorant. Occasional Peregrine, Sedge Warbler, Water Rail, Snipe. *Spring/ autumn*: Passage waders, wildfowl, Kittiwake. *Summer*: Reed Bunting, Dipper, Common Sandpiper, Curlew, Oystercatcher, Black Tern, 'Commic' Tern, Grey Partridge, Blackcap. *Winter*: Goosander, Goldeneye, Siskin, Redpoll, Golden Plover.
Contact: The Ranger, Hollingworth Lake Visitor Centre, Rakewood Road, Littleborough, OL15 0AQ. 01706 373 421. www.rochdale.gov.uk

4. PENNINGTON FLASH COUNTRY PARK

Wigan Leisure and Culture Trust
Location: SJ 640 990. One mile from Leigh town centre. Main entrance on A572 (St Helens Road).
Access: Park is signposted from A580 (East Lancs Road) and is permanently open. Five largest hides, toilets and information point open 9am-dusk (except Christmas Day). Main paths flat and suitable for disabled. Main car park pay & display with coach parking available if booked in advance.
Facilities: Toilets (including disabled) and information point. Total of eight bird hides. Site leaflet available and Rangers based on site. Group visits welcome but please book your visit in advance.
Public transport: Only 1 mile from Leigh bus station. Several services stop on St Helens Road near entrance to park. Contact GMPTE on 0161 228 7811.
Habitat: Lowland lake, ponds and scrapes, fringed with reeds, rough grassland, scrub and woodland.
Key birds: Waterfowl all year, waders (14-plus species) and terns (4-plus species) mainly on

passage in both spring and autumn. Breeding birds include nine species of warbler. Feeding station attracts Willow Tit, Stock Dove and up to 40 Bullfinches all year. Large gull roost in winter. Over 240 species recorded, including seven county firsts in the last decade alone.
Other notable flora and fauna: Several species of orchid including bee orchid. Wide variety of butterflies and dragonflies.
Contact: Peter Alker, WLCT, Pennington Flash Country Park, St Helens Road, Leigh, WN7 3PA. 01942 605 253 (Also Fax number); e-mail: pfcp@wlct.org

5. WIGAN FLASHES LNR

Lancashire Wildlife Trust/Wigan Council.
Location: SD 580 035. Leave M6 at J25 head N on A49, turn R on to Poolstock Lane (B5238). There are several entrances to the site; at end of Carr Lane near Hawkley Hall School, one off Poolstock Lane, two on Warington Road (A573). Also accessible from banks of Leeds and Liverpool Canal.
Access: Open at all times. Areas suitable for wheelchairs but there are some motorcycle barriers (gates can be opened by reserve manager for large groups). Paths being upgraded. Access for coaches - contact reserve manager for details.
Facilities: Six hide screens.
Public transport: 610 bus (Hawkley Hall Circular). Local timetable info - call 0161 228 7811.
Habitat: Wetland with reedbed.
Key birds: Black Tern on migration. *Summer*: Nationally important for Reed Warbler and breeding Common Tern. Willow Tit, Cetti's and Grasshopper Warblers, Kingfisher. *Winter*: Wildfowl, especially diving duck and Gadwall. Bittern (especially winter).
Other notable flora and fauna: Interesting orchids, with the eight species including marsh and dune helleborines. One of the UK's largest feeding assemblage of noctule bats. Eighteen species of dragonfly has included red-veined darter.
Contact: Mark Champion, Lancashire Wildlife Trust, Highfield Grange, Wigan, Lancs WN3 6SU. 01942 233 976. e-mail: wiganflashes@lancswt.org.uk

Merseyside

1. AINSDALE & BIRKDALE SANDHILLS LNR

Sefton Council.
Location: SD 300 115. SD 310 138. Leave the A565 just N of Formby. Car parking areas are off the un-numbered coastal road.
Access: Track from Ainsdale or Southport along the shore. Wheelchair access across boardwalks at Ainsdale Sands Lake and Queen's Jubilee nature trails opposite Weld Road.
Facilities: Ainsdale Discovery Centre open summer. Shore Road toilets open Easter-Oct.
Public transport: Ainsdale and Southport stations 20 minute walk. Hillside Station is a 30 minute walk across the Birkdale Sandhills to beach.

Habitat: Foreshore, dune scrub and pine woodland.
Key birds: *Spring/summer*: Grasshopper Warbler, Chiffchaff, waders. *Winter*: Blackcap, Stonechat, Redwing, Fieldfare, waders and wildfowl. *All year*: Skylark, Grey Partridge.
Other notable flora and fauna: Red squirrel, natterjack toad, early marsh orchid.
Contact: Sefton Council Leisure Services, 0151 934 2967; e-mail: coast-countryside@leisure.sefton.gov.uk www.visitsouthport.com/sefton/nature-and-wildlife

2. DEE ESTUARY

Metropolitan Borough of Wirral.
Location: SJ 255 815. Leave A540 Chester to Hoylake road at Heswall and head downhill (one mile) to the free car park at the shore end of Banks Road. Heswall

is 30 mins from South Liverpool and Chester by car.
Access: Open at all times. Best viewpoint 600 yards along shore N of Banks Road. No disabled access along shore, but good birdwatching from bottom of Banks Road. Arrive 2.5 hours before high tide. Coach parking available.
Facilities: Information board. No toilets in car park. Wirral Country Park Centre three miles N off A540 has toilets, hide, café, kiosk (all accessible to wheelchairs). Birdwatching events programme on RSPB website.
Public transport: Bus service to Banks Road car park from Heswall bus station, or bus to Irby village then walk one mile. Mersey Travel (0151 236 7676).
Habitat: Saltflats and mudflats.
Key birds: *Autumn/winter*: Large passage and winter wader roosts — Redshank, Curlew, Black-tailed Godwit, Oystercatcher, Golden Plover, Knot, Shelduck, Teal, Red-breasted Merganser, Peregrine, Merlin, Hen Harrier, Short-eared Owl. Smaller numbers of Pintail, Wigeon, Bar-tailed Godwit, Greenshank, Spotted Redshank, Grey and Ringed Plovers, Whimbrel, Curlew Sandpiper, Little Stint, occasional Scaup and Little Egret.
Contact: The Senior Ranger, Wirral Country Park Centre, 01516 484 371/3884; www.wirral.gov.uk/er e-mail: wirralcountrypark@wirral.gov.uk

3. HILBRE ISLAND LNR

Wirral Country Park Centre (Metropolitan Borough of Wirral).
Location: SJ 184 880. Three tidal islands in the mouth of the Dee Estuary. Park in West Kirby which is on the A540 Chester-to-Hoylake road – 30 minutes from Liverpool, 45 minutes from Chester. Follow the brown Marine Lake signs to Dee Lane pay and display car park. Coach parking

available at West Kirby but please apply for permit to visit island well in advance as numbers limited.
Access: Two mile walk across the sands from Dee Lane slipway. No disabled access. Do not cross either way within 3.5 hours of high water – tide times and suggested safe route on noticeboard at slipway. Prior booking and permit needed for parties of five or more – maximum of 50. Book early.
Facilities: Hilbre Bird Observatory. Toilets at Hilbre (primitive!) and Marine Lake. Permits, leaflets and tide times from Wirral Country Park Centre.
Public transport: Bus and train station (from Liverpool) within 0.5 mile of Dee Lane slipway. Contact Mersey Travel, tel 0151 236 7676.
Habitat: Sandflats, rocky shore and open sea.
Key birds: *Late summer/autumn*: Seabird passage – Gannets, terns, skuas, shearwaters and after NW gales good numbers of Leach's Petrel. *Winter*: Wader roosts at high tide, Purple Sandpiper, Turnstone, sea ducks, divers, grebes. Passage migrants.
Other notable flora and fauna: Nationally scarce rock sea lavender.
Contact: The Senior Ranger, Wirral Country Park Centre, 01516 484 371/3884; www.wirral.gov.uk/er e-mail: wirralcountrypark@wirral.gov.uk

4. MARSHSIDE

RSPB (Northern England).
Location: SD 355 202. On S shore of Ribble Estuary, one mile N of Southport centre on Marine Drive.
Access: Open 8.30am-5pm all year. Toilets. No dogs please. Coach parties please book in advance. Donations welcomed. Park in Sefton Council car park along Marine Drive.
Facilities: Information centre, toilets (inc disabled), two hides and trails accessible to wheelchairs. Two viewing screens and a viewing platform.
Public transport: Bus service to Elswick Road/Marshside Road half-hourly, bus No 44, from Lord Street. Contact Traveline (0870 608 2608).
Habitat: Coastal grazing marsh and lagoons.
Key birds: *Winter*: Pink-footed Goose, wildfowl, waders, raptors. *Spring*: Breeding waders, inc. Avocet and wildfowl, Garganey, migrants inc Black-tailed Godwit, Ruff and Wheatear. *Autumn*: Migrants.
Other notable flora and fauna: Hares, various plants including marsh orchid, migrant hawker dragonfly.
Contact: Graham Clarkson, Warden, RSPB, 24 Hoghton Street, Southport, PR9 0PA. 01704 536 378. e-mail: graham.clarkson@rspb.org.uk

5. N.WIRRAL COASTAL PARK

Metropolitan Borough of Wirral.
Location: SJ 241 909. Located SW of new Brighton, between the outer Dee and Mersey Estuaries. From Moreton take A553 E then A551 N. Turn left onto Tarran Way South then R onto Lingham Lane. Parking available by lighthouse. Foreshore can be viewed from footpath which runs alongside.

Access: Open at all times.
Facilities: Visitor centre, several car parks, three toilet blocks (one summer-only), extensive footpath network and public bridleways, four picnic areas.
Public transport: The area is served by Grove Road (Wallasey), Leasowe, Moreton, and Meols Merseyrail Stations, and bus routes along Leasowe Road, Pasture Road and Harrison Drive.
Habitat: Saltmarsh.
Key birds: Important as a feeding and roosting site for passage and wintering flocks of waders, wildfowl, terns and gulls. Wintering populations of Knot (20,000+), Bar-tailed Godwit (2,000+) and Dunlin (10,000). Redshank (1,000+) and Turnstone (500+) feed on the rocky shore at Perch Rock and on the rocky sea walls. Oystercatcher (500+), Curlew, Grey Plover and Black-tailed Godwit also regularly roost here in relatively high numbers. Small populations of wildfowl, including Common Scoter, Scaup and Goldeneye, Red-throated Diver and Great Crested Grebe also frequently winter on this site.
Other notable flora and fauna: Sea holly, marram grass, storksbill, burnet rose and rarities like the Isle of Man cabbage can be found. This area is one of only two known sites in the world for the very rare British sub-species of the belted beauty moth.
Contact: Ranger Service, North Wirral Coastal Park, Leasowe Lighthouse, Moreton Common, Wirral CH46 4TA. 0151 678 5488. www.wirral.gov.uk
e-mail: coastalpark@wirral.gov.uk

6. RED ROCKS MARSH

Cheshire Wildlife Trust.
Location: SJ 206 880. 9 km west of Birkenhead immediately W of Hoylake and adjacent to the Dee estuary.
Access: Open all year.

Facilities: Car park, hide.
Habitat: Sand dune, reedbed.
Key birds: *Spring/summer*: Wildfowl, warblers. *Passage*: Finches, Snow Bunting, thrushes.
Other notable flora and fauna: The only breeding colony of natterjack toads on the Wirral Peninsula. More than 50 species of flowering plant recorded, including parsley, quaking grass, Danish scurvy grass, wild asparagus and various orchid species.
Contact: Trust HQ, 01948 820 728;
e-mail: info@cheshirewt.cix.co.uk
www.cheshirewildlifetrust.co.uk

7. SEAFORTH NATURE RESERVE

The Wildlife Trust for Lancashire, Manchester and North Merseyside.
Location: SJ 315 970. Five miles from Liverpool city centre. From M57/M58 take A5036 to docks.
Access: Only organised groups which pre-book are now allowed access. Groups should contact the reserve office (see below) at least seven days in advance of their planned trip. Coaches welcome.
Facilities: Toilets at visitor centre when open, three hides.
Public transport: Train to Waterloo or Seaforth stations from Liverpool. Buses to dock gates from Liverpool.
Habitat: Saltwater and freshwater lagoons, scrub grassland.
Key birds: Noted site for Little Gull on passage (Apr), plus Roseate, Little and Black Terns. Breeding and passage Common Tern (Apr-Sept). Passage and winter waders and gulls. Passage passerines, especially White Wagtail, pipits and Wheatear.
Contact: Steve White, Seaforth Nature Reserve, Port of Liverpool, L21 1JD. 0151 9203 769.
e-mail: swhite@lancswt.org.uk

Northumberland

1. ARNOLD MEMORIAL, CRASTER

Northumberland Wildlife Trust.
Location: NU255197. Lies NE of Alnwick on Sw edge of Craster village. Take minor road to coast off B1339.
Access: Public footpath from car park in disused quarry.
Facilities: Information centre (not NWT) open in summer. Interpretation boards.Toilets (incl disabled) and picnic site in quarry car park. Easy going access along path through site. Coach parking in adjacent public car park.
Public transport: Arriva Northumberland nos. 500, 505. Travelsure No 401
Habitat: Semi-natural woodland and scrub near coast.
Key birds: Good site for migrant passerines to rest and feed. Interesting visitors can inc. Bluethroat, Red-breasted Flycatcher, Barred and Icterine Warblers, Wryneck; moulting site for Lesser Redpoll.

Breeding warblers in summer.
Other notable flora and fauna: Spring flora including primrose and non-native periwinkle.
Contact: Trust HQ, 01912 846 884;
e-mail: mail@northwt.org.uk www.nwt.org.uk

2. DRURIDGE POOLS - CRESSWELL POND

Northumberland Wildlife Trust.
Location: Two sites lying on coast between Newbiggin and Amble, off A1068. 1. Druridge Pools NZ 272 965. 2. Cresswell Pond NZ 283 945. Half mile N of Cresswell.
Access: Wheelchair users can view northern part of Cresswell Pond from public footpath or roadside.
Facilities: 1. Three hides. 2. Hide.
Public transport: Arriva No 420 (to within 2 miles).
Habitat: 1. Deep lake and wet meadows with pools behind dunes. 2. Shallow brackish lagoon behind dunes fringed with saltmarsh and reedbed, some mudflats.
Key birds: 1. Especially good in spring. Winter and breeding wildfowl; passage and breeding waders. 2.

Good for waders, esp. on passage.
Other notable flora and fauna: The sheltered sunny banks are good for a range of butterflies and dragonflies in summer at Druridge Pools. Otters are often seen on the lakes.
Contact: Trust HQ, 01912 846 884;
e-mail: mail@northwt.org.uk www.nwt.org.uk

3. EAST CHEVINGTON

Northumberland Wildlife Trust.
Location: NZ 265 985. Overlooking Druridge Bay, off A 1068 between Hauxley and Cresswell.
Access: Main access from overflow car park at Druridge Bay Country Park (signed from main road).
Facilities: Four public hides, café, toilets and information at Country Park (County Council). ID boards for coastal plants.
Public transport: Arriva 420 and 423 bus services.
Habitat: Ponds and reedbeds created from former open cast coal mine. Areas of scrub and grassland.
Key birds: Large numbers of wildfowl, including Greylag and Pinkfooted Geese in winter. Breeding Skylark, Stonechat, Reed Bunting, plus Reed, Sedge and Grasshopper Warblers. Capable of attracting rarities at any time of year. Marsh Harriers around the reedbeds.
Other notable flora and fauna: Coastal wildflowers.
Contact: Trust HQ, 01912 846 884;
e-mail: mail@northwt.org.uk www.nwt.org.uk

4. FARNE ISLANDS

The National Trust.
Location: NU 230 370. Access by boat from Seahou Harbour. Access from A1.
Access: Inner Farne and Staple 10.30am-6pm (majority of boats land at Inner Farne when conditions are calm). In April and between Aug 1 a Oct 31: Staple Island 10.30am-1.30pm, Inner Farn 1.30pm-5pm between May 1 and July 31. Disabled access possible on Inner Farne, telephone Propert Manager for details. Dogs allowed on boats but no on islands.
Facilities: Toilets on Inner Farne.
Public transport: Nearest rail stations at Alnmout and Berwick. Hourly Travelsure buses between Bu and Beadnell Bays (Mon-Sat). Call 01665 720 955.
Habitat: Maritime islands – between 15-28 depending on height of tide.
Key birds: 18 species of seabirds/waders, four species of tern (including Roseate), 55,000-plus pairs of Puffin, 1,200 Eider, Rock Pipit, Pied Wagtail etc.
Other notable flora and fauna: Grey seals.
Contact: John Walton, 8 St Aidans, Seahouses, Northumberland NE68 7SR. 01665 720 651.

5. HAUXLEY

Northumberland Wildlife Trust
Location: NU 285 023. South of Amble.
Access: Day permit required available from Reception hide. Access through High Hauxley villa

Site is signposted off A1068.
Facilities: Reception hide open daily from 10am-5pm (summer) or 10am-3pm (winter) and six public hides. Toilets and information.
Public transport: Arriva 420 and 423 bus services.
Habitat: Ponds created from former opencast coal mine. Areas of woodland and grassland.
Key birds: Waders use the site at high tide. Roseate Terns sometimes join commoner species in late summer. Waders and migrants on passage. *Winter*: Bewick's Swan, Shoveler, plus larg number of other wildfowl species, Lapwing and Purple Sandpiper.
Other notable flora and fauna: A variety of invertebrates, including butterflies, dragonflies and amphibians such as great crested newt.
Contact: Trust HQ, 01912 846 884;
e-mail: mail@northwt.org.uk www.nwt.org.uk

6. KIELDER FOREST PARK

Forestry Commission
Location: NY 632 934. Kielder Castle is situated at N end of Kielder Water, NW of Bellingham.
Access: Forest open all year. Toll charge on 12 mile forest drive and car park charge applies. Visitor centre has limited opening in winter.
Facilities: Three visitor centres (Castle, Tower Knowe and Leapish Waterside Park), exhibition, toilets, shop, access for disabled, licensed café. Local facilities include youth hostel, camp site, pub and

Public transport: Bus: 814, 815, 816 from Hexham and seasonal service 714 from Newcastle.
Habitat: Commercial woodland, mixed and broadleaved trees.
Key birds: *Spring/summer*: Goshawk, Chiffchaff, Willow Warbler, Redstart, Siskin. *Winter*: Crossbill. *Resident*: Jay, Dipper, Great Spotted Woodpecker, Tawny Owl, Song Thrush, Goldcrest.
Other notable flora and fauna: Impressive display of northern marsh orchids at entrance to Kielder Castle. Red Squirrel hide at Leapish WP.
Contact: Forestry Commission, 01434 220 242. e-mail: richard.gilchrist@forestry.gsi.gov.uk

7. LINDISFARNE NNR

Natural England (Northumbria Team).
Location: NU 090 430. Island access lies two miles E of A1 at Beal, eight miles S of Berwick-on-Tweed.
Access: Causeway floods at high tide, so check when it is safe to cross. Some restricted access (bird refuges). Coach parking available on Holy Island.
Facilities: Toilets, visitor centre in village. Hide on island (new hide with disabled access at Fenham-le-Moor). Self-guided trail on island.
Public transport: Irregular bus service to Holy Island, mainly in summer. Main bus route follows mainland boundary of site north-south.
Habitat: Dunes, sand, mudflats and saltmarsh.
Key birds: *Passage and winter*: Wildfowl and waders, including pale-bellied Brent Goose, Long-tailed Duck and Whooper Swan. Rare migrants.
Other notable flora and fauna: Butterflies include dark green fritillary (July) and grayling (August). Guided walks advertised for nine species of orchid

Tyne & Wear

1. BIG WATERS

Northumberland Wildlife Trust.
Location: NZ 227 734 N of Newcastle upon Tyne. Drive under A1 flyover, W of B1318 in Wideopen and through Brunswick Village, turning R after last house. Reserve is entered from car park via a path that meets public right of way from access road just S of the car park.
Access: Hides are locked, keys available to NWT members. Public viewing areas.
Facilities: Two hides, viewing areas, easy going footpath access.
Public transport: Arriva Northumberland nos 45, 45a, 45b.
Habitat: Pond with surrounding reedbed.
Key birds: Wintering wildfowl including Teal, Tufted Duck and Shoveler. Breeding species include Great Crested and Little Grebe and Coot. Tree Sparrow, Yellowhammer and Great Spotted Woodpecker use feeding station all year.
Other notable flora and fauna: Otters are frequently seen from the hide. The small pond on site is used by dragonflies, while woodland edges and fields are used

including coralroot and Lindisfarne helleborine.
Contact: Phil Davey, Senior Reserve Manager, Beal Station, Berwick-on-Tweed, TD15 2PB. 01289 381 470.

8. WHITELEE MOOR

Northumberland Wildlife Trust
Location: NT 700 040. Reserve located at head of Redesdale, south of A68 Newcastle to Jedburgh road where it crosses Scottish Border at Carter Bar.
Access: There is parking at tourist car park at Carter Bar and on laybys on forest track at reservoir end. A public footpath leads along old track to Whitelee Limeworks and then southwards. This footpath extends to southern boundary of site and eastwards along it to link up with a bridleway from White Kielder Burn via Girdle Fell to Chattlehope Burn. Additionally there is access on foot via Forest Enterprise road near eastern corner of reserve. Reserve is remote and wild, and weather can change quickly. Visitors should have hill-walking experience if attempting long walks.
Facilities: Car park and laybys.
Habitat: Active blanket bog and heather heath.
Key birds: The River Rede and its tributaries add to the habitat and bird diversity. Notable breeding birds include Merlin and Stonechat. Black Grouse, Skylark, Meadow Pipit, Dunlin, Curlew, Golden Plover, Grey Wagtail, Dipper and Ring Ouzel regularly visit the reserve.
Other notable flora and fauna: Otters often hunt along the Rede and a herd of feral goats may be seen.
Contact: Trust HQ, 01912 846 884; e-mail: mail@northwt.org.uk www.nwt.org.uk

by a variety of butterflies, including large skipper and small copper.
Contact: Trust HQ, 01912 846 884; www.nwt.org.uk
e-mail: mail@northwt.org.uk

2. BOLDON FLATS

South Tyneside Council.
Location: NZ 377 614. Turn west along Moor Lane at Cleadon on A1018 (Sunderland to South Shields Road).
Access: View from limited lay-by parking along Moor Lane.
Facilities: None.
Public transport: East Boldon Metro Station approx. 800 metres from site. www.nexus.org.uk
Habitat: Managed winter flood, ponds, ditches, summer meadow.
Key birds: *Winter*: Large numbers of wildfowl, inc Wigeon, Teal, occasional Whooper Swan and Bean Goose. Waders include Golden Plover. *Spring*: Little Ringed Plover, Lapwing, Tree Sparrow. *Summer*: Farmland species.
Other notable flora and fauna: Good range of dragonflies, inc occasional vagrants in late summer.
Contact: Countryside Officer, South Tyneside Metropolitan Council, 01914 271 717.
www.southtyneside.info

NATURE RESERVES - NORTHERN ENGLAND

3. DERWENT WALK COUNTRY PARK AND DERWENTHAUGH PARK

Gateshead Council.
Location: NZ 178 604. Along River Derwent, four miles SW of Newcastle and Gateshead. Several car parks along A694.
Access: Site open all times. Thornley visitor centre open weekends and Bank Holidays (12-5pm). Keys for hides available from Thornley Woodlands Centre. Swalwell visitor centre open daily (9am-5pm).
Facilities: Toilets at Thornley and Swalwell visitor centres. Hides at Far Pasture Ponds and Thornley feeding station.
Public transport: 45, 46, 46A, 47/47A/47B buses from Newcastle/Gateshead to Swalwell/Rowlands Gill. Bus stop Thornley Woodlands Centre. (Regular bus service from Newcastle). Information from Nexus Travel Information, 0919 203 3333.
www.nexus.org.uk
Habitat: Mixed woodland, river, ponds, meadows.
Key birds: *All year*: Kingfisher, Green and Great Spotted Woodpecker, Nuthatch. *Summer*: Red Kite, Grasshopper Warbler, Lesser Whitethroat, Dipper, Blackcap, Garden Warbler. *Winter*: Teal, Tufted Duck, Brambling, Marsh Tit, Bullfinch, Great Spotted Woodpecker, Nuthatch, Goosander, Kingfisher.
Contact: Trevor Weston, Thornley Woodlands Centre, 01207 545 212. e-mail: countryside@gateshead.gov.uk
www.gatesheadbirders.co.uk
www.gateshead.gov.uk

4. RYTON WILLOWS

Gateshead Council.
Location: NZ 155 650. Five miles W of Newcastle. Access along several tracks running N from Ryton.
Access: Open at all times.
Facilities: Nature trail and free leaflet.
Public transport: Regular service to Ryton from Newcastle/Gateshead. Information from Nexus Traveline on 0191 232 5325.
Habitat: Deciduous woodland, scrub, riverside, tidal river.
Key birds: *Winter*: Goldeneye (now rare), Goosander, Green Woodpecker, Nuthatch, Treecreeper. *Autumn*: Greenshank. *Summer*: Lesser Whitethroat, Sedge Warbler, Yellowhammer, Linnet, Reed Bunting, Common Sandpiper.
Other notable flora and fauna: Invertebrate species associated with acid grassland.
Contact: Brian Pollinger, Thornley Woodlands Centre, 1208 545 212. e-mail: countryside@gateshead.gov.uk
www.gatesheadbirders.co.uk

5. SHIBDON POND

Gateshead Council.
Location: NZ 192 628. E of Blaydon, S of Scotswood Bridge, close to A1. Car park at Blaydon swimming baths. Open access from B6317 (Shibdon Road).
Access: Open at all times. Disabled access to hide.
Facilities: Hide in SW corner of pond. Free leaflet available.
Public transport: At least six buses per hour from Newcastle/Gateshead to Blaydon (bus stop Shibdon Road). Information from Nexus Travel Line (0191 232 5325).
Habitat: Pond, marsh, scrub and damp grassland.
Key birds: *Winter*: Wildfowl, Water Rail, occasional white-winged gulls. *Summer*: Reed Warbler, Sedge Warbler, Lesser Whitethroat, Grasshopper Warbler, Water Rail. *Autumn*: Passage waders and wildfowl, Kingfisher.
Other notable flora and fauna: 18 species of butterfly, inc dingy skipper. Dragonflies inc ruddy darter, migrant hawker, occasional emperor and vagrants.
Contact: Brian Pollinger, Thornley Woodlands Centre, 1208 545 212. e-mail: countryside@gateshead.gov.uk
www.gatesheadbirders.co.uk

6. TYNE RIVERSIDE COUNTRY PARK

Newcastle City Council
Location: NZ 158 658 in Newburn on W edge of Newcastle. From the Newcastle to Carlisle by-pass on the A69(T) take A6085 into Newburn. Park is signposted from road to Blaydon. 0.25 miles after this junction, turn due W (the Newburn Hotel is on the corner) and after 0.5 miles the parking and

information area is signed just beyond the Newburn Leisure Centre.
Access: Open all year.
Facilities: Visitor centre (open weekend afternoons and other times when staff available. Toilets open 9am-5pm in summer and most winter days. Car park. Leaflets and walk details available.
Habitat: River, pond with reed and willow stands, mixed woodland, open grassland.
Key birds: *Spring/summer*: Swift, Swallow, Whitethroat, Lesser Whitethroat. *Winter*: Sparrowhawk, Kingfisher, Little Grebe, finches, Siskin, Fieldfare, Redwing, Goosander.
All year: Grey Partridge, Green and Great Spotted Woodpecker, Bullfinch, Yellowhammer.
Contact: Newcastle City Council, The Riverside Country Park, Newburn, Newcastle upon Tyne, NE15 8BW. 0191 264 8501; www.newcastle.gov.uk
e-mail: newburn.countrypark@newcastle.gov.uk

7. WASHINGTON

The Wildfowl & Wetlands Trust.
Location: NZ 331 566. In Washington. On N bank of River Wear, W of Sunderland. Signposted from A195, A19, A1231 and A182.

Access: Open 9.30am-5pm (summer), 9.30am-4pm (winter). Free to WWT members. Admission charge for non-members. No dogs except guide dogs. Good access for people with disabilities.
Facilities: Visitor centre, toilets, parent and baby room, range of hides. Shop and café.
Public transport: Buses to Waterview Park (250 yards walk) from Washington, from Sunderland, Newcastle-upon-Tyne, Durham and South Shields. Tel: 0845 6060 260 for details.
Habitat: Wetlands, woodland and meadows.
Key birds: *Spring/summer*: Nesting colony of Grey Heron, other breeders include Common Tern, Oystercatcher, Lapwing.
Winter: Bird-feeding station visited by Great Spotted Woodpecker, Bullfinch, Jay and Sparrowhawk. Goldeneye and other ducks.
Other notable flora and fauna: Wildflower meadows – cuckoo flower, bee orchid and yellow rattle. Dragonfly and amphibian ponds.
Contact: Dean Heward (Conservation Manager), Wildfowl & Wetlands Trust, Pottinson, Washington, NE38 8LE. 01914 165 454 ext 231.
e-mail: dean.heward@wwt.org.uk
www.wwt.org.uk

Yorkshire, East Riding

1. BEMPTON CLIFFS

RSPB (Northern England).
Location: TA 197 738. Near Bridlington. Take Cliff Lane N from Bempton Village off B1229 to car park and visitor centre.
Access: Visitor centre open year round - 9.30am to 5pm March - Oct; 9.30am - 4pm Nov - Feb. Public footpath along cliff top with observation points. Access for wheelchairs to main observation points along gravel paths.
Facilities: Visitor centre, toilets, light refreshments, observation points, picnic area, limited coach parking. Four miles of stunning chalk cliffs, highest in county.
Public transport: Bempton railway station (limited service) 1.5 miles — irregular bus service to village 1.25 miles.
Habitat: Seabird nesting cliffs, farmland, coastal scrub.
Key birds: Largest mainland seabird colony in UK; only Gannet colony in England. Birds present Jan-Oct with peak between Apr-Jun. Includes Kittiwake, Puffin, Guillemot, Razorbill And Fulmar. Nesting Tree Sparrow and Corn Bunting. Passage skua, shearwater, tern and passerine migrants.
Other notable flora and fauna: Harbour porpoise regularly offshore. Also bee and northern marsh orchid occur.
Contact: RSPB Bempton Cliffs Nature Reserve, Cliff Lane, Bempton, E Yorks, YO15 1JF. 01262 851179. YO15 1JF. 01262 851 179.

2. BLACKTOFT SANDS

RSPB (Northern England).
Location: SE 843 232. Eight miles E of Goole on minor road between Ousefleet and Adlingfleet.
Access: Open 9am-9pm or dusk if earlier. RSPB members free, £3 permit for non-members, £2 concessionary, £1 children, £6 family.
Facilities: Car park, toilets, visitor centre (open 9am to 5pm April to Oct and weekends between Nov and March), six hides, footpaths suitable for wheelchairs.
Public transport: Goole/Scunthorpe bus (Sweynes' Coaches stops outside reserve entrance). Bus timetable on main RSPB website (see Blacktoft Reserve details).
Habitat: Reedbed, saline lagoons, lowland wet grassland, willow scrub.
Key birds: *Summer*: Breeding Avocet, Marsh Harrier, Bittern, Bearded Tit, passage waders (exceptional list inc many rarities). *Winter*: Hen Harrier, Merlin, Peregrine, wildfowl.
Other notable flora and fauna: Good place to see water vole. Small number of dragonflies and damselflies including black-tailed skimmer, four-spotted chaser, large red damselfly. Marsh sow thistle easily seen from footpaths in summer.
Contact: Mike Andrews, Visitor Development Officer, Blacktoft Sands RSPB reserve, Hillcrest, Whitgift, Nr Goole, E Yorks DN14 8HL. 01405 704 665.
e-mail: michael.andrews@rspb.org.uk

3. FLAMBOROUGH CLIFFS NATURE RESERVE

Yorkshire Wildlife Trust
Location: TA 240 722. The reserve is part of the Flamborough headland, approx 4 miles NE

of Bridlington. From Bridlington take B1255 to Flamborough and follow the signs for the North Landing.

Access: Open all year. Public pay and display car park at North Landing gives access to both parts of the reserve. Paths not suitable for wheelchairs.

Facilities: Car park (pay and display), trails, refreshments available at café at North Landing (open Apr-Oct 10am-5pm), toilets.

Public transport: Flamborough is served by buses from Bridlington and Bempton. Phone 01482 222 222 for details.

Habitat: Coastal cliffs, species rich and rough grassland and scrub. Spectacular views of this chalk coastline and living seas beyond.

Key birds: *Summer:* Puffin, Guillemot, Razorbill, Kittiwake, Shag, Fulmar, Skylark, Meadow Pipit, Linnet, Whitethroat, Yellowhammer, Tree Sparrow, occasional Corn Bunting. *Passage migrants:* Fieldfare, Redwing and occasional rarities such as Wryneck and Red-backed Shrike.

Other notable flora and fauna: Pyramidal and northern marsh orchids, harebell, thrift on cliff tops. Migrant butterflies such as painted ladies.

Contact: Yorkshire Wildlife Trust, 01904 659 570; e-mail:info@ywt.org.uk - www.ywt.org.uk

4. NORTH CAVE WETLANDS

Yorkshire Wildlife Trust

Location: SE 887 328. At NW of North Cave village, approx 10 miles W of Hull. From junction 28 of M62, follow signs to North Cave on B1230. In village, turn L and follow road to next crossroads where you go L, then take next L onto Dryham Lane.

Access: Open all year with car parking on Dryham Lane. Some of the footpaths are suitable for all abilities.

Facilities: Five bird-viewing hides and screen including unique straw bale constructions, four are accessible to wheelchair users. Portaloo available on site and Wild Bird Café open seven days a week for refreshments on Dryham Lane, adjacent to reserve.

Public transport: Buses serve North Cave from Hull and Goole: telephone 01482 222 222 for details.

Habitat: Former gravel pits have been converted into various lagoons for wetland birds, including one reedbed. There is also scrub and hedgerows, and since 2010 a large area of wet grassland.

Key birds: More than 200 different species have been recorded including Great Crested Grebe, Gadwall, Pochard, Sparrowhawk, Avocet, Ringed Plover, Golden Plover, Dunlin, Ruff, Redshank, Green Sandpiper, Common Sandpiper and Tree Sparrow.

Other notable flora and fauna: Dragon and damselflies, several butterfly species.

Contact: Trust HQ, 01904 659 570; e-mail:info@ywt.org.uk www.ywt.org.uk

5. SPURN NNR

Yorkshire Wildlife Trust.

Location: Entrance Gate TA 417 151. 26 miles from Hull. Take A1033 from Hull to Patrington then B1445 from Patrington to Easington and unclassified roads on to Kilnsea and Spurn Point.

Access: Normally open at all times. Vehicle admission fee (at present £3). No charge for pedestrians. No dogs allowed under any circumstances, not even in cars. Coaches by permit only (must be in advance).

Facilities: Reserve open all year, Blue Bell café open daily. Four hides. Public toilets in Blue Bell car park.

Public transport: Nearest bus service is at Easington (3.5 miles away). 2011 Sunday service to the Point, hail and ride, Easter to last weekend of October.

Habitat: Sand dunes with marram and sea buckthorn scrub. Mudflats around Humber Estuary.

Key birds: *Spring:* Many migrants on passage and often rare birds such as Red-backed Shrike, Bluethroat etc. *Autumn:* Passage migrants and rarities such as Wryneck, Pallas's Warbler. *Winter:* Waders and Brent Goose.

Other notable flora and fauna: Unique habitats and geographical position makes Spurn a very interesting site for butterflies (25 species recorded) and moths.

Contact: Outer Humber Officer, Spurn NNR, Blue Bell, Kilnsea, Hull HU12 0UB. e-mail:andrew.gibson@ywt.org.uk

6. TOPHILL LOW NATURE RESERVE

Yorkshire Water.

Location: TA 071 482. Nine miles SE of Driffield and ten miles NE of Beverley. Signposted from village of Watton on A164.

Access: Open daily (9am-6pm). Charges: £2.50 per

person. £1 concessions. No dogs allowed. Provision for disabled visitors (paths, ramps, hides, toilet etc). Coaches welcome.
Facilities: Visitor Centre with toilets open every weekend and most week days. Disabled toilet open at all times, 12 hides (five with access for wheelchairs), good paths and sightings board.
Public transport: None.
Habitat: Open water (two reservoirs), marshes, wader scrapes, woodland and thorn scrub.
Key birds: 160 to 170 species each year. *Winter:* SSSI for wildfowl numbers, plus one of the UK's largest Black-headed and Common Gull roosts. Regular wintering Bittern. Active feeding station with

Brambling. Woodcock. *Spring/early summer:* Passage waders, Black Tern and Black-necked Grebe. Breeding Little Ringed Plover, Common Tern, Kingfisher and Barn Owl, plus a diverse variety of warblers. *Late summer/autumn:* Up to 20 species of passage wader.
Other notable flora and fauna: Specialist grassland and wetland flora including orchids. Fauna includes red-eyed damselfly, marbled white and brown argus butterflies, grass snake, otter, water vole and roe deer.
Contact: Richard Hampshire, Tophill Low Nature Reserve, 01377 270 690.
e-mail: richard.hampshire@yorkshirewater.co.uk

Yorkshire, North

1. COATHAM MARSH

Tees Valley Wildlife Trust.
Location: NZ 585 250. Located on W edge of Redcar. Access from minor road to Warrenby from A1085/A1042.
Access: Reserve is open throughout daylight hours. Please keep to permissive footpaths only.
Facilities: Good footpaths around site. Shops and facilities available in Redcar close by.
Public transport: Very frequent bus service between Middlesbrough and Redcar. Nearest stops are in Coatham 0.25 mile from reserve (Arriva tel 0871 200 2233). Redcar Central Station one mile from site. Frequent trains from Middlesbrough and Darlington.
Habitat: Freshwater wetlands, lakes, reedbeds.
Key birds: *Spring/autumn:* Wader passage (including Wood Sandpiper and Greenshank). *Summer:* Passerines include Sedge Warbler, Yellow Wagtail. *Winter:* Ducks (including Smew). *Occasional rarities:* Water Rail, Great White Egret, Avocet, Bearded Tit and Bittern.
Other notable flora and fauna: The lime-rich soil allows wildflower meadows to grow around the site, including northern marsh orchid. Also good for insects incuding migrant hawker dragonfly.
Contact: Tees Valley Wildlife Trust, 01287 636 382; e-mail: info@teeswildlife.org

2. FILEY BRIGG ORNITHOLOGICAL GROUP BIRD OBSERVATORY

FBOG and Yorkshire Wildlife Trust (The Dams).
Location: TA 10 68 07. Two access roads into Filey from A165 (Scarborough to Bridlington road). Filey is ten miles N of Bridlington and eight miles S of Scarborough.
Access: Open at all times. Dogs only in Parish Wood and The Old Tip (on lead). Coaches welcome. Park in the North Cliff Country Park.
Facilities: No provisions for disabled at present. Two hides at The Dams, one on The Brigg (open most weekends from late Jul-Oct, key can be hired from Country Park café). Toilets in Country Park (Apr-

Nov 1) and town centre. Nature trails at The Dams, Parish Wood/Old Tip. Cliff top walk for seabirds along Cleveland Way.
Public transport: All areas within a mile of Filey railway station. Trains into Filey tel. 08457 484 950; buses into Filey tel. 01723 503 020
Habitat: The Dams — two freshwater lakes, fringed with some tree cover and small reedbeds. Parish Wood — a newly planted wood which leads to the Old Tip, the latter has been fenced (for stock and crop strips) though there is a public trail. Carr Naze has a pond and can produce newly arrived migrants.
Key birds: The Dams: Breeding and wintering water birds, breeding Sedge Warbler, Reed Warbler and Tree Sparrow. The Tip: Important for breeding Skylark, Meadow Pipit, common warblers and Grey Partridge. *Winter:* Buntings, including Lapland. *Seawatch Hide - Jul-Oct:* All four skuas, shearwaters, terns. *Winter:* Divers and grebes. Totem Pole Field: A new project should encourage breeding species and wintering larks, buntings etc. Many sub-rare/rare migrants possible at all sites.
Contact: e-mail: secretary-at-fbog.co.uk www.fbog.co.uk

3. FYLINGDALES MOOR CONSERVATION AREA

Hawk and Owl Trust /Strickland Estate/Fylingdales Moor ESS Co Ltd.
Location: NZ 947 003. Off A171 S of Whitby. On eastern side of North York Moors National Park, stretching between Sneaton High Moor (Newton House Plantation) and the coast at Ravenscar. Crossed by A171 Scarborough to Whitby road.
Access: Open access. Parking (inc for coaches) available at Jugger Howe Layby (OS NZ 947 003) on A171 Scarborough to Whitby road.
Facilities: Numerous footpaths including the Jugger Howe Nature Trail, Lyke Wake Walk and Robin Hood's Bay Road.
Public transport: Half-hourly bus service (No. 93 and X93) between Scarborough and Whitby, nearest stop at Flask Inn (approx. 1 mile N of Jugger Howe Layby). Services run by Arriva (0191 281 1313) www.arrivabus.co.uk
Habitat: About 6,800 acres (2,750 hectares) of

heather moorland (former grouse moor), with scattered trees and wooded valleys and gulleys. Managed exclusively for wildlife and archaeological remains, the moor is an SSSI and SPA (Merlin and Golden Plover) and a special area of conservation.

Key birds: As well as more than 80 more common bird species, rare and endangered breeding birds include harriers, Merlin, Golden Plover, Red Grouse, Curlew, Wheatear, Stonechat, Whinchat, Skylark, Marsh Tit, Willow Tit, Linnet, Bullfinch, Reed Bunting and Yellowhammer. The moor is also home to Kestrel, Lapwing, Snipe, Cuckoo, Meadow Pipit, Grey Wagtail and Wood Warbler and visited by Peregrine.

Other notable flora and fauna: Mammals include otter, roe deer, brown hare, stoat, weasel and badger. Important for water vole. Three species of heather, plus cranberry, cowberry, moonwort and, in wetter parts, bog myrtle, lesser twayblade, bog asphodel, butterwort, marsh helleborine, and sundews can be found. Also rare orchids and sedges. Insect species include large heath and small pearl-bordered fritillary butterflies and emperor moth.

Contact: Professor John Edwards, The Hawk and Owl Trust., 01751 417 398. www.hawkandowl.org e-mail: john.edwards@wildfylingdales.co.uk

4. GOUTHWAITE RESERVOIR

Yorkshire Water.

Location: SE 12 69. 2.5miles NW of Pately Bridge on the B6265.

Access: Open all hours, all year.

Facilities: Three viewing areas on edge of reservoir.

Public transport: Nidderdale Rambler route 24/25 (summer Sundays and bank holidays). Harrogate and District Travel 01423 566 061.

Habitat: Reservoir, deciduous woodland shoreline, moors.

Key birds: Green Woodpecker, Nuthatch, Merlin and Buzzard all year. Summer warblers with passage Osprey. *Winter*: Surrounding morland good for raptors such as Red Kite, Buzzard, Hen Harrier, Merlin and Kestrel as well as Red Grouse and Lapwing. Goosander, Goldeneye and Whooper Swan.

Contact: Geoff Lomas, Catchment & Recreation Officer, PO Box 52, Bradford, BD6 2LZ. www.yorkshirewater.co.uk (turn to recreation page).

5. LOWER DERWENT VALLEY

Natural England (Yorkshire and Humber Region), Yorkshire Wildlife Trust and Countryside Trust.

Location: Six miles SE of York, stretching 12 miles S along the River Derwent from Newton-on-Derwent to Wressle and along the Pocklington Canal. Visitor facilities at Bank Island (SE 691 448), Wheldrake Ings YWT (SE 691 444 see separate entry), Thorganby (SE 692 418) and North Duffield Carrs (SE 697 367).

Access: Open all year. No dogs. Disabled access at North Duffield Carrs.

Facilities: Bank Island — two hides, viewing tower. Wheldrake Ings — four hides. Thorganby — viewing platform. North Duffield Carrs — two hides and wheelchair access. Car parks at all sites, height restriction of 2.1m at Bank Island and North Duffield Carrs. Bicycle stands in car parks at Bank Island and North Duffield Carrs.

Public transport: Bus from York/Selby — contact First (01904 622 992).

Habitat: Hay meadow and pasture, swamp, open water and alder/willow woodland.

Key birds: *Spring/summer*: Breeding wildfowl and waders, incl. Garganey, Snipe and Ruff. Barn Owl and warblers. *Winter/spring*: 20,000-plus waterfowl including Whooper Swan, wild geese, Teal and Wigeon. Large gull roost, incl. white-winged gulls. Also passage waders, incl. Whimbrel.

Other notable flora and fauna: A walk alongside the Pocklington Canal is particularly good for a wide range of aquatic plants and animals.

Contact: Peter Roworth, Senior Reserve Manager, 01904 435 500; email: york@naturalengland.org.uk www.naturalengland.org.uk Pocklington Canal: www.pocklington.gov.uk/pcas

6. NOSTERFIELD LOCAL NATURE RESERVE

Lower Ure Conservation Trust

Location: SE 278 795 Six miles north of Ripon, between villages of West Tanfield and Nosterfield, via A6108 (Ripon to Masham road) and approximately 4 miles west of A1.

Access: Reserve open all year, two hides, one roofed

viewing screen. Main car park, a lower 'viewing area' beyond car park permits viewing from cars only. Please keep to permissive footpath at all times. Dogs permitted, on short lead, only on part of the permissive footpath network.

Facilities: Permissive footpath from Main Hide to Tanfield Hide (500 m) is disabled-friendly. Terrain is more uneven from car park to Northern Viewing Screen (1000 m). Two disabled-friendly hides, interpretation panels (Main Hide), comfortable "woolly" seats, lowered windows for wheelchair users. No other on-site facilities.

Habitat: Primarily wetland grassland and open water. Also Magnesian limestone grassland, gravel banks, hedgerows and scrub.

Key species: Primarily for wet grassland waders and waterfowl and site of North Yorkshire's first breeding Avocets (2008). Annually 150 species recorded – more than 225 species recorded overall (including rarities). *Spring/autumn:* Wader passage between 25 to 30 species recorded annually, also terns.
Summer: Breeding species include Redshank, Lapwing, Avocet, Oystercatcher, Curlew, Ringed Plover, Shoveler, Gadwall, Barn Owl, Skylark, Lesser Whitethroat, Tree Sparrow, Linnet, Reed Bunting.
Autumn: passage waders including near-annual Pectoral Sandpiper. *Winter:* Wildfowl (Wigeon, Teal, Greylag Geese), waders (Golden Plover, Lapwing, Curlew) and Peregrine.

Other notable flora and fauna: Specialist grassland and wetland flora, including seven species of orchid, mudwort, yellow rattle, golden dock. Butterflies include white-letter hairstreak, brown argus, wall

and large colony of common blue. Dragonflies include emperor, black-tailed skimmer, red-veined darter (has bred). Also, brown hare and water shrew.
Contact: email:luct@luct.org.uk www.luct.org.uk

7. TIMBLE INGS

Yorkshire Water
Location: SE 15 53. West of Harrogate, north of Otley. Off the A59 south of Blubberhouses, near Timble village.
Access: Open at all times, all year.
Facilities: Toilets, cafes, pubs, coach parking all nearby. Hard forest tracks.
Habitat: Woodland and nearby reservoir.
Key birds: Bradford OG species list stands at 134. Habitat management work by Yorkshire Water makes site attractive to Long-eared and Tawny Owls, Nightjars and Tree Pipits. Buzzards now nest and Red Kites seen regularly. Goshawk numbers in decline. *Summer:* Breeding species inc Redpoll, Siskin, Crossbill, Woodcock, Redstart and Grasshopper Warbler. Short-eared Owls hunt adjacent moorland. *Winter:* Fieldfare, Redwing, Brambling, occasional Waxwings and Hawfinches.
Other notable flora and fauna: Roe deer, badger, brown hare, shrew, vole and mouse species (all detected from owl pellets). New ponds attractive to amphibians and dragonflies, inc broad-bodied chaser, emperor and black darter.
Contact: Geoff Lomas, Catchment & Recreation Officer, Yorkshire Water, Western House, Halifax Road, Bradford BD6 2LZ.
www.yorkshirewater.co.uk (turn to recreation page).

Yorkshire South & West

1. BOLTON INGS (DEARNE VALLEY)

RSPB (Northern England)
Location: SE 425 020. Park at RSPB Old Moor and walk east along Trans Pennine Trail to Bolton Ings. By car, Old Moor is just off Manvers Way (A633). From the M1, take junction 36 then follow the A6195. From the A1M, take junction 37 then follow the A635 towards the A6195.
Access: Open all year round. Dearne Way footpath and Trans-Pennine Trail open at all times, but not suitable for wheelchair users.
Facilities: Cormorant View hide. More facilities at RSPB Old Moor.
Public transport: Wombwell and Swinton train stations approximatley 3 miles from reserve. Buses run to Old Moor reserve from Barnsley, Doncaster and Meadowhall – call Traveline on 01709 515 151 for details. Trans-Pennine Trail runs along southern edge of reserve.
Habitat: 43 hectares of reedbed and scrub. Excellent warbler habitat.

Key birds: *All year:* Kingfisher, Grey Heron. *Winter:* Stonechat. *Spring/Summer:* Reed Bunting. breeding waders and warblers, Cuckoo, Garganey. *Autumn:* Passage waders including Greenshank, Green Sandpiper, Golden Plover. *Winter:* Wildfowl, including Goosander, Wigeon and Teal.
Other notable flora and fauna: Dragonflies inc. banded demoiselle, brown hare.
Contact: RSPB Old Moor, Old Moor Lane, Wombwell, Barnsley, South Yorkshire, S73 0YF. 01226 751 593 e-mail: old.moor@rspb.org.uk - www.rspb.org.uk

2. DENABY INGS NATURE RESERVE

Yorkshire Wildlife Trust.
Location: Reserve on Pastures Rd, off A6023 near Mexborough. Jucntion signed Denaby Ings Nature Reserve. Proceed along Pastures Road for 0.5 miles and watch for a sign on R marking entrance to car park. From car park, climb flight of concrete steps to enter reserve.
Access: Open all year.
Facilities: Car park, 2 hides, interpretation panels, circular trail.
Public transport: None.
Habitat: Water, deciduous woodland, marsh, willows.

NATURE RESERVES - NORTHERN ENGLAND

Key birds: *Spring/Summer:* Waterfowl, Barn Owl, Tawny Owl, Sand Martin, Swallow, Whinchat, Grasshopper Warbler, Lesser Whitethroat, Whitethroat, other warblers, Kingfisher. *Passage:* Waders, Common, Arctic and Black Terns, Redstart, Wheatear. *Winter:* Whooper Swan, wildfowl, Jack Snipe, waders, Grey Wagtail, Fieldfare, Redwing, Brambling, Siskin. *All year:* Corn Bunting, Yellowhammer, all three woodpeckers, common woodland birds, possible Willow Tit.
Other notable flora and fauna:
Contact: Yorkshire Wildlife Trust, 01904 659 570. e-mail:info@ywt.org.uk - www.ywt.org.

3. FAIRBURN INGS

RSPB (Northern England).
Location: SE 452 277. 12 miles from Leeds, six miles from Pontefract, three miles from Castleford, situated next to A1246 from J42 of A1.
Access: Reserve and hides open every day except Dec 25/26. Centre and shop open each day (9am-5pm). Dogs on leads welcome. Boardwalks leading to Pickup Pool, feeding station and Kingfisher viewpoint are all wheelchair-friendly.
Facilities: Five hides open at all times. Toilets open 9am-5pm. Disabled toilets and baby-changing facilities. Hot and cold drinks, snacks available. Wildlife garden, pond-dipping and mini beast areas, plus duck feeding platform. Coach parking for club visits.
Public transport: Nearest train stations are Castleford, Micklefield and Garforth. No bus service.
Habitat: Open water, wet grassland, marsh and fen scrub, reedbed, reclaimed colliery spoil heaps.
Key birds: *All year:* Tree Sparrow, Willow Tit, Green Woodpecker, Bullfinch. *Winter:* Smew, Goldeneye, Goosander, Wigeon, Peregrine. *Spring:* Osprey, Little Gull, Wheatear, five species of tern inc annual Black Tern.

Summer: Nine species of breeding warbler, Grey Heron, Gadwall, Little Ringed Plover.
Other notable flora and fauna: Brown hare, harvest mouse, roe deer, Leisler's and Daubenton's bats, 28 species of butterfly and 20 species of dragonfly.
Contact: Laura Bentley, Visitor Services Manager, Fairburn Ings Visitor Centre, 01977 628 191.

4. HARDCASTLE CRAGS

National Trust.
Location: From Halifax, follow A646 W for five miles to Hebden Bridge and pick up National Trust signs in town centre on the A6033 Keighley Road. Follow this for 0.75 miles. Turn L at the National Trust sign to the car parks. Alternate pay-and-display car park at Clough Hole on Widdop Road, Heptonstall.
Access: Open all year. NT car park charges: £3.50 all day weekdays and for up to 3 hours at weekends, £5 at weekends and bank holidays. No charge for NT members and disabled badge holders.
Facilities: 2 small pay car parks, cycle racks and several way-marked trails. Gibson Mill visitor centre (not NT property) has toilets, café, exhibitions. Not connected to any mains services, in extreme conditions the mill may be closed for health and safety reasons.
Public transport: Good public transport links. Trains to Hebden Bridge from Manchester or Leeds every 30 minutes. Call 08457 484 950. Weekday buses every 30 minutes to Keighley Road, then 1 mile walk to Midghole. Summer weekend bus 906 Widdop-Hardcastle Crags leaves Hebden Bridge rail station every 90 minutes 9.20am-6.05pm. Tel: 0113 245 7676.
Habitat: 400 acres of unspoilt wooded valleys, ravines, streams, hay meadows and moorland edge.
Key birds: *Spring/summer:* Cuckoo, Redstart, Lesser Whitethroat, Garden Warbler, Blackcap, Wood Warbler, Chiffchaff, Spotted Flycatcher, Pied Flycatcher, Curlew, Lapwing, Meadow Pipit. *All year:* Sparrowhawk, Kestrel, Green and Greater Spotted Woodpeckers, Lesser Spotted Woodpecker, Tawny Owl, Barn Owl, Little Owl, Jay, Coal Tit, Dipper, Grey Wagtail and other woodland species. Goshawk in Crimsworth Dean.
Other notable flora and fauna: Northern hairy wood ant, moss carder bee, tree bumble bee, killarney fern, brittle bladder fern.
Contact: National Trust, Hardcastle Crags, 01422 844 518. www.nationaltrust.org.uk

5. INGBIRCHWORTH RESERVOIR

Yorkshire Water.
Location: Leave the M1 at J37 and take the A628 towards Manchester and Penistone. After five miles you reach a roundabout. Turn R onto the A629 Huddersfield road. After 2.5 miles you reach Ingbirchworth. At a sign for The Fountain Inn, turn L. Pass a pub. The road bears L to cross the dam, proceed straight forward onto the track

leading to the car park.

Access: Open all year. One of the few reservoirs in the area with footpath access.

Facilities: Car park, picnic tables.

Habitat: Reservoir, small strip of deciduous woodland.

Key birds: *Spring/summer*: Whinchat, warblers, woodland birds, House Martin. *Spring/autumn passage*: Little Ringed Plover, Ringed Plover, Dotterel, other waders, Common Tern, Arctic Tern, Black Tern, Yellow Wagtail, Wheatear. *Winter*: Wildfowl, Golden Plover, waders, occasional rare gull such as Iceland or Glaucous, Grey Wagtail, Fieldfare, Redwing, Brambling, Redpoll.

Contact: Yorkshire Water, PO Box 52, Bradford, BD6 2LZ. www.yorkshirewater.co.uk (recreation page).

6. OLD MOOR (DEARNE VALLEY)

RSPB (Northern England).

Location: SE 422 022. By car, Old Moor is just off Manvers Way (A633). From the M1, take junction 36 then follow the A6195. From the A1M, take junction 37 then follow the A635 towards the A6195.

Access: Open all year except Christmas day and Boxing day. April 1-Sept 30 (9.30am-8pm, visitor centre closes at 5pm). Oct 1-March 31 (9.30am-4pm). Entry fees for non-RSPB members: adults £3.00, children £1.50, Concessions £2.00.

Facilities: Visitor centre, café, shop, education and meeting rooms. Accessible toilets. Two trails with seven hides, all suitable for wheelchair users. Family explorer backpacks and binoculars available to hire. Free electric scooters available on request.

Public transport: Wombwell and Swinton train stations approx 3 miles from reserve. Buses run to Old Moor reserve from Barnsley, Doncaster and Meadowhall – call 01709 515 151 for details. Trans-Pennine Trail runs along southern edge of reserve.

Habitat: Lakes, flood meadows, wader scrape and reedbeds.

Key birds: *All year*: Kingfisher, Little Owl. *Winter*: Large numbers of wildfowl, spectacular flocks of Lapwing and Golden Plover, Peregrine, Tree Sparrow in garden feeding area. *Summer*: Breeding waders, inc drumming Snipe, and wildfowl.

Other notable flora and fauna: Water vole, brown hare, pygmy shrew, wildflowers including orchids and adders tongue fern.

Contact: RSPB Old Moor, 01226 751 593; e-mail: old. moor@rspb.org.uk - www.rspb.org.uk

7. POTTERIC CARR

Yorkshire Wildlife Trust.

Location: SE 589 007. From M18 junction 3 take A6182 (Doncaster) and at first roundabout take third exit; entrance and car park are on R after 50m.

Access: Open daily 9am-5pm. Obtain ticket on arrival, YWT members free; Single £3; family £6.50 (two adults and up to three children); concession £2.50; child £1.50. Groups of ten or more should book

in advance.

Facilities: Around 8 km of paths (5 km accessible to wheelchairs, unassisted), 14 viewing hides (10 suitable for the disabled) and a Field Centre with café, open daily (10am-4pm) with hot and cold drinks, snacks and meals. Toilets at entrance reception, in Field Centre (during café opening times), and outside Field Centre.

Public transport: Nearest railway station is Doncaster. From Frenchgate Interchange, take bus number 72 or 75, and alight at B&Q on Woodfield Way. Cross White Rose Way, walk down Mallard Way. Cross car park to reserve entrance in Sedum House.

Habitat: Reed fen, subsidence ponds, artificial pools, grassland, woodland.

Key birds: 96 species have bred. Nesting waterfowl (inc. Shoveler, Gadwall, Pochard), Water Rail, Kingfisher, all three woodpeckers, Lesser Whitethroat, Reed and Sedge Warblers, Willow Tit. *Passage/winter*: Bittern, Marsh Harrier, Black Tern, waders, wildfowl.

Other notable flora and fauna: 20 species of dragonfly recorded, 28 species of butterfly including purple hairstreak and dingy skipper. Palmate and great crested newt.

Contact: Trust HQ, 01904 659 570.
e-mail: potteric.carr@ywt.org.uk
www.potteric-carr.org.uk

8. SPROTBOROUGH FLASH RESERVE AND THE DON GORGE

Yorkshire Wildlife Trust.

Location: From A1, follow A630 to Rotherham 4.8km W of Doncaster. After 0.8km, turn R at traffic lights to Sprotborough. After approx 1.6km the road drops down into Don Gorge. Cross a bridge over river, then another over a canal, turn immediately L. Public car park on left.

Access: Open all year.

Facilities: Three hides, footpaths, interpretation panels.

Public transport: River bus from Doncaster in summer months. Bus service from Doncaster to Sprotbrough village (10 minute walk to reserve).

Habitat: River, reed, gorge, woodland, limestone grassland

Key birds: *Summer*: Hirundines, Lesser Whitethroat, Whitethroat, Garden Warbler, Blackcap, Chiffchaff, Willow Warbler, Cuckoo. *Spring/autumn passage*: Little Ringed Plover, Dunlin, Greenshank, Green Sandpiper, waders, Yellow Wagtail. *Winter/All year*: Wildfowl, Water Rail, Snipe, Little Owl, Tawny Owl, all three woodpeckers, thrushes, Siskin, possible Corn Bunting.

Other notable flora and fauna:

Contact: Trust HQ . 01904 659 570.
e-mail:info@ywt.org.uk
www.ywt.org.uk

South East England

Berkshire, Buckinghamshire, Hampshire, Kent, London (Greater), Surrey, East Sussex, West Sussex

Berkshire

1. DINTON PASTURES

Wokingham District Council.
Location: SU 784 718. Country Park, E of Reading off B3030 between Hurst and Winnersh.
Access: Open all year, dawn to dusk. Car parking charges apply 8am to 6pm each day. Dogs allowed.
Facilities: Three hides (one adapted for wheelchairs), information centre, car park, café, toilets (suitable for wheelchairs). Electric buggies for hire. Various trails between one and three miles in length.
Public transport: Not known.
Habitat: Mature gravel pits and banks of River Loddon. Sandford Lake managed for wildfowl, Lavell's Lake best for waders and scrub species.
Key birds: *All year*: Kingfisher, Water Rail. *Spring/summer*: Hobby, Little Ringed Plover, Common Tern, Nightingale, common warblers. *Winter*: Bittern, wildfowl (inc. Goldeneye, Wigeon, Teal, Gadwall), thrushes. Waders include Green and Common Sandpipers, Snipe, Redshank.
Other notable flora and fauna: Water vole, harvest mouse, great crested newt, Loddon pondweed and Loddon lily. Good range of dragonflies inc emperor, black-tailed skimmer, white-legged and banded agrion damselfies and migrant hawker.
Contact: The Ranger, Dinton Pastures Country Park, Davis Street, Hurst, Berks. 0118 934 2 016.
e-mail: countryside@wokingham.gov.uk

2. HUNGERFORD MARSH

Berks, Bucks & Oxon Wildlife Trust.
Location: SU 333 687. On W side of Hungerford, beside the Kennet and Avon Canal. From town centre, go along Church Street past the town hall. Turn R under the railway. Follow public footpath over swing bridge on the canal near the church. The reserve is separated from Freeman's Marsh by a line of willows and bushes.
Access: Open all year. Please keep to the footpath. Dogs on leads please.
Facilities: Car park.
Public transport: Hungerford railway station half mile from reserve.
Habitat: An idyllic waterside site with chalk stream, unimproved rough grazing and reedbed.
Key birds: 120 species recorded. *Spring/summer*: Reed and Grasshopper Warblers. *Winter*: Siskin and Water Rail. *All year*: Kingfisher, Mute Swan, Mallard, Little Grebe.
Other notable fauna: Water vole, otter and grass snake.
Contact: BBOWT, The Lodge, 1 Armstrong Road, Littlemore, Oxford OX4 4XT. 01865 775 476.
e-mail: info@bbowt.org.uk www.bbowt.org.uk

3. LAVELL'S LAKE

Wokingham District Council.
Location: SU 785 727. Via Sandford Lane off B3030 between Hurst and Winnersh E of Reading.
Access: Dawn to dusk. No permit required. Dogs on leads all year.
Facilities: Car park, two public hides, one with disabled access, one members-only hide (see below), viewing screen.
Public transport: Thames Travel bus services 128/129 run between Reading and Wokingham, stopping outside Dinton Pastures main entrance. Nearest train services are at either Winnersh, or Winnersh Triangle.
Habitat: Gravel pits, two wader scrapes, reed beds, rough grassland, marshy area, Sand Martin banks, between River Loddon and Emm Brook. To N of Lavell's Lake gravel pits are being restored to attract birds. The lake at Lea Farm is viewable walking N along the River Loddon from Lavell's Lake over small

green bridge. It is on R and can be seen through a viewing screen and a members-only hide for Friends of Lavell's Lake (see www.foll.org.uk). No access is permitted.
Key birds: *All year:* Great Crested Grebe, Gadwall, Sparrowhawk, Kingfisher, Red Kite, Buzzard, Cetti's Warbler. *Summer:* Common Tern, Redshank, Lapwing, Hobby, warblers include Reed, Sedge, Whitethroat. *Passage:* Garganey, Little Ringed Plover, Common and Green Sandpiper and Greenshank. *Winter:* Water Rail, Bittern, Little Egret, Teal, Shoveler, Pochard, Goldeneye, occasional Smew and Goosander along River Loddon. Siskin, Lesser Redpoll, Fieldfare and Redwing.
Contact: As for Dinton Pastures or via www.foll.org.uk

4. MOOR GREEN LAKES

Blackwater Valley Countryside Partnership.
Location: SU 805 628. Main access and parking off Lower Sandhurst Road, Finchampstead (RG40 3TH). Alternatively, Rambler's car park, Chandlers Lane, Yateley near junction with Mill Lane (SU 820 619).
Access: Car parks open dawn-dusk. Dogs on leads. Site can be used by wheelchairs, though surface not particularly suitable.
Facilities: Two bird hides open to members of Moor Green Lakes Group (contact BVCP for details), two viewing screens. Feeder station viewable from bench on adjacent path. Footpaths along western, southern and eastern perimeter of site: Blackwater Valley long distance footpath passes alongside site.
Public transport: Nearest railway station, South West Trains Crowthorne.
Habitat: Thirty-six hectares (90 acres) in total. Three lakes with gravel islands, beaches and scrapes. River Blackwater, grassland, surrounded by willow, ash, hazel and thorn hedgerows.

Key birds: *Spring/Summer:* Redshank, Little Ringed Plover, Willow Warbler. Also Whitethroat, Sedge Warbler, Common Sandpiper, Common Tern, Barn Owl. Dunlin and Black Tern on passage. Lapwings breed on site and several sightings of Red Kite. *Winter:* Wigeon, Teal, Gadwall and of particular interest, a flock of Goosander.
Other notable flora and fauna: 27 species of butterfly and 15 species of dragonfly have been recorded. See www.mglg.org.uk for more details.
Contact: Blackwater Valley Countryside Partnership. 01252 331 353. www.blackwater-valley.org.uk e-mail:blackwater.valley@hants.gov.uk

5. WILDMOOR HEATH

Berks, Bucks & Oxon Wildlife Trust.
Location: SU 842 627. Between Bracknell and Sandhurst. From Sandhurst shopping area, take the A321 NW towards Wokingham. Turn E at the mini-roundabout on to Crowthorne Road. Continue for about one mile through one set of traffic lights. Car park is on the R at the bottom of the hill.
Access: Open all year. No access to woodland N of Rackstraw Road at Broadmoor Bottom. Please keep dogs on a lead.
Facilities: Car park.
Public transport: The reserve is one mile north of Sandhurst railway station.
Habitat: Wet and dry lowland heath, bog, mixed woodland and mature Scots pine plantation.
Key birds: *Spring/summer:* Wood Lark, Nightjar, Dartford Warbler and Stonechat.
Other notable flora and fauna: Good range of dragonflies including keeled skimmer and ruddy darter, slow worm, adder, grass snake, lizard. Bog plants inc sundews.
Contact: Trust HQ. 01865 775 476. e-mail: info@bbowt.org.uk www.bbowt.org.uk

---

Buckinghamshire

1. BURNHAM BEECHES NNR

City of London.
Location: SU 950 850. N of Slough and on W side of A355, running between J2 of the M40 and J6 of M4. Entry from A355 via Beeches Road. Also smaller parking areas in Hawthorn Lane and Pumpkin Hill to the S and Park Lane to the W.
Access: Open all year, except Dec 25. Main Lord Mayor's Drive open from 8am-dusk. Beeches Café, public toilets and information point open 10am to 5pm. Motorised buggy available for hire. Network of wheelchair accessible roads and paths.
Facilities: Car parks, toilets, café, visitor information centre. Easy access path network, suitable for wheelchairs, most start at Victory Cross. Coach parking possible, additional coach parking on request.
Public transport: Train: nearest station Slough on the

main line from Paddington. Arriva, First and Jason Tours buses 40 and 74 stop at reserve. Call Traveline on 0870 608 2608.
Habitat: Ancient woodland, streams, pools, heathland, grassland, scrub.
Key birds: *Spring/summer:* Cuckoo, possible Turtle Dove. *Winter:* Siskin, Crossbill, regular large flocks c100 Brambling. Possible Woodcock. *All year:* Mandarin (good population), all three woodpeckers, Sparrowhawk, Marsh Tit, possible Willow Tit, Red Kite and Buzzard.
Other notable flora and fauna: Ancient beech and oak pollards with associated wildlife. Rich array of fungi.
Contact: City of London Corporation, Burnham Beeches Office, Hawthorn Lane, Farnham Common, SL2 3TE . 01753 647 358.
e-mail: burnham.beeches@cityoflondon.gov.uk www.cityoflondon.gov.uk

NATURE RESERVES - SOUTH EAST ENGLAND

2. CALVERT JUBILEE

Berks, Bucks & Oxon Wildlife Trust.
Location: SP 849 425. Near Steeple Claydon, NW of Aylesbury, Bucks.
Access: Access by permit (free) only. Apply to Trust who provide map and information with permit. Please keep to network of paths.
Facilities: Two hides, small car park.
Public transport: None.
Habitat: Ex-clay pit, railway and landfill site. Now with deep lake, marginal reedbed and scrub habitat.
Key birds: *Summer:* Nesting Common Tern on rafts, Kingfisher, Hobby, warblers and occasional Nightingale. *Passage migrants:* Include Black Tern and flyover waders. *Winter:* Bittern, Water Rail and large gull roost with occasional Glaucous and Iceland Gull. Rarer birds turn up regularly.
Other notable flora and fauna: Rare butterflies, including dingy and grizzled skippers andblack hairstreak.
Contact: Trust HQ. 01865 775 476.
e-mail: info@bbowt.org.uk www.bbowt.org.uk

3. CHURCH WOOD RESERVE

RSPB (Midlands Regional Office).
Location: SU 971 872. Reserve lies three miles from J2 of M40 in Hedgerley. Park in village, walk down small track beside pond for approx 200m. Reserve entrance is on L.
Access: Open all year. Not suitable for wheelchair users.
Facilities: Two marked paths with some inclines.
Public transport: None.
Habitat: Mixed woodland.
Key birds: *Spring/summer:* Red Kite, Buzzard, Blackcap, Garden Warbler, Swallow. *Winter:* Redpoll, Siskin. *All year:* Marsh Tit, Willow Tit, Nuthatch, Treecreeper, Great Spotted and Green Woodpeckers.
Other notable flora and fauna: Wood anenome, wood sorrel, bluebell and other woodland plants. Brimstone, comma, white admiral and peacock butterflies. Good range of fungi species.
Contact: RSPB Central England Office, 01865 351 163. www.rspb.org.uk/wildlife/reserves

4. COLLEGE LAKE

Berks, Bucks & Oxon Wildlife Trust.
Location: SU 934 140. 2 miles N of Tring on B488, quarter mile N of canal bridge at Bulbourne turn L into gated entrance.
Access: Open Apr-Oct (10am-5pm); Nov-Mar (10am-4pm), closed Mondays. Wheelchair access to hides and disabled toilets.
Facilities: Large car park, coach park, many hides, interpretive buildings. Network of wheelchair-friendly paths, visitor centre, toilets.
Public transport: Tring railway station, two miles walk mostly on canal towpath.
Habitat: Deep lake in former chalk pit, shallow pools, wet, chalk and rough grasslands, scrub.
Key birds: *Spring/Summer:* Lapwing, Redshank, Little

Ringed Plover, Sand Martin, Hobby, Common Tern, Sky Lark. *Winter:* Wildfowl (Wigeon, Shoveler, Teal, Gadwall), waders, inc. Snipe, Peregrine Falcon. Rarer birds turn up regularly.
Other notable flora and fauna: Chalk grassland flowers. Butterflies include small blue and green hairstreak. Good numbers of dragonflies (16 species). Brown Hare.
Contact: The Warden, College Lake, Upper Icknield Way, Bulbourne, Tring, Herts HP23 5QG. 01442 826 774; (M)07711 821 303. www.bbowt.org.uk

5. LITTLE MARLOW GRAVEL PITS

Lefarge Redland Aggregates.
Location: SU 880 880. NE of Marlow from J4 of M40. Use permissive path from Coldmoorholm Lane to Little Marlow village. Follow path over a wooden bridge to N end of lake. Permissive path ends just past the cottages where it joins a concrete road to sewage treatment works.
Access: Open all year. Please do not enter the gravel works.
Facilities: Paths. **Public transport:** None.
Habitat: Gravel pit, lake, scrub.
Key birds: *Spring:* Passage migrants, Sand Martin, Garganey, Hobby. *Summer:* Reedbed warblers, Kingfisher, wildfowl. *Autumn:* Passage migrants. *Winter:* Wildfowl, possible Smew, Goldeneye, Yellow-legged Gull, Lapwing, Snipe.
Contact: Ranger Service, Wycombe District Council, Queen Victoria Road, High Wycombe, Buckinghamshire HP11 1BB.

Hampshire

1. BLASHFORD LAKES

Hampshire & Isle of Wight Wildlife Trust in partnership with Wessex Water, Bournemouth and West Hampshire Water and New Forest District Council.
Location: SU 153 080. From Ringwood take A338 for two miles towards Fordingbridge/Salisbury, pass Ivy Lane R and take next R to Moyles Court / Linwood at Ellingham Cross, into Ellingham Drove. Main car park for hides is first L (entrance shared with Hanson works) after 400 yards. For Education Centre turn R opposite (entrance shared with Wessex Water and water-ski club) and straight on through gate and bear R between wooden pillars. Parking is just inside pillars or in front of centre.
Access: A network of permissive paths in the reserve link to New Forest and Avon Valley Long Distance footpaths. These paths and a number of wildlife viewing screens are always open. The six hides and Centre are open daily (9am-4.30pm). The Centre is also used for school and other organised visits, please phone for further details. No dogs allowed. The paths are fully wheelchair accessible and kissing gates are RADAR key-operated to allow passage of disability buggies.
Facilities: Parking, footpaths, six hides, viewing screens, toilets and information including recent sightings board. Coach parking by arrangement. Picnic tables available beside the centre when not being used by booked groups.
Public transport: Bus service on the A338 Ringwood to Salisbury/Fordingbridge road stops just north of Ivy Lane, Ellingham Cross and Ibsley Church.
Habitat: Flooded gravel pits, areas of wet woodland, some of it ancient also dry grassland and lichen heath.
Key birds: *Winter*: Large number of over-wintering wildfowl, inc. Tufted Duck, Pochard, Wigeon, Shoveler, Goosander and internationally important numbers of Gadwall. Also a large gull roost.
Spring/summer: Breeding birds include Common Tern, Lapwing, Redshank, Oystercatcher, Kingfisher, Garden Warblers are especially common.
Autumn: Waders on migration including Green and Common Sandpipers and Greenshank, also Hobby, Black Tern and passerines.
Other notable flora and fauna: Dragonflies (23 species recorded) including brown hawker, scarce chaser and large and small red-eyed damselfly. Roe deer are regular, also present badgers, otters, foxes, reptiles include adders and grass snakes.
Contact: Blashford Lakes Centre, Ellingham Drove, Ringwood, Hampshire BH24 3PJ. 01425 472 760.
e mail: feedback@hwt.org.uk www.hwt.org.uk

2. FARLINGTON MARSHES

Hampshire & Isle of Wight Wildlife Trust.
Location: SU 685 045. North of Langstone Harbour. Main entrance off roundabout junction A2030/A27.
Access: Open at all times, no charge or permits, but donations welcome. Dogs on leads only. Wheelchair access via RADAR gates. Short slopes up to sea wall. Paths around site are mostly level but the main path running along the sea wall can be uneven in places and muddy in wet weather. Groups — please book to avoid clash of dates.
Facilities: 2.5 mile trail. Information at entrance and shelter. No toilets.
Public transport: By bus: Several bus routes pass along the A2030 (Easter Road), close to the western entrance to the marsh. Contact First bus service on 023 8058 4321. By train: Hilsea station is one mile from reserve. Contact South West Trains on 0845 6000 650.
Habitat: Coastal grazing marsh with pools and reedbed within reserve. Views over intertidal mudflats/saltmarshes of Langstone Harbour.
Key birds: *Summer*: Breeding waders and wildfowl (including Lapwing, Redshank and Shelduck) also breeding Cetti's, Sedge and Reed Warblers, Bearded Tit. *Autumn to spring*: Waders and wildfowl, good numbers of migrating Yellow Wagtail among the cattle. *Winter*: Brent Goose, Wigeon, Pintail etc and waders (Dunlin, Grey Plover etc). On migration wide range of waders including rarities. Reedbeds with Bearded Tit, Water Rail etc, scrub areas attract small migrants (Redstart, Wryneck, warblers etc).
Contact: Jamie Marsh, Hampshire and Isle of Wight Wildlife Trust, Beechcroft House, Vicarage Lane, Curdridge, Hants SO32 2DP. 1489 774 429.
www.hwt.org.uk - go to 'Reserves' and then 'news' for sightings, etc

3. FLEET POND LNR

Hart District Council Service/Fleet Pond Society.
Location: SY 85. Located in Fleet, W of Farnborough. From the B3013, head to Fleet Station. Park in the long-stay car park at Fleet Station. Parking also available in Chestnut Grove and Westover Road. Pond car park off B3013.
Access: Open all year.
Facilities: Some surfaced paths, boardwalks in wet areas.
Public transport: Fleet railway station lies N of site.
Habitat: Lake, marshes, reedbeds, heathland, wet and dry woodland.
Key birds: *Spring/autumn*: Migrant waders incl. Little Ringed Plover, Dunlin, Greenshank, Little Gull, Lesser Spotted Woodpecker, occasional Kittiwake, terns, Woodlark, Skylark, occasional Ring Ouzel, Firecrest, Pied Flycatcher. *Summer*: Hobby, Common Tern, Tree Pipit, occasional Red Kite and Osprey. *Winter*: Bittern, wildfowl, occasional Smew, Snipe, occasional Jack Snipe, Siskin, Redpoll.

Other notable flora and fauna: Dragonflies and damselflies in wet areas of marshes and heathlands. Butterflies, roe deer. Plants include ling and bell heather, phragmites reeds.
Contact: Hart District Council, Civic Office,, Harlington Way, Fleet, Hampshire, GU51 4AE. 01252 622 122, e-mail: countryside@hart.gov.uk

4. LANGSTONE HARBOUR

RSPB (South East Region Office).
Location: SU 695 035. Harbour lies E of Portsmouth, one mile S of Havant. Car parks at Broadmarsh (SE of A27/A3(M) junction) and West Hayling LNR (first R on A2030 after Esso garage).
Access: Restricted access to ensure birds not disturbed. Good views from West Hayling LNR, Broadmarsh and Farlington Marshes LNR (qv).
Facilities: Mainline trains all stop at Havant. Local bus service to W Hayling LNR.
Public transport: See Farlington Marshes.
Habitat: Intertidal mud, saltmarsh, shingle islands.
Key birds: *Summer:* Breeding waders and seabirds inc. Mediterranean Gull and Little Tern. *Passage/winter:* Waterfowl, inc. Black-necked Grebes, c5,000 dark-bellied Brent Geese, Shoveler, Goldeneye and Red-breasted Merganser. Waders inc. Oystercatcher, Ringed and Grey Plover, Dunlin, Black and Bar-tailed Godwits and Greenshank. Peregrine, Merlin and Short-eared Owl.
Contact: Chris Cockburn (Warden), RSPB Langstone Harbour, 389 Havant Road, Farlington, Portsmouth PO6 1AA. 02392 378 686.
e-mail: chris.cockburn@rspb.org.uk

5. LOWER TEST

Hampshire & Isle of Wight Wildlife Trust.
Location: SU 364 150. From M271 N of Southampton take A36 (Commercial Road) W to Totton. Viewing screens accessed from Compton Road.
Access: Open at all times, guide dogs only. No coach parking facilities. Disabled access limited. Park on Testwood Lane near Salmon Leap pub.
Facilities: One hide and two screens. Hide open 9.30-4.30pm every day, screens open at all times.
Public transport: Totton train station and bus stops within easy walking distance. Tel 01983 827 005 for bus details.
Habitat: Saltmarsh, brackish grassland, wet meadows, reedbed, scrapes, meres, estuary.
Key birds: *Summer:* Breeding Little, Sandwich and Common Terns, Black-headed and Mediterranean Gulls, waders. *Passage/winter:* Waders. *Autumn/winter:* Waders (inc. Black-tailed and Bar-tailed Godwits, Oystercatcher, Ringed and Grey Plover, Dunlin). Wildfowl (inc. Shelduck, Shoveler, Goldeneye, Red-breasted Merganser and c7000 dark-bellied Brent Geese). Black-necked Grebe, Short-eared Owl, Peregrine.

Other notable flora and fauna: Good range of common butterflies. Dragonflies including scarce chaser, emperor and migrant hawker. Plants include early marsh, green winged, southern marsh orchids and green flowered helleborine. Otter, water vole.
Contact: Clare Bishop, Trust HQ, 02380 424 206. e-mail: clareb@hwt.org.uk www.hwt.org.uk

6. LYMINGTON REEDBEDS

Hampshire & Isle of Wight Wildlife Trust.
Location: SZ 324 965. From Lyndhurst in New Forest take A337 to Lymington. Turn L after railway bridge into Marsh Lane. Park in the lay-by next to allotments. The reserve entrance is on opposite side, to R of the house and over railway crossing. The footpath exits the reserve near the Old Ampress Works, leading to a minor road between the A337 and Boldre.
Access: Open all year. The best viewpoint over the reedbeds is from Bridge Road or from the Undershore leading from the B3054.
Facilities: None.
Public transport: Bus: at either end of the footpath through site, Marsh Lane and on the A337 (route 112). Five minutes walk from train station.
Habitat: One of largest reedbeds on S coast, fringed by alder and willow woodland.
Key birds: One of highest concentrations of Water Rail in the country; resident but most evident in winter. *Spring/summer:* Cetti's Warbler, Bearded Tit, Yellow Wagtail, Swallow, martins, Reed Warbler.

Passage: Snipe, ducks. Otters are in the area.
Contact: Michael Boxall, Hampshire and Isle of Wight
Wildlife Trust, 01489 774 400.
e-mail: feedback@hwt.org.uk www.hwt.org.uk

7. LYMINGTON-KEYHAVEN NNR

Hampshire County Council.
Location: SZ 315 920. S of Lymington along seawall
footpath; car parks at Bath Road, Lymington and at
Keyhaven Harbour.
Access: Open all year.
Facilities: None.
Habitat: Coastal marshland and lagoons.
Key birds: *Spring*: Passage waders (inc. Knot,
Sanderling, Bar-tailed and Black-tailed Godwits,
Whimbrel, Spotted Redshank), Pomarine and Great
Skuas. Breeding Oystercatcher, Ringed Plover,
Sandwich, Common and Little Terns. *Autumn*:
Passage raptors, waders and passerines. *Winter*:
Wildfowl (inc. Brent Goose, Wigeon, Pintail, Red-
breasted Merganser), waders (inc. Golden Plover),
Little Egret, gulls.
Contact: Hampshire County Council, Mottisfont Court,
High Street, Winchester, Hants SO23 8ZF.
www3.hants.gov.uk/countryside/lymington-keyhaven

8. MARTIN DOWN

Natural England (Wiltshire Team).
Location: SU 05 19. Nine miles SW of Salisbury. Car
park on A354.
Access: Open access, organised groups of 10+ should
book in advance. Car park height barrier of 7ft 6 ins.
Coaches only by prior arrangement. Hard flat track
from A354 car park suitable for wheelchairs.
Facilities: Two car parks, interpretative boards.
Public transport: One bus Salisbury/Blandford. Call
01722 336 855 or visit www.wdbus.co.uk
Habitat: Chalk downland and scub.
Key birds: *Spring/summer*: Grey Partridge, Turtle
Dove, warblers, Nightingale. *Winter*: Occasional
Merlin, Hen Harrier.
Other notable flora and fauna: Species-rich chalk
downland with a variety of orchids. *The Times online*
rates Martin Down in its Britain's Best 50 Days Out
list.
Contact: South Wiltshire NNR Office, Parsonage Down
NNR, Cherry Lodge, Shrewton, Nr Salisbury, Wilts, SP3
4ET 01980 620 485, www.naturalengland.org.uk
e-mail: wiltshire@naturalengland.org.uk

9. TESTWOOD LAKES

Hampshire & Isle of Wight Wildlife Trust
Location: SU 347 155. M271 West J2 towards Totton.

Left at first roundabout, then left onto A36. Left at
next roundabout onto Brunel Rd. Entrance on left
after ¼ mile.
Access: Car parks open 8am until 4pm in winter
and from 8am until 6pm in summer. Surfaced paths
around lakes and to hides are relatively flat. Dogs
under control allowed in some parts of the reserve
but not the conservation and education areas.
Facilities: Two hides and two screens. Hides open
10am-4pm daily. Disabled toilet in the Education
Centre.
Public Transport: Totton rail station is 1.5 miles from
the reserve. Bluestar and Wilts & Dorset buses stop
¼ mile from entrance. Tel 01983 827 005.
Habitat: Flooded gravel pits, scrapes, wet and dry
grasslands, woodland and hedgerows.
Key Birds: *Winter*: Various wildfowl (inc. Tufted
Duck, Wigeon, Pochard, Teal, Gadwall, Goosander),
Siskin, Hawfinch, Meadow Pipit, Common Sandpiper,
Green Sandpiper, Pochard, Redwing, Fieldfare.
Spring: Shelduck, Sand Martin, Little Ringed Plover,
Willow Warbler. *Summer*: Swift, Swallow, Blackcap,
Whitethroat. *Autumn*: Wheatear, Yellow Wagtail,
Goldfinch.
Other notable flora and fauna: Good range of
butterflies. Dragonflies including emperor, scarce
chaser, southern and migrant hawker and golden ring.
Contact: Clare Bishop, Trust HQ, 02380 424 206.
e-mail: clareb@hwt.org.uk www.hwt.org.uk

10. TITCHFIELD HAVEN

Hampshire County Council.
Location: SU 535 025. From A27 W of Fareham; public
footpath follows derelict canal along W of reserve
and road skirts S edge.
Access: Open Wed-Sun all year, plus Bank Hols,
except Christmas and Boxing Days.
Facilities: Centre has information desk, toilets, tea
room and shop. Guided tours (book in advance).
Hides.
Public transport: None.
Habitat: Reedbeds, freshwater scrapes, wet grazing
meadows.
Key birds: *Spring/summer*: Bearded Tit, waders
(inc. Black-tailed Godwit), wildfowl, Common Tern,
breeding Cetti's Warbler, Water Rail. Offshore
seabirds include Gannet, Common Scoter, Yellow-
legged Gull, Kittiwake and Little Tern. *Winter*:
Bittern.
Contact: Barry Duffin, Titchfield Haven Visitor
Centre, Cliff Road, Hill Head, Fareham, Hants PO14
3JT. 01329 662 145; Fax 01329 667 113.

Kent

1. BLEAN WOODS NNR

RSPB (South East Region Office).
Location: TR 126 592 (postcode CT2 9DD). From Rough Common (off A290, one and a half miles NW of Canterbury).
Access: Open 8am-9pm for cars, open at all times for visitors on foot. No parking for coaches — please drop passengers off in Rough Common village. Green Trail suitable for wheelchair users.
Facilities: Public footpaths and five waymarked trails.
Public transport: No 27 from Canterbury hourly, stops at reserve entrance (ask for Lovell Road). No 4/4A every 20 minutes from Canterbury to Whitstable. Ask for Rough Common Road, 500m walk from site entrance. Local bus company Stagecoach 0870 243 3711.
Habitat: Mature oak woodland, plus birch, sweet chestnut, hazel and hornbeam coppice. Grazed and ungrazed heathland.
Key birds: Good for Woodpeckers, warblers and Nightingale in spring, fairly quiet the rest of the year. *All year:* Woodpecker (3 species), Nuthatch, Treecreeper, tits (5 species). *Spring:* Nightingale, Blackcap, Garden Warbler, Hobby, Nightjar.
Other notable flora and fauna: Badger, dormouse. Heath fritillary, white admiral, silver-washed fritillary. Common spotted orchid, wild service.
Contact: Michael Walter, Site Manager, 11 Garden Close, Rough Common, Canterbury, Kent CT2 9BP. 01227 455 972.

2. BOUGH BEECH RESERVOIR

Kent Wildlife Trust.
Location: TQ 49 64 89. Bough Beech is situated 3.5 miles S of Ide Hill.

From Sevenoaks, site is signposted off B2042.
Access: Confined to holders of permits granted for recording and study purposes only on application to the warden. The whole of the reserve may be viewed from the public road just S of Winkhurst Green (TQ 496 494). Park on roadside (one side only).
Facilities: Toilets and visitor centre open between Apr-Oct, Wed, Sat, Sun & Bank Holiday Mon (11am-4.30pm).
Public transport: Rail service to Penshurst Station (two miles south)
Habitat: Reservoir and adjacent woodland and farmland.
Key birds: Approx 60 species of birds breed in and around the reserve annually, with Mallard, Tufted Duck, Mandarin, Canada Goose, Coot and Great Crested Grebe notable among the waterfowl. Little Ringed Plover nest most years. *Autumn:* Especially good for numbers of waders like Green and Common Sandpipers and Greenshank. Many rarities have been recorded. Ospreys recorded most years. *Winter:* wildfowl numbers are much higher than summer and include Goldeneye and Goosander.
Other notable flora and fauna: Great crested newt, toad, dragonflies (black-tailed skimmer, ruddy darter, emperor, southern aeshna, migrant hawker, red-eyed damselfly), common lizard, Roesel's bush cricket, long-winged conehead, dormouse, water shrew, white admiral butterfly, glow-worm, bats (pipistrelle, Daubenton, noctule, brown long-eared).
Contact: Dave Hutton, Bough Beech Visitor Centre, 01732 453 880. e-mail: info@kentwildlife.org.uk www.kentwildlifetrust.org.uk

3. CLIFFE POOLS

RSPB (South East Region Office).
Location: TQ 722 757. On S bank of River Thames, N of Rochester. Take A289 off the A2 at Strood and follow B2000 to reserve. See RSPB website for more detailed directions.
Access: Free admission at all times, but donations welcome. Group bookings welcome. Monthly guided walks available. Dogs only on public footpaths.
Facilities: Six viewing points. Public rights of way encircle reserve and bisect it.
Public transport: Nearest bus stop at Six Bells pub in Cliffe.
Habitat: A mix of saline lagoons, freshwater pools, grassland, saltmarsh and scrub.
Key birds: Massed flocks of waders in winter, plus a wide range of wildfowl. A great variety of passage birds in spring and autumn. Breeding species include

Lapwing, Redshank, Avocet, Ringed Plover, Shelduck. Also look out for Nightingale, Hobby and Turtle Dove. **Other notable flora and fauna:** Good range of insects (rare bumblebees include shrill carder bee, brown-banded carder bee). Butterflies, including marbled white, common blue, Essex skipper and the migrant clouded yellow, plus large range of grasshoppers and bush crickets, including Roes **Contact:** Jason Mitchell, RSPB Nature Reserve, Northwood Hill, Bromhey Farm, Eastborough, Cooling, Rochester, Kent ME3 8DS. 01634 222 480

4. DUNGENESS NATURE RESERVE

RSPB (South East Region Office).
Location: TR 063 196. SE of Lydd.
Access: Open daily (9am-9pm) or sunset when earlier. Visitor centre open (10am-5pm, or 4pm Nov-Feb). Parties over 12 by prior arrangement. Closed Dec 25 & 26.
Facilities: Visitor centre, toilets (including disabled access), seven hides, viewing screen, two nature trails, wheelchair access to visitor centre and six hides. Fully equipped classroom/meeting room. Coach parking available.
Public transport: Limited service. Bus 11 from Ashford stops at reserve entrance on request — one mile walk to visitor centre. Contact reserve for details.
Habitat: Shingle, flooded gravel pits, sallow scrub, reedbed, wet grassland.
Key birds: *All year:* Bittern, Marsh Harrier, Bearded Tit. *Spring:* Little Ringed Plover, Wheatear, Yellow Wagtail, Lesser Whitethroat. *Autumn:* Migrant waders and passerines.
Winter: Smew, Goldeneye, Slavonian Grebe, Wigeon, Goosander and Bewick's Swan.
Other notable flora and fauna: Jersey cudweed, Nottingham catchfly, brown hare.
Contact: Christine Hawkins/Bob Gomes, Boulderwall Farm, Dungeness Road, Lydd, Romney Marsh, Kent, TN29 9PN. 01797 320 588,www.rspb.org.uk e-mail: dungeness@rspb.org.uk

5. DUNGENESS BIRD OBSERVATORY

Dungeness Bird Observatory Trust.
Location: TR 085 173. Three miles SE of Lydd. Turn south off Dungeness Road at TR 087 185 and continue to end of road.
Access: Observatory open throughout the year. No wheelchair access.
Facilities: Accommodation available. Bring own sleeping bag/sheets and toiletries. Shared facilities including fully-equipped kitchen. Coach parking available at railway station.
Public transport: Bus service between Rye and Folkestone, numbers 11, 12, 711, 712. Alight at the Pilot Inn, Lydd-on-Sea. Tel: 01227 472 082.
Habitat: Shingle promontory with scrub and gravel pits. RSPB reserve nearby.
Key birds: Breeding birds include Wheatear and Black Redstart and seabirds on RSPB Reserve. Important

migration site. Excellent seawatching when weather conditions are suitable. Power station outfall, 'The Patch' good for gulls and terns.
Other notable flora and fauna: Long Pits are excellent for dragonflies, including small red-eyed damselfly. Moth trapping throughout the year.
Contact: David Walker, Dungeness Bird Observatory, 11 RNSSS, Dungeness, Kent TN29 9NA. 01797 321 309, e-mail: dungeness.obs@tinyonline.co.uk www.dungenessbirdobs.org.uk

6. ELMLEY MARSHES

RSPB (South East Region Office).
Location: TQ 93 86 80. Isle of Sheppey signposted from A249, one mile beyond old Kingsferry Bridge. Reserve car park is two miles from the main road.
Access: Use old bridge road - access road is one mile from bridge. Open every day (9am-9pm or dusk if earlier) except Tue, Christmas and Boxing days. No charge to RSPB members. Dogs are not allowed on the reserve. Less able may drive closer to the hides.
Facilities: Five hides. Disabled access to Wellmarsh hide. No visitor centre. Toilets located in car park 1.25 miles from hides.
Public transport: Swale Halt nearest railway station on Sittingbourne to Sheerness line. From there it is a three mile walk to reserve.
Habitat: Coastal grazing marsh, ditches and pools alongside the Swale Estuary with extensive intertidal mudflats and saltmarsh.
Key birds: *Spring/Summer:* Breeding waders — Redshank, Lapwing, Avocet, Yellow Wagtail, passage waders, Hobby. *Autumn:* Passage waders. *Winter:* Spectacular numbers of wildfowl, especially Wigeon and White-fronted Goose. Waders. Hunting raptors - Peregrine, Merlin, Hen Harrier and Short-eared Owl.
Contact: Gordon Allison, Warden (RSPB North Kent Marshes), Elmley RSPB Reserve, Kingshill Farm, Elmley, Sheerness, Kent ME12 3RW. 01795 665 969.

7. NOR MARSH

RSPB (South East Region Office).
Location: TQ 810 700. One mile NE of Gillingham in the Medway Estuary.
Access: No access as it is an island. It is viewable from Riverside Country Park (B2004) at the Horrid Hill Peninsula, or from nearby Motney Hill RSPB Reserve, giving overviews of the Medway Estuary saltmarsh and mudflats.
Facilities: None.
Public transport: Buses can be caught to Riverside Country Park. Phone Medway Council for the bus numbers, 01634 727 777.
Habitat: Saltmarsh and mudflats.
Key birds: *Winter:* Large numbers of wildfowl, including Brent Geese, Pintail, Dunlin and Avocets. *Spring and autumn:* Look out for Mediterranean Gull, Black-tailed Godwit, Whimbrel and Greenshank.
Contact: RSPB North Kent Marshes, Bromhey Farm, Eastborough, Cooling, Rochester ME3 8DS. 01634 222 480.

NATURE RESERVES - SOUTH EAST ENGLAND

8. NORTHWARD HILL

RSPB (South East Region Office).
Location: TQ 781 757. Adjacent to High Halstow, off A228, approx four miles NE of Rochester.
Access: Open all year, free access, trails in public area of wood joining Saxon Shoreway link to grazing marsh. Dogs allowed in public area on leads. Trails often steep and not suitable for wheelchair users.
Facilities: Four trails vary in length from 0.5 to 4km. The Toddler trail is surfaced and suitable for 'off-road' push-chairs. Woodland trail is entirely within the public area of the wood. Heron trail takes in heronry viewpoints.
Public transport: Buses to village of High Halstow. Contact Arriva buses (01634 283 600) for timetable details.
Habitat: Ancient and scrub woodland (approximately 130 acres), grazing marsh (approximately 350 acres).
Key birds: *Spring/summer:* Wood holds UK's largest heronry, with c.130 pairs of Grey Heron and c.120 pairs of Little Egret (in 2009), breeding Nightingale, Turtle Dove, scrub warblers and woodpeckers. Marshes — breeding Lapwing, Redshank, Avocet, Marsh Harrier, Shoveler, Pochard. *Winter:* Wigeon, Teal, Shoveler. Passage waders (ie Black-tailed Godwit), raptors, Corn Bunting. Long-eared Owl.
Other notable flora and fauna: Good range of dragonflies over the marsh, white-letter hairstreak butterfly in the woods.
Contact: Jason Mitchell, RSPB North Kent Marshes, Bromhey Farm, Eastborough, Cooling, Rochester ME3 8DS. 01634 222 480.

9. OARE MARSHES LNR

Kent Wildlife Trust.
Location: TR 01 36 48 (car park). Two miles N of Faversham. From A2 follow signs to Oare and Harty Ferry.
Access: Open at all times. Access along marked paths only. Dogs under strict control to avoid disturbance to birds and livestock.
Facilities: Three hides. Roadside viewpoint of East Hide accessible to wheelchair users.Those with pneumatic tyres can reach seawall path and hide. Small car park, restricted turning space, not suitable for coaches.
Public transport: Bus to Oare Village one mile from reserve. Arriva service (Mon-Sat), Jaycrest (Sun) — call Traveline on 0870 608 2608. Train: Faversham (two miles distance).
Habitat: Grazing marsh, mudflats/estuary.
Key birds: *All year:* Waders and wildfowl. *Winter:* Merlin, Peregrine. Divers, grebes and sea ducks on Swale. *Spring/summer:* Avocet, Garganey, Green, Wood and Curlew Sandpipers, Little Stint, Black-tailed Godwit, Little Tern, Marsh Harrier.
Contact: Tony Swandale, Kent Wildlife Trust, 01622 662 012. e-mail: info@kentwildlife.org.uk www.kentwildlifetrust.org.uk

10. SANDWICH BAY BIRD OBSERVATORY

Sandwich Bay Bird Observatory Trust.
Location: TR 355 575. 2.5 miles from Sandwich, five miles from Deal. A256 to Sandwich from Dover or Ramsgate. Follow signs to Sandwich Station and then Sandwich Bay.
Access: Open daily. Disabled access.
Facilities: New Field Study Centre. Visitor centre, toilets, refreshments, hostel-type accommodation, plus self-contained flat.
Public transport: Sandwich train station two miles from Observatory.
Habitat: Coastal, dune land, farmland, marsh, two small scrapes.
Key birds: *Spring/autumn passage:* Good variety of migrants and waders, specially Corn Bunting. Annual Golden Oriole. *Winter:* Golden Plover.
Other notable flora and fauna: Sand dune plants such as lady's bedstraw and sand sedge.
Contact: The Secretary, Sandwich Bay Bird Observatory, Guildford Road, Sandwich Bay, Sandwich, Kent, CT13 9PF. 01304 617 341. e-mail: sbbot@talk21.com www.sbbo.co.uk

11. STODMARSH NNR

Natural England (Kent Team).
Location: TR 222 618. Lies alongside River Stour and A28, five miles NE of Canterbury.
Access: Open at all times. Keep to paths. No dogs.
Facilities: Fully accessible toilets are available at the Stodmarsh entrance car park. Five hides (one fully accessible), easy access nature trail, footpaths and information panels. Car park, picnic area and toilets adjoining the Grove Ferry entrance with easily accessible path, viewing mound and two hides.
Public transport: There is a regular Stagecoach bus service from Canterbury to Margate/Ramsgate. Alight at Upstreet for Grove Ferry. Hourly on Sun.
Habitat: Open water, reedbeds, wet meadows, dry meadows, woodland.
Key birds: *Spring/summer:* Breeding Bearded Tit, Cetti's Warbler, Garganey, Reed, Sedge and Willow Warblers, Nightingale. Migrant Black Tern, Hobby, Osprey, Little Egret. *Winter:* Wildfowl, Hen Harrier, Bittern.
Other notable flora and fauna: Nationally rare plants and invertebrates, including shining ram's horn snail.
Contact: David Feast, Natural England, 07767 321 058 (mobile).

London, Greater

1. BEDFONT LAKES COUNTRY PARK

Continental Landscapes Ltd.
Location: TQ 080 728. OS map sheet 176 (west London). 0.5 miles from Ashford, Middx, 0.5 miles S of A30, Clockhouse Roundabout, on B3003 (Clockhouse Lane).
Access: Park open (7.30am-9pm or dusk, whichever is earlier), all days except Christmas Day. Disabled friendly. Dogs on leads. Main nature reserve only open Sun (2pm-4pm). Keyholder membership available.
Facilities: Toilets, information centre, several hides, nature trail, free parking, up-to-date information.
Public transport: Train to Feltham and Ashford. Bus – H26 and 116 from Hounslow.
Habitat: Lakes, reedbed, wildflower meadows, wet woodland, scrub.
Key birds: *Winter*: Water Rail, Bittern, Smew and other wildfowl, Meadow Pipit. *Summer*: Common Tern, Willow, Garden, Reed and Sedge Warblers, Whitethroat, Lesser Whitethroat, hirundines, Hobby, Blackcap, Chiffchaff, Skylark. *Passage*: Wheatear, Wood Warbler, Spotted Flycatcher, Ring Ouzel, Redstart, Yellow Wagtail.
Other notable flora and fauna: 140 plant species inc bee and pyramidal orchid. Nathusius pipistrelle bat, emperor dragonfly plus other butterflies and dragonflies.
Contact: James Herd, Ranger, BLCP, Clockhouse Lane, Bedfont, Middx, TW14 8QA. 0845 456 2796. e-mail: bedfont.lakes@continental-landscapes.co.uk

2. CHASE (THE) LNR

London Wildlife Trust.
Location: TQ 515 860. Lies in the Dagenham Corridor, an area of green belt between the London Boroughs of Barking & Dagenham and Havering.
Access: Open throughout the year and at all times. Reserve not suitable for wheelchair access. Eastbrookend Country Park which borders The Chase LNR has surfaced footpaths for wheelchair use.
Facilities: Millennium visitor centre, toilets, ample car parking, Timberland Trail walk.
Public transport: Rail: Dagenham East (District Line) 15 minute walk. Bus: 174 from Romford five minute walk.
Habitat: Shallow wetlands, reedbeds, horse-grazed pasture, scrub and wetland. These harbour an impressive range of animals and plants including the nationally rare black poplar tree. A haven for birds, with approx 190 different species recorded.
Key birds: *Summer*: Breeding Reed Warbler, Lapwing, Water Rail, Lesser Whitethroat, Little Ringed Plover, Kingfisher, Reed Bunting. *Winter*: Significant numbers of Teal, Shoveler, Redwing, Fieldfare and Snipe dominate the scene. *Spring/autumn migration*: Yellow Wagtail, Wheatear, Ruff, Wood Sandpiper, Sand Martin, Ring Ouzel, Black Redstart and Hobby regularly seen.

Other notable flora and fauna: 140 plant species, wasp spider, butterflies and dragonflies.
Contact: The Millennium Centre, 02085 938 096, e-mail: lwtchase@cix.co.uk
www.wildlifetrust.org.uk/london/

3. LONDON WETLAND CENTRE

The Wildfowl & Wetlands Trust.
Location: TQ 228 770. Less than 1 mile from South Circular (A205) at Roehampton. In London, Zone 2/3, one mile from Hammersmith.
Access: Winter (9.30am-5pm: last admission 4pm), summer (9.30am-6pm: last admission 5pm). Charge for admission. Coach parking by arrangement.
Facilities: Visitor centre, hides, nature trails, discovery centre and children's adventure area, restaurant (hot and cold food), cinema, shop, observatory building, six hides (all wheelchair accessible), sustainable gardens, interactive pond zone, three interpretative buildings.
Public transport: Train: Barnes. Tube: Hammersmith then bus 283 (comes into centre). Other buses from Hammersmith are 33, 72, 209; from Richmond, 33.
Habitat: Main lake, reedbeds, wader scrape, open water lakes, wet woodland, grazing marsh.
Key birds: Nationally important numbers of wintering waterfowl, including Gadwall and Shoveler. Important numbers of wetland breeding birds, including grebes, swans, a range of duck species such as Pochard, plus Lapwing, Little Ringed Plover, Redshank, warblers, Reed Bunting and Bittern. Cetti's Warblers remain on site all year round and bred for the first time in 2010.
Other notable flora and fauna: Water voles, slow worm, grass snake, common lizard. Seven species of bat. 22 species of dragonfly and 25 of butterfly. Notable plants inc snake's head fritillaries, cowslip, pyramidal and bee orchids.
Contact: London Wetland Centre 020 8409 4400. email:info.london@wwt.org.uk - www.wwt.org.uk/london Twitter:@wwtlondon.

4. SYDENHAM HILL WOOD

London Wildlife Trust.
Location: TQ 335 722. Forest Hill, SE London, SE26, between Forest Hill and Crystal Palace, just off South Circular (A205). Entrances as Crescent Wood Road and Coxs Walk.
Access: Open at all times, no permits required. Some steep slopes, so wheelchair access is difficult.
Facilities: Nature trail, information boards. No toilets.
Public transport: Train stations: Forest Hill (from London Bridge) or Sydenham Hill (from Victoria). Buses 363, 202, 356, 185, 312, 176, P4. Call Transport for London 0207 5657 299 for details.
Habitat: Ancient woodland, reclaimed Victorian gardens, meadow and small pond.
Key birds: Woodland and gardens species all year round. *All year*: All three woodpeckers, Tawny Owl, Kestrel, Sparrowhawk, Goldcrest, Nuthatch, Treecreeper, Stock Dove. *Summer*: Blackcap,

Chiffchaff, Willow Warbler. *Winter*: Fieldfare, Redwing.
Other notable flora and fauna: Five species of bat, including noctule and brown long-eared. Bluebell, wood anemone, dog violet and primrose. Oak and hornbeam. Speckled wood, comma, painted lady and orange-tip butterflies.
Contact: Chantal Brown, London Wildlife Trust, Centre for Wildlife Gardening, 28 Marsden Road, London SE15 4EE. 0207 252 9186.
e-mail: cbrown@wildlondon.org.uk
www.wildlondon.org.uk

Surrey

1. BRENTMOOR HEATH LNR

Surrey Wildlife Trust.
Location: SU 936 612. The reserve runs along the A322 Guildford to Bagshot road, at the intersection with the A319/B311 between Chobham and Camberley. Best access is by Brentmoor Road, which runs W from West End past Donkey Town.
Access: Open all year.
Facilities: Local buses, nos 34, 590 and 591 stop less than half a miles away.
Public transport: None.
Habitat: Heathland, woodland, grassland, ponds.
Key birds: *Spring/summer:* Stonechat, Nightjar, Hobby. *All year:* Usual woodland birds.
Contact: Surrey Wildlife Trust, 01483 795 440.
e-mail: surreywt@cix.co.uk
www.surreywildlifetrust.org.uk

2. FARNHAM HEATH

RSPB (South East Region Office).
Location: SU 859 433. S of Farnham. Take the B3001 south from Farnham. Take the right hand fork, signposted Tilford, immediately past level crossing. Keep to that road. Just outside Tilford village it is signed to the Rural Life Centre. Follow those signs. Entrance is on the right after 0.5 mile.
Access: Reserve open at all times. Car park opens 9.30 am weekdays and 10.30 am weekends. Parking lay-bys on adjacent roads outside those hours.

Rural Life Centre open Wed-Fri and Sundays all year. Open on Saturdays April-September. Tea room opens at 11 am.
Facilities: Large grass car park, shared with Rural Life Centre. No height barrier, but gates may be locked outside opening hours. No bike racks. Toilets (including disabled), picnic area, refreshments. Group bookings accepted, guided walks available. Good for walking, pushchair friendly.
Public transport: Bus route is number 19 (Farnham to Hindhead service). Nearest stop is in Millbridge village, outside entrance to Pierrepont House. Reserve is a mile away, along Reeds Road (follow signs to the Rural Life Centre).
Habitat: Heathland and pine woodland.
Key birds: *Spring:* Blackcap, Tree Pipit, Woodcock, Woodlark. *Summer:* Woodcock and Nightjar, woodland birds, including Stock Dove and Green and Great Spotted Woodpeckers. *Winter:* Crossbills in the pine woods, winter finches, including Brambling around the feeders, winter thrushes.
Other notable flora and fauna: Fungi — more than 150 species. Bats in summer.
Contact: Mike Coates, c/o The Rural Life Centre, Reeds Road, Tilford, Surrey GU10 2DL. 01252 795 632.

3. FRENSHAM COMMON AND COUNTRY PARK

Waverley BC and National Trust .
Location: SU 855 405. Common lies on either side of A287 between Farnham and Hindhead.
Access: Open at all times. Car park (locked 9pm-9am). Keep to paths.
Facilities: Information rooms, toilets and refreshment kiosk at Great Pond.
Public transport: Call Trust for advice.
Habitat: Dry and humid heath, woodland, two large ponds, reedbeds.
Key birds: *Summer:* Dartford Warbler, Woodlark, Hobby, Nightjar, Stonechat. *Winter:* Wildfowl (inc. occasional Smew), Bittern, Great Grey Shrike.
Other notable flora and fauna: Tiger beetle, purple hairstreak and silver-studded blue butterflies, sand lizard, smooth snake.
Contact: Steve Webster, Rangers Office, Bacon Lane, Churt, Surrey, GU10 2QB. 01252 792 416.

NATURE RESERVES - SOUTH EAST ENGLAND

4. LIGHTWATER COUNTRY PARK

Surreyheath Council
Location: SU 921 622. From J3 of M3, take the A322 and follow brown Country Park signs. From the Guildford Road in Lightwater, turn into The Avenue. Entrance to the park is at the bottom of the road.
Access: Open all year, dawn-dusk.
Facilities: Car park, toilets, waymarked trails with leaflets available.
Public transport: Train: Bagshot two miles. SW Trains 0845 6000 650. Arriva Bus: No 34. 01483 306 397.
Habitat: Heathland, woodland, three ponds and meadows.
Key birds: *All year*: All three woodpeckers, Goldcrest in woods, Coot, Moorhen, Grey Heron and Kingfisher on ponds. *Summer*: Nightjar, Willow Warbler, Chiffchaff, Blackcap, Whitethroat. *Winter*: Fieldfare, Redwing, Siskin.
Other notable flora and fauna: Flora includes ox-eye daisies, knapweed and common spotted orchid in meadow, three heathers and two gorse species on heath. Wood ant nests in woodlands. Good range of dragonflies and butterflies.
Contact: Surreyheath Ranger Service, Lightwater Country Park, The Avenue, Lightwater, Surrey, GU18 5RG. 01276 479 582. www.surreyheath.gov.uk
e-mail: rangers@surreyheath.gov.uk

5. THURSLEY COMMON

Natural England (Sussex and Surrey Team).
Location: SU 900 417. From Guildford, take A3 SW to B3001 (Elstead/Churt road). Use the Moat car park, S of Elstead village.
Access: Open access. Parties must obtain prior permission.
Facilities: Boardwalk in wetter areas.
Public transport: None.
Habitat: Wet and dry heathland, woodland, bog.
Key birds: *Winter*: Hen Harrier and Great Grey Shrike. *Summer*: Hobby, Woodlark, Dartford Warbler, Stonechat, Curlew, Snipe, Nightjar.
Other notable flora and fauna: Large populations of silver-studded blue, grayling and purple emperor butterflies can be seen here, alongside 26 recorded dragonfly species. Sandier sites on the reserve provide homes for many species of solitary bees and wasps. Damp areas support carnivorous plants such as sundew and bladderwort. Bog asphodel and marsh orchid may also be seen.
Contact: Simon Nobes, Natural England, The Barn, Heathhall Farm, Bowlhead Green, Godalming, Surrey GU8 6NW. 01483 307 703.
e-mail: enquiries.southeast@naturalengland.org.uk
www.naturalengland.org.uk

Sussex, East

1. CASTLE WATER, RYE HARBOUR

Sussex Wildlife Trust.
Location: TQ 942 189. Reserve is one mile SE of Rye along Harbour Road.
Access: Open at all times, entry is free. Information centre at Limekiln Cottage open every day 10am-4pm. The site is flat with some wheelchair access to all four hides, although there are stiles where the sheep are grazing the fields.
Facilities: Information centre, large car park at Rye Harbour with nearby toilets.
Habitat: Intertidal, saltmarsh, marsh, drainage ditches, shingle ridges, pits, sand, scrub, woodland.
Key birds: Many birds occur here in nationally important numbers, such as Shoveler and Sanderling in the winter and breeding Little Tern and Mediterranean Gull. Nesting Black-headed Gull colony, Common and Sandwich Terns and a good range of waders and ducks. Barn and Short-eared Owls.
Other notable flora and fauna: The saltmarsh supports such unusual plants as sea-heath and marsh mallow, and even highly specialised insects including the star-wort moth and saltmarsh bee.
Contact: Sussex Wildlife Trust, Woods Mill, Henfield, West Sussex, BN5 9SD. 01273 492 630.
e-mail: enquiries@sussexwt.org.uk
www.sussexwt.org.uk

2. ERIDGE ROCKS RESERVE

Sussex Wildlife Trust.
Location: Located at Eridge Green 4 miles S of Tunbridge Wells. Car park at TQ 555 355. From A26, turn into Warren Farm Lane, next to a church and small printing works.
Access: Open all year.
Facilities: Car park.
Public transport: Bus stop on A26. Call Traveline on 0871 200 2223. Nearest railway station at Eridge (one mile).
Habitat: Sandstone rock outcrop, mixed woodland.
Key birds: *All year*: Range of common woodland birds. *Spring/summer*: Warblers.
Other notable flora and fauna: Mosses and liverworts on the rocks. Good for general woodland butterflies, inc white admiral.
Contact: Trust HQ, 01273 492 630.
e-mail: enquiries@sussexwt.org.uk

3. FORE WOOD

RSPB (South East Region Office).
Location: TQ 758 123. From the A2100 (Battle/Hastings) take lane to Crowhurst at Crowhurst Park Caravan Park. Park at Crowhurst village hall and walk up Forewood Lane for 500 yards. Look for the finger post on L and follow the public footpath across farmland to reserve entrance.
Access: Open all year. No disabled facilities. No dogs. No coaches.
Facilities: Two nature trails.
Public transport: Station at Crowhurst, about 0.5

NATURE RESERVES - SOUTH EAST ENGLAND

5. PEVENSEY LEVELS

Natural England (Sussex and Surrey Team).
Location: TQ 665 054. A small reserve of 12 fields, within the 3,500 ha SSSI/Ramsar site of Pevensey Levels. NE of Eastbourne. S of A259, one mile along minor road from Pevensey E towards Norman's Bay.
Access: Please view from road to avoid disturbance to summer nesting birds and sheltering flocks in winter. Access on foot allowed at Rockhouse Bank (TQ 675 057) — panoramic view of whole reserve.
Facilities: None. Nearest toilets at Star Inn (TQ 687 062) or petrol station (TQ 652 052).
Public transport: Nearest railway stations: Pevensey Bay or Cooden Beach. Eastbourne buses to Pevensey Bay — call 01323 416416.
Habitat: Freshwater grazing marsh with extensive ditch system, subject to flooding.
Key birds: *Summer:* Breeding Reed and Sedge Warblers, Yellow Wagtail, Snipe, Redshank, Lapwing. Raptors include Peregrine and Hobby. Passage migrants include Whimbrel, Curlew, Brent Geese. *Winter:* Flocks of wildfowl and waders, Short-eared Owl, Merlin and other raptors.
Other notable flora and fauna: Variable damselfly, many rare snails and other molluscs, the most important site in the UK for fen raft spider. Unusual wetland plants.
Contact: Site Manager, East Sussex NNRs, Natural England, 01273 476 595;
e-mail sussex.surrey@natural-england.org.uk;
www.natural-england.org.uk

6. RYE HARBOUR

Rye Harbour LNR Management Committee.
Location: TQ 941 188. One mile from Rye off A259 signed Rye Harbour. From J10 of M20 take A2070 until it joins A259.
Access: Open at all times by footpaths. Organised groups please book.
Facilities: Car park in Rye Harbour village. Information kiosk in car park. Shop, two pubs, toilets and disabled facilities near car park, four hides (wheelchair access), information centre open most days (10am-4pm) by volunteers.
Public transport: Train (08457 484 950), bus (0870 608 2608), tourist information (tel: 01797 226 696).
Habitat: Sea, sand, shingle, pits and grassland.
Key birds: *Spring:* Passage waders, especially roosting Whimbrel. *Summer:* Turtle Dove, terns (3 species), waders (7 species), gulls (6 species), Garganey, Shoveler, Cetti's Warbler, Bearded Tit. *Winter:* Wildfowl, Water Rail, Bittern, Smew.
Other notable flora and fauna: Good shingle flora

---

mile walk. Charing Cross/Hastings line. No buses within one mile.
Habitat: Semi-natural ancient woodland.
Key birds: A wide range of woodland birds. *Spring:* Chiffchaff, Greater Spotted Woodpecker, Nuthatch, Treecreeper. *Summer:* Blackcap, Bullfinch, Mistle Thrush, Green Woodpecker. *Autumn:* Goldcrest, Jay, Marsh Tit. *Winter:* Fieldfare, Rook, Redwing.
Other notable flora and fauna: Rare ferns, bluebells, wood anemonies, purple orchid. Butterflies including silver-washed fritillary and white admiral.
Contact: Martin Allison, RSPB Broadwater Warren, Unit 10, Sham Farm Business Units, Eridge Green, Tunbridge Wells, Kent TN3 9JA.

4. LULLINGTON HEATH

Natural England (Sussex and Surrey Team).
Location: TQ 525 026. W of Eastbourne, between Jevington and Litlington, on northern edge of Friston Forest.
Access: Via footpaths and bridleways. Site open for access on foot as defined by CROW Act 2000.
Facilities: None. Nearest toilets/refreshments at pubs in Jevington, Litlington or Seven Sisters CP, 2km to S.
Public transport: Nearest bus stop is Seven Sisters Country Park. Phone Brighton and Hove services on 01273 886 200 or visit: www.buses.co.uk/bustimes/
Habitat: Grazed chalk downland and heath, with mixed scrub and gorse.
Key birds: *Summer:* Breeding Nightingale, Turtle Dove, Nightjar and diverse range of grassland/scrub-nesting species. Passage migrants include Wheatear, Redstart, Ring Ouzel. *Winter:* Raptors (inc. Hen Harrier), Woodcock.
Other notable flora and fauna: Bell heather, ling and gorse on chalk heath; orchid species in grassland.
Contact: Senior Reserve Manager, East Sussex NNRs, Natural England, 01273 476 595;
e-mail sussex.surrey@natural-england.org.uk;
www.natural-england.org.uk

including sea kale, sea pea, least lettuce and stinging hawksbeard. Excellent range of dragonflies including breeding red-veined darter and scarce emerald

damselfly.
Contact: Barry Yates, (Manager), 2 Watch Cottages, Winchelsea, East Sussex, TN36 4LU. 01797 223 862.

Sussex, West

1. ARUNDEL

The Wildfowl and Wetlands Trust.
Location: TQ 020 081. Clearly signposted from Arundel, just N of A27.
Access: Summer (9.30am-5.30pm) winter (9.30am-4.30pm). Closed Christmas Day. Approx 1.5 miles of level footpaths, suitable for wheelchairs. No dogs except guide dogs. Admission charges for non-WWT members.
Facilities: Visitor centre, restaurant, shop, hides, picnic area, seasonal nature trails. Corporate hire facilities.
Public transport: Arundel station, 15-20 minute walk. Tel: 01903 882 131.
Habitat: Lakes, wader scrapes, reedbed.
Key birds: *Summer*: Nesting Redshank, Lapwing, Oystercatcher, Common Tern, Sedge, Reed and Cetti's Warblers, Peregrine, Hobby. *Winter*: Teal, Wigeon, Reed Bunting, Water Rail, Cetti's Warbler and occasionally roosting Bewick's Swan.
Contact: James Sharpe, Mill Road, Arundel, West Sussex, BN18 9PB. 01903 883 355, www.wwt.org.uk e-mail: info.arundel@wwt.org.uk

2. PAGHAM HARBOUR

West Sussex County Council.
Location: SZ 857 966. Five miles S of Chichester on B2145 towards Selsey.
Access: Open at all times, dogs must be on leads, disabled trail with accessible hide. All groups and coach parties must book in advance.
Facilities: Visitor Centre open weekends in winter (10am-4pm) and in summer (10am-5pm). Open most of the week throughout the year but check first. Toilets (including disabled), three hides, one trail.
Public transport: Bus stop by visitor centre.
Habitat: Mudflats, intertidal saltmarsh, shingle beaches, lagoons and farmland.
Key birds: *Spring*: Passage migrants. *Autumn*: Passage waders, other migrants. *Winter*: Brent Goose, Slavonian Grebe, wildfowl and waders. *All year*: Little Egret.
Other notable flora and fauna: Wide range of grasses, butterflies and dragonflies.
Contact: Kathryn Hampson, Pagham Harbour LNR, Selsey Road, Sidlesham, Chichester, West Sussex, PO20 7NE. 01243 641 508.
e-mail: pagham.nr@westsussex.gov.uk

3. PULBOROUGH BROOKS

RSPB (South East Region Office).
Location: TQ 054 170. Signposted on A283 between Pulborough (via A29) and Storrington (via A24). Two

miles SE of Pulborough.
Access: Open daily. Visitor centre open 9.30am-5pm (tea-room 4.30pm), closed Christmas Day and Boxing Day. Nature trail and hides (9am-9pm or sunset), closed Christmas Day. Admission fee for nature trail (free to RSPB members). No dogs. All four hides accessible to wheelchair users, though strong helper is needed.
Facilities: Visitor centre (incl RSPB shop, tea room with terrace, displays, toilets). Nature trail, four hides and additional viewpoints. Large car park including coach area. Play and picnic areas. An electric buggy is available for free hire, for use on trail.
Public transport: Two miles from Pulborough train station. Connecting bus service regularly passes reserve entrance (not Sun). Compass Travel (01903 690 025). Cycle stands.
Habitat: Lowland wet grassland (wet meadows and ditches). Hedgerows and woodland.
Key birds: *Winter*: Wintering waterbirds, Bewick's Swan. *Spring*: Breeding wading birds and songbirds (incl Lapwing and Nightingale). *Autumn*: Passage wading birds, Redstart, Whinchat.
Other notable flora and fauna: Good range of butterflies and dragonflies.
Contact: The Administrator, Pulborough Brooks Nature Reserve, Upperton's Barn, Wiggonholt, Pulborough RH20 2EL. 01798 875 851.
e-mail: pulborough.brooks@rspb.org.uk

4. THORNEY/PILSEY

RSPB (South East Region Office).
Location: SW of Chichester. Park in Emsworth and walk over sea walls to view both Thorney and Pilsey islands.
Access: No vehicle access to Thorney Island, viewing from footpaths only. Pilsey Island can also be viewed from coastal path (the Sussex Border Path) that runs around the Thorney Island MoD base. Long, exposed walk.
Facilities: Footpath.
Public transport: None.
Habitat: Intertidal sandflats and mudflats, fore dunes and yellow dunes, bare and vegetated shingle and saltmarsh.
Key birds: The reserve, together with the adjacent area of Pilsey Sand, forms one of the most important pre-roost and roost site for passage and wintering waders in the area.
Contact: Tim callaway, RSPB Pulborough Brooks, Wiggonholt, Pulborough, West Sussex RH20 2EL. 01798 875 851.

5. WARNHAM LNR

Horsham District Council.
Location: TQ 167 324. One mile from Horsham town

centre, just off A24 'Robin Hood' roundabout on B2237.

Access: Open every day, all year, including bank holidays (10am-6pm or dusk if earlier). Day permits: Adults £1, children under 16 free. Annual permits also available. No dogs or cycling allowed. Good wheelchair access over most of the Reserve.

Facilities: Visitor centre and café open every day except Christmas Day and Boxing Day (10am-5.30pm). Also new stag beetle loggery. Ample car park – coaches by request. Toilets (including disabled), two hides, reserve leaflets, millpond nature trail, bird feeding station, boardwalks, benches and hardstanding paths.

Public transport: From Horsham Railway Station it is a mile walk along Hurst Road, with a R turn onto Warnham Road. Buses from 'CarFax' in Horsham Centre stop within 150 yards of the reserve. Travel line, 0870 608 2608.

Habitat: 17 acre millpond, reedbeds, marsh, meadow and woodland (deciduous and coniferous).

Key birds: *Summer:* Common Tern, Kingfisher, woodpeckers, Mandarin Duck, Marsh Tit, Goldcrest, hirundines, Hobby, warblers. *Winter:* Cormorant, gulls, Little Grebe, Water Rail, Brambling, Siskin, Lesser Redpoll, thrushes and wildfowl. *Passage:* Waders, pipits, terns and hirundines.

Other notable flora and fauna: Extensive invertebrate interest, including 33 species of butterfly and 25 species of dragonfly. Mammals including harvest mouse, water vole and badger. More than 450 species of plant, including broad-leaved helleborine and common spotted orchid.

Contact: Sam Bayley, Countryside Warden, Leisure Services, Park House Lodge, North Street, Horsham, W Sussex, RH12 1RL. 01403 256 890.
e-mail: sam.bayley@horsham.gov.uk
www.visithorsham.co.uk www.market-towns.info

6. WOODS MILL

Sussex Wildlife Trust.

Location: TQ 218 138. Located NW of Brighton, one mile S of Henfield on A2037.

Access: Open every day except Christmas week. All-weather surface nature trail suitable for wheelchairs. HQ of Sussex Wildlife Trust.

Facilities: Toilets (including disabled), nature trail, car parking and parking for two coaches.

Public transport: Bus route 100 stops outside. Compass Travel 01903 690 025.

Habitat: Wetland, woodland and meadow habitats.

Key birds: General woodland birds and Kingfisher all year. *Summer:* Warblers (Reed and Garden Warblers), Blackcap, Whitethroat, Lesser Whitethroat) and Nightingales.

Other notable flora and fauna: Dragon and damselflies including beautiful demoiselle, red and ruddy darter and the rare scarce chaser. Wide range of water, woodland and meadow plants. Spring flowers include bluebells, wood anemones and common spotted orchids.

Contact: Woods Mill, 01273 492 630.
e-mail: enquiries@sussexwt.co.uk

South West England

Cornwall, Devon, Dorset, Somerset, Wiltshire

Cornwall

1. BRENEY COMMON

Cornwall Wildlife Trust.
Location: SX 054 610. 2.5 miles S of Bodmin. Take minor road off A390 one mile W of Lostwithiel to Lowertown. For Breney Common entrance, turn R at Reperry Cross, then L fork to Trebell Green and on towards Gurtla. The entrance track is on the left in Gurtla, after the Methodist church, opposite The Barn.
Access: Open at all times but please keep to paths. Disabled access from small car park at Breney.
Facilities: Wilderness trail. Boardwalk sections the only suitable surface for wheelchairs.
Public transport: None.
Habitat: Huge site (536 acres) includes wetland, grassland, heath and scrub.
Key birds: Willow Tit, Nightjar, Tree Pipit, Sparrowhawk, Lesser Whitethroat, Curlew.
Other notable flora and fauna: Royal fern, sundews and other bog plants. Butterflies (inc marsh and small pearl-bordered fritillaries, silver-studded blue).
Contact: Sean O'Hea, Cornwall Wildlife Trust, 01872 273 939. e-mail: info@cornwt.demon.co.uk
www.cornwallwildlifetrust.org.uk

2. CROWDY RESERVOIR

South West Lakes Trust.
Location: Follow signs from A39 at Camelford to Davidstow Airfield and pick up signs to reservoir. On edge of forestry plantation, park in pull-in spot near cattle grid. A track leads to a hide via stiles. Main car park located a little further down the lane.
Access: Open all year.
Facilities: Hide. **Public transport:** None.
Habitat: Reservoir, bog, moorland, forestry.
Key birds: *Spring:* Passage migrants, inc Wheatear, Whimbrel, Ruff. *Summer:* Black-headed Gull, Reed and Sedge Warblers, returning waders. *Autumn:* Waders, raptors possible inc Peregrine, Goshawk, Merlin. *Winter:* Wild swans, wildfowl, possible Smew. Golden Plover, Woodcock, Fieldfare, Redwing.
Other notable flora: Mire floral communities.
Contact: South West Lakes Trust, 01566 771 930. www.swlakestrust.org.uk

3. HAYLE ESTUARY

RSPB (South West England Office).
Location: SW 550 370. In town of Hayle. Follow signs to Hayle from A30. Take B3301 through Hayle past the Tempest factory, turn L

into Chenells Rd and R into Ryans Field.
Access: Open at all times. No permits required. No admission charges. Not suitable for wheelchair users. Dogs on leads please. Sorry — no coaches.
Facilities: Eric Grace Memorial Hide at Ryan's Field has parking and viewing, but birds here only at high tide. Nearest toilets in town of Hayle. No visitor centre but information board at hide.
Public transport: Buses and trains at Hayle. Call 0871 200 2233 for details.
Habitat: Intertidal mudflats, saltmarsh, lagoon and islands, sandy beaches and sand dunes.
Key birds: *Winter:* Wildfowl, gulls, Kingfisher, Great Northern Diver and waders. *Spring/summer:* Migrant waders, breeding Shelduck. *Autumn:* Rare waders, often from N America. Terns, gulls.
Contact: RSPB South West Regional Office, 01392 432 691; www.rspb.org.uk

4. MARAZION MARSH

RSPB (South West England Office).
Location: SW 510 315. Reserve is one mile E of Penzance, 500 yards W of Marazion. Entrance off seafront road near Marazion.
Access: Open at all times. No permits required. No admission charges. Not suitable for wheelchair users. Dogs on leads please. Sorry — no coaches.
Facilities: No toilets or visitor centre. Nearest toilets in Marazion and seafront car park.
Public transport: First Group Nos 2, 7 and 8, plus Sunset Bay2Bay service 340 from

NATURE RESERVES - SOUTH WEST ENGLAND

Penzance. Call 0871 200 2233 for details.
Habitat: Wet reedbed, willow carr.
Key birds: *Winter*: Wildfowl, Snipe, occasional Bittern. *Spring/summer*: Breeding Reed, Sedge and Cetti's Warblers, herons, swans. *Autumn*: Large roost of swallows and martins in reedbeds, migrant warblers and Water Rail.
Other notable flora and fauna: Up to 22 species of dragonfly, plus 500 species of vascular plants, inc lawn camomile and yellow flag.
Contact: RSPB South West Regional Office, 01392 432 691; www.rspb.org.uk

5. NARE HEAD

National Trust.
Location: Approx ten miles SE of Truro. from A390 head S on A307 to two miles S of Tregony just past the garage. Follow signs to Veryan then L signposted to Carne. Go straight over at crossroad, following Carne and Pendower. Turn L on a bend following NT signs for Nare Head. Bearing R, cross over a cattle grid to the car park. From the garage, Nare Head is about four miles.
Access: Open all year.
Facilities: Car park.
Public transport: None.
Habitat: Headland.
Key birds: *Spring/summer*: Razorbill, Guillemot, Sandwich, Common and Arctic Terns, possible Whimbrel, Fulmar. *Winter*: Black-throated and Great Northern Divers. Red-throated Diver possible. Common Scoter, Velvet Scoter, Slavonian, Black-necked and Red-necked Grebes.
Contact: National Trust, Lanhydrock House, Lanhydrock, Cornwall, PL30 4DE. 01208 432 691.

6. STITHIANS RESERVOIR

South West Lakes Trust.
Location: SS 715 365. From B3297 S of Redruth.
Access: Good viewing from causeway.
Facilities: New hide near main centre open to all.
Public transport: None.
Habitat: Open water, marshland.
Key birds: County's best open water site for winter wildfowl. Good for waders such as Common, Green and Wood Sandpipers, plus rarities, eg. Pectoral and Semipalmated Sandpipers, Lesser Yellowlegs.
Contact: South West Lakes Trust, Centre Manager, 01209 860 301. www.swlakestrust.org.uk

7. TAMAR ESTUARY

Cornwall Wildlife Trust.
Location: SX 434 631 (Northern Boundary). SX 421 604 (Southern Boundary). From Plymouth head W on A38. Access parking at Cargreen and Landulph from minor roads off A388.
Access: Open at all times. Access bird hides from China Fleet Club car park, Saltash. Follow path alongside golf course — do not walk on course itself. Combination number for hide locks available at club reception.
Facilities: Two hides on foreshore, first (0.25 miles from car park) overlooks estuary, second (0.5 miles) has excellent views across Kingsmill Lake.
Public transport: None.
Habitat: Tidal mudflat with some saltmarsh.
Key birds: *Winter*: Avocet, Snipe, Black-tailed Godwit, Redshank, Dunlin, Curlew, Whimbrel, Spotted Redshank, Green Sandpiper, Golden Plover, Kingfisher.
Contact: Cornwall Wildlife Trust, St Dominick, Cornwall PL12 6TA. 01579 351 155.
e-mail: peter@cornwt.demon.co.uk
www.cornwallwildlifetrust.org.uk

8. TAMAR LAKES

South West Lakes Trust
Location: SS 295 115. Follow brown tourist signs from Holsworthy or Kilkhampton.
Access: Open all year. Limited wheelchair access.
Facilities: Bird hides on Upper and Lower lakes. Café (limited opening) at Upper Tamar. Toilets at Upper open all year, those at Lower only open in summer.
Public transport: None.
Habitat: Two lfreshwater lakes, plus swamp, scrub and grassland.
Key birds: *All year*: Great Crested Grebe, Black-headed Gull, Kingfisher, Willow Tit, Reed Bunting. *Spring*: Black Tern. *Summer*: Breeding Sedge, Reed and Willow Warblers and House Martin. *Winter*: Moderate numbers of wildfowl, inc Wigeon and Teal and gulls.
Other notable flora and fauna: Badger, roe deer, otter, southern marsh orchid, wood white butterfly, grass snake.
Contact: Mark Green, Conservation Officer, Upper Tamar Lakes Visitor Centre, Kilkhampton, Bude, Cornwall EX23 9SA. 01288 321 262.

For a comprehensive survey of bird reserves in the county and The Isles of Scilly, see the latest, highly acclaimed *Best Birdwatching Sites: Cornwall and Scilly* book from Buckingham Press. See page 94 for more details.

199

Devon

1. AYLESBEARE COMMON

RSPB (South West England Office).
Location: SY 058 897. Five miles E of J30 of M5 at
Exeter, 0.5 miles past Halfway Inn on B3052. Turn R
to Hawkerland, car park is on L. The reserve is on the
opposite side of the main road.
Access: Open all year. One track suitable for
wheelchairs and pushchairs.
Facilities: Car park, picnic area, group bookings,
guided walks and special events. Disabled access via
metalled track to private farm.
Public transport: Buses (Exeter to Sidmouth,
52a, 52b). Request stop at Joneys Cross (reserve
entrance). Tel: 01392 427 711.
Habitat: Heathland, wood fringes, streams and ponds.
Key birds: *Spring/summer*: Hobby, Nightjar, Tree
Pipit, Stonechat. *All year*: Dartford Warbler, Buzzard,
Yellowhammer. *Winter*: Possible Hen Harrier.
Other notable flora and fauna: Good range of
dragonflies and butterflies.
Contact: Toby Taylor, Hawkerland Brake Barn,
Exmouth Road, Aylesbeare, Nr Exeter EX5 2JS. 01395
233 655.
www.rspb.org.uk/reserves/guide/a/
aylesbearecommon/

2. BOVEY HEATHFIELD

Devon Wildlife Trust.
Location: SX 824 765. On the outskirts of Bovey
Tracey on SE edge of Dartmoor. From A382 Bovey
Straight take Battle Road into Heathfield Industrial
estate. Turn L into Cavalier Road, then Dragoon Close
– the reserve is along a gravel path.
Access: Open all year. Dogs allowed on leads.
Please keep to paths. Rough paths not suitable for
wheelchairs. No coach access.
Facilities: Information hut open when warden is on
site.
Public transport: Buses to Battle Road, Heathfield.
Habitat: Heathland.
Key birds: Breeding Nightjar, Tree Pipit, Stonechat
and Dartford Warbler, plus commoner species.
Other notable flora and fauna: Heathers, wet and
dry heathland plants, more than 60 endangered insect
species, plus grayling and green hairstreak butterflies,
slow worm, adder.
Contact: Devon Wildlife Trust, Cricklepit Mill,
Commercial Road, Exeter, EX1 4AB. 01392 279 244.
e-mail: devonwt@cix.co.uk

3. BOWLING GREEN MARSH

RSPB (South West England Office).
Location: SX 972 876. On the E side of River Exe, four
miles SE of Exeter, 0.5 miles SE of Topsham.
Access: Open at all times. Please park at the public
car parks in Topsham, not in the lane by the reserve.
Facilities: RSPB shop at Darts Farm, 1.5km from
reserve, east of Topsham across River Clyst.

Public transport: Exeter to Exmouth railway has
regular (every 30 mins) service to Topsham station
(half a mile from reserve). Stagecoach Devon 57 bus
has frequent service (Mon-Sat every 12 mins, Sun
every half-hour) from Exeter to Topsham. Traveline
0871 200 2233.
Habitat: Coastal grassland, open water/marsh.
Key birds: *Winter*: Wigeon, Shoveler, Teal, Black-
tailed Godwit, Curlew, Golden Plover. *Spring*:
Shelduck, passage waders, Whimbrel, passage
Garganey and Yellow Wagtail. *Summer*: Gull/tern
roosts, high tide wader roosts contain many passage
birds. *Autumn*: Wildfowl, Peregrine, wader roosts.
Other notable flora and fauna: Hairy dragonfly, wasp
spider.
Contact: RSPB, Darts Farm Shopping Village, Clyst
St. George, Exeter EX3 0QH. 01392 879 438 or the
reserve on 01392 824 614.
www.rspb.org.uk

4. BURRATOR RESERVOIR

South West Lakes Trust.
Location: SX 551 681. Lies 10 miles NE of Plymouth,
off A386 (Tavistock road). At Yelverton take B3212
towards Princeton. Turn R at Burrator Inn and follow
signs to reservoir.
Access: Open all year. Numerous free parking areas
around reservoir. Main route is suitable for disabled
but is also used by motorists and cyclists. There are
about 25 stiles around the reservoir but not on main
route.
Facilities: Toilets (including disabled at Burrator
Lodge). Snacks and ice-creams available during
summer.
Public transport: Bus: daily from Plymouth to
Dousland (a short walk from the reservoir). No 82
Western National or No 48 (Sun). Tel: 01752 402 060.
Train: nearest station is Plymouth. Tel: 08457 484
950.
Habitat: Pine forests, wooded streams, open
moorland scrub.
Key birds: *Winter*: Goosander, Dipper, Grey Wagtail,
Green Sandpiper, Brambling, Crossbill, Siskin,
Redpoll. *All year*: All three woodpeckers, Buzzard,
Sparrowhawk, Kestrel, Barn Owl, Tree Sparrow.
Other notable flora and fauna: Marsh fritillary
butterfly, dragonflies and damselflies, particularly in
the arboretum, bats (various species), otter.
Contact: South West Lakes Trust, Lidn Park, Quarry
Crescent, Pennygillam Industrial Estate, Launceston,
Cornwall PL15 7PF. 01566 771 930.
www.swlakestrust.org.uk

5. DART VALLEY

Devon Wildlife Trust.
Location: SX 680 727. On Dartmoor nine miles NW
from Ashburton. From A38 'Peartree Cross' near
Ashburton, follow signs towards Princetown. Access
from National Park car parks at New Bridge (S) or
Dartmeet (N).
Access: Designated 'access land' but terrain is

avoid beach beyond groyne nine around high tide due to roosting birds. Parking charges apply. Restricted access for dogs (none allowed in hide).
Facilities: Visitor centre (tel 01626 863 980) open most weekends all year (10.30am-1pm and 2pm-5pm). Summer also open most weekdays as before, but can be closed if warden is on site. Toilets at entrance tunnel and in resort area only. Hide open at all times — best around high tide.
Public transport: Train station at site, also regular bus service operated by Stagecoach.
Habitat: High tide roost site for wildfowl and waders of Exe estuary on mudflats and shore. Dunes, dune grassland, woodland, scrub, ponds.
Key birds: *Winter*: Waders and wildfowl - large numbers. Also good for divers and Slavonian Grebe offshore. *Summer*: Particularly good for terns. Excellent variety of birds all year, especially on migration.
Contact: Steve Ayres/Philip Chambers, Countryside Management Section, Teignbridge District Council, Forde House, Brunel Road, Newton Abbot, Devon, TQ12 4XX. Visitor centre: 01626 863 980. Teignbridge District Council: 01626 361 101 (Ext 5754). www. dawlishwarren.co.uk

rough with few paths. It is possible to walk the length of the river (eight miles). A level, well-made track runs for a mile from Newbridge to give easy access to some interesting areas. Not suitable for large coaches (narrow bridges). Probably too rough for wheelchairs.
Facilities: Dartmoor National Park toilets in car parks at New Bridge and Dartmeet.
Public transport: Enquiry line 01392 382 800. Summer service only from Newton Abbot/Totnes to Dartmeet.
Habitat: Upland moor, wooded valley and river.
Key birds: *All year*: Raven, Buzzard. *Spring/summer*: Wood Warbler, Pied Flycatcher, Redstart in woodland, Stonechat and Whinchat on moorland, Dipper, Grey Wagtail, Goosander on river.
Contact: Devon Wildlife Trust, Cricklepit Mill, Commercial Road, Exeter, EX1 4AB. 01392 279 244. www.devonwildlifetrust.org

6. DAWLISH WARREN NNR

Teignbridge District Council.
Location: SX 983 788. At Dawlish Warren on S side of Exe estuary mouth. Turn off A379 at sign to Warren Golf Club, between Cockwood and Dawlish. Turn into car park adjacent to Lea Cliff Holiday Park. Pass under tunnel and turn L away from amusements. Park at far end of car park and pass through two pedestrian gates.
Access: Open public access, but avoid mudflats. Also

7. EAST DARTMOOR NNR

Natural England.
Location: SX 778 787. The NNR is two miles from Bovey Tracey on road to Becky Falls and Manaton. Road continues across Trendlebere Down, where there are roadside car parks and adjacent paths.
Access: Yarner Wood car park open from 8.30am-7pm or dusk if earlier. Outside these hours, access on foot from Trendlebere Down. Dogs welcome but must be kept under close control.
Facilities: Information/interpretation display and self-guided trails available in Yarner Wood car park also hide with feeding station (Nov-Mar).
Public transport: Nearest bus stops are in Bovey Tracey. Buses from here to Exeter and Newton Abbot (hourly).
Habitat: The reserve consists of three connected sites (Yarner Wood, Trendlebere Down and Bovey Valley Woodlands) totalling 365 hectares of upland oakwood and heathland.
Key birds: *All year*: Raven, Buzzard, Goshawk, Sparrowhawk, Lesser Spotted, Great Spotted and Green Woodpeckers, Grey Wagtail and Dartford Warbler (on Trendlebere Down). *Spring/summer*: Pied Flycatcher, Wood Warbler, Redstart, Tree Pipit, Linnet, Stonechat, Cuckoo, Whitethroat, Skylark. *Autumn/winter*: Good range of birds with feeding

at hide, inc Siskin, Redpoll, plus Hen Harrier on Trendlebere Down.
Contact: Site Manager, Natural England, Yarner Wood, Bovey Tracey, Devon, TQ13 9LJ. 01626 832 330. www.natural-england.org.uk

8. EXMINSTER MARSHES

RSPB (South West England Office).
Location: SX 954 872. Five miles S of Exeter on W bank of River Exe. Marshes lie between Exminster and the estuary.
Access: Open at all times.
Facilities: No toilets or visitor centre. Information in RSPB car park and marked footpaths across reserve.
Public transport: Exeter to Newton Abbot/Torquay buses — stops are 400 yds from car park. Traveline 0871 200 2233. No 2 buses Mon-Sat every 15 mins, Sun half-hourly.
Habitat: Coastal grazing marsh with freshwater ditches and pools, reeds, scrub-covered canal banks, winter stubbles and crops managed for farmland birds.
Key birds: *Winter*: Brent Goose, Wigeon, Water Rail, Short-eared Owl. *Spring*: Lapwing, Redshank and wildfowl breed, Cetti's Warbler on canal banks. *Summer*: Gull roosts, passage waders. *Autumn*: Peregrine, winter wildfowl, finch flocks. There are also records of Cirl Bunting and Woodlark.
Other notable flora and fauna: 23 species of dragonfly, including hairy and scarce chaser.
Contact: RSPB, Unit 3, Lions Rest Estate, Station Road, Exminster, Exeter, EX6 8DZ. 01392 824 614. www.rspb.org.uk

9. HALDON FOREST RAPTOR VIEWPOINT

Forestry Commission.
Location: Five miles W of Exeter.Turn off A38 at Haldon Racecourse junction, then follow signs for Dunchideock and Forest Walks. After just over 1 mile, turn L into Haldon Forest Park car park. Follow all-ability trail to the viewpoint.
Access: Open all year.
Facilities: Toilets in car park. Viewing point with benches. Path suitable for wheelchairs.
Habitat: Plantations, clearings.
Key birds: *Summer*: Hobby, Nightjar, Turtle Dove, Tree Pipit. *All year*: Goshawk, Sparrowhawk, Buzzard, all woodpeckers, Crossbill, Siskin.
Contact: Forestry Commission, Bullers Hill, Kennford, Exeter, Devon, EX6 7XR. 01392 832 262.. www.forestry.gov.uk/england

10. PLYMBRIDGE WOOD

National Trust/Forest Enterprise.
Location: At the Estover roundabout, Plymouth (near the Wrigley company factory), take the narrow, steep Plymbridge Road. Park at the bridge area at the bottom of the hill. Coming from Plympton, pick up Plymbridge Road from either Plymouth Road or Glen Road.
Access: Open all year.
Facilities: Car park, woodland paths, picnic area.
Public transport: None.
Habitat: Mixed woodland, river, conifers.
Key birds: *Spring/summer*: Cuckoo, Wood Warbler, Redstart, Blackcap, possible Nightjar, Crossbill. *Winter*: Woodcock, Snipe, Fieldfare, Redwing, Brambling, Siskin, Redpoll, possible Crossbill. *All year*: Mandarin Duck, Sparrowhawk, Buzzard, Kestrel, Tawny Owl, all three woodpeckers, Kingfisher, Grey Wagtail, Dipper, Goldcrest, common woodland passerines, Marsh Tit, Raven.
Contact: National Trust, Lanhydrock House, Lanhydrock, Cornwall, PL30 4DE. 01208 432 691.

11. STOVER LAKE COUNTRY PARK

Devon County Council.
Location: Two miles N of Newton Abbot off A38 Exeter-Plymouth road. Follow the A382 L at Drumbridges roundabout, signed to Newton Abbot. After 0.25 miles follow the brown tourist sign L into the car park (fee payable).
Access: Open all year. Wheelchairs available for visitor use.
Facilities: Car park, information centre, notice board display, site leaflets, maps, feeding station, 90 metre aerial walkway.
Public transport: From Newton Abbot, Exeter or Plymouth. Info from Traveline 0871 200 2233.
Habitat: Mixed woodland, lake and lowland heath. SSSI.
Key birds: *Spring/summer*: Sand Martin, Chiffchaff, Willow Warbler, Spotted Flycatcher, Nightjar, Great Crested Grebe. *Winter*: Water Rail, Marsh Tit, Snipe. *All year*: Woodpeckers, Jay, Siskin, Kingfisher.
Other notable flora and fauna: More than 20 species of dragonfly and damselfly, including hairy dragonfly, downy, emerald and red-eyed damselflies. 34 species of butterfly have been recorded, including white admiral, pearl-bordered and silver-washed fritillaries. A good site for bat watching with 10 species identified.
Contact: Rangers Office, Stover Country Park, Stover, Newton Abbot TQ12 6QG. 01626 835 236. www.devon.gov.uk/stover_country_park

Visit www.buckinghampress.co.uk for details of the *Best Birdwatching Sites* series of guides to key UK locations.

Dorset

1. ARNE

RSPB (South West England Office).
Location: SY 973 882. Four miles SE of Wareham, turn off A351 at Stoborough.
Access: Shipstal Point and Coombe Birdwatchers' trails open all year. Coombe birdwatchers' screen on Middlebere Channel and overlooking estuary open all year. Visitor centre open all year except Christmas. Bird hides available on both trails. Accessed from car park. Coaches and escorted parties by prior arrangement.
Facilities: Toilets in car park. Car park charge applies to non-members. Various footpaths. Visitor centre.
Public transport: None to reserve. Nearest station is Wareham.
Habitat: Lowland heath, woodland reedbed and saltmarsh, extensive mudflats of Poole Harbour.
Key birds: *All year*: Dartford Warbler, Little Egret, Stonechat. *Winter*: Hen Harrier, Red-breasted Merganser, Black-tailed Godwit. *Summer*: Nightjar, warblers. *Passage*: Spotted Redshank, Whimbrel, Greenshank, Osprey.
Other notable flora and fauna: Sika deer, all six species of UK reptile, silver-studded blue and 32 other butterflies, 23 dragonflies, 850 moths and 500 flowering plants.
Contact: Alaxia Hollinshead, Arne Nature Reserve, RSPB Work Centre, Arne, Wareham, Dorset, BH20 5BJ. 01929 553 360, e-mail: arne@rspb.org.uk www.rspb.org.uk/reserves/guide/a/arne/

2. BROWNSEA ISLAND

Dorset Wildlife Trust.
Location: SZ 026 883. Half hour boat rides from Poole Quay with Greenslade Pleasure Boats (01202 631 828) and Brownsea Island Ferries (01929 462 383). Ten minutes from Sandbanks Quay (next to Studland chain-ferry).
Access: Apr, May, Jun, Sept and Oct. Access by self-guided nature trail. Costs £2 adults, £1 children. Jul, Aug access by afternoon guided tour (2pm daily, duration 105 minutes). Costs £2 adults, £1 children.
Facilities: Toilets, information centre and shop, six hides, nature trail.
Public transport: Poole rail/bus station for access to Poole Quay and boats. Tel: 01202 673 555.
Habitat: Saline lagoon, reedbed, lakes, coniferous and mixed woodland.
Key birds: *Spring*: Avocet, Black-tailed Godwit, waders, gulls and wildfowl. *Summer*: Common and Sandwich Terns, Yellow-legged Gull, Little Egret, Little Grebe, Golden Pheasant. *Autumn*: Curlew Sandpiper, Little Stint.
Other notable flora and fauna: Red squirrel, water vole, Bechstein's bat found 2007.
Contact: Dorset Wildlife Trust, 01202 709 445. e-mail: brownseaisland@dorsetwildlife.co.uk www.wildlifetrust.org.uk/dorset

3. DURLSTON NNR AND COUNTRY PARK

Dorset County Council.
Location: SZ 032 774. One mile S of Swanage (signposted).
Access: Open between sunrise and sunset. Visitor centre open weekends and holidays during winter and daily in other seasons.
Facilities: Guided walks, visitor centre, café, toilets, hide, waymarked trails.
Habitat: Grassland, hedges, cliff, meadows.
Key birds: Cliff-nesting seabird colonies; good variety of scrub and woodland breeding species; spring and autumn migrants; seawatching esp. Apr/May and Aug/Nov.
Other notable flora and fauna: 34 species of butterfly and 500-plus species of flowering plants, inc nine species of orchid.
Contact: The Ranger, Durlston Country Park, 01929 424 443, e-mail: info@durlston.co.uk www.durlston.co.uk

4. GARSTON WOOD

RSPB (South West England Office).
Location: SU 004 194. SW from Salisbury. From A354 take turn to Sixpenny Handley then take Bowerchalke road (Dean Lane). Keeping R, proceed for approximately 1.5 miles. Garston Wood car park on L of road indicated by a finger post on R side of road.
Access: Pushchairs can be negotiated around all of the rides, though the terrain is best in dry weather. Dogs are only allowed on public footpaths and bridleways must be kept on a lead.
Facilities: Car park, reserve leaflet, picnic area, group bookings accepted, guided walks available, remote location, good for walking, pushchair friendly.
Public transport: The nearest train station is in Salisbury: from the bus station, take Wilts and Dorset 184 service to Sixpenny Handley (Roebuck Inn).
Habitat: Ancient woodland includes large area of coppiced hazel and maple. Other habitats include oak woodland, scrub and mixed plantation, with important features such as glades, rides and dead wood.
Key birds: Common woodland birds plus Turtle Dove and migrant warblers including Blackcap, Willow Warbler, Garden Warbler and Nightingale. Spotted Flycatcher. Raptors include Buzzard, Sparrowhawk and Goshawk. Winter thrushes.
Other notable flora and fauna: Butterflies, including silver-washed fritillary and elusive white admiral. Adders can be seen on the ride side. Good range of fungi. Fallow deer.
Contact: Alaxia Hollinshead, Arne Nature Reserve, RSPB Work Centre, Arne, Wareham, Dorset BH20 5BJ. www.rspb.org.uk/reserves/guide/g/garstonwood//

5. HAM COMMON LNR

Poole Borough Council.
Location: SY 99. W of Poole. In Hamworthy, take the Blandford Road S along Lake Road, W along Lake Drive and Napier Road, leading to Rockley Park. Park

NATURE RESERVES - SOUTH WEST ENGLAND

in the beach car park by Hamworthy Pier or Rockley Viewpoint car park, off Napier Road, opposite the entrance to Gorse Hill Central Park.
Access: Open all year. Not suitable for coaches.
Facilities: None.
Habitat: LNR consisting of heathland, scrub, reedbeds, lake. Views over Wareham Channel and Poole Harbour.
Key birds: *Spring/summer*: Stonechat, Dartford Warbler. *Winter*: Brent Goose, Red-breasted Merganser, occasional divers, rarer grebes, Scaup. Waders inc Whimbrel, Greenshank and Common Sandpiper. *All year*: Little Egret.
Contact: Poole Borough Council, Civic Centre, Poole, BH15 2RU. 01202 633 633.
e-mail: information@poole.gov.uk

6. LODMOOR

RSPB (South West England Office).
Location: SY 686 807. Adjacent Lodmoor Country Park, in Weymouth, off A353 to Wareham.
Access: Open all times.
Facilities: One viewing shelter, network of paths.
Public transport: Local bus service.
Habitat: Marsh, shallow pools, reeds and scrub, remnant saltmarsh.
Key birds: *Spring/summer*: Breeding Common Tern, warblers (including Reed, Sedge, Grasshopper and Cetti's), Bearded Tit. *Winter*: Wildfowl, waders. *Passage*: Waders and other migrants.
Contact: Nick Tomlinson, RSPB Visitor Centre, Swannery Car Park, Weymouth, DT4 7TZ. 01305 778 313. www.rspb.org.uk

7. MOORS VALLEY COUNTRY PARK AND RINGWOOD FOREST

East Dorset District Council/Forestry Commission
Location: Two miles W of Ringwood, well-signposted from A31 between Ringwood and Three Legged Cross.
Access: Open every day (except Christmas Day) 8am-dusk. Visitor centre open 9am to 4.30pm daily. Many trails wheelchair friendly.
Facilities: Visitor centre, toilets, tea-room, country shop. Coach parking. Way-marked trails in good condition.
Public transport: Accessible by Wilts and Dorset No 36 service. Call 01988 827 005 or visit: www.wdbus.co.uk
Habitat: River, wet meadow, lakes, scrub, broad-leaved woodland, extensive coniferous forest, golf course.
Key birds: *Spring/summer*: Cuckoo, Nightjar, Sand Martin, Tree Pipit, Whitethroat. Occasional

Woodlark, Sedge Warbler. *Winter*: Teal, Pochard, Gadwall, Snipe, Redpoll. Occasional Brambling, Goosander. *Passage*: Whimbrel, Common Sandpiper, waders.
All year: Buzzard, Lapwing, Woodcock, Little Owl, Grey Wagtail, Kingfisher, Dartford Warbler, Crossbill, usual woodland species.
Other notable flora and fauna: 27 species of dragonfly. Good numbers of butterflies and other invertebrates. Roe deer, muntjac, badger, fox, rabbit, grey squirrel.
Contact: Moors Valley Country Park, Horton Road, Ashley Heath, Nr Ringwood, Dorset, BH24 2ET. 01425 470 721, e-mail: moorsvalley@eastdorset.gov.uk www.moors-valley.co.uk

8. PORTLAND BIRD OBSERVATORY

Portland Bird Observatory (registered charity).
Location: SY 681 690. Six miles S of Weymouth beside the road to Portland Bill.
Access: Open at all times. Parking only for members of Portland Bird Observatory. Self-catering accommodation for up to 20. Take own towels, sheets, sleeping bags.
Facilities: Displays and information, toilets, natural history bookshop, equipped kitchen.
Public transport: Bus service from Weymouth (First Dorset Transit Route 1).
Habitat: World famous migration watchpoint. Scrub and ponds.
Key birds: *Spring/autumn*: Migrants including many rarities. *Summer*: Breeding auks, Fulmar, Kittiwake. A total of 355 species recorded.
Contact: Martin Cade, Old Lower Light, Portland Bill, Dorset, DT5 2JT. 01305 820 553.
e-mail: obs@btinternet.com
www.portlandbirdobs.org.uk

9. RADIPOLE LAKE

RSPB (South West England Office).
Location: SY 677 796. In Weymouth. Enter from Swannery car park on footpaths.
Access: Visitor centre and nature trail open every day, summer (9am-5pm), winter (9am-4pm). Hide open (8.30am-4.30pm). Permit (available from visitor centre) required by non-RSPB members.
Facilities: Network of paths, one hide, one viewing shelter.
Public transport: Close to train station serving London and Bristol.
Habitat: Lake, reedbeds.
Key birds: *Winter:* Wildfowl. *Summer:* Breeding reedbed warblers (including Cetti's), Bearded Tit, passage waders and other migrants. Garganey regular in spring. Good for rarer gulls.
Contact: Nick Tomlinson, RSPB Visitor Centre, Swannery Car Park, Weymouth, DT4 7TZ. 01305 778 313. www.rspb.org.uk

10. SOPLEY COMMON

Dorset Wildlife Trust.
Location: SZ 132 975. Four miles NW of Christchurch near Hurn village.
Access: Open at all times. Permits required for surveying and group visits. Dogs under close control and on leads Apr to Aug. Limited disabled access.
Facilities: None.
Public transport: None.
Habitat: Lowland heath (dry and wet) and deciduous woodland.
Key birds: *Summer:* Breeding Dartford Warbler, Nightjar, Woodlark, Stonechat. Also Hobby. *Winter:* Snipe.
Other notable flora and fauna: Rare fauna includes sand lizard, smooth snake, green and wood tiger beetles, silver-studded blue butterfly. Wide range of dragonflies on many ponds.
Contact: Rob Brunt, Dorset Wildlife Trust, 01305 264 620, e-mail: rbrunt@dorsetwildlife.co.uk www.wildlifetrust.org.uk/dorset

Somerset

1. BREAN DOWN

National Trust (North Somerset).
Location: ST 290 590. 182 map. Juts into Bristol Channel five miles N of Burnham on Sea. J22 of M5, head for Weston-super-Mare on A370 and then head for Brean at Lympsham.
Access: Open all year. Dogs on lead. Steep slope — not suitable for wheelchair-users.
Facilities: Toilets one mile before property, not NT.
Public transport: Call Tourist Information Centre for details 01934 888 800 (bus services differ in winter/ summer).
Habitat: Limestone and neutral grassland, scrub and steep cliffs.
Key birds: *All year:* Peregrine, Raven. *Summer:* Blackcap, Garden Warbler, Whitethroat, Stonechat. *Winter:* Curlew, Shelduck, Dunlin on mudflat. Migrants.
Other notable flora and fauna: Chalkhill blue, marbled white and commoner butterflies. Extremely rare white rock rose in June. Somerset hair grass, dwarf sedge.
Contact: The National Trust, Barton Rocks, 01934 844 518.

2. BRIDGWATER BAY NNR

Natural England (Dorset and Somerset Team)
Location: ST 270 470. Five kilometres N of Bridgwater and extends to Burnham-on-Sea. Take J23 or 24 off M5. Turn N off A39 at Cannington.
Access: Hides open every day except Christmas Day. Permits needed for Steart Island (by boat only). Dogs on leads to protect grazing animals/nesting birds. Disabled access to hides by arrangement, other areas accessible.
Facilities: Car park, interpretive panels and leaflet dispenser at Steart. Footpath approx 0.5 miles to tower and hides.
Public transport: Train and bus stations in Bridgwater. First Group buses on A39 stop at Stockland Bristol, 2km SW of Steart. www.firstgroup. com
Habitat: Estuary, intertidal mudflats, saltmarsh.
Key birds: *All year:* Approx 190 species recorded on this Ramsar and SPA site. Wildfowl includes large population of Shelduck and nationally important numbers of Wigeon. Internationally important numbers of Whimbrel and Black-tailed Godwit. Resident Curlews and Oystercatchers joined by many other waders on passage. Good for birds of prey. *Spring/autumn:* Passage migrants, including occasional vagrants.
Other notable flora and fauna: Saltmarsh flora. Rare invertebrates include great silver water beetle, aquatic snail and hairy dragonfly.
Contact: Senior Reserves Manager, Natural England, 0300 060 2570, www.naturalengland.org.uk

3. CATCOTT LOWS

Somerset Wildlife Trust.
Location: ST 400 415. Approx one mile N of Catcott village (off A39 from J23 of M5).
Access: Open at all times.
Facilities: River Parrett Trail passes through reserve.
Public transport: None.
Habitat: Wet meadows with winter flooding and summer grazing.
Key birds: *Winter:* Wigeon, Teal, Pintail, Shoveler, Gadwall, Bewick's Swan, Peregrine. *Spring:* Little Egret, passage waders, breeding Lapwing, Snipe, Redshank, Yellow Wagtail.
Contact: Mark Blake, Reserve Officer, Somerset Wildlife Trust. 01823 652 400.
e-mail: enquires@somersetwildlife.org www.somersetwildlife.org

4. CHEW VALLEY LAKE

Avon Wildlife Trust, Bristol Water Plc.
Location: ST 570 600. Nine miles S of Bristol. Take B3114 south from Chew Stoke, bear L for West Harptree and head NE on A368. View reserve from causeway at Herriott's Bridge where there is car parking.
Access: Permit needed for access to hides (five at Chew, two at Blagdon). Best roadside viewing from causeways at Herriott's Bridge (nature reserve) and Herons Green Bay. Day, half-year and year permits from Bristol Water, Recreation Department, Woodford Lodge, Chew Stoke, Bristol BS18 8SH. Tel/Fax 01275 332 339. Parking for coaches available.
Facilities: Hides.
Public transport: Traveline, 0870 6082 608.
Habitat: Largest artificial lake in SW England with important reedbed.
Key birds: Often attracts rarities. *Winter and passage:* Wildfowl include important numbers of Shoveler, Gadwall, Teal and Tufted Duck. Large numbers of Goosander, Great Crested Grebe and Cormorant, with the grebe numbers often the highest in Britain in autumn. Plus Bewick's Swan, Goldeneye, Smew, Ruddy Duck. Huge winter gull roost (up to 50,000+), mostly Black-headed, Common and Mediterranean Gull. *Summer:* Breeding birds include Great Crested and Little Grebe, Gadwall, Tufted Duck, Shoveler, Pochard, Reed Warbler. Hobbies hunt in late summer. When the water level low, mud can attract waders such as Dunlin, Ringed Plover and Green Sandpiper.
Other notable flora and fauna: Ruddy darter and migrant hawker dragonflies.
Contact: Avon Wildlife Trust HQ or Bristol Water Recreation Dept, 01275 332 339.
e-mail: mail@avonwildlifetrust.org.uk
www.avonwildlifetrust.org.uk

5. GREYLAKE

RSPB (South West England Office).
Location: ST 399 346. Off A361 Taunton to Glastonbury road, between Othery and Greinton.
Access: Open all year, dawn to dusk, free admission. No dogs, apart from guide-dogs. Wheelchair users can access a 700 metre-long boardwalk and viewing hide.
Facilities: Surfaced nature trail, interpretive signs. No toilets on site.
Public transport: Bus No 29 (First Group). Nearest stop is one mile along main road at Greinton phone box, but drivers may stop at reserve on request.
Habitat: A large wet grassland reserve bought by RSPB in 2003. Formerly arable farmland.
Key birds: *Spring/summer:* Kingfisher, Grey Heron, Little Egret and Breeding Snipe, Lapwing, Redshank, Skylark, Meadow Pipit, Yellow Wagtail. *Autumn:* Green Sandpiper, waders on passage. *Winter:* Waders, wildfowl (including Lapwing, Golden Plover, Shoveler, Pintail, Teal and Wigeon). Peregrine, Hen Harrier.
Other notable flora and fauna: Roe deer, water vole, stoat, otter, dragonflies including four-spotted chaser.
Contact: Site Manager, 01458 252 805; e-mail:west.sedgemoor@rspb.org.uk
www.rspb.org.uk/reserves/guide/g/greylake

6. HAM WALL

RSPB (South West England Office).
Location: ST 449 397. W of Glastonbury. From A39 turn N in Ashcott and follow road onto the moor. After three miles pass Church Farm Horticultural building. Shortly after, at metal bridge, reserve is opposite side of road to Shapwick Heath NNR.
Access: Open all year. 2m height restriction on car park. Coach parking available at Avalon Marshes Centre, Shapwick Road. Dogs only on public footpaths and disused railway line. Wheelchair users can access viewing areas from main track (use RADAR key). Other rougher tracks cover 3.8 miles.
Facilities: Two open-air viewing platforms, four roofed viewing screens.
Public transport: By bus: Service 668 to Avalon Marshes Centre (BA6 9TT) at Westhay village, approx I mile or St Mary's Road, Meare (approx 1.2 miles from reserve entrance).
Habitat: 200-plus hectare wetland, including region's largest reedbed.
Key birds: *Spring/Summer:* Bittern, Cetti's Warbler, Water Rail, warblers, Hobby, Barn Owl. *Autumn:* Migrant thrushes, Lesser Redpoll, Siskin, Kingfisher, Bearded Tit. *Winter:* Million+ Starling roost, plus

NATURE RESERVES - SOUTH WEST ENGLAND

large flocks of ducks, Bittern, Little Egret, Peregrine, Merlin, Short-eared Owl.
Other notable flora and fauna: Otter, water vole, dragonflies, butterflies.
Contact: RSPB Ham Wall,1458 860494.
e-mail:ham.wall@rspb.org.uk;
www.rspb.org.uk/reserves/guide/h/hamwall

7. HORNER WOOD NATURE RESERVE

National Trust
Location: SS 897 454. From Minehead, take A39 W to a minor road 0.8km E of Porlock signed to Horner. Park in village car park.
Access: Open all year. Car parking in Horner village, extensive footpath system.
Facilities: Tea-room and toilets. Walks leaflets available from Holnicote Estate office and Porlock visitor centre. Interpretation boards in car parks.
Public transport: Bus: Porlock.
Habitat: Oak woodland, moorland.
Key birds: *Spring/summer*: Wood Warbler, Pied Flycatcher, Redstart, Stonechat, Whinchat, Tree Pipit, Dartford Warbler possible. *All year*: Dipper, Grey Wagtail, woodpeckers, Buzzard, Sparrowhawk.
Other notable flora and fauna: Silver-washed fritillary in July.
Contact: National Trust, 01643 862 452.
e-mail: holnicote@nationaltrust.org.uk
www.nationaltrust.org.uk

8. SHAPWICK HEATH NNR

Natural England (Dorset and Somerset Team)
Location: ST 426 415. Situated between Shapwick and Westhay, near Glastonbury. The nearest car park is 400 metres away at the Peat Moors Centre, south of Westhay.
Access: Open all year. Disabled access to displays, hides. No dogs.
Facilities: Network of paths, hides, elevated boardwalk. Toilets, leaflets and refreshments available at the Peat Moors Centre.
Public transport: None.
Habitat: Traditionally managed herb-rich grassland, ferny wet woodland, fen, scrub, ditches, open water, reedswamp and reedbed.
Key birds: *All year*: Ducks and waders. *Summer*: Bittern, Hobby, Cuckoo, Cetti's Warbler. *Winter*: Starling roost, large flocks of wildfowl.
Other notable flora and fauna: Wetland plants, otter and roe deer.
Contact: Senior Reserves Manager, Natural England, 0300 060 2570, www.naturalengland.org.uk

9. SHAPWICK MOOR RESERVE

Hawk and Owl Trust
Location: ST417 398. On the Somerset Levels. Take A39 between Bridgwater and Glastonbury and turn N, signposted Shapwick, on to minor road, straight over crossroads and through Shapwick village, turn L at T- junction following signs for Westhay. The reserve is

about a mile north of Shapwick village.
Access: Open all year. Access only along public footpaths and permissive path (closed on Christmas Day). Dogs must be kept on leads.
Facilities: Information panels. No toilets on site but public toilets at nearby Avalon Marshes Centre (ST 425 414).
Public transport: Train to Bridgwater, then First Bus (01278 434 574) No 375 Bridgwater-Glastonbury, to Shapwick village. Sustrans National Route 3 passes through Shapwick village.
Habitat: A wet grassland reserve being created from arable farmland as part of the Avalon Marshes project. Grazing pasture with rough grass edges, fen, open ditches (known as rhynes), pollard willows and hedges.
Key birds: *Spring/summer*: Hobby, Barn Owl, Reed Bunting, and Cetti's Warbler. Whimbrel and other waders on passage. Skylark. Passerines such as Bullfinch and Yellowhammer. *Autumn/winter*: Flocks of finches, Snipe, Shoveler, Gadwall, Stonechat, Brambling. Peregrine and harriers may fly over.
All year: Buzzard, Kestrel, Sparrowhawk, Kingfisher, Lapwing, Grey Heron, Mute Swan.
Other notable flora and fauna: Roe deer, brown hare, badger, otter and water vole.
Contact: Hawk and Owl Trust, 0844 984 2824.
e-mail: enquiries@hawkandowl.org
www.hawkandowl.org

10. SWELL WOOD

(RSPB South West England Office).
Location: ST 361 238. Entrance down by-road off A378 Taunton-Langport road, one mile E of Fivehead.
Access: Access at all times to Swell Wood car park and heronry hide. Coach parking in lay-by across main road. Heronry hide and part of woodland trail are wheelchair accessible.
Facilities: Heronry hide, two nature trails: woodland trail and scarp trail link to public footpaths, disabled parking area.
Public transport: Bus from Taunton to Fivehead. First Southern National Ltd 01823 272 033.
Habitat: Semi-natural ancient oak woodland and views across wet grassland from woodland trails. Part of the Somerset Levels and Moors.
Key birds: *Spring/summer*: Breeding Grey Heron, Little Egret, Buzzard, Bullfinch, Spotted Flycatcher, Song Thrush, warblers such as Chiffchaff, Blackcap and Garden Warbler.
On escorted walks: Curlew, Snipe, Sedge Warbler, Yellow Wagtail, Skylark, Nightingale. *Autumn*: Green Woodpecker, Robin, Wren, Coal Tit. *Winter*: Long-tailed tit, Treecreeper, Great Spotted Woodpecker, Nuthatch.
Other notable flora and fauna: Roe deer, woodland flora such as bluebells, wood anemone, lesser celandine, dragonflies, damselflies, butterflies.
Contact: Site Manager, 01458 252 805.
e-mail: swell.wood@rspb.org.uk
www.rspb.org.uk/reserves/guide/s/swellwood/

Scottish Border Counties

Borders

1. DUNS CASTLE

Scottish Wildlife Trust.
Location: NT 778 550. Located N of the centre of Duns (W of Berwick upon Tweed).
Access: Access from Castle Street or at N end of reserve from B6365.
Facilities: None. **Public transport:** None.
Habitat: Loch and woodland.
Key birds: Woodland birds, waterfowl.
Other notable flora and fauna: Occasional otter.
Contact: SWT headquarters132 312 7765.

2. GUNKNOWE LOCH AND PARK

Scottish Borders Council.
Location: NT 518 345. 3.2km from Galashiels on the A6091. Park at Gunknowe Loch.
Access: Open all year. Surfaced paths suitable for wheelchair use.
Facilities: Car park, paths.
Public transport: Tweedbank is on the Melrose to Peebles bus route.
Habitat: River, parkland, scrub, woodland.
Key birds: *Spring/summer*: Grey Wagtail, Kingfisher, Sand Martin, Blackcap, Sedge and Grasshopper Warblers. *Passage*: Yellow Wagtail, Whinchat, Wheatear. *Winter*: Thrushes, Brambling, Wigeon, Tufted Duck, Pochard, Goldeneye. *All year*: Great Spotted and Green Woodpeckers, Redpoll, Goosander, possible Marsh Tit.
Contact: Scottish Borders Council Ranger Service, 01835 825 060. www.scotborders.gov.uk

3. ST ABB'S HEAD

National Trust for Scotland.
Location: NT 914 693. Lies five miles N of Eyemouth. Follow A1107 from A1.
Access: Reserve open all year. Keep dogs under control. Viewpoint at Starney accessible for disabled visitors. Coach parking at Northfield Farm by prior arrangement.
Facilities: Visitor centre and toilets open daily Apr-Oct.
Public transport: Nearest rail station is Berwick-upon-Tweed. Bus service from Berwick, tel 01289 308 719.
Habitat: Cliffs, coastal grasslands and freshwater loch.
Key birds: Apr-Aug: Seabird colonies with large numbers of Kittiwake, auks, Shag, Fulmar, migrants. *Apr-*

May and Sept-Oct: Good autumn seawatching.
Other notable flora and fauna: Northern brown argus butterfly. Rock-rose, purple milk-vetch, spring sandwort.
Contact: Kevin Rideout, Rangers Cottage, Northfield, St Abbs, Borders TD14 5QF. 0844 493 2256.
e-mail:krideout@nts.org.uk www.nts.org.uk

4. THE HIRSEL

The Estate Office, The Hirsel.
Location: NT 827 403. Signed off the A698 on the outskirts of Coldstream.
Access: Open all year. Private estate so please stay on the public paths. Coaches by appointment.
Facilities: Car parks, visitor centre, toilets, hide, walks, tea-room.
Public transport: Bus: Coldstream, Kelso, Berwick-upon-Tweed, Edinburgh.
Habitat: Freshwater loch, reeds, woods.
Key birds: *Spring/summer*: Redstart, Garden Warbler, Blackcap, flycatchers, possible Water Rail, wildfowl. *Autumn*: Wildfowl, Goosander, possible Green Sandpiper. *Winter*: Whooper Swan, Pink-footed Goose, Wigeon, Goldeneye, Pochard, occasional Smew, Scaup, Slavonian Grebe.
Other notable flora and fauna: Rhododendrons.
Contact: The Managing Factor Roger Dodd, Bridge Street, Kelso ATD5 7JD. 01573 224 144.

Dumfries and Galloway

5. CAERLAVEROCK WETLAND CENTRE

The Wildfowl and Wetlands Trust.
Location: NY 051 656. Overlooks the Solway. From Dumfries take B725 towards Bankend.
Access: Open daily (10am-5pm), except Christmas Day.
Facilities: 20 hides, heated observatory, four towers,

Salcot Merse Observatory, sheltered picnic area. Self-catering accommodation and camping facilities. Nature trails in summer. Old Granary visitor building with fair-trade coffee shop serving light meals and snacks; natural history bookshop; binoculars and telescopes for sale. Theatre/conference room. Binoculars for hire. Parking for coaches.
Public transport: Bus 371 from Dumfries stops 30 mins walk from reserve. Stagecoach 01387 253 496.
Habitat: Saltmarsh, grassland, wetland.
Key birds: *Winter:* Wildfowl esp. Barnacle Geese (max 30,000) and Whooper Swans. *Summer:* Osprey, Barn Owl, Skylark.
Other notable flora and fauna: Natterjack toad. Northern marsh, common spotted and twayblade orchids.
Contact: The Wildfowl and Wetlands Trust, Eastpark Farm, Caerlaverock DG1 4RS. 01387 770 200.

6. KEN/DEE MARSHES

RSPB (South and West Scotland Office).
Location: NX 699 684. Six miles from Castle Douglas — good views from A762 and A713 roads to New Galloway.
Access: From car park at entrance to farm Mains of Duchrae. Open during daylight hours. No dogs.
Facilities: Hides, nature trails. Three miles of trails available. Closer parking for elderly and disabled is available, but phone warden first. Part of Red Kite trail.
Public transport: None.
Habitat: Marshes, woodlands, open water.
Key birds: *All year:* Mallard, Grey Heron, Buzzard, Nuthatch, Willow Tit. *Spring/summer:* Pied Flycatcher, Redstart, Tree Pipit, Sedge Warbler. *Winter:* Greenland White-fronted and Greylag Geese, birds of prey (Hen Harrier, Peregrine, Merlin, Red Kite).
Other notable flora and fauna: Red squirrel.
Contact: Gus Keys, RSPB Scotland, 01671 404 975.

7. KIRKCONNELL MERSE

RSPB (South and West Scotland Office).
Location: NX990 690. Lies between Dumfries and Glencaple (B725) on banks of River Nith.
Access: None. View reserve from B725 on east side of River Nith.
Facilities: None. **Public transport:** None.
Habitat: Saltmarsh, inter-tidal sand flats and grassland.
Key birds: *Winter:* Whooper Swan, Pink-footed and Barnacle Geese, Pintail, waders.
Contact: Dave Fairlamb, RSPB Scotland, Mersehead Reserve, Southwick DG2 8AH. 01387 780 579

8. MERSEHEAD

RSPB (South and West Scotland Office).
Location: From Dumfries, take A710 Solway Coast road, passing through several villages, reserve is signposted just before Caulkerbush on L. Single track road with passing places runs for a mile down to car

park by visitor centre. From Castle Douglas, take A745, then A711 to Dalbeattie before joining the A710 Solway Coast road. Reserve is signposted just after Caulkerbush bridge, on R. Follow above directions for single track road to reserve.
Access: Open at all times.
Facilities: Hide, nature trails, information centre and toilets.
Habitat: Wet grassland, arable farmland, saltmarsh, inter-tidal mudflats.
Key birds: *Winter:* Up to 9,500 Barnacle Geese, 4,000 Teal, 2,000 Wigeon, 1,000 Pintail, waders (inc. Dunlin, Knot, Oystercatcher). *Summer:* Breeding birds include Lapwing, Redshank, Skylark.
Contact: Eric Nielson, Mersehead, Southwick, Mersehead, Dumfries DG2 8AH. 01387 780 298.

9. MULL OF GALLOWAY

RSPB (South and West Scotland Office).
Location: NX 156 304. Most southerly tip of Scotland — five miles from village of Drummore, S of Stranraer.
Access: Open at all times. Access suitable for disabled. Disabled parking by centre. Centre open summer only (Apr-Oct).
Facilities: Visitor centre, toilets, nature trails, CCTV on cliffs.
Habitat: Sea cliffs, coastal heath.
Key birds: *Spring/summer:* Guillemot, Razorbill, Kittiwake, Black Guillemot, Puffin, Fulmar, Raven, Wheatear, Rock Pipit, Twite. Migrating Manx Shearwater. *All year:* Peregrine.
Contact: Gus Keys, RSPB Scotland, 01671 404 975.

10. WIGTOWN BAY LNR

Dumfries and Galloway Council.
Location: NX 465 545. Between Wigtown and Creetown, S of Newton Stewart. It is the largest LNR in Britain at 2,845 ha. The A75 runs along E side with A714 S to Wigtown and B7004 providing superb views of the LNR.
Access: Reserve open at all times. The hide is disabled-friendly. Main accesses: Roadside lay-bys on A75 near Creetown and parking at Martyr's Stake and Wigtown Harbour. All suitable for coaches. Visitor Centre in Wigtown County Building has coach parking and welcomes groups. It has full disabled access, including lift and toilets.
Facilities: Hide at Wigtown Harbour overlooking River Bladnoch, saltmarsh and fresh water wetland has disabled access from harbour car park. Walks and interpretation in this area. Visitor centre has a commanding view of the bay. CCTV of Ospreys breeding in Galloway during summer and wetland birds in winter. Open Mon-Sat (10am-5pm, later some days), Sun (2pm-5pm).
Public transport: Travel Information Line 08457 090 510 (local rate 9am-5pm Mon-Fri). Bus No 415 for Wigtown and W side. Bus No 431 or 500 X75 for Creetown and E side.
Habitat: Estuary with extensive saltmarsh/merse and mudflats with developed fresh water wetland at Wigtown Harbour.

Key birds: *Winter:* Internationally important for Pink-footed Goose, nationally important for Curlew, Whooper Swan and Pintail, with major gull roost and other migratory coastal birds. *Summer:* Breeding waders and duck.
Other notable flora and fauna: Lax-flowered sea-lavender, thrift, sea aster.
Contact: Elizabeth Tindal, Countryside Ranger, Wigtown Bay Visitor Centre, 01988 402 401, mobile 07702 212 728. e-mail:wblLNR@dumgal.gov.uk www.dgcommunity.net/wblr

11. WOOD OF CREE

RSPB (South and West Scotland Office).
Location: NX 382 708. Four miles N of Newton

Stewart on minor road from Minnigaff, parallel to A714.
Access: Open during daylight hours. Dogs on lead. Not suitable for disabled.
Facilities: Car park, viewing platform, nature trails.
Habitat: The largest ancient oak woodland in southern Scotland, marshes, river.
Key birds: *Spring/summer:* Pied Flycatcher, Wood Warbler, Tree Pipit, Redstart, Buzzard, Great Spotted Woodpecker.
Dipper and Grey Wagtail on River Cree.
Other notable flora and fauna: Red squirrel, otter, Leisler's bat, carpet of bluebells and other spring wildflowers. Wilsons filmy fern. 21 species of butterfly recorded.
Contact: Gus Keys, RSPB Scotland, 01671 404 975.

Central Scotland

Argyll, Ayrshire, Clyde, Fife, Forth, Lothian

Argyll

1. COLL RESERVE

RSPB (South and West Scotland Office).
Location: NM 167 563. By ferry from Oban to island of Coll. Take the B8070 W from Arinagour for five miles. Turn R at Arileod. Continue for about one mile. Park at end of the road. Reception point at Totronald.
Access: Open all year. A natural site with unimproved paths not suitable for wheelchairs. Please avoid walking through fields and crops.
Facilities: Car park, information bothy at Totronald, guided walks in summer. Corncrake viewing bench.
Public transport: None.
Habitat: Sand dunes, beaches, machair grassland, moorland, farmland.
Key birds: *Spring:* Gt Northern Diver offshore. Corncrake arrive in late April. Displaying waders, inc Redshank, Lapwing, Snipe. *Summer:* Auks offshore, plus Gannet, shearwaters and terns. *Autumn:* Barnacle and Greenland White-fronted Geese arrive, thrushes on passage. Waders inc Purple Sandpiper. *Winter:* Long-tailed Duck, divers offshore. Hunting Hen Harrier and Merlin. Twite.
Other notable flora and fauna: Good for cetaceans and basking shark. Otter, 300-plus machair wildflowers inc rare orchids, great yellow bumblebee.
Contact: RSPB Coll Nature Reserve, 01879 230 301.

2. LOCH GRUINART, ISLAY

RSPB (South & West Scotland Office).
Location: NR 275 672. Sea loch on N coast of Islay, seven miles NW from Bridgend.
Access: Hide open all hours, visitor centre open (10am-5pm), disabled access to hide, viewing area and toilets. Assistance required for wheelchair users.

Coach parking at visitor centre only. No dogs in hides.
Facilities: Toilets (inc disabled), visitor centre (offers hot drinks), hide, trail. Two car parks — the one opposite the viewpoint is level and made from rolled stone. Group bookings accepted. Weekly guided walks every Thursday at 10am (April to Oct)
Public Transport: Nearest bus stops three miles from reserve.
Habitat: Lowland wet grasslands, sea loch, moorland.
Key birds: *Oct-Apr:* Large numbers of Barnacle and White-fronted Geese, plus other wildfowl and waders. *May-Aug:* Breeding and displaying waders and Corncrake. *Sept-Nov:* Many passage migrants and arriving wildfowl. Birds of prey are present all year, esp Hen Harrier and Peregrine, while Chough can be seen feeding in nearby fields. *Spring:* Displaying Snipe, Lapwing, Curlew and Redshank.
Other notable flora and fauna: Good chance of seeing otter, red and roe deer. Marsh fritillary butterflies during May and June. Herb-rich meadows.
Contact: Liz Hathaway, RSPB Scotland, 01496 850 505; e-mail: loch.gruinart@rspb.org.uk or Liz.Hathaway@rspb.org.uk or www.rspb.org.uk/scotland

3. MACHRIHANISH SEABIRD OBSERVATORY

(sponsored by SNH and Leader+) John McGlynn, Nancie Smith and Eddie Maguire.
Location: NR 628 209. Southwest Kintyre, Argyll. Six miles W of Campbeltown on A83, then B843.
Access: Daily April-Oct. Wheelchair access. Dogs welcome. Parking for three cars. Digiscoping facilities include electricity and monitor.
Facilities: Seawatching hide, toilets in nearby village. Coach parking.
Public transport: Regular buses from Campbeltown (West Coast Motors, tel 01586 552 319).

Habitat: Marine, rocky shore and upland habitats.
Key birds: *Summer:* Golden Eagle, Peregrine, Storm Petrel and Twite. *Autumn:* Passage seabirds and waders. On-shore gales often produce inshore movements of Leach's Petrel and other scarce seabirds, including Balearic Shearwater, Sabine's Gull and Grey Phalarope.
Winter: Great Northern Diver, Purple Sandpiper, Ruddy Turnstone with occasional Glaucous and Iceland Gulls.
Other notable flora and fauna: Grey and common seals, otter, wild goat.
Contact: Eddie Maguire, Warden, Seabird and Wildlife Observatory, Lossit Park, Machrihanish, SW Kintyre, Argyll PA28 6PZ. 07919 660 292.
e-mail:machrihanishbirds@btinternet.com
www.machrihanishbirds.org.uk

4. THE OA, ISLE OF ISLAY

RSPB (South and West Scotland Office).
Location: NR 282 423. Six miles SW of Port Ellen, Islay.
Access: Open all year.
Facilities: Car park and waymarked trail. No toilets or other facilities. Weekly guided walks every Tuesday at 10am (April to September).
Public transport: None.
Habitat: Open moorland, freshwater loch, seacliffs, coastal grassland and heath.
Key birds: Breeding Golden Eagle, Red-throated Diver, Peregrine, Hen Harrier, Chough, Corncrake and farmland birds. *Winter:* Greenland White-fronted Geese and winter thrushes.
Other notable flora and fauna: Narrow-bordered bee hawkmoth, feral goats on cliffs.
Contact: Andy Schofield, RSPB Scotland, Kinnabus Farm, The Oa, Port Ellen PA42 7AU, 01496 300 118.

Ayrshire

5. AILSA CRAIG

RSPB (South and West Scotland Office).
Location: NX 020 998. Island is nine miles offshore, nearest town on mainland is Girvan.
Access: Accessible only by boat — no landing possible. Boat trips on the MFV Glorious (tel: 01465 713 219) or Kintyre Express (tel: 01294 270 160) from Girvan during the summer period. Also from Campbeltown by Mull of Kintyre Seatours' fast rib (Tel: 07785 542 811).
Facilities: None. **Public transport:** None.
Habitat: Dramatic seacliffs.
Key birds: Ailsa Craig is the third largest gannetry in the UK and supports 73,000 breeding seabirds, including Guillemot, Razorbill, Puffin, Black Guillemot, Kittiwake and up to 36,000 pairs of Gannet. Twite can also be found here.
Other notable flora and fauna: Slow worm.
Contact: RSPB South and West Scotland Office, 0141 331 0993, e-mail:glasgow@rspb.org.uk

6. CULZEAN CASTLE COUNTRY PARK

National Trust for Scotland.
Location: NS 234 103. 12 miles SW of Ayr on A719.
Access: Country Park open all year during daylight hours. Restaurant/shops open daily between April and Oct and weekends Nov-March. Access leaflet available.
Facilities: Car park, visitor centre, children's playground, picnic areas, 21 miles of footpath and estate tracks, ranging from unsurfaced woodland paths to metalled roads.
Public transport: Stagecoach bus No 60 (Ayr to Girvan) stops at site entrance. One mile walk downhill to visitor centre and castle. (Stagecoach 01292 613 700)
Habitat: Shoreline, parkland, woodland, gardens, streams, ponds.
Key birds: *All year:* Good populations of common woodland species, inc Jay, Great Spotted Woodpecker and thrushes, plus recent new resident — Nuthatch.
Spring/summer: Arriving migrants, esp Blackcap, Chiffchaff and Willow Warbler. Nesting Raven and Fulmar on cliffs, Gannet and terns offshore.
Autumn/winter: Regular flocks of Redwing and Fieldfare, Waxwing, crossbills. Wildfowl on pond inc Little Grebe, Tufted Duck, Goldeneye. Offshore divers and Eider.
Other notable flora and fauna: The high diversity of flora and fauna due to range of habitats merits site being listed as SWT Wildlife Site. Roe deer, otter, water vole, several species of bat. Shoreline SSSI rich in rock pool life.
Contact: The Ranger Service, Culzean Castle and Country Park, Maybole KA19 8LE. 0844 493 2148.

Clyde

7. BARON'S HAUGH

RSPB (South and West Scotland Office).
Location: NS 756 553. On SW edge of Motherwell, overlooking River Clyde. Via Adele Street, then lane off North Lodge Avenue.
Access: Open all year. Most paths suitable for wheelchairs, except circular nature trail, which has some steep sections.
Facilities: Four hides, information board in car park.
Habitat: Marshland, flooded areas, woodland, parkland, meadows, scrub, river.
Key birds: *Summer:* Breeding Gadwall, warblers (inc. Garden, Grasshopper), Whinchat, Common Sandpiper, Kingfisher, Sand Martin.
Autumn: Excellent for waders (22 species). *Winter:* Whooper Swan, Pochard, Wigeon, Sparrowhawk.
Contact: RSPB, 0141 331 0993.

8. FALLS OF CLYDE

Scottish Wildlife Trust.
Location: NS 88 34 14. Approx one mile S of Lanark. Directions from Glasgow – travel S on M74 until J7 then along A72, following signs for Lanark and New

211

NATURE RESERVES - CENTRAL SCOTLAND

Lanark.
Access: Open during daylight hours all year. Disabled access limited.
Facilities: Visitor centre open 11am-5pm Mar-Dec, 12-4pm Jan-Feb. Toilets and cafeteria on site. Seasonal viewing facility for Peregrines. Numerous walkways and ranger service offers comprehensive guided walks programme.
Public transport: Scotrail trains run to Lanark (0845 7484 950). Local bus service from Lanark to New Lanark.
Habitat: River Clyde gorge, waterfalls, mixed woodland and broadleaved riparian gorge, meadow, pond.
Key birds: More than 100 species of bird recorded on the reserve, including unrivalled views of breeding Peregrine. Others include Tawny Owl, Kingfisher, Dipper, Great Spotted Woodpecker, Spotted Flycatcher and Goosander.
Contact: Miss Lindsay Cook, The Falls of Clyde Visitor Centre, 01555 665 262; e-mail:fallsofclyde@swt.co.uk

9. LOCHWINNOCH

RSPB (South & West Scotland Office).
Location: NS 358 582. 18 miles SW of Glasgow, adjacent to A760.
Access: Open every day except Christmas and Boxing Day, Jan 1 and Jan 2. (10am-5pm).
Facilities: Special facilities for schools and disabled access in hides and toilets. Fairtrade refreshments available. Visitor centre, hides.
Public transport: Rail station adjacent, bus services nearby.
Habitat: Shallow lochs, marsh, mixed woodland.
Key birds: *Winter:* Wildfowl (esp. Whooper Swan, Wigeon, Goosander, Goldeneye). Occasional passage migrants inc. Whimbrel, Greenshank. *Summer:* Breeding Great Crested Grebe, Water Rail, Sedge and Grasshopper Warblers, Reed Bunting.
Other notable flora and fauna: Possible otters, roe deer, butterflies, moths and dragon/damselflies.
Contact: RSPB Nature Centre, 01505 842 663; e-mail lochwinnoch@rspb.org.uk.
www.rspb.org.uk/lochwinnoch.
www.facebook.com/RSPBLochwinnochNR

Fife

10. EDEN ESTUARY LNR

Fife Council.
Location: 470 195 (centre of site). The LNR can be accessed from Guardbridge, St Andrews (one mile) on A91, and from Leuchars via Tentsmuir Forest off A919 (four miles). Use Outhead at St Andrews off West Sands beach to access Balgove Bay. Tentsmuir Forest car park best for northern access and Guardbridge village best for the River Eden section of reserve. Coble Shore southern access at GR 467 188.
Access: Eden Estuary Centre, Guardbridge: open (9am-5pm) all days except Dec 25, Jan 1 and Leuchars airshow day. Evans Hide: at GR 483 183, parking at Pilmuir Links golf course car park. Combination number required from ranger service.
Facilities: Visitor centre at Guardbridge. Information panels at Outhead. Hide at Balgove Bay (key from Ranger Service).
Public transport: Leuchars train station (1.5 miles), regular bus service from Cupar and Dundee. Tel 08457 484 950.
Habitat: Intertidal mudflats, saltmarsh, river, reed, sand dunes and wetland.
Key birds: *Winter and passage:* Significant numbers of waders and wildfowl. Outer estuary is good place for sea duck such as scoters, Eider and Long-tailed Duck, plus Gannet, terns and skuas. Mudflats ideal for godwits, plovers, sandpipers and Shelduck. River good for Kingfisher, Common Sandpiper and Goosander. Surrounding area is good for Short-eared and Long-eared Owls, Peregrine, Marsh Harrier and Merlin. Osprey visit daily throughout the season.
Other notable flora and fauna: Northern marsh orchid, dune grasses, herbs, maiden pink, saltmarsh grasses and reed systems. Common harbour seal, bottle-nosed dolphin, porpoise, brown hare, stoat. Butterflies include comma, grayling, small pearl-bordered, dark green fritilliary, painted lady and orange tip.
Contact: Ranald Strachan, Fife Ranger Service, Harbourmaster House, Hot Pot Wynd, Dysart, KY1 2TQ. 01592 656 080, mobile: 07985 707 593.
E-mail: Ranald.Strachan@fife.gov.uk

11. ISLE OF MAY NNR

Scottish Natural Heritage.
Location: NT 655 995. This small island lying six miles off Fife Ness in the Firth of Forth is a NNR.
Access: Boats run from Anstruther and North Berwick. Contact SNH for details on 01334 654038. Keep to paths. RIB from Anstruther arranged for those using Observatory accommodation. Delays are possible, both arriving and leaving, because of weather.
Facilities: A small visitor centre. A permit is required to carry out research, filming or photography. Permit application forms can be obtained from SNH.
Public transport: Regular bus service to Anstruther and North Berwick harbour.
Habitat: Sea cliffs, rocky shoreline.
Key birds: *Early Summer:* Breeding auks and terns, Kittiwake, Shag, Eider, Fulmar. More than 45,000 pairs of Puffins. *Autumn/spring:* Weather-related migrations include rarities each year.
Other notable flora and fauna: Breeding grey seal colony.
Contact: For Observatory accomodation: David Thorne, Craigurd House, Blyth Bridge, West Linton, Peeblesshire EH46 7AH. For all other enquiries: SNH, 46 Crossgate, Cupar, Fife KY15 5HS.
www.nnr-scotland.org

Forth

12. CAMBUS POOLS

Scottish Wildlife Trust.
Location: NS 846 937. Take A907 from Stirling towards Alloa, then Station Road to Cambus village. Park by river in village.
Access: Cross River Devon by bridge at NS 853 940 and walk down stream on R bank past bonded warehouses. Open all year.
Facilities: Bench on S side of western pool.
Public transport: None.
Habitat: Wet grassland with two salty pools.
Key birds: Used extensively by migrants in spring and autumn, inc. wildfowl and waders such as Black-tailed Godwit and Greenshank. Gadwall have bred here and Kingfisher is seen regularly.
Other notable flora and fauna: Brown hare, stoat, short-tailed vole, 115 species of vascular plants. Harbour porpoise seen in Forth.
Contact: SWT headquarters, 01313 127 765.

13. INVERSNAID

RSPB (South and West Scotland Office).
Location: NN 337 088. On E side of Loch Lomond. Via B829 W from Aberfoyle, then along minor road to car park by Inversnaid Hotel.
Access: Open all year.
Facilities: New car park and trail at Garrison Farm (NN 348 095).
Habitat: Deciduous woodland rises to craggy ridge and moorland.
Key birds: *Summer:* Breeding Black Grouse, Snipe,

Cuckoo, Wheatear and Twite. Raven, Grey Wagtail, Dipper, Wood Warbler, Redstart, Pied Flycatcher, Tree Pipit. The loch is on a migration route, especially for wildfowl and waders. Look for Red-throated and Black-throated Divers in spring. *Winter:* Hen Harrier and thrushes.
Other notable flora and fauna: Pine marten, slow worm, 17 species of butterfly inc small pearl-bordered fritillary on nature trail at Inversaid. Wilson's and Tunbridge filmy ferns on boulders through woodland.
Contact: RSPB South and West Scotland Office, 01413 310 993.

Lothian

14. ABERLADY BAY

East Lothian Council (LNR).
Location: NT 472 806. From Edinburgh take A198 E to Aberlady. Reserve is 1.5 miles E of Aberlady village.
Access: Open at all times. Please stay on footpaths to avoid disturbance. Disabled access from reserve car park. No dogs please.
Facilities: Small car park and toilets. Notice board with recent sightings at end of footbridge. SOC HQ, Waterston House, located W of Aberlady village. Includes shop, library, hot and cold drinks.
Public transport: Edinburgh to N Berwick bus service stops at reserve (request), service no 124. Nearest train station 4 miles away at Longniddry.
Habitat: Tidal mudflats, saltmarsh, freshwater marsh, dune grassland, scrub, open sea.
Key birds: *Summer:* Breeding birds include Shelduck, Eider, Reed Bunting and up to eight species of warbler. Passage waders inc. Green, Wood and Curlew Sandpipers, Little Stint, Greenshank, Whimbrel, Black-tailed Godwit. *Winter:* Divers (esp. Red-throated), Red-necked and Slavonian Grebes and geese (large numbers of Pink-footed roost); sea-ducks, waders.
Contact: John Harrison, Reserve Warden, Landscape and Countryside Management, East Lothian Council, 01875 870 588. email:jharrison@eastlothian.gov.uk
www.aberlady.org

15. ALMONDELL & CALDERWOOD COUNTRY PARK

West Lothian Council.
Location: NT 091 697. North entrance, the closest to the visitor centre is signposted off A89, two miles S of Broxburn.
Access: Open all year. Parking available at N entrance. S entrance at East Calder. Mid Calder and Oakbank on A71 (furthest from visitor centre). Disabled car park at visitor centre. Coach parking available with prior notice.
Facilities: Car park, picnic area,hot and cold drinks, toilets, pushchair access, partial access for wheelchairs, visitor centre (open every day), gift shop, countryside ranger service.
Habitat: Woodland, river.
Key birds: *Spring/summer:* Woodcock, Tawny Owl,

Grasshopper Warbler, Yellowhammer, Blackcap, Garden Warbler. *Winter*: Goldcrest, Redpoll, Willow Tit. *All year*: Dipper, Grey Wagtail, Sparrowhawk.
Contact: Head Ranger, Visitor Centre, Broxburn, West Lothian, EH52 5PE, 01506 882 254;
www.beecraigs.com
e-mail:almondellandcalderwood@westlothian.gov.uk

16. BASS ROCK

Location: NT 605 875. Island NE of North Berwick.
Access: Private property. Regular daily sailings from N Berwick around Rock; local boatman has owner's permission to land individuals or parties by prior arrangement. For details contact 01620 892 838 or The Scottish Seabird Centre 01620 890 202;
www.seabird.org
Facilities: None. **Habitat:** Sea cliffs.
Key birds: The spectacular cliffs hold a large Gannet colony, (up to 9,000 pairs), plus auks, Kittiwake, Shag and Fulmar.

17. BAWSINCH & DUDDINGSTON LOCH

Scottish Wildlife Trust.
Location: NT 284 725. Centre of Edinburgh, below Arthur's Seat. Use car park on Duddingston Road West and Holyrood Park Gate.
Access: Open access to north shore of loch and Cavalry ground to SE. Remainder of site and hide by

prior arrangement with C.McLean, 88 Gilmore Place, Edinburgh.
Facilities: Hide with bird and plant lists.
Habitat: Reedbed, marsh, loch, ponds, mixed woodland, flower meadow and scrub. Developed from former waste area.
Key birds: Heronry. Loch has breeding swans, geese, ducks and grebes. Summer migrants, winter-roosting wildfowl.
Other notable flora and fauna: Fox and otter. Damselfly, four species of amphibian.
Contact: SWT headquarters, 01313 127 765.

18. GLADHOUSE RESERVOIR

Scottish Water.
Location: NT 295 535. S of Edinburgh off the A703.
Access: Open all year although there is no access to the reservoir itself. Most viewing can be done from the road (telescope required).
Facilities: Small car park on north side. Not suitable for coaches.
Habitat: Reservoir, grassland, farmland.
Key birds: *Spring/summer*: Oystercatcher, Lapwing, Curlew. Possible Black Grouse. *Winter*: Geese, including Pinkfeet, Twite, Brambling, Hen Harrier.
Contact: Scottish Water, PO Box 8855, Edinburgh, EH10 6YQ, 084 6 018 855.
e-mail:customer.service@scottishwater.co.uk
www.scottishwater.co.uk

Eastern Scotland

Angus & Dundee, Moray & Nairn, NE Scotland, Perth & Kinross

Angus & Dundee

1. BALGAVIES LOCH

Scottish Wildlife Trust.
Location: NO523 516. From car park on A932, four miles E of Forfar.
Access: All areas apart from hide restricted. Groups should apply in advance.
Facilities: Hide, path.
Public transport: None.
Habitat: Loch, fen and woodland.
Key birds: *Winter*: Wildfowl and wetland breeding birds.
Contact: Montrose Basin Wildlife Centre, 01674 676 336.

2. LOCH OF LINTRATHEN

Scottish Wildlife Trust.
Location: NO 278 550. Seven miles W of Kirriemuir.

Take B951 and choose circular route on unclassified roads round loch.
Access: Two public hides (one wheelchair-accessible) open 24 hours a day. Rest of reserve is private, but good viewing is possible from several places along unclassified roads.
Facilities: Viewpoint can accommodate five cars.
Public transport: None.
Habitat: Mesotrophic loch designated a Ramsar site because of its value to waterbirds. Surrounded by mainly coniferous woodland.
Key birds: *Summer*: Grey Heron, Great Crested Grebe and other water birds. Osprey. *Winter*: Internationally-important numbers of Icelandic Greylag Geese, plus Goosander, Whooper Swan, Wigeon, Teal and other wildfowl.
Other notable flora and fauna: Red squirrel.
Contact: Robert Potter, Reserves Manager North East, SWT, The Kennels, Nr Cortachy, by Kirriemuir, Angus DD8 4QE. 01575 540 396; (M)07920 468 568.
e-mail:rpotter@swt.org.uk

Moray & Nairn

3. CULBIN SANDS

RSPB (North Scotland Office).
Location: NH 900 576. Approx ½ mile NE of Nairn, overlooking Moray Firth. Access to parking at East Beach car park, signed off A96.
Access: Open at all times. 750m path to Minster's Pool suitable for all abilities.
Facilities: Toilets (inc disabled) and bike racks at car park. Track along dunes and saltmarsh.
Public transport: Buses stop in St Ninian's Road, Nairn, half mile W of site. Call Rapsons on 0870 608 2608 or Stagecoach on 01862 892 683. Train station in Nairn three-quarters mile W of reserve.
Habitat: Saltmarsh, sandflats, dunes.
Key birds: *Winter:* Flocks of Common Scoter, Long-tailed Duck, Knot, Bar-tailed Godwit, Red-breasted Merganser. Raptors including Peregrine, Merlin and Hen Harrier attracted by wader flocks. Roosting geese, Snow Bunting flocks. *Spring:* Tern flock, esp Sandwich, passage waders. *Summer:* Breeding Ringed Plover and Oystercatcher. Osprey on passage.
Other notable flora and fauna: Dolphins in Firth. Otters sometimes seen.
Contact: RSPB North Scotland Office, 01463 715 000. e-mail:nsro@rspb.org.uk www.rspb.org.uk

4. SPEY BAY

Scottish Wildlife Trust.
Location: NJ 335 657. Eight miles NE of Elgin. From Elgin take A96 and B9015 to Kingston. Reserve is immediately E of village. Car parks at Kingston and Tugnet.

Access: Open all year.
Facilities: Car park, information board.
Public transport: None.
Habitat: Shingle, rivermouth and coastal habitats.
Key birds: *Summer:* Osprey, waders, wildfowl. *Winter:* Seaduck and divers offshore, esp. Long-tailed Duck, Common and Velvet Scoters, Red-throated Diver.
Other notable flora and fauna: Otter, plus dolphin offshore. Good range of dragonflies.
Contact: Robert Potter, Gardener's Cottage, Balhary Estate, Alyth PH11 8LT. 07920 468 568, e-mail:rpotter@swt.org.uk

5. TROUP HEAD

RSPB (East Scotland).
Location: NJ 825 672. Troup Head is between Pennan and Gardenstown on B9031, E along coast from Macduff. It is signposted off B9031. Look for small RSPB signs which direct you past the farm buildings to car park.
Access: Unrestricted, but not suitable for wheelchair users.
Facilities: Parking for small number of cars. Not suitable for coaches. Live pictures are beamed from the reserve to the Macduff Marine Aquarium during the summer with free entry to the aquarium for RSPB members on Tuesdays between April — August. Boat trips run from Macduff (contact Puffin Cruises 07900 920 445) and Banff or Gardenstown (contact North 58° Sea Adventures) 01261 819 900).
Habitat: Sea cliffs, farmland.
Key birds: Spectacular seabird colony, including Scotland's only mainland nesting Gannets. Bonxies linger in summer. Migrants occur during spring/autumn.
Other notable flora and fauna: Impressive common flower assemblage in spring. Ceteceans possible offshore in summer including minke whale. Brown hare common.
Contact: RSPB Troup Head warden, c/o Starnafin Farmhouse, Crimond, Fraserburgh AB43 8QN. 01346 532 017. E-mail:troup@rspb.org.uk

NE Scotland

6. CORRIE FEE NNR

Scottish Natural Heritage.
Location: NO 283 761. Take the B955 from Kirriemuir to the Ranger Base in Glen Doll at the head of Glen Clova (car park with a small charge).
Access: Walk 3 km up through Glen Doll Forest to Corrie Fee. There is also a path up through Corrie Fee itself.
Facilities: Ranger Base, toilets (24hr), picnic benches and paths around accessible from the Glen Doll car park.

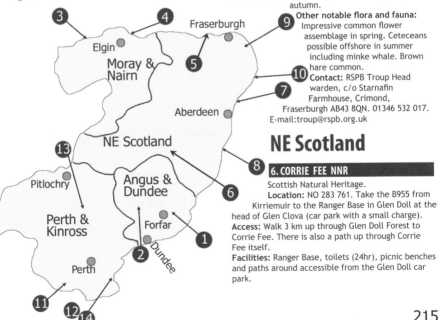

Fraserburgh
Elgin
Moray & Nairn
Aberdeen
NE Scotland
Pitlochry
Angus & Dundee
Forfar
Perth & Kinross
Perth
Dundee

Public transport: Post bus.

Habitat: Upland habitats.

Key birds: *Summer:* Golden Eagles nest nearby, Peregrine, Raven, cliff-nesting House Martins nest in the Corrie. Also Ring Ouzel, Twite.

Other notable flora and fauna: Very rare Arctic-alpine plants including UK's largest population of dwarf willows (woolly and downy) plus, more common species like tormentil, opposite leaved saxifrage, chickweed wintergreen and mountain everlasting.

Contact: Shona Hill, SNH, West Lodge, Airlie, Kirriemuir DD8 5NP. 01575 530 333; e-mail: Shona.Hill@snh.gov.uk - www.snh.org.uk

7. FORVIE NNR

Scottish Natural Heritage.

Location: NK 034 289. 12 miles N of Aberdeen. Through Newburgh off A975 road.

Access: Reserve open at all times but ternery closed Apr 1 to end of Aug annually. Stevenson Forvie Centre open every day (Apr-Sept) and, outside these months when staff are available. Centre and short trail are wheelchair-accessible.

Facilities: Interpretive display and toilets at Stevenson Forvie Centre. Bird hide, waymarked trails. Coach parking at Waterside car park and Stevenson Forvie Centre.

Public transport: Bluebird No 263 to Cruden Bay. Ask for the Newburgh or Collieston Crossroads stop. Tel: 01224 591 381.

Habitat: Estuary, dunes, coastal heath.

Key birds: *Spring/summer:* Breeding Eider and terns. Migrant waders and seabirds offshore. *Autumn:* Pink-footed Goose, migrant seabirds, waders and passerines inc occasional scarce species or rarity. *Winter:* Waders and wildfowl, inc Whooper Swan, Long-tailed Duck and Golden Plover.

Other notable flora and fauna: Occasional cetaceans offshore, esp in summer.

Contact: Annabel Drysdale (Reserve Manager), Scottish Natural Heritage, Stevenson Forvie Centre, Little Collieston Croft, Collieston, Aberdeenshire AB41 8RU. 01358 751 330; www.nnr-scotland.org

8. FOWLSHEUGH

RSPB

Location: NO 879 80. Cliff top path N from Crawton, signposted from A92, three miles S of Stonehaven.

Access: Unrestricted. Not suitable for wheelchair users.

Facilities: Car park with 12 spaces, 200 yards from reserve.

Public transport: Request bus stop (Stonehaven to Johnshaven route). Mile walk to reserve entrance. Details at www.travelinescotland.com.

Habitat: Sea cliffs.

Key birds: Spectacular 130,000-strong seabird colony, mainly Kittiwake and Guillemot plus Razorbill, Fulmar and Puffin. Gannet, Eider and skuas offshore, inc Bonxies lingering in summer. *Autumn:* Red-throated Diver on sea, terns on passage.

Other notable flora and fauna: Grey and common seals, bottle-nosed dolphin regular, white-beaked dolphin and minke whale occasional in summer. Spring flowers, common butterflies and moths.

Contact: The Warden, c/o Starnafin Farmhouse, Crimond, Fraserburgh AB43 8QN. 01346 532 017, e-mail:strathbeg@rspb.org.uk

9. LOCH OF STRATHBEG

RSPB.

Location: NK 057 581. Britain's largest dune loch is near Crimond on the A90, nine miles S of Fraserburgh.

Access: Visitor Centre open daily 10am-4pm (Nov-Feb), 8am-6pm (later if staff time allows — check website for details) (Mar-Oct). Tower Pool, Bay and Fen Hides open dawn-dusk. Visitor centre wheelchair accessible. Coach parking available — book in advance.

Facilities: Visitor centre, with telescope, toilets, baby changing table and coffee machine. Tower Pool hide accessible via 700 metre footpath. Two hides overlooking Loch accessed via short drive to Airfield. Coastal section of reserve accessed from track behind Tufted Duck hotel in St Combs village. Wildlife garden, indoor children's area — kid's backpacks.

Public transport: Access to whole reserve difficult without vehicle. Buses from Fraserburgh and Peterhead to Crimond, one mile from centre. Details at www.travelin escotland.com.

Habitat: Dune loch with surrounding marshes, reedbeds, grasslands and dunes.

Key birds: 200 species a year. Breeding wetland species, passage waders, internationally important numbers of wintering wildfowl. Scarcities year round. *Winter:* Pink-footed and Barnacle Geese, Whooper Swan, large numbers of duck. Snow Goose and Slavonian Grebe annual. Raptors including Hen and Marsh Harriers. Great Northern Diver offshore. *Summer:* Common Tern, Water Rail, Corn Bunting. *Spring/autumn:* Little Egret, Spoonbill, Avocet, Marsh Harrier, Garganey, Little Gull, Pectoral Sandpiper.

Other notable flora and fauna: Otter, badger, stoat, roe deer. Early purple, butterfly and northern marsh orchids, dark green fritillary butterfly.

Contact: RSPB Loch of Strathbeg, Starnafin, Crimond, Fraserburgh, AB43 8QN. 01346 532 017. e-mail:strathbeg@rspb.org.uk

10. LONGHAVEN CLIFFS

Scottish Wildlife Trust.

Location: NK 116 394. 3.8 miles S of Peterhead. Take A952 S from Peterhead and then A975 to Bullers of Buchan (gorge).

Access: Access from car park at Blackhills quarry or Bullers of Buchan.

Facilities: Leaflet available. Parking.

Habitat: Rugged red granite cliffs and cliff-top vegetation.

Key birds: Nine species of breeding seabird, including Kittiwake, Shag, Guillemot, Razorbill, Puffin.

Other notable flora and fauna: Unusual form of

coastal heath has developed, with plants such as bell heather, crowberry, devil's-bit scabious and grass-of-Parnassus.

Grey seals in sheltered inlets. Porpoise, dolphin and minke whale occasionally seen.

Contact: SWT headquarters 0131 312 7765.

Perth & Kinross

11. DOUNE PONDS

Stirling Council.

Location: NN 726 019. Take A820 Dunblane road E from the junction with the A84 Callander-Stirling road. First left turn to Station Wynd.

Access: Wheelchair access to both hides. Open all year.

Facilities: Information board, paths, hides. Leaflet from local tourist information offices, local library.

Public Transport: Bus: from Stirling and Callander to Doune. Traveline 0870 608 2608.

Habitat: Pools, scrape, birch and willow woodlands.

Key birds: *All year:* Grey Heron, Buzzard, Snipe, Goldcrest, Siskin, Red Kite. *Spring/Summer:* Common Sandpiper, Whitethroat, warblers.

Other notable flora and fauna: Excellent site for fungi.

Contact: Stirling Council Countryside Ranger Service, Viewforth, Stirling FK8 2ET. 0845 2777 000; e-mail: birdc@stirling.gov.uk

12. LOCH LEVEN NNR

SNH, Loch Leven Laboratory.

Location: NO 150 010. Head S from Perth and leave M90 at exit 6, Kinross.

Access: An all-abilities trail covers eight miles of the western shore between Kinross and Vane Farm. Access with car parking is available at Kinross, Burleigh, Findatie and RSPB Vane Farm Local access guidance is in place at the site see www.snh.org.uk for details or pick up leaflet locally.

Facilities: Viewing hides at Kirkgate, Burleigh, Kinross, and RSPB Vane Farm. Seasonal tourist information, toilets and facilities available at the pier in Kinross. Further toilets and facilities available at Findatie and Channel Farm. RSPB Vane farm has observation room, natural trail, cafe, shop and toilets (see www.rspb.org.uk/vanefarm).

Public transport: Bus from Perth or Edinburgh to Kinross.

Habitat: Lowland loch with islands.

Key birds: *Winter:* Flocks of geese (more than 20,000 Pinkfeet), huge numbers of the full range of ducks, Whooper Swan. *Summer:* Greatest concentration of inland breeding ducks in Britain (10 species), Osprey and grebes. *Passage:* Waders and hirundines.

Other notable flora and fauna: Lesser butterfly orchid, otter.

Contact: SNH, Loch Leven Laboratory, The Pier, Kinross KY13 8UF. 01577 864 439, www.snh.org.uk

13. LOCH OF THE LOWES

Scottish Wildlife Trust.

Location: NO 042 435. Sixteen miles N of Perth, two miles NE of Dunkeld, just off A923 (signposted).

Access: Visitor centre open all year (10am-5pm). Observation hide open all year during daylight hours. No dogs allowed. Full access for wheelchairs.

Facilities: Visitor centre, toilets, observation hide.

Public transport: Railway station at Birnam/Dunkeld, three miles from reserve. Bus from Dunkeld two miles from reserve.

Habitat: Freshwater loch with fringing woodland.

Key birds: Breeding Ospreys (Apr-end Aug). Nest in view 200 metres from hide. Wildfowl and woodland birds. Greylag roost (Oct-Mar).

Other notable flora and fauna: Red squirrel.

Contact: Peter Ferns, (Manager), Scottish Wildlife Trust, Loch of the Lowes, Visitor Centre, Dunkeld, Perthshire PH8 0HH. 01350 727 337.

14. VANE FARM (LOCH LEVEN NNR)

RSPB Scotland

Location: NT 160 990. Part of Loch Leven NNR. Seven miles from Cowdenbeath, signposted two miles E of J5 from M90 onto B9097. Drive for approx two miles. Car park on R.

Access: Open daily (10am-5pm) except Christmas Day, Boxing Day, Jan 1 and Jan 2. Cost £3 adults, £2 concessions, 50p children, £6 family. Free to members. Disabled access to shop, coffee shop, observation room and toilets. Coach parking available for up to two coaches. Free car parking.

Facilities: Shop, coffee shop and observation room with five telescopes overlooking Loch Leven and the reserve. There is a 1.25 mile trail through woodland and moorland. Wetland trail with three observation hides. Toilets, including disabled. binoculars can be hired from shop.

Public transport: Trains to Cowdenbeath (7 miles), but no bus service from here. Limited bus service (204) runs to the reserve from Kinross (4 miles) on Wednesdays, Saturdays and Sundays. Contact Stagecoach Fife on 01383 511 911 for further details. Eight-mile cycle path around loch.

Habitat: Wet grassland and flooded areas by Loch Leven. Arable farmland. Native woodland and heath moorland.

Key birds: *Spring/summer:* Breeding and passage waders (including Lapwing, Redshank, Snipe, Curlew). Farmland birds (including Skylark and Yellowhammer), Tree Pipit. *Autumn:* Migrating waders on exposed mud.

Winter: Whooper Swan, Bewick's Swan, Pink-footed Goose, finch and tit flocks.

Other notable flora and fauna: 237 butterfly and moth species. 25 mammal species including pipstrelle bat and roe deer.

Contact: Uwe Stoneman, Business Manager, Vane Farm Nature Centre, Kinross, Tayside KY13 9LX. 01577 862 355; e-mail:vanefarm@rspb.co.uk

Highlands & Islands

Caithness, Highlands and Sutherland

1. BEINN EIGHE

Scottish Natural Heritage (East Highland Area).
Location: NG 990 620. By Kinlochewe, Wester Ross, 50 miles from Inverness and 20 miles from Gairloch on A832.
Access: Reserve open at all times, no charge. Visitor centre open Easter-Oct (10am-5pm).
Facilities: Visitor centre, toilets, woodland trail and mountain trail (self-guided with leaflets from visitor centre). Trails suitable for all abilities.
Public transport: Very limited.
Habitat: Caledonian pine forest, dwarf shrub heath, mountain tops, freshwater loch shore.
Key birds: *All year*: Golden Eagle, Scottish Crossbill, Ptarmigan, Red Grouse, Siskin. *Summer*: Black-throated Diver, Redwing, Snow Bunting.
Other notable flora and fauna: Wide range of dragonflies, including golden ringed and common hawker.
Contact: Eoghain Maclean, Reserve Manager, SNH, Anancaun, Kinlochewe, Ross-shire IV22 2PD. 01445 760 254; e-mail:eoghain.maclean@snh.gov.uk

2. CORRIMONY

RSPB (North Scotland Office).
Location: NH 379 304. Lies SW of Inverness between Glen Affric and Loch Ness, off A 831.
Access: Open at all times. Unimproved paths, so terrain may not be suitable for disabled visitors.
Facilities: Way-marked trail (8.5 miles long) passes through farm. Please leave gates as you find them. Guided minibus safaris to see Black Grouse leks in April and May.
Public transport: No 17 bus from Inverness to Cannich stops 1.5 miles from reserve.
Habitat: Pine woodland, moorland, blanket bog.
Key birds: Black Grouse, Crested Tit, crossbill species, occasional Golden Eagle and Osprey. Breeding Greenshank, Red Grouse, Black-throated Diver. *Autumn*: Whooper Swan, Pinkfooted Goose, Woodcock.
Other notable flora and fauna: Red deer, pine marten. Many orchids in July.
Contact: RSPB North Scotland Office, 01463 715 000. e-mail:nsro@rspb.org.uk

3. FAIRY GLEN

RSPB (North Scotland Office).
Location: NH 732 580. On the Black Isle, by Rosemarkie on the A832.
Access: Open all year.
Facilities: Car park, nature trail. Coach parking available.

Public transport: Buses between Inverness and Cromarty stops in reserve car park). Bus info: Rapsons on 0870 608 2608.
Habitat: Broadleaved woodland in a steep-sided valley, stream, waterfalls.
Key birds: *All year*: Large rookery, Dipper, Buzzard, Grey Wagtail, usual woodland species. Migrant warblers in spring/summer.
Other notable flora and fauna: Roe deer. Range of dragonflies, pipistrelle bat, bluebells and other spring woodland plants.
Contact: RSPB North Scotland Office, 01463 715 000. e-mail:nsro@rspb.org.uk

4. FORSINARD

RSPB (North Scotland Region).
Location: NC 890 425. 30 miles SW of Thurso on A897. From S turn off at Helmsdale (24 miles) or from N coast road (A836) turn 2 miles E of Melvich (14 miles).
Access: Open at all times. Contact reserve office during breeding season (mid-Apr to end Jul) and during deerstalking season (Jul 1 to Feb 15) for advice. Families welcome. Two self-guided trails open all year, requested no dogs, farm section of one walk suitable for wheelchairs.
Facilities: Visitor centre open Apr 1 to Oct 31 (9am-5.30pm), seven days per week. Static and AV displays, Hen Harrier nest CCTV. Wheelchair access to centre and toilet. Guided walks Tue and Thu afternoon, May-Aug. Hotel and B&B nearby.
Public Transport: Train from Inverness and Thurso (08457 484 950). RSPB visitor centre is in former Forsinard Station building.
Habitat: Blanket bog, upland hill farm.
Key birds: The best time to visit for birds is May-July. Join a guided walk for the best chance of views of Red-throated Diver, Golden Plover, Greenshank, Dunlin, Hen Harrier, Merlin, Short-eared Owl. Few birds between Sep-Feb.
Other notable flora and fauna: Red deer, azure hawker dragonfly, emperor moth.
Contact: RSPB, Forsinard Flows Reserve, Reserve Office, Forsinard, Sutherland KW13 6YT. 01641 571 225; e-mail: forsinard@rspb.org.uk - www.rspb.org.uk

5. HANDA

Scottish Wildlife Trust.
Location: NC 138 480. Island accessible by boat from Tarbet, near Scourie — follow A894 N from Ullapool 40 miles. Continue another three miles, turn L down single track road another three miles to Tarbet.
Access: Open April-Sept. Boats leave 9.30am-2pm (last boat back 5pm). Dogs not allowed. Visitors are asked for a contribution of £2 towards costs. Not suitable for disabled due to uneven terrain.
Facilities: Three mile circular path, shelter (no toilets on island — use those in Tarbet car park). Visitors are given introductory talk and a leaflet with

map on arrival.

Public transport: Post bus to Scourie (tel 01549 402 357 Lairg Post Office). Train to Lairg (tel 0845 484 950 National Train enquiries). No connecting public transport between Scourie and Tarbet.

Habitat: Sea cliffs, blanket bog.

Key birds: *Spring/summer*: Biggest Guillemot and Razorbill colony in Britain and Ireland. Also nationally important for Kittiwakes, Arctic and Great Skuas. Puffin, Shag, Fulmar and Common and Arctic Terns also present.

Contact: Mark Foxwell, Conservation Manager, Unit 4A, 3 Carsegate Road North, Inverness IV3 8PU. 01463 714 746. Charles Thomson (Boatman) 01971 502 347. e-mail:mfoxwell@swt.org.uk www.swt.org.uk

6. INSH MARSHES

RSPB (North Scotland Office).

Location: NN 775 998. In Spey Valley, two miles NE of Kingussie on B970 minor road.

Access: Open at all times. Disabled access to the information viewpoint. Coach parking available at car park.

Facilities: Information viewpoint, two hides, three nature trails. Access for disabled to Information Viewpoint only. No toilets.

Public transport: Nearest rail station and bus stop at Kingussie (two miles).

Habitat: Marshes, woodland, river, open water.

Key birds: *Spring/summer*: Waders (Lapwing, Curlew, Redshank, Snipe), wildfowl (including Goldeneye and Wigeon), Osprey, Wood Warbler, Redstart, Tree Pipit. *Winter*: Hen Harrier, Whooper Swan, other wildfowl.

Other notable flora and fauna: Black darter dragonflies along Invertromie trail plus northern brown argus butterflies. Five species of orchid in Tromie Meadow. Roe deer.

Contact: Pete Moore, Ivy Cottage, Insh, Kingussie PH21 1NT. 01540 661 518; www.visitkincraig.com e-mail: pete.moore@rspb.org.uk

7. ISLE OF EIGG

Scottish Wildlife Trust.

Location: NM 38 48. Small island S of Skye, reached by ferry from Mallaig or Arisaig (approx 12 miles).

Access: Ferries seven days per week (weather permitting) during summer. Four days per week (weather permitting) between Sept-Apr. Coach parties would need to transfer to ferries for visit to Eigg. Please contact ferry companies

prior to trip. Mix of roads, hardcore tracks and rough paths on island.

Facilities: Pier centre: shop/post office, tea-room, craftshop, toilets.

Public transport: Train service from Glasgow, via Arisaig to Mallaig. Cal-Mac (01687 462 403) ferries (no sailing Wed and Sun), MV Sheerwater (no sailing Thurs, tel: 01687 450 224). Island minibus/taxi usually available at the pier.

Habitat: Moorland (leading to Sgurr pitchstone ridge), extensive woodland and scrub, marshland,and bog, hay meadows, sandy bays and rocky shorelines.

Key birds: *All year*: Resident species include Red-throated Diver, Golden Eagle, Hen Harrier, Woodcock and Raven. *Summer*: Cuckoo, Wheatear, Whitethroat, Whinchat, Sedge and Willow Warblers, Twite. Large numbers of Manx Shearwaters offshore with Storm-petrels regularly seen from boats between June-Sept.

Other notable flora and fauna: 17 species of butterfly recorded, including green hairstreak, small pearl-bordered and dark green fritillaries. Nine species of damsel/dragonfly occur with golden ringed, common hawker and highland darter the most numerous. Approx 500 species of 'higher' plants listed, including 12 species of orchid, and alpine/arctic species such as mountain aven and moss campion. Carpet of primroses, bluebells and wild garlic in spring. Otters not uncommon and minke whales, bottle-nosed and common dolphins and harbour porpoises regularly recorded offshore. Basking sharks can be quite numerous in early summer.

Contact: John Chester, Millers Cottage, Isle of Eigg, Small Isles PH42 4RL. 01687 482 477. www.isleofeigg.org

8. ISLE OF RUM

Scottish Natural Heritage
Location: NM 370 970. Island lying S of Skye. Passenger ferry from Mallaig, take A830 from Fort William.
Access: Contact Reserve Office for details of special access arrangements relating to breeding birds, deer stalking and deer research.
Facilities: Kinloch Castle Hostel, 01687 462 037, Lea Cottage B&B, 01687 462 036. General store and post office, Kinloch Castle tea shop and bar. Guided walks in summer.
Public transport: The Shearwater boat from Arisaig — 01687 450 224, also Caledonian MacBrayne ferry from Mallaig, 01687 450224, www.arisaig.co.uk
Habitat: Coast, moorland, woodland restoration, montane.
Key birds: *Summer:* Unique mountain-top Manx Shearwater colony (a third of the world population). Seabird breeding colony including auks, Kittiwake, Fulmar, Eider, Shag. Gull colonies including Common, Herring, Lesser and Greater Black-backed. Upland breeding species including Golden Plover, Wheatear, Merlin, Kestrel. *Late autumn/spring:* Thrush passage. *Winter:* Greylag Geese, Oystercatcher, Red-breasted Merganser.
Other notable flora and fauna: Butterflies including small white, green veined, green hairstreak, small copper, red admiral, small tortoiseshell, dark green fritillary, peacock etc. Various dragonflies. Heath spotted orchid. Feral goat, red deer, otter, Rhum highland pony, palmate newt, lizard.
Contact: SNH Reserve Office, Isle of Rum, PH43 4RR. 01687 462 026; www.nnr-scotland.org

9. LOCH FLEET

Scottish Wildlife Trust.
Location: NH 794 965. Site lies two miles S of Golspie on the A9 and five miles N of Dornoch. View across tidal basin from A9 or unclassified road to Skelbo.
Access: Park at Little Ferry or in lay-bys around the basin.
Facilities: Guided walks in summer. Interpretive centre. **Public transport:** None.
Habitat: Tidal basin, sand dunes, shingle, woodland, marshes.
Key birds: *Winter:* Important feeding place for ducks and waders. The sea off the mouth of Loch Fleet is a major wintering area for Long-tailed Duck, Common and Velvet Scoters, Eider Duck. In pine wood off minor road S from Golspie to Little Ferry: Crossbill, occasional Crested Tit.
Contact: SWT headquarters, 01313 127 765.

10. LOCH RUTHVEN

RSPB (North Scotland Office).
Location: NH 638 280. From Inverness, take A9 SE to junction with B851. Head SW until the minor road NE at Croachy (reserve is signposted); car park one mile.
Access: Open at all times. **Facilities:** Hide, car park.
Public transport: Nearest bus-stop at Croachy (one mile from reserve). Service is not frequent.
Habitat: Freshwater loch and woodland.
Key birds: Best breeding site in Britain for Slavonian Grebe, which arrive in late March. *Spring/summer:* Red-throated Diver and Osprey. Teal, Wigeon and other wildfowl breed. Peregrine, Buzzard often seen.
Other notable flora and fauna: Toad (mid-April).
Contact: RSPB North Scotland Office. 01463 715 000. e-mail:nsro@rspb.org.uk

11. UDALE BAY RSPB RESERVE

RSPB (North Scotland Office).
Location: NH 712 651. On the Black Isle, one mile W of Jemimaville on the B9163.
Access: Open all year. View wader roost from lay-by. Nearest adapted unisex toilet in Allen Street, Cromarty (one mile away).
Facilities: Hide, large lay-by. No coach parking.
Public transport: No 26 bus stops in Jemimaville six times a day (approx 5 min walk to reserve). Bus Info
Contact: Rapsons, 0870 608 2608 or Stagecoach on 01862 892 683.
Habitat: Mudflat, saltmarsh and wet grassland.
Key birds: *Spring/summer:* 10,000 Pinkfeet on passage each year, other wildfowl, Oystercatcher, Redshank, waders. Possible Osprey fishing. *Autumn/winter:* Large flocks of wildfowl (approx 10,000 Wigeon), geese, waders.
Contact: RSPB North Scotland Office, 01463 715 000. e-mail:nsro@rspb.org.uk

Orkney

12. BRODGAR

RSPB (East Scotland).
Location: HY 296 134. Reserve surrounds the Ring of Brodgar, part of the Heart of Neolithic Orkney World Heritage Site on the B9055 off the Stromness-Finstown Road.
Access: Open all year.
Facilities: Footpath, circular route approx one mile.
Public transport: Orkney Coaches. Service within 0.5 mile of reserve. Tel: 01856 870 555. Occasional service past reserve.
Habitat: Wetland and farmland including species-rich grassland, loch shores.
Key birds: *Spring/summer:* Breeding waterfowl on farmland and nine species of waders breed here. The farmed grassland is suitable for Corncrake and provides water, food and shelter for finches, larks and buntings. *Winter:* large numbers of Golden Plover, Curlew and Lapwing.
Other notable flora and fauna: A hotspot for great yellow bumblebee in August. Possibility of otter, while common seals haul out nearby on Loch of Stenness.
Contact: The Warden,12/14 North End Road,

NATURE RESERVES - HIGHLANDS AND ISLANDS

Stromness, Orkney KW16 3AG. 01856 850 176.
e-mail:orkney@rspb.org.ukwww.rspb.co.uk

13. COPINSAY

RSPB (East Scotland).
Location: HY 610 010. Small island accessed by private boat or hire boat from mainland Orkney.
Access: Open all year round.
Facilities: House on island open to visitors, but no facilities. No toilets or hides.
Habitat: Sea cliffs, farmland.
Key birds: *Summer*: Stunning seabird-cliffs with breeding Kittiwake, Guillemot, Black Guillemot, Puffin, Razorbill, Shag, Fulmar, Rock Dove, Eider, Twite, Raven and Greater Black-backed Gull, Great Skua (new breeding species in recent years). Passage migrants esp. during periods of E winds.
Other notable flora and fauna: The island is a key breeding location for more than 2,000 Atlantic grey seals from Oct-Dec. 2,385 pups counted in 2006.
Contact: The Warden, 12/14 North End Road, Stromness, Orkney KW16 3AG. 01856 850 176.
e-mail:orkney@rspb.org.ukwww.rspb.co.ukS Foubisher (boatman) 01856 741252 — cannot sail if wind is in the east.

14. HOBBISTER

RSPB (East Scotland).
Location: HY 396 070 or HY 381 068. Near Kirkwall.
Access: Open access between A964 and the sea. Dogs on leads please.
Facilities: A council-maintained footpath to Waulkmill Bay, two car parks. New circular walk from RSPB car park along cliff top and Scapa Flow.
Public transport: Orkney Coaches, 01856 877 500.
Habitat: Orkney moorland, bog, fen, saltmarsh, coastal cliffs, scrub.
Key birds: *Summer*: Breeding Hen Harrier, Merlin, Short-eared Owl, Red Grouse, Red-throated Diver, Eider, Merganser, Black Guillemot. Wildfowl and waders at Waulkmill Bay. *Autumn/winter*: Waulkmill for sea ducks, divers, auks and grebes (Long-tailed Duck, Red-throated, Black-throated and Great Northern Divers, Slavonian Grebe).
Other notable flora and fauna: Otter occasionally seen from the Scapa trail. Grey and common seal both possible from footpath looking towards Scapa Flow.
Contact: The Warden, 12/14 North End Road, Stromness, Orkney KW16 3AG. 01856 850 176.
e-mail:orkney@rspb.org.uk www.rspb.co.uk

15. MARWICK HEAD

RSPB (East Scotland).
Location: HY 229 242. On W coast of mainland Orkney, near Dounby. Path N from Marwick Bay, or from council car park at Cumlaquoy at HY 232 252.
Access: Open all year. Rough terrain not suitable for wheelchairs.
Facilities: Cliff top path.
Public transport: Orkney Coaches (01856 877 500), nearest stop one mile from reserve.

Habitat: Rocky bay, sandstone cliffs. Beach path good place for great yellow bumblebee in Aug.
Key birds: May-Jul best. Huge numbers of Kittiwakes and auks, inc. Puffins, also nesting Fulmar, Rock Dove, Raven, Rock Pipit.
Other notable flora and fauna: Cetaceans are a possibility from Marwick with porpoise and minke whale occasionally seen.
Contact: The Warden, 12/14 North End Road, Stromness, Orkney KW16 3AG. 01856 850 176.
e-mail:orkney@rspb.org.uk www.rspb.co.uk

16. NORTH HILL, PAPA WESTRAY

RSPB (East Scotland).
Location: HY 496 538. Small island lying NE of Westray, reserve at N end of island's main road.
Access: Access at all times. During breeding season report to summer warden at Rose Cottage, 650 yards S of reserve entrance (Tel 01857 644 240) or use trail guide.
Facilities: Nature trails, hide/info hut.
Public transport: Orkney Ferries (01856 872 044), Loganair (01856 872 494).
Habitat: Sea cliffs, maritime heath.
Key birds: *Summer*: Close views of colony of Puffin, Guillemot, Razorbill and Kittiwake. Black Guillemot nest under flagstones around reserve's coastline. One of UK's largest colonies of Arctic Tern, also Arctic Skua.
Other notable flora and fauna: North Hill is one of the best areas to see 'Scottish primrose' (*primula scotica*) which has two flowering periods that just overlap (May-Aug).
Contact: Apr-Aug, The Warden at Rose Cottage, Papay Westray DW17 2BU. 01857 644 240 or RSPB Orkney Office, 01856 850 176.
e-mail:orkney@rspb.org.uk www.rspb.co.uk

17. NORTH RONALDSAY BIRD OBSERVATORY

Location: HY 64 52. 35 miles from Kirkwall, Orkney mainland.
Access: Open all year except Christmas.
Facilities: Three star guest house and hostel accommodation, restaurant, cafe, fully licenced, croft walk.
Public transport: Daily subsidised flights from Kirkwall (Loganair 01856 872 494). Once weekly ferry from Kirkwall (Fri or Sat), Tuesday and some Sunday sailings in summer (Orkney Ferries Ltd 01856 872 044).
Habitat: Crofting island with a number of eutrophic and oligotrophic wetlands. Coastline has both sandy bays and rocky shore. Walled gardens concentrate passerines.
Key birds: *Spring/Autumn*: Prime migration site including regular BBRC species. Wide variety of breeding seabirds, wildfowl and waders. *Winter*: Waders and wildfowl include Whooper Swan and hard weather movements occur.
Contact: Alison Duncan, North Ronaldsay Bird Observatory, 01857 633 200.
e-mail:alison@nrbo.prestel.co.uk www.nrbo.f2s.com

Outer Hebrides

18. BALRANALD

RSPB (North Scotland Office).
Location: NF 705 707. From Skye take ferry to Lochmaddy, North Uist. Drive W on A865 for 20 miles to reserve. Turn off main road three miles NW of Bayhead at signpost to Houghharry.
Access: Open at all times, no charge. Dogs on leads. Circular walk not suitable for wheelchairs.
Facilities: Visitor Centre and toilets (disabled access). Marked nature trail. Group bookings welcome.
Public transport: Post bus service (tel 01876 560 244).
Habitat: Freshwater loch, machair, coast and croft lands.
Key birds: *Spring:* Skuas and divers at sea, Purple Sandpiper and other waders on shore. Dotterel. *Summer:* Corncrake, Corn Bunting, Lapwing, Oystercatcher, Dunlin, Ringed Plover, Redshank, Snipe, terns. *Autumn:* Hen Harrier, Peregrine, Greylag Goose. *Winter:* Twite, Snow Bunting, Whooper Swan, Greylag Goose, Wigeon, Teal, Shoveler, sightings of Golden and White-tailed Eagles becoming commoner. *Passage:* Barnacle Goose, Pomarine Skua, Long-tailed Skua.
Other notable flora and fauna: Blanket bog and machair plants reach their peak in July.
Contact: Jamie Boyle, 9 Grenitote, Isle of North Uist, H56 5BP. 01876 560 287.
e-mail:james.boyle3@btinternet.com

19. LOCH DRUIDIBEG NNR

SNH (Western Isles Area).
Location: NF 782 378. Reserve of 1,577 ha on South Uist. Turn off A865 at B890 road for Loch Sgioport. Track to reserve is 1.5 miles further on — park at side of road.
Access: Open all year. Several tracks and one walk covering a range of habitats — most not suitable for wheelchair use. Stout footwear essential. Observe Scottish Outdoor Access Code in all areas with livestock. View E part of reserve from public roads but parking and turning areas for coaches is limited.
Facilities: None.
Public transport: Regular bus service stops at reserve. Hebridean Coaches 01870 620 345, MacDonald Coaches 01870 620 288. Large print timetable — call 01851 709 592.
Habitat: Range of freshwater lochs and marshes, machair, coast and moorland.
Key birds: *Summer:* Breeding waders, Corncrake, wildfowl, terns and raptors. *Spring and autumn:* Migrant waders and wildfowl. *Winter:* Waders, wildfowl and raptors.
Contact: SNH Area Officer, SNH Office, 01870 620 238; e-mail:western.isles@snh.gov.uk
www.nnr-scotland.org.uk

Shetland

20. FAIR ISLE BIRD OBSERVATORY

Fair Isle Bird Observatory.
Location: HZ 2172. Famous island for rarities located SE of mainland Shetland.
Access: Open from end Apr-end Oct. No access restrictions.
Facilities: Public toilets at Airstrip and Stackhoull Stores (shop). Accommodation at Fair Isle Bird Observatory (phone/e-mail: for brochure/details). Guests can be involved in observatory work and get to see birds in the hand. Slide shows, guided walks through Ranger Service.
Public transport: Tue, Thurs, Sat — ferry (12 passengers) from Grutness, Shetland. Tel: Neil or Pat Thomson on 01595 760 363. Mon, Wed, Fri, Sat — air (7 seater) from Tingwall, Shetland. Tel: Direct Flight 01595 840 246.
Habitat: Heather moor and lowland pasture/crofting land. Cliffs.
Key birds: Large breeding seabird colonies (auks, Gannet, Arctic Tern, Kittiwake, Shag, Arctic Skua and Great Skua). Many common and rare migrants Apr/May/early Jun, late Aug-Nov.
Other notable flora and fauna: Northern marsh, heath spotted and frog orchid, lesser twayblade, small adders tongue, oyster plant. Orcas, minke whale, white-backed, white-sided and Risso's dolphins. Endemic field mouse.
Contact: Fair Isle Bird Observatory, 01595 760 258.
e-mail:fairisle.birdobs@zetnet.co.uk
www.fairislebirdobs.co.uk

21. FETLAR

RSPB Scotland
Location: HU 603 917. Small island lying E of Yell. Take car ferry from Gutcher, N Yell. Booking advised. Tel: 01957 722 259.
Access: Apart from the footpath to Hjaltadance circle, Vord Hill, the Special Protection Area is closed mid May to end July. Entry during this period is only by arrangement with warden.
Facilities: Hide at Mires of Funzie open Apr-Nov. Toilets and payphone at ferry terminal, interpretive centre at Houbie, campsite, shop.
Public transport: None.
Habitat: Serpentine heath, rough hill lane, upland mire.
Key birds: *Summer:* Breeding Red-throated Diver, Eider, Shag, Whimbrel, Golden Plover, Dunlin, skuas, Manx Shearwater, Storm Petrel. Red-necked Phalarope on Loch of Funzie (HU 655 899) viewed from road or RSPB hide overlooking Mires of Funzie.
Other notable flora and fauna: Heath spotted orchid and autumn gentian. Otters are common, harbour and grey seals breed.
Contact: RSPB North Isles Warden, Bealance, Fetlar, Shetland ZE2 9DJ. Tel/Fax: 01957 733 246.
e-mail:malcolm.smith@rspb.org.uk

NATURE RESERVES - EASTERN WALES

22. NOSS NNR

Scottish Natural Heritage (Shetland Office).
Location: HU 531 410. Take car ferry to Bressay from Lerwick and follow signs for Noss (5km). At end of road walk to shore (600 mtrs) where inflatable ferry (passenger only) to island will collect you. If red flag is flying, island is closed due to sea conditions. Information updated daily in season on 0800 107 7818.
Access: Open Tue, Wed, Fri, Sat, Sun (10am-5pm) between late Apr-late Aug. Access by zodiac inflatable. Sorry, no dogs on ferry.
Steep rough track down to ferry. Groups or anyone requiring asistance to board ferry should contact SNH as far in advance as possible.
Facilities: Visitor centre, toilets. Bike rack/car park

on Bressay side. Parking for small coaches.
Public transport: None. Cycle hire in Lerwick.
Habitat: Dune and coastal grassland, moorland, heath, blanket bog, sea cliffs.
Key birds: *Spring/summer*: Breeding Fulmar, Shag, Gannet, Arctic Tern, Kittiwake, Herring and Great Black-backed Gull, Great Skua, Arctic Skua, Guillemot, Razorbill, Puffin, Black Guillemot, Eider, Lapwing, Dunlin, Snipe, Wheatear, Twite plus migrant birds at any time.
Other notable flora and fauna: Grey and common seals, otter porpoise regularly seen, killer whales annual in recent years.
Contact: Glen Tyler, SNH, Stewart Building, Alexandra Wharf, Lerwick, Shetland ZE1 0LL. 01595 693 345; e-mail:noss_nnr@snh.gov.uk
www.nnr-scotland.org

Eastern Wales

Breconshire, Montgomeryshire, Radnorshire

1. BAILEY EINON LNR

Radnorshire Wildlife Trust.
Location: SO 083 613. From Llandrindod Wells, take the Craig Road leading to Cefnllys Lane. Down this road is Shaky Bridge with a car park and picnic site. A kissing-gate downstream from the picnic site marks the reserve entrance. Please do not park in front of the kissing-gate.
Access: Open all year.
Facilities: Car park, picnic site, waymarked trail.
Public transport: None.
Habitat: Woodland, river.
Key birds: *Spring/summer*: Pied Flycatcher, Redstart, Wood Warbler. *All year*: Great Spotted Woodpecker, Buzzard, usual woodland birds.
Other notable flora and fauna: Orange tip and ringlet butterflies. Red campion, yellow archangel.
Contact: Radnorshire Wildlife Trust, 01597 823 298, e-mail:info@rwtwales.org
www.radnorshirewildlifetrust.org.uk

2. BRECHFA POOL

Brecknock Wildlife Trust.
Location: SO 118 377. Travelling NE from Brecon look for lane off A470, 1.5 miles SW of Llyswen; on Brechfa Common, pool is on R after cattle grid.
Access: Open dawn to dusk. Road runs around three-quarters of pool, giving good access.
Facilities: None.
Public transport: None.
Habitat: Marshy grassland, large shallow pool.
Key birds: Good numbers of wintering wildfowl are replaced by breeding gulls and commoner waterfowl. Species recorded inc Teal, Gadwall, Tufted Duck, Shoveler, Wigeon, Little Grebe, Black-headed Gull,

Lapwing, Dunlin, Redshank, Kestrel.**Other notable flora and fauna:** Rare pillwort around pond margins, plus crowfoot, penny royal and orange foxtail.
Contact: Trust HQ, Lion House, Bethel Square, Brecon, Powys LD3 7AY. 01874 625 708.
e-mail:enquiries@bricknockwildlifetrust.org.uk
www.brecknockwildlifetrust.org.uk

3. CARNGAFALLT

RSPB Wales
Location: SN 935 653. From Rhayader take the B4518 W to Elan village. Turn into village and carry on over bridge into Elan village. Continue through village to cattle grid where nature trail starts.
Access: The nature trail is open at all times.
Facilities: None apart from trail.
Public transport: None.
Habitat: Ancient oak woodland, grassland and moorland. Spectacular upland scenery.
Key birds: Red Kite, Buzzard, Sparrowhawk, Peregrine, Raven, Green Woodpecker, Grey Wagtail and Marsh Tit are joined in the summer by Pied Flycatcher, Spotted Flycatcher, Wood Warbler, Redstart, Tree Pipit and Cuckoo.**Other notable flora and fauna:** Golden-ringed dragonfly, silver-washed, small pearl-bordered and dark-green fritillaries and purple hairstreak butterflies.
Contact: RSPB Ynys-Hir Reserve, 01654 700 222.
e-mail:ynyshir@rspb.org.uk

4. ELAN VALLEY

Dwr Cymru /Welsh Water.
Location: SN 928 646 (visitor centre). Three miles SW of Rhayader, off B4518.
Access: Mostly open access.

223

NATURE RESERVES - EASTERN WALES

Facilities: Visitor centre and toilets (open between mid Mar-end Oct), nature trails all year and hide at SN 905 617.
Public transport: Local bus service discontinued.
Habitat: 45,000 acres of moorland, woodland, river and reservoir.
Key birds: *Spring/summer*: Birds of prey, upland birds including Golden Plover and Dunlin. Woodland birds include Redstart and Pied Flycatcher.
Other notable flora and fauna: Internationally important oak woodlands. More than 3,000 species of flora and fauna recorded.
Contact: Pete Jennings, Rangers Office, Elan Valley Visitor Centre, 01597 810 880, www.elanvalley.org.uk e-mail:peter.jennings@dwrcymru.com

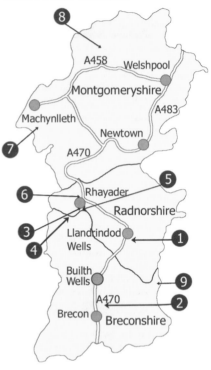

5. GIGRIN FARM

Location: Farm lies half a mile south of Rhayader, Powys off A470.
Access: Open for kite feeding sessions from 1pm each day, except Dec 25. Feeding at 2pm (winter) and 3pm (summer). No booking required. See website for admission charges.
Facilities: Red Kite Shop, five hides (three with disabled access), plus specialist photography hides.
Habitat: 200-acre upland sheep farm rising to 1,200 feet above sea level.
Details: Brilliant views of Red Kites. For the past 18 years, Gigrin has been the official Red Kite feeding station for Wales helping young birds survive in winter. By attracting large numbers of birdwatchers it relieves pressure on nest sites in summer.
Key birds: Daily feeds attract a wide range of species including Carrion Crow, Raven, Jackdaw, Buzzard and Red Kite. Kite numbers vary from a few dozen to around 400 when weather is bad . Other feeding stations attract smaller birds such as Brambling, Yellowhammer and Siskin. A 1.5ml trail links to the RSPB Dyffryn reserve while a wetland area attracts wild ducks, Grey Heron and wagtails.
Contact: Chris Powell, Gigrin Farm, South Street, Rhayader, Powys LD6 5BL. 01597 810 243; www.gigrinfarm.co.uk

6. GILFACH

Radnorshire Wildlife Trust.
Location: SN 952 714. Two miles NW from Rhayader/Rhaeadr-Gwy. Take minor road to St Harmon from A470 at Marteg Bridge.
Access: Open every day, all year.
Facilities: Visitor centre opening times may vary – contact Trust for details.
Public transport: None.
Habitat: Upland hill farm, river, oak woods, meadows, hill-land.
Key birds: *Spring/summer*: Pied Flycatcher, Redstart. *All year*: Dipper, Red Kite.
Other notable flora and fauna: Green hairstreak, wall brown and ringlet butterflies, mountain pansy, bloody-nosed beetle.
Contact: Reserve manager, St Harmon, Gilfach, St

Harmon, Rhaeadr-Gwy, Powys LD6 5LF. 01597 823 298, e-mail:info@rwtwales.org www.radnorshirewildlifetrust.org.uk

7. GLASLYN, PLYNLIMON

Montgomeryshire Wildlife Trust.
Location: SN 826 941. Nine miles SE of Machynlleth. Off minor road between the B4518 near Staylittle and the A489 at Machynlleth. Go down the track for about a mile to the car park.
Access: Open at all times – dogs on lead at all times.
Facilities: Footpath.
Public transport: None.
Habitat: Heather moorland and upland lake.
Key birds: Red Grouse, Short-eared Owl, Meadow Pipit, Skylark, Wheatear and Ring Ouzel, Red Kite, Merlin, Peregrine. Goldeneye occasional.
Contact: Montgomeryshire Wildlife Trust, Collot House, 20 Severn Street, Welshpool, Powys SY21 7AD. 01938 555 654, e-mail:info@montwt.co.uk www.montwt.co.uk

7. LAKE VYRNWY

RSPB Mid-Wales Office
Location: SJ 020 193. Located WSW of Oswestry. Nearest village is Llanfyllin on A490. Take B4393 to lake.
Access: Reserve open all year. Visitor centre open

Apr-Oct (10.30am-5.00pm), Nov-March (10.30am-4.00pm).
Facilities: Toilets, visitor centre, hides, nature trails, coffee shop, RSPB shop, craft workshops.
Public transport: Train and bus Welshpool (25 miles away).
Habitat: Heather moorland, woodland, meadows, rocky streams and large reservoir.
Key birds: Dipper, Kingfisher, Pied Flycatcher, Wood Warbler, Redstart, Peregrine and Buzzard.
Other notable flora and fauna: Mammals include otter, polecat, brown hare. Golden-ringed dragonflies frequent in summer.
Contact: Centre Manager, RSPB Lake Vyrnwy Reserve, Bryn Awel, Llanwddyn, Oswestry, Salop SY10 0LZ. 01691 870 278 or e-mail: vyrnwy@rspb.org.uk

8. PWLL-Y-WRACH

Brecknock Wildlife Trust.
Location: SO 165 326. From Talgarth town centre take Bell Street and then Hospital Road. After 1.5 miles, reserve is on the right.
Access: Reserve open all year. Please keep to footpaths. Level wheelchair-friendly path runs half way into site. Elsewhere, paths can be muddy and there are steps in places.
Facilities: No facilities.
Public transport: No local services.
Habitat: 8.5 hectares of ancient woodland, river and spectacular waterfall.
Key birds: Large variety of resident woodland birds, with migrant boost in spring. Dipper, Kingfisher, Pied Wagtail, Great Spotted Woodpecker, Chiffchaff, Wood Warbler, Pied Flycatcher, Mistle and Song Thrushes, Nuthatch.
Other notable flora and fauna: Otter, dormouse, bats, common lizard. Early purple and birds' nest orchids, herb paris, bluebell, wood anenome.
Contact: Trust HQ. 01874 625 708.
e-mail: enquiries@brecknockwildlifetrust.org.uk

Northern Wales

Anglesey, Caernarfonshire, Denbighshire, Flintshire, Merioneth

1. BARDSEY BIRD OBSERVATORY

Bardsey Bird Observatory.
Location: SH 11 21. Private 444-acre island. Twenty minute boat journey from Aberdaron.
Access: Mar-Nov. No dogs. Visitor accommodation in 150-year-old farmhouse (two single, two double, one x four bed dorm). To stay at the Observatory contact Alicia Normand (tel 01626 773 908)
e-mail: bookings@bbfo.org.uk.
Day visitors by Bardsey Ferries (07971 769 895).
Facilities: Public toilets available for day visitors. Three hides, one on small bay, two seawatching. Gift shops and payphone.
Public transport: Trains from Birmingham to Pwllheli. Tel: 0345 484 950. Arriva bus from Bangor to Pwllheli. Tel: 0870 6082 608.
Habitat: Sea-birds cliffs viewable from boat only. Farm and scrubland, Spruce plantation, willow copses and gorse-covered hillside.
Key birds: *All year*: Chough, Peregrine. *Spring/summer*: Manx Shearwaters (16,000 pairs), other seabirds. Migrant warblers, chats, Redstart, thrushes. *Autumn*: Many rarities including Eye-browed Thrush, Lanceolated Warbler, American Robin, Yellowthroat, Summer Tanager.
Other notable flora and fauna: Autumn ladies' tresses.
Contact: Steven Stansfield, Cristin, Ynys Enlli (Bardsey), off Aberaron, via Pwllheil, Gwynedd LL53 8DE. 07855 264 151; e-mail:warden@bbfo.org.uk
www.bbfo.org.uk

2. CEMLYN

North Wales Wildlife Trust.
Location: SH 329 936 and SH 336 932. Cemlyn is signposted from Tregele on A5025 between Valley and Amlwch on Anglesey.
Access: Open all the time. Dogs on leads. No wheelchair access. During summer months walk on seaward side of ridge and follow signs.
Facilities: Car parks at either end of reserve.
Public transport: None within a mile.
Habitat: Brackish lagoon, shingle ridge, salt marsh, mixed scrub.
Key birds: Wintering wildfowl and waders, breeding terns, gulls and warblers, pipits and passing migrants. *Spring*: Wheatear, Whitethroat, Sedge Warbler, Manx Shearwater, Sandwich Tern, Whimbrel, Dunlin, Knot and Black-tailed Godwit. *Summer*: Breeding Arctic, Common and Sandwich Terns, Black-headed Gull, Oystercatcher and Ringed Plover. *Autumn*: Golden Plover, Lapwing, Curlew, Manx Shearwater, Gannet, Kittiwake, Guillemot. *Winter*: Little and Great Crested Grebes, Shoveler, Shelduck, Wigeon, Red-breasted Merganser, Coot, Turnstone, Purple Sandpiper.
Other notable flora and fauna: 20 species of butterfly recorded. Sea kale, yellow horned poppy, sea purselane, sea beet, glasswort. Grey seal, harbour porpoise, bottlenose dolphin.
Contact: Trust HQ. 01248 351 541.
e-mail: nwwt@wildlifetrustswales.org
www.wildlifetrust.org.uk/northwales

NATURE RESERVES - NORTHERN WALES

Hollyhead, Isle of Anglesey, A5, Colwyn Bay, A55, Flintshire, Bangor, Caernarfon, Denbighshire, A5, Caernarfon, A487, Wrexham, A483, Merioneth, A494, Bardsey Island, Dolgellau

Access: Open daily (9.30am-5pm). Closed for Christmas Day. Ample parking for coaches. Toilets, buildings and trails accessible to pushchairs and wheelchairs.
Facilities: Visitor centre, gift shop, coffee shop, toilets including disabled. Four hides (accessible to wheelchairs) two viewing screens. Trails firm and level, though a little rough in places and wet in winter.
Public transport: Train service to Llandudno Junction, 10 minute walk. Bus service to Tesco supermarket, Llandudno Junction 5 minutes walk. Tel: 0871 200 2233.
Habitat: Lagoons, islands, reedbed, scrub, estuary.
Key birds: Wildfowl and waders in winter, warblers and wetland breeding birds in summer. *Spring*: Passage waders, hirundines and wagtails. *Summer*: Lapwing, waterbirds and warblers. *Winter*: Kingfisher, Goldeneye, Water Rail, Red-breasted Merganser, wildfowl, huge Starling roost.
Other notable flora and fauna: Common butterflies through summer, especially common blues. Great display of cowslips in March, bee orchids in June. Otters seen early mornings.
Contact: Conwy RSPB Nature Reserve, Llandudno Junction, Conwy LL31 9XZ. 01492 584 091.

3. CONNAHS QUAY POWER STATION NR

Deeside Naturalists' Society and Eon UK.
Location: SJ 275 715. From England: Take A550 from Liverpool/N Wirral or A5117 from Ellesmere Port/ M56, follow road to Queensferry. 200 metres after junction of A550 and A5117, turn L at A548 and follow signs to Flint. Cross Dee Bridge and turn off dual carriageway at B5129, Connah's Quay exit. Turn R under A548 then L, following signs to power station. From Flint: Take A548 towards Connah' Quay/ Queensferry. After 2.5 miles, take B5129 (Connah's Quay exit). Turn L following signs to power station. From Connah's Quay: Take B5129 towards Flint. Go under A548, turn L following signs to power station.
Access: Advance permit required (group bookings only). Wheelchair access. Public welcome on open days — see website for details.
Facilities: Field studies centre, five hides.
Public transport: Arriva Cymru — 01745 343 492.
Habitat: Saltmarsh, mudflats, grassland scrub, open water, wetland meadow.
Key birds: *Summer*: Small roosts of non-breeding estuarine birds. *Winter*: High water roosts of waders and wildfowl including, Black-tailed Godwit, Oystercatcher, Redshank, Spotted Redshank, Curlew, Lapwing, Teal, Pintail and Wigeon.
Contact: Secretary, Deeside Naturalists' Society, 01244 537 440, www.deesidenaturalists.org.uk e-mail:deenaturalists@btinternet.com

4. CONWY

RSPB (North Wales Office).
Location: SH 799 773. On E bank of Conwy Estuary. Access from A55 at exit 18 signed to Conwy and Deganwy. Footpath and cycleway accessed from Conwy Cob.

5. GORS MAEN LLWYD

North Wales Wildlife Trust.
Location: SH 975 580. Follow A5 to Cerrigydrudion (seven miles S of site), then take B4501 and go past the Llyn Brennig Visitor Centre. Approx two miles beyond centre, turn R (still on B4501). First car park on R approx 300 yards after the cattle grid.
Access: Open all the time. Dogs on leads. Rare breeding birds on the heather so keep to paths.
Facilities: In second car park by lake shore there are toilets and short walk to bird hide. Paths are waymarked, but can be very wet and muddy in poor weather.
Habitat: Heathland. Heather and grass overlooking large lake.
Key birds: *Summer*: Red and Black Grouse, Hen Harrier, Merlin, Skylark, Curlew. *Winter*: Wildfowl on lake.
Contact: Graham Berry, Trust HQ, 01248 351 541; e-mail: nwwt@wildlifetrustswales.org

6. LLYN ALAW

Welsh Water/United Utilities.
Location: SH 390 865. North Anglesey, SW of Amlwch. Signposted from J5 of A55. Car park at SH375 856.
Access: Open all year. No dogs to hides or sanctuary area but dogs allowed (maximum two per adult) other areas. Limited wheelchair access. Coach parking in main car park (SH 373 856).

Facilities: Visitor centre, Toilets (including disabled), earth paths, boardwalks. Two hides, car parks, network of mapped walks, picnic sites, information boards. Coach parking at main car park.
Public transport: Not to within a mile.
Habitat: Large area of standing water, shallow reedy bays, hedges, scrub, woodland, marsh, grassland.
Key birds: *Winter*: Wildfowl and thrushes, breeding warblers/waterfowl. *Summer*: Lesser Whitethroat, Sedge and Grasshopper Warblers, Little and Great Crested Grebes, Tawny Owl, Barn Owl, Buzzard. *Winter*: Whooper Swan, Goldeneye, Hen Harrier, Short-eared Owl, Redwing, Fieldfare, Peregrine, Raven. *All year*: Bullfinch, Siskin, Redpoll, Goldfinch, Stonechat. *Passage waders*: Ruff, Spotted Redshank, Curlew Sandpiper, Green Sandpiper.
Other notable flora and fauna: Bee and northern marsh orchid, royal fern, skullcap, needle spikerush. Migrant hawker, hairy, four-spotted chaser dragonflies, banded demoiselle, wall brown, gatekeeper, clouded yellow and orange tip butterflies. Brown hare, water vole.
Contact: The Warden, Llyn Alaw, Llantrisant, Holyhead LL65 4TW. 01407 730 762.

7. LLYN CEFNI

Welsh Water/Forestry Commission/United Utilities.
Location: Entrance at Bodffordd SH 433 775 and Rhosmeirch SH 451 783. A reservoir located two miles NW of Llangefni, in central Anglesey. Follow B5111 or B5109 from the village.
Access: Open at all times. Dogs allowed except in sanctuary area. Good footpath (wheelchair accessible) for most of the site, bridges over streams.
Facilities: Two picnic sites, good footpath, coach parking at Rhosmeirch car prk SH451 783.
Public transport: Bus 32, 4 (44 Sun only, 52 Thu only). Tel 0871 200 2233 for information.
Habitat: Large area of open water, reedy bays, coniferous woodland, scrub, carr.
Key birds: *Summer*: Sedge and Grasshopper Warblers, Whitethroat, Buzzard, Tawny Owl, Little Grebe, Gadwall, Shoveler, Kingfisher. *Winter*: Waterfowl (Whooper Swan, Goldeneye), Crossbill, Redpoll, Siskin, Redwing. *All year*: Stonechat, Treecreeper, Song Thrush.
Other notable flora and fauna: Northern marsh orchid, rustyback fern, needle spikerush. Banded demoiselle, migrant hawker, golden ringed dragonfly, emerald damselfly. Ringlet, gatekeeper, clouded yellow and wall butterflies. Bloody nose beetle.
Contact: The Warden, Llyn Alaw, 01407 730 762.

8. MAWDDACH VALLEY

RSPB (North Wales Office).
Location: Coed Garth Gell (SH 688 192) is adjacent to the main Dolgellau to Barmouth road (A496) near Taicynhaeaf. No reserve parking is available but lay-bys are found close to the reserve's entrances. Arthog Bog (SH630138) is off the main Dolgellau to Tywyn road (A493) west of Arthog. Parking is available near by at the Morfa Mawddach station.

Access: Nature trails are open at all times.
Facilities: Nature trails and information boards.
Public transport: A regular bus service runs between Dolgellau and Barmouth and stops close to the reserve entrance at Coed Garth Gell. The Arthog Bog part of the reserve is served by the Dolgallau to Tywyn bus services which stops close by at Arthog. The Arthog Bog reserve is a short distance from the Morfa Mawddach railway station.
Habitat: Oak woodland, bracken and heathland at Coed Garth Gell. Willow and alder scrub and raised bog at Arthog bog.
Key birds: *At Coed Garth Gell*: Buzzard, Sparrowhawk, Peregrine, Raven, Lesser Spotted Woodpecker, Grey Wagtail, Dipper and Hawfinch are joined in the summer by Pied Flycatcher, Spotted Flycatcher, Wood Warbler, Redstart, Tree Pipit and Cuckoo. *At Arthog Bog*: Buzzard, Sparrowhawk, Peregrine, Raven are resident. Summer migrants include Tree Pipit, Grasshopper Warbler and Cuckoo. In winter flocks of Redpolls and Siskins are common and Red-breasted Merganser, Pintail and Little Egret are on the nearby estuary.
Other notable flora and fauna: Coed Garth Gell has Tunbridge filmy and beech ferns and a wide variety of butterflies. Golden-ringed dragonflies are regular at both reserves.
Contact: RSPB Ynys-Hir Reserve, 01654 700 222. e-mail:ynyshir@rspb.org.uk

9. MORFA HARLECH NNR

CCW (North West Area).
Location: SH 574 317, NW of Harlech. On the A496 Harlech road.
Access: Open all year.
Facilities: Car park. Disabled parking bays and three coach parking spaces.
Public transport: The site is served by both bus and train. Train stations are at Harlech and Ty Gwyn (Ty Gwyn is near the saltmarsh wintering birds.) Contact Arriva for details (0844 8004 411).
Habitat: Shingle (except at Harlech), coast, marsh, dunes. Also forestry plantation, grassland, swamp.
Key birds: *Spring/summer*: Whitethroat, Spotted Flycatcher, Grasshopper Warbler, migrants. *Passage*: Waders, Manx Shearwater, ducks. *Winter*: Divers, Whooper Swan, Wigeon, Teal, Pintail, Scaup, Common Scoter, Hen Harrier, Merlin, Peregrine, Short-eared Owl, Little Egret, Water Pipit, Snow Bunting, Twite. *All year/breeding*: Redshank, Lapwing, Ringed Plover, Snipe, Curlew, Shelduck, Oystercatcher, Stonechat, Whinchat, Wheatear, Linnet, Reed Bunting, Sedge Warbler. Also Red-breasted Merganser, Kestrel, gulls.
Other notable fauna: Sand lizard, otter, water vole.
Contact: CCW, 0845 1306 229; www.ccw.gov.uk e-mail:enquiries@ccw.gov.uk

10. SOUTH STACK CLIFFS

RSPB (North Wales Office).
Location: RSPB Car Park SH 211 818, Ellins Tower information centre SH 206 820. Follow A55 to W end in Holyhead, proceed straight on at roundabout,

continue straight on through traffic lights. After another half mile turn L and follow the Brown Tourist signs for RSPB Ynys Lawd/South Stack.
Access: RSPB car park with disabled parking, 'Access for all' track leading to a viewing area overlooking the lighthouse adjacent to Ellins Tower visitor centre. Access to Ellins Tower gained via staircase. Reserve covered by an extensive network of paths, some of which are steep and uneven. Coach parking by prior arrangement at The South Stack Kitchen Tel: 01407 762 181 (privately owned).
Facilities: Free access to Ellins Tower which has windows overlooking main auk colony open daily (10am-5.30pm Easter-Sep).
Public transport: Mainline station Holyhead. Infrequent local bus service, Holyhead-South Stack. Tel. 0870 608 2608.
Habitat: Sea cliffs, maritime grassland, maritime heath, lowland heath.
Key birds: Peregrine, Chough, Fulmar, Puffin, Guillemot, Razorbill, Rock Pipit, Skylark, Stonechat, Linnet, Shag, migrant warblers and passage seabirds.
Contact: Dave Bateson, 01407 764 973. www.rspb.org.uk

11. SPINNIES ABER OGWEN
North Wales Wildlife Trust.
Location: SH 613 721. From Bangor follow the Tal-y-Bont road from roundabout on A5122 near Penrhyn Castle entrance. Road to reserve is signposted on L after 1km. Reserve can also be approached from aroad at J 12 off A55. Minor road leads to car park where reserve entrance is signposted.
Access: Open all year. Dogs on leads. Keep to the paths. Wheelchair accessible to the main hide.
Facilities: Two hides clearly signposted from the car park, main hide is wheelchair accessible and offers views of Traeth Lafan sands and the Spinnies lagoon. There is a drop-off point at the main entrance. Footpaths are good throughout.
Public transport: Take the 5 or 5X bus from Bangor or Llandudno.
Habitat: Woodland, scrub, grassland, shingle beach mudflats, reed swamp and open water.
Key birds: Autumn/*winter:* Large numbers of wintering wildfowl and waders such as Redshank, Greenshank, Wigeon and Teal. Kingfisher can be seen from Sep-Mar. *Spring/summer:* Mergansers, feeding Sandwich Terns, large numbers of Mute Swans, Little Grebe, Blackcap and Sedge Warbler.
Other notable flora and fauna: Broad-leaved helleborine, snowdrops, dog's mercury, bluebells. Red admiral, Speckled wood, holly blue, orange tip and small copper butterflies.
Contact: Chris Wynne, Conservation Officer, 01248 351 541. E-mail: ChrisWynne@wildlifetrustswales.org www.wildlifetrust.org.uk/northwales

12. TRAETH LAFAN
Gwynedd Council.
Location: NE of Bangor, stretching to Llanfairfechan. 1) Minor road from old A55 near Tal-y-Bont (SH 610 710) to Aber Ogwen car park by coast (SH 614 723). 2) Also access from minor road from Abergwyngregyn village to Morfa Aber Reserve (SH 646 731). 3) Access on foot to Morfa Madryn Reserve 1 mile W from Llanfairfechan promenade (SH 679 754).
Access: Open access from 1, 2, and 3. All sites are wheelchair accessible.
Facilities: Public paths. 1) Car park, hides 200m away at Spinnies Reserve. 2) Car park and hide. 3) Car and coach park with toilets and café, hides at reserve.
Public transport: For local bus and train timetables call 0870 60 82 608 or log on to www.gwynedd.gov.uk
Habitat: Intertidal sands and mudflats, wetlands, streams. SPA SAC SSSI and LNR.
Key birds: Third most important area in Wales for wintering waders; of national importance for moulting Great Crested Grebe and Red-breasted Merganser; internationally important for Oystercatcher and Curlew; passage waders; winter concentrations of Goldeneye and Greenshank, and of regional significance for wintering populations of Black-throated, Red-throated and Great Northern Divers and Black-necked and Slavonian Grebes and breeding Lapwings at Morfa Madryn.
Contact: Countryside Wardens, 01766 771000. E-mail: HaydnEHughes@gwynedd.gov.uk www.gwynedd.gov.uk LL55 1SH.

Southern Wales

Glamorgan, Gower, Gwent

1. CWM CLYDACH
RSPB Wales
Location: SN 684 026. N of Swansea. Three miles N of J45 on M4, through the village of Clydach on B4291, follow the signs for Craig Cefn Parc , the car park is close to the New Inn pub.
Access: Open at all times along public footpaths and waymarked trails. Not suitable for wheelchairs. Coach parking not available.
Facilities: Two nature trails, car park, information boards.
Public transport: Hourly buses from Swansea stop at reserve entrance. Nearest railway station is in

Swansea.
Habitat: Oak woodland on steep slopes lining the banks of the fast-flowing Lower Clydach River.
Key birds: Red Kite, Sparrowhawk, Buzzard, Raven, Green Woodpecker, Dipper and Grey Wagtail are joined in the summer by Spotted Flycatcher, Garden Warbler, Wood Warbler and Cuckoo. In winter Siskins, Lesser Redpolls and Woodcock are regular.
Other notable flora and fauna: Wood sorrel, silver-washed fritillary and speckled wood butterflies. Good range of fungi.
Contact: RSPB Ynys-Hir Reserve, 01654 700 222; e-mail:ynys -hir@rspb.org.uk

2. CWM COL-HUW
The Wildlife Trust of South and West Wales.
Location: SS 957 674. SE from Bridgend, site includes Iron Age fort, overlooking Bristol Channel. From Bridgend take B4265 S to Llanwit Major. Follow beach road from village.
Access: Park in seafront car park. Climb steps. Open all year.
Facilities: All year toilets and café. Information boards.
Public transport: None.
Habitat: Unimproved grassland, woodland, scrub and Jurassic blue lias cliff.
Key birds: Cliff-nesting House Martin colony, breeding Fulmar, Grasshopper Warbler. Large autumn passerine passage. Peregrine. Seawatching vantage point. Occasional Chough.
Contact: Trust HQ, 01656 724 100.
e-mail:information@wtsww.cix.co.uk

3. KENFIG NNR
Bridgend County Borough Council.
Location: SS 802 811. Seven miles W of Bridgend. From J37 on M4, drive towards Porthcawl, then North Cornelly, then follow signs.
Access: Open at all times. Unsurfaced sandy paths, not suitable for wheelchairs. Flooding possible in winter and spring. Coach parking available.
Facilities: Toilets, hides, free car parking and sign-posted paths. Visitor centre and shop open weekends and holidays (10am-4.30pm), weekdays (2pm-4.30pm). Rooms available for hire.
Public transport: Local bus service: contact reserve for details.

Habitat: 1,300 acre sand dune system, freshwater lake with reeds, numerous wet dune slacks, sandy coastline with some rocky outcrops.
Key birds: *Summer*: Warblers and migrants including Cetti's, Grasshopper, Sedge, Reed, Lesser Whitethroat and Whitethroat. *Winter*: Coastal waders and divers, wildfowl, Water Rail, Bittern and Merlin.
Other notable flora and fauna: 16 species of orchid, hairy dragonfly, red-veined and ruddy darters, small blue, dark green fritillary, grayling, brown argus butterflies.
Contact: David Carrington, Ton Kenfig, Bridgend, CF33. 4PT. 01656 743 386.
e-mail:david.carrington@bridgend.gov.uk

4. MAGOR MARSH
Gwent Wildlife Trust.
Location: ST 427 867. Magor can be reached from junctions 23 and 23A of the M4 motorway. Reserve lies to S of Magor. Leave M4 at exit 23, turning R onto B4245. Follow signs for Redwick in Magor village. Take first L after railway bridge. Reserve entrance is half mile further on R.
Access: Open all year. Keep to path. Wheelchair access to bird hide.
Facilities: Hide. Car park, footpaths and boardwalks.
Public transport: Bus service to Magor village. Reserve is approx 10 mins walk along Redwick road.
Habitat: Sedge fen, reedswamp, willow carr, damp hay meadows and open water.
Key birds: Important for wetland birds. *Spring*: Reed, Sedge and Grasshopper Warblers, occasional Garganey and Green Sandpiper on passage, Hobby. *Winter*: Teal, Peregrine, Jack Snipe, Snipe, occasional Shoveler and Gadwall, Bittern records in two recent years. *All year*: Little Egret, Little Grebe, Reed Bunting, Cetti's Warbler and Water Rail.
Contact: Gwent Wildlife Trust, 01600 740 358; e-mail:info@gwentwildlife.co.uk
www.gwentwildlife.org

5. NEWPORT WETLANDS NNR
CCW/ RSPB/ Newport City Council.
Location: ST 334 834. SW of Newport. Reserve car park on West Nash Road, just before entrance to Uskmouth power station. From M4 J 24 take the A48 to Newport Retail Park, turn towards steelworks and follow brown 'duck' signs to the reserve car park.
Access: Free entry 9am to 5pm each day apart from Dec 25. Six disabled parking bays. All nature trails are

accessible by wheelchair. Dogs only on perimeter footpath.
Facilities: Information centre, tea-rooms, shop, toilets (inc disabled), viewing screens.
Public transport: No 65 bus from Queensway bus station in Newport stops at West Nash Community Hall, a 15 min walk from reserve. Contact Newport bus services, tel: 01633 263 600. Nearest train station: Newport.
Habitat: 438 hectares of wet meadows, saline lagoons, reedbed, scrub and mudflats on Severn estuary.
Key birds: *Spring/summer*: Breeding waders such as Lapwing and Oystercatcher, Bearded Tit, Cetti's Warbler, Cuckoo and regular migrants on passage. *Autumn*: Large numbers of migrating wildfowl and waders arrive at the reserve — regulars include Curlew, Dunlin, Ringed Plover, Shoveler. *Winter*: Massive Starling roost (up to 50,000 birds). Bittern, nationally important numbers of Black-tailed Godwit, Shoveler and Dunlin.
Other notable flora and fauna: Badger, wood mouse, otter. Great crested newt. Orchids in spring, 16 species of dragonfly, 23 species of butterfly and around 200 species of moth.
Contact: Newport Wetlands Reserve, West Nash Road, Newport NP18 2BZ. RSPB visitor centre — 01633 636 363.

6. OXWICH

CCW (Swansea Office).
Location: SS 872 773. 12 miles from Swansea, off A4118.

Access: NNR open at all times. No permit required for access to foreshore, dunes, woodlands and facilities.
Facilities: Private car park, summer only. Toilets summer only. Marsh boardwalk and marsh lookout. No visitor centre, no facilities for disabled visitors.
Public transport: Bus service Swansea/Oxwich. First Cymru, tel 01792 580 580.
Habitat: Freshwater marsh, saltmarsh, foreshore, dunes, woodlands.
Key birds: *Summer*: Breeding Reed, Sedge and Cetti's Warblers, Treecreeper, Nuthatch, woodpeckers. *Winter*: Wildfowl.
Contact: CCW, 01792 634 960; e-mail:enquiries@ccw.gov.uk - www.ccw.gov.uk

7. PARC SLIP NATURE PARK

The Wildlife Trust of South and West Wales.
Location: SS 880 840. Tondu, half mile W of Aberkenfig. From Bridgend take A4063 N, turning L onto B4281 after passing M4. Reserve is signposted from this road.
Access: Open dawn to dusk. Space for coach parking.
Facilities: Three hides, nature trail, interpretation centre.
Public transport: None.
Habitat: Restored opencast mining site, wader scrape, lagoons.
Key birds: *Summer*: Breeding Tufted Duck, Lapwing, Sky Lark. Migrant waders (inc. Little Ringed Plover, Green Sandpiper), Little Gull. Kingfisher, Green Woodpecker.
Contact: Trust HQ, 01656 724 100. e-mail:info@welshwildlife.org

Western Wales

Carmarthenshire, Ceredigion, Pembrokeshire

1. CASTLE WOODS

Location: SN 615 217. About 60 acres of woodland overlooking River Tywi, W of Llandeilo town centre.
Access: Open all year by footpath from Tywi Bridge, Llandeilo (SN 627 221).
Facilities: Call for advice.
Public transport: None.
Habitat: Old mixed deciduous woodlands.
Key birds: All three woodpeckers, Buzzard, Raven, Sparrowhawk. *Summer*: Pied and Spotted Flycatchers, Redstart, Wood Warbler. *Winter*: On water meadows below, look for Teal, Wigeon, Goosander, Shoveler, Tufted Duck and Pochard.
Contact: Carmarthenshire Officer, The Wildlife Trust of South and West Wales, 01239 621 212; e-mail: info@welshwildlife.org - www.welshwildlife.org

2. CORS CARON

CCW (West Wales Area).
Location: SN 692 625 (car park). Reached from B4343 N of Tregaron.
Access: Open access to S of car park along the railway to boardwalk (which is wheelchair accessible), out to SE bog. Access to rest of the reserve by permit.
Dogs (on lead) allowed on boardwalk and old railway line walk but not on Riverside Walk. Access for coaches.
Facilities: New car park with toilets (one with disabled access) and picnic space. Bird hide along boardwalk. Riverside walk is open access. For access to the rest of the reserve please contact the reserve manager.
Public transport: None.

NATURE RESERVES - WESTERN WALES

Habitat: Raised bog, river, fen, wet grassland, willow woodland, reedbed.
Key birds: *Summer*: Lapwing, Redshank, Curlew, Red Kite, Hobby, Grasshopper Warbler, Whinchat. *Winter*: Teal, Wigeon, Whooper Swan, Hen Harrier, Red Kite. **Other notable flora and fauna:** Small red damselfy among the abundant dragonflies seen from boardwalk.
Contact: CCW, 01974 298 480;
e-mail:p.culyer@ccw.gov.uk www.ccw.gov.uk

3. DYFI

CCW (West Wales Area).
Location: SN 610 942. Large estuary area W of Machynlleth. Public footpaths off A493 E of Aberdyfi, and off B4353 (S of river); minor road from B4353 at Ynyslas to dunes and parking area.
Access: Ynyslas dunes and the estuary have unrestricted access. No access to Cors Fochno (raised bog) for casual birdwatching; permit required for study and research purposes. Good views over the bog and Aberleri marshes from W bank of Afon Leri.
Facilities: Public hide overlooking marshes beside footpath at SN 611 911.
Public transport: None.
Habitat: Sandflats, mudflats, saltmarsh, creeks, dunes, raised bog, grazing marsh.
Key birds: *Winter*: Greenland White-fronted Goose, wildfowl, waders and raptors. *Summer*: Breeding wildfowl and waders (inc. Teal, Shoveler, Merganser, Lapwing, Curlew, Redshank).
Contact: CCW Warden, Plas Gogerddan, Aberystwyth, Ceredigion SY23 3EE. 01970 821 100.

4. GWENFFRWD & DINAS

Location: SN 788 471. North of Llandovery.From A483 take B road signposted to Llyn Brianne Reservoir.
Access: Public nature trail at Dinas open at all times.
Facilities: Nature trail including a boardwalk. Other parts of the trail are rugged. Car park and information board at start of trail. Coach parking can be arranged.
Public transport: Nearest train station at Llandovery, 10 miles away.
Habitat: Hillside oak woods, streams and bracken slopes. Spectacular upland scenery.
Key birds: Upland species such as Red Kite, Buzzard, Peregrine, Raven, Goosander, Dipper and Grey Wagtail are joined in the summer by Pied Flycatcher, Spotted Flycatcher, Wood Warbler, Redstart, Tree Pipit, Common Sandpiper and Cuckoo. Marsh Tit and all three woodpecker species are present.
Other notable flora and fauna: Golden-ringed dragonfly, purple hairstreak, silver-washed fritillary and Wilson's filmy fern.
Contact: RSPB Ynys-Hir Reserve, 01654 700 222. e-mail: ynyshir@rspb.org.uk

5. NATIONAL WETLANDS CENTRE WALES

The Wildfowl & Wetlands Trust.
Location: SS 533 984. Overlooks the Burry Inlet near Llanelli. Leave M4 at junction 48. Signposted from A484, E of Llanelli.
Access: Open daily 9.30am-5pm, except Christmas Eve and Christmas Day. Grounds are open until 6pm in summer. The centre is fully accessible with disabled toilets. Mobility scooters and wheelchairs are free to hire.
Facilities: Visitor centre with toilets, hides, restaurant, shop, education facilities, free car and coach parking. The centre has level access and hard-surfaced paths.
Public transport: Bus from Llanelli to Lllwydhendy, approx 1 mile from the centre. Telephone Traveline Cymru 0871 200 2233 (7am-10pm daily).
Habitat: Inter-tidal mudflats, reedbeds, pools, marsh, waterfowl collection.
Key birds: Large flocks of Curlew, Oystercatcher, Redshank on saltmarsh. *Winter*: Pintail, Wigeon, Teal. Also Little Egret, Short-eared Owl, Peregrine.
Other notable flora and fauna: Bee and southern marsh orchids, yellow bartisa. Damselflies and dragonflies, water voles and otters.
Contact: Centre Manager, WWT National Wetlands Centre Wales, 01554 741 087; www.wwt.org.uk
e-mail:info.llanelli@wwt.org.uk

6. RAMSEY ISLAND

R**Location:** SM 706 237. One mile offshore from St Justinians lifeboat station. Two miles west of St Davids, Pembrokeshire.
Access: Open every day, weather permitting, 1 April - 31 Oct. No wheelchair access. Coach and car parking available at St Justinians. For boat bookings Contact: Thousand Island Expeditions, 01437 721721; e-mail. sales@thousandislands. co.uk
Facilities: Toilets, small RSPB shop selling snacks and hot and cold drinks. Self-guiding

231

trail with introduction from resident wardens. Guided walks are also available.
Public transport: Trains to Haverfordwest Station. Hourly buses to St Davids and then Celtic Coaster shuttle bus to boat embarkation point (Tel 01348 840539)
Habitat: Acid grassland, maritime heath, seacliffs.
Key birds: *Spring/summer:* Cliff-nesting auks (Guillemot, Razorbill), Kittiwake, Fulmar, Lesser Black-backed, Great Black-backed and Herring Gulls, Shag, Wheatear, Stonechat. Skylark, Linnet, Lapwing. *All year:* Peregrine, Raven, Chough.
Other notable flora and fauna: Largest grey seal colony is southern Britain, red deer, harbour porpoise.
Contact: The Warden: 07836 535 733; e-mail: ramsey.island@rspb.org.uk
www.rspb.org.uk/ramseyisland

7. SKOKHOLM ISLAND

The Wildlife Trust of South and West Wales.
Location: SM 735 050. Island lying S of Skomer.
Access: Occasional day visits, also 3 or 4 night stays available. Weekly accomm. Apr-Sep, tel 01239 621 212 for details and booking.
Facilities: Call for details. **Public transport:** None.
Habitat: Cliffs, bays and inlets.
Key birds: *Summer:* Large colonies of Razorbill, Puffin, Guillemot, Manx Shearwater, Storm Petrel, Lesser Black-backed Gull. Migrants inc. rare species.
Contact: 01239 621 212.

8. SKOMER ISLAND

The Wildlife Trust of South and West Wales.
Location: SM 725 095. Fifteen miles from Haverfordwest. Take B4327 turn-off for Marloes, embarkation point at Martin's Haven, two miles past village.
Access: Apr 1-Oct 31. Boats sail at 10am, 11am and noon every day except Mon (Bank Holidays excluded). Closed four days beginning of Jun for seabird counts. Not suitable for infirm (steep landing steps and rough ground).
Facilities: Information centre, toilets, two hides, wardens, booklets, guides, nature trails.
Habitat: Maritime cliff, heathland, freshwater ponds.
Key birds: Largest colony of Manx Shearwater in the world. Puffin, Guillemot, Razorbill (Apr-end Jul). Kittiwake (until end Aug), Fulmar (absent Oct), Short-eared Owl (during day Jun and Jul), Chough, Peregrine, Buzzard (all year), migrants.
Contact: Skomer Island, Marloes, Pembs SA62 2BJ. 07971 114 302; e-mail: skomer@wtww.co.uk

9. WELSH WILDLIFE CENTRE

The Wildlife Trust of South and West Wales.
Location: SN 188 451. Two miles SE of Cardigan. River Teifi is N boundary. Sign-posted from Cardigan to Fishguard road.

Access: Open 10.30am-5pm all year. Free parking for WTSWW members, £3 non-members. Dogs on leads welcome. Disabled access to visitor centre, paths, four hides.
Facilities: Visitor centre, restaurant, network of paths and seven hides.
Public transport: Train station, Haverfordwest (23 miles). Bus station in Cardigan. Access on foot from Cardigan centre, ten mins.
Habitat: Wetlands, marsh, swamp, reedbed, open water, creek (tidal), river, saltmarsh, woodland.
Key birds: Cetti's Warbler, Kingfisher, Water Rail, Great Spotted Woodpecker, Dipper, gulls, Marsh Harrier, Sand Martin, Hobby, Redstart, occasional Bittern and Red Kite.
Contact: The Welsh Wildlife Centre, Cilgerran, Cardigan SA43 2TB. 01239 621 212.
e-mail:wwc@welshwildlife.org
www.welshwildlife.org

10. YNYS-HIR

RSPB (CYMRU).
Location: SN 68 29 63. Off A487 Aberystwyth − Machynlleth road in Eglwys-fach village. Six miles SW of Machynlleth.
Access: Open every day (9am-9pm or dusk if earlier) except Christmas Day. Visitor centre open daily Apr-Oct (10am-5pm), Wed-Sun Nov-Mar (10am-4pm). Coaches welcome but please call for parking information. Sorry, no dogs allowed.
Facilities: Visitor centre and toilets. Numerous trails, six hides, drinks machine.
Public transport: Bus service to Eglwys-fach from either Machynlleth or Aberystwyth, tel. 01970 617 951. Rail service to Machynlleth.
Habitat: Estuary, freshwater pools, woodland and wet grassland.
Key birds: Large numbers of wintering waders, wildfowl and birds of prey on the estuary are replaced with breeding woodland birds in spring and summer. *All year:* Red Kite, Buzzard, Little Egret, Lapwing, Teal. *Spring:* Wood Warbler, Redstart, Pied Flycatcher, nine species of warbler. *Winter:* Greenland white-fronted Goose, Barnacle Goose, Wigeon, Hen Harrier.
Other notable flora and fauna: Sixteen species of dragonfly and damselfly include small red damselfly and golden-ringed damselfly. Butterflies include dark green fritillary, brimstone and speckled wood. Otters and brown hares are resident though the former are rarely seen.
Contact: RSPB Ynys-Hir Reserve, Eglwys-fach, Machynlleth, Powys SY20 8TA. 01654 700 222.
e-mail:ynyshir@rspb.org.uk

Is there a reserve in your area that you think should be included in this annually-updated survey? E-mail your nominations to the Editor at: d.cromack@btinternet.com

COUNTY DIRECTORY

David Cromack

Want to get involved in counting wildfowl species like these Shovelers for the Wetlands Bird Survey? *The Yearbook* **provides a county-by-county guide to all the local organisers.**

ENGLAND

THE INFORMATION in the directory has been obtained either from the persons listed or from the appropriate national or other bodies. In some cases, where it has not proved possible to verify the details directly, alternative responsible sources have been relied upon. When no satisfactory record was available, previously included entries have sometimes had to be deleted. Readers are requested to advise the editor of any errors or omissions.

AVON
See Somerset.

BEDFORDSHIRE

Bird Atlas/Avifauna
An Atlas of the Breeding Birds of Bedfordshire 1988-92 by R A Dazley and P Trodd (Bedfordshire Natural History Society, 1994).

The Birds of Bedfordshire by P.Trodd & D.Kramer (Castlemead, 1991) - out of print.

Bird Recorders
Steve Blain, 9 Devon Drive, Biggleswade, Bedfordshire SG18 0FJ. 07979 606 300;
e-mail: recorder@bedsbirdclub.org.uk

Bird Report
BEDFORDSHIRE BIRD REPORT (1946-), from Mary Sheridan, 28 Chestnut Hill, Linslade, Leighton Buzzard, Beds LU7 2TR. 01525 378 245;
e-mail: membership@bnhs.org.uk

BTO Regional Representative
Nigel Willits, Orchard Cottage, 68 High Street, Wilden, Beds MK44 2QD. 01234 771 948;
e-mail: willits1960@hotmail.com

Club
BEDFORDSHIRE BIRD CLUB. (1992; 300). Miss Sheila Alliez, Flat 61 Adamson Court, Adamson Walk, Kempston, Bedford MK42 8QZ. E-mail: alliezsec@peewit. freeserve.co.uk
www.bedsbirdclub.org.uk
Meetings: 8.00pm, last Tuesday of the month (Sep-Mar), Maulden Village Hall, Maulden, Beds.

Ringing Groups
IVEL RG. Graham Buss, 11 Northall Close, Eaton Bray, Dunstable, LU6 2EB. 01525 221 023;
e-mail: g1j2buss@yahoo.co.uk

RSPB. WB Kirby. E-mail: will.kirby@rspb.org.uk

RSPB Local Groups
BEDFORD. (1970; 80). Bob Montgomery, 36 Princes Road, Bromham, Beds MK43 8QD. 01234 822 035;
e-mail: montgomery547@btinternet.com
www.rspb.org.uk/groups/bedford/

Meetings: 7.30pm, 3rd Thursday of the month, A.R.A. Manton Lane, Bedford.
LUTON AND SOUTH BEDFORDSHIRE. (1973; 120+). Allyn Hill. 01582 666 297;
e-mail: cah_halfmoon@yahoo.com
www.rspb.org.uk/groups/luton
Meetings: 7.45pm, 2nd Wednesday of the month, Houghton Regis Social Centre, Parkside Drive, Houghton Regis, LU5 5QN.

Wetland Bird Survey Organiser
BEDFORDSHIRE. Mr R I Bashford, 6 Brook Road, St Neots, Cambridgeshire PE19 7AX.
E-mail: richard.bashford@rspb.org.uk

Wildlife Trust
See Cambridgeshire.

BERKSHIRE

BirdAtlas/Avifauna
The Birds of Berkshire by P E Standley et al (Berkshire Atlas Group/Reading Ornithological Club, 1996).

Bird Recorder
Chris DR Heard, 3 Waterside Lodge, Ray Mead Road, Maidenhead, Berkshire SL6 8NP. 01628 633 828;
e-mail: chris.heard@virgin.net

Bird Reports
BERKSHIRE BIRD BULLETIN (Monthly, 1986-), from Brian Clews, 118 Broomhill, Cookham, Berks SL6 9LQ. 01628 525314; e-mail: brian.clews@btconnect.com

THE BIRDS OF BERKSHIRE (1974-), from Secretary of the Berkshire Ornithological Club.
E-mail: mike.turton@berksoc.org.uk
www.berksoc.org.uk

BIRDS OF THE THEALE AREA (1988-), from Secretary, Theale Area Bird Conservation Group.

NEWBURY DISTRICT BIRD REPORT (1959-) - covering West Berkshire (approx 12 miles from centre of Newbury), plus parts of north Hants, south Oxon, from Secretary, Newbury District Ornithological Club.

BTO Regional Representatives
Sarah Priest and Kent White. 01635 268 442;
e-mail: btoberks.ken.sarah@googlemail.com

234

Clubs
BERKSHIRE BIRD BULLETIN GROUP. (1986; 100).
Berkshire Bird Bulletin Group, PO Box 680,
Maidenhead, Berks, SL6 9ST. 01628 525 314;
e-mail: brian.clews@btconnect.com

NEWBURY DISTRICT ORNITHOLOGICAL
CLUB. (1959; 110). John L Swallow,
Yew Tree House, High Street,
Kintbury, Hungerford RG17 9TN.
07795 027 490; e-mail:
jls4015-ndoc@yahoo.co.uk
www.ndoc.org.uk
Meetings: Indoor lectures from
October to March and regular bird watching days
around Newbury, throughout the summer and winter.
Please see website for details.

THEALE AREA BIRD CONSERVATION GROUP. (1988;
75). Catherine McEwan, Secretary. 01189 415 792;
e-mail: catherine_j_mcewan@fsmail.net
www.freewebs.com/tabcg/index.htm
Meetings: 8pm, 1st Tuesday of the month, Englefield
Social Club.

Ringing Groups
NEWBURY RG. J Legg, 31 Haysoms Drive, Greenham,
Thatcham, Nr Newbury, Berks RG19 8EY.
E-mail: janlegg@btinternet.com
www.newburyrg.co.uk

RUNNYMEDE RG. D G Harris, 22 Blossom Waye,
Hounslow, TW5 9HD.
E-mail: daveharris@tinyonline.co.uk
www.rmxrg.org.uk

RSPB Local Groups
EAST BERKSHIRE. (1974; 200). Gerry Studd, 5 Cherry
Grove, Holmer Green, High Wycombe, Bucks HP15
6RG. 01494 715 609; e-mail: gerrystudd@aol.com
www.eastberksrspb.org.uk
Meetings: 7.30pm, Thursdays (Sept-April), Methodist
Church Hall, King Street, Maidenhead, SL6 1EA

READING. (1986; 130). Carl Feltham. 0118 941 1713;
e-mail: carl.feltham@virginmedia.com
www.reading-rspb.org.uk
Meetings: 8.00Pm, 2nd Tuesday of the month (Sep-
Jun), Pangbourne Village Hall, Pangbourne.

WOKINGHAM & BRACKNELL. (1979; 200). Les Blundell,
Folly Cottage, Buckle Lane, Warfield, RG42 5SB.
01344 861964; e-mail: lesblundell@ymail.com
www.rspb.org.uk/groups/wokinghamandbracknell
Meetings: 8.00pm, 2nd Tuesday of the month (Sep-
Jun), Finchampstead Memorial Hall, Wokingham,
RG40 4JU.

Wetland Bird Survey Organisers
BERKSHIRE. Ken White & Sarah Priest,
e-mail: btoberks.ken.sarah@googlemail.com

Wildlife Hospital
LIFELINE. Wendy Hermon, Treatment Centre Co-
ordinator, Swan Treatment Centre, Cuckoo Weir
Island, South Meadow Lane, Eton, Windsor, Berks SL4
6SS. 01753 859 397;
e-mail: wendyhermon@swanlifeline.org.uk
www.swanlifeline.org.uk Registered charity. Thames
Valley 24-hour swan rescue and treatment service.
Veterinary support and hospital unit. Operates
membership scheme.

Wildlife Trust
Director, See Oxfordshire,

BUCKINGHAMSHIRE

BirdAtlas/Avifauna
The Birds of Buckinghamshire ed by P Lack and D
Ferguson (Buckinghamshire Bird Club, 1993). Now out
of print.

Bird Recorder
Andy Harding, 01908 565 896 (home/evening/
weekends); 01908 653 328 (work/weekdays);
e-mail: a.v.harding@open.ac.uk

Bird Reports
BUCKINGHAMSHIRE BIRD REPORT (1980-) - only some
reports since 1990 are available, from John Gearing,
Valentines, Dinton, Aylesbury, Bucks, HP17 8UW.
E-mail: john_gearing@hotmail.com

NORTH BUCKS BIRD REPORT (12 pa), from John
Gearing. 01296 748 245;
e-mail: clubrecorder@bucksbirdclub.co.uk

BTO Regional Representative
Roger Warren. 01491 638 691;
e-mail: rcwarren@btinternet.com

BTO Garden BirdWatch Ambassador
Stephanie Plaster;
e-mail: steph.plaster@googlemail.com

Clubs
BUCKINGHAMSHIRE BIRD CLUB. (1981; 340). Neill
Foster, Secretary. 01296 748 597;
e-mail: Secretary@bucksbirdclub.co.uk
www.bucksbirdclub.co.uk

NORTH BUCKS BIRDERS. (1977; 30). Ted Reed, c/o
AACS, The Open University, Walton Hall,Milton Keynes
MK7 6AA. 01908 653 517 (work);
e-mail: E.J.Reed@open.ac.uk
Meetings: No meetings. Contact is via North Bucks
email group. To join contact the Group Administrator,
Simon Nichols (si.nich@yahoo.com)

RSPB Local Groups
See also Herts: Chorleywood.

AYLESBURY. (1981; 220). Brian Fisher. 01844 215 924;
e-mail: brian.fisher45@yahoo.co.uk
www.rspb.org.uk/groups/aylesburyPrebendal Farm
Meetings: Community Centre, Fowler Road, Aylesbury
HP19 7QW.

ENGLAND

NORTH BUCKINGHAMSHIRE. (1976; 440). Chris Ward,
41 William Smith Close, Woolstone, Milton Keynes,
MK15 0AN. 01908 669 448;
e-mail: northbucksrspb@hotmail.com
www.rspb.org.uk/groups/northbucks
Meetings: 8.00pm, 2nd Thursday of the month, Cruck
Barn, City Discovery Centre, Bradwell Abbey, MK13
9AP.

Wetland Bird Survey Organiser
BUCKINGHAMSHIRE. Position vacant.

Wildlife Hospitals
WILDLIFE HOSPITAL TRUST. St Tiggywinkles, Aston
Road, Haddenham, Aylesbury, Bucks, HP17 8AF.
01844 292 292 (24hr helpline);
e-mail: mail@sttiggywinkles.org.uk
www.sttiggywinkles.org.uk
Registered charity. All British species. Veterinary
referrals and helpline for vets and others on wild bird
treatments. Full veterinary unit and staff.
Pub: *Bright Eyes* (free to members - sae).

Wildlife Trust
Director, See Oxfordshire,

CAMBRIDGESHIRE

BirdAtlas/Avifauna
*An Atlas of the Breeding Birds of Cambridgeshire (VC
29)* P M M Bircham et al (Cambridge Bird Club, 1994).

The Birds of Cambridgeshire: checklist 2000
(Cambridge Bird Club).

Bird Recorders
CAMBRIDGESHIRE. Mark Hawkes, 7 Cook Drive,
Eynesbury, St Neots, Cambs PE19 2JU. 01480 215 305;
e-mail: marklhawkes@yahoo.co.uk

Bird Reports
CAMBRIDGESHIRE BIRD REPORT (1925-), from Bruce
Martin, 178 Nuns Way, Cambridge, CB4 2NS. (H)01223
700 656; e-mail: bruce.s.martin@ntlworld.com

PETERBOROUGH BIRD CLUB REPORT (1999-), from
Secretary, Peterborough Bird Club.

BTO Regional Representatives
CAMBRIDGESHIRE. Mark Welch.
E-mail: m.welch@nhm.ac.uk

HUNTINGDON & PETERBOROUGH. Position vacant.

Clubs
CAMBRIDGESHIRE BIRD CLUB. (1925; 329). John
Harding, 3 Cotton's Field, Dry Drayton, Cambs CB23
8DG. E-mail: johnharding44@googlemail.com
Meetings: 2nd Friday of the month, St John's Church
Hall, Hills Road, Cambridge/Cottenham Village
College.

PETERBOROUGH BIRD CLUB. (1999; 150) Keith
Stapleford, 01733 555 973;
e-mail: keith.stapleford@talktalk.net

www.peterboroughbirdclub.co.uk
Meetings: Indoor last Tuesday
of each month from Sep-Apr
inclusive at 7.30pm at the Post
Office Club, Bourges Boulevard,
Peterborough. Outdoor meeting
monthly throughout most of year.

THE FRIENDS OF PAXTON PITS (1995; 2200).
Secretary, Gill Butt, 01480 473 848;
www.paxton-pits.org.uk
Meetings: Regular indoor and outdoor meetings
held at Paxton Pits Nature Reserve. See website for
details.

Ringing Group
WICKEN FEN RG. Dr C J R Thorne, 17 The Footpath,
Coton, Cambs CB23 7PX. 01954 210 566;
e-mail: cjrt@cam.ac.uk

RSPB Local Groups
CAMBRIDGE. (1977; 150). Melvyn Smith. 01799 500
482; e-mail: mel_brensmith@hotmail.co.uk
www.RSPB.org.uk/groups/cambridge
Meetings: 3rd Wednesday of every month Jan-May
and Sept-Dec 8pm. The Wilkinson Room, St John's the
Evangelist, Hills Road, Cambridge, CB2 8RN

HUNTINGDONSHIRE. (1982; 180). Pam Peacock. 01487
840 615; e-mail: pam.evan@btinternet.com
www.rspb.org.uk/groups/huntingdonshire
Meetings: 7.30pm, last Wednesday of the month
(Sep-Apr), Free Church, St Ives.

Wetland Bird Survey Organisers
CAMBRIDGESHIRE (including Huntingdonshire). Bruce
Martin, 178 Nuns Way, Cambridge, CB4 2NS. (H)01223
700 656; e-mail: bruce.s.martin@ntlworld.com

NENE WASHES. Charlie Kitchin, RSPB Nene Washes,
21a East Delph, Whittlesey, Cambs PE7 1RH. 01733
205 140; e-mail: Charlie.kitchin@rspb.org.uk

OUSE WASHES. Paul Harrington, Ouse Washes RSPB
Reserve, E-mail: paul.harrington@rspb.org.uk

SOUTH LINCOLNSHIRE/PETERBOROUGH (inland). Bob
Titman; e-mail: titman@nildram.co.uk

Wildlife Trust
THE WILDLIFE TRUST FOR BEDFORDSHIRE,
CAMBRIDGESHIRE, NORTHAMPTONSHIRE AND
PETERBOROUGH. (1990; 36,000). The Manor House,
Broad Street, Great Cambourne, Cambridgeshire CB23
6DH. 01954 713 500;
e-mail: cambridgeshire@wildlifebcnp.org
www.wildlifebcnp.org

CHESHIRE & WIRRAL

BirdAtlas/Avifauna
*Birds in Cheshire and Wirral - A Breeding and
Wintering Atlas 2004-2007* by Professor David
Norman, Liverpool University Press, Autumn 2008.

ENGLAND

The Birds of Sandbach Flashes 1935-1999 by Andrew Goodwin and Colin Lythgoe (The Printing House, Crewe, 2000).

Bird Recorder (inc Wirral)
CHESHIRE & WIRRAL. Hugh Pulsford, 6 Buttermere Drive, Great Warford, Alderley Edge, Cheshire SK9 7WA. 01565 880 171; e-mail: countyrec@cawos.org

Bird Reports
CHESHIRE & WIRRAL BIRD REPORT (1969-), from Andrew Duncalf, 25 Monarch Drive, Northwich, Cheshire CW9 8UN. 07771 774 5210; e-mail: andrewduncalf@cawos.org
www.cawos.org

SOUTH EAST CHESHIRE ORNITHOLOGICAL SOCIETY BIRD REPORT (1985-), from Secretary, South East Cheshire Ornithol Soc. 01270 582 642.

BTO Regional Representatives
MID. Paul Miller. 01928 787 535;
e-mail: paulandhilarymiller@live.co.uk

NORTH & EAST. Mark Eddowes, 59 Westfield Drive, Knutsford, Cheshire WA16 0BH. 01925 843 422; e-mail: mark.eddowes@esrtechnology.com

SOUTH. Charles Hull, Edleston Cottage, Edleston Hall Lane, Nantwich, Cheshire CW5 8PL. 01270 628194; e-mail: edleston@yahoo.co.uk

BTO Garden BirdWatch Ambassador
George Pilkington;
e-mail: george.pilkington@ntlworld.com

Clubs
CHESHIRE & WIRRAL ORNITHOLOGICAL SOCIETY. (1988; 375). Dr Ted Lock, 2 Bourne Street, Wilmslow, Cheshire, SK9 5HD. 01625 540 466;
e-mail: secretary@cawos.org - ww.cawos.org
Meetings: 7.45pm, 1st Friday of the month, Knutsford Civic Centre.

CHESTER & DISTRICT ORNITHOLOGICAL SOCIETY. (1967; 50). David King, 13 Bennett Close, Willaston, South Wirral, CH64 2XF. 0151 327 7212.
Meetings: 7.30pm, 1st Thursday of the month (Oct-Mar), Caldy Valley Community Centre.

KNUTSFORD ORNITHOLOGICAL SOCIETY. (1974; 55). Derek A Pike, 2 Lilac Avenue, Knutsford, Cheshire, WA16 0AZ. 01565 653 811;
e-mail: tony@mobberley.eu - www.10X50.com
Meetings: 7.30pm, 4th Friday of the month (not Dec), Jubilee Hall, Stanley Road, Knutsford.

LANCASHIRE & CHESHIRE FAUNA SOCIETY. (1914; 140). Dave Bickerton, 64 Petre Crescent, Rishton, Blackburn, Lancs, BB1 4RB. 01254 886 257;
e-mail: bickertond@aol.com
www.lacfs.org.uk

LYMM ORNITHOLOGY GROUP. (1975; 60). Mandy Tonge. E-mail: mandy.tonge@zetnet.co.uk
www.users.zetnet.co.uk/lymmog/

Meetings: 8.00pm, last Friday of the month (Aug-May), Lymm Village Hall.

MID-CHESHIRE ORNITHOLOGICAL SOCIETY. (1963; 80). John Drake, 17 Wisenholme Close, Beechwood West, Runcorn, Cheshire WA7 2RU. 01928 561 133; E-mail: contact@ midcheshireos.co.uk
www.midcheshireos.co.uk
Meetings: 7:30pm, 2nd Friday of the month (Oct-Mar), Cuddington and Sandiway Village Hall.

SOUTH EAST CHESHIRE ORNITHOLOGICAL SOCIETY. (1964; 140). Colin Lythgoe, 11 Waterloo Road, Haslington, Crewe, CW1 5TF. 01270 582 642.
www.secos.org.uk
Meetings: 2nd Friday (Sept-Apr), 7.30pm, Ettiley Heath Church Community Centre, Sandbach.

WILMSLOW GUILD BIRDWATCHING GROUP. (1965; 67). Tom Gibbons, Chestnut Cottage, 37 Strawberry Lane, Wilmslow, Cheshire SK9 4AQ. 01625 520317.
http://wgbw.wikidot.com
Meetings: 7.30pm last Friday of the month, Wilmslow Guild, Bourne St, Wilmslow.

Ringing Groups
MERSEYSIDE RG. Bob Harris, 3 Mossleigh, Whixalll, Whitchurch, Shropshire SY13 2SA. Work 0151 706 4311; e-mail: harris@liv.ac.uk

SOUTH MANCHESTER RG. Mr N.B. Powell,
email: neville.powell@tiscali.co.uk

RSPB Local Groups
CHESTER. (1988; 220). Norman Sadler. 01244 335 670;
e-mail: chester1RSPB@btinternet.com
www.rspb.org.uk/groups/chester
Meetings: 7.30pm, 3rd Wednesday of the month (Sep-Apr), St Mary's Centre, Chester.

MACCLESFIELD. (1979; 250). Anne Bennett. 01260 271 231; e-mail: secretary@macclesfieldrspb.org.uk
www.macclesfieldrspb.org.uk
Meetings: 7.45pm, 2nd Tuesday of the month (Sept-May), Senior Citizens Hall, Duke Street, MACCLESFIELD, Cheshire, SK11 6UR

NORTH CHESHIRE. (1976; 100). Paul Grimmett. 01925 268 770; e-mail: paulwtwitcher@hotmail.com
www.rspb.org.uk/groups/north_cheshire
Meetings: 7.45pm, 3rd Friday (Jan-April and Sept-Nov), Appleton Parish Hall, Dudlow Green Road, Appleton, Warrington.

Wetland Bird Survey Organiser
CHESHIRE NORTH. Vacant position.

CHESHIRE SOUTH. David Cookson, 01270 567 526;
e-mail: cheshireswans@aol.com

MERSEY ESTUARY. Graham Thomason;
e-mail: webs@bto.org

237

ENGLAND

Wildlife Hospital
RSPCA STAPELEY GRANGE WILDLIFE CENTRE. London Road, Stapeley, Nantwich, Cheshire, CW5 7JW. 0300 123 0722. All wild birds. Oiled bird wash facilities and pools. Veterinary support.

Wildlife Trust
CHESHIRE WILDLIFE TRUST. (1962; 13,100). Bickley Hall Farm, Bickley, Malpas, Cheshire SY14 8EF. 01948 820 728; e-mail: info@cheshirewt.org.uk
www.cheshirewildlifetrust.co.uk

CLEVELAND

Bird Atlas/Avifauna
Birds of Cleveland. M.A Blick. Tees Valley Wildlife Trust, 2010.

The Breeding Birds of Cleveland. Teesmouth Bird Club, 2008.

Bird Recorder
CLEVELAND. Tom Francis.
E-mail: mot.francis@ntlworld.com

Bird Report
CLEVELAND BIRD REPORT (1974-), from Mr J Fletcher, 43 Glaisdale Avenue, Middlesbrough TS5 7PF. 01642 818 825.

BTO Regional Representative
CLEVELAND. Vic Fairbrother, 8, Whitby Avenue, Guisborough, Cleveland, TS14 7AP. 01287 633 744; e-mail: vic.fairbrother@ntlworld.com

Club
TEESMOUTH BIRD CLUB. (1960; 425). Chris Sharp (Hon Sec.), 20 Auckland Way, Hartlepool, TS26 0AN. 01429 865 163; www.teesmouthbc.com
Meetings: 7.30pm, 1st Monday of the month (Sep-Apr), Stockton Library, Church Road, Stockton.

Ringing Group
SOUTH CLEVELAND RG. W Norman, 2 Station Cottages, Grosmont, Whitby, N Yorks YO22 5PB. 01947 895 226; e-mail: wilfgros@btinternet.com

RSPB Local Group
CLEVELAND. (1974; 150). Terry Reeve.
E-mail: ClevelandRSPB@googlemail.com
www.rspb.org.uk/groups/cleveland
Meetings: 7.00 for 7.30pm, 2nd Monday of each month (Sep-Apr), Nature's World, Ladgate Lane, Middlesbrough, Cleveland.

Wetland Bird Survey Organisers
CLEVELAND (EXLUDING TEES ESTUARY). Chris Sharpe, 01429 865 163; e-mail: chrisandlucia@ntlworld.com

TEES ESTUARY. Mike Leakey, c/o Natural England, British Energy, Tees Road, Hartlepool TS25 2BZ. 01429 853 325;
e-mail: mike.leakey@naturalengland.org.uk

Wildlife Trust
TEES VALLEY WILDLIFE TRUST. (1979; 5,000). Margrove Heritage Centre, Margrove Park, Boosbeck, Saltburn-by-the-Sea, TS12 3BZ. 01287 636 382; e-mail: info@teeswildlife.org
www.teeswildlife.org

CORNWALL AND ISLES OF SCILLY

Bird Recorders
CORNWALL. Darrell Clegg, 55 Lower Fore Street, Saltash, Cornwall PL12 6JQ.
E-mail: recorder@cbwps.org.uk

ISLES OF SCILLY. Nigel Hudson, Carn Ithen, Trench Lane, Old Town, St Mary's, Isles of Scilly TR21 0PA. 01720 422 917; e-mail: nigel@carnithen.co.uk
www.carnithen.co.uk

Bird Atlas/Avifauna
The Essential Guide to Birds of The Isles of Scilly 2007 by RL Flood, N Hudson and B Thomas, published by authors.

Bird Reports
BIRDS IN CORNWALL (1931-), from Cornwall Birding, www.cornwall-birding.co.uk

ISLES OF SCILLY BIRD REPORT and NATURAL HISTORY REVIEW 2000 (1969-), see website; www.scilly-birding.co.uk

BTO Regional Representatives
CORNWALL. Stephen Jackson, 2, Trelawney Cottages, Falmouth, Cornwall TR11 3NY. 01326 313 533; e-mail: stephen.f.jackson@btinternet.com

ISLES OF SCILLY. Will Wagstaff, 42 Sally Port, St Mary's, Isles of Scilly, TR21 0JE. 01720 422 212; e-mail: will@islandwildlifetours.co.uk

Clubs
CORNWALL BIRDWATCHING & PRESERVATION SOCIETY. (1931; 762). Tony Bertenshaw, (Honorary Secretary), Hantergantick, St. Breward, Cornwall PL30 4NH. 01208 850 419; www.cbwps.org.uk
e-mail: secretary@cbwps.org.uk

CORNWALL WILDLIFE TRUST PHOTOGRAPHIC GROUP. (40). David Chapman, 41 Bosence Road, Townshend, Nr Hayle, Cornwall TR27 6AL. 01736 850 287; e-mail: david@ruralimages.freeserve.co.uk
www.ruralimages.freeserve.co.uk
Meetings: Mixture of indoor and outdoor meetings, please phone for details.

ISLES OF SCILLY BIRD GROUP. (2000; 510). Membership Secretary. 01720 422 917.
E-mail: danni@carnithen.co.uk
www.scilly-birding.co.uk

ENGLAND

Ringing Group
SCILLONIA SEABIRD GROUP. Peter Robinson, Secretary, 19 Pine Park Road, Honiton, Devon EX14 2HR. 01404 549 873 (M)07768 538 132; e-mail: pjrobinson2@aol.com www.birdexpertuk.com

RSPB Local Group
CORNWALL. (1972; 420). Roger Hooper. 01209 820 610; e-mail: rogerhooper@talktalk.net www.rspb.org.uk/groups/cornwall
Meetings: Indoor meetings (Oct-Apr), outdoor throughout the year.

Wetland Bird Survey Organisers
CORNWALL (excl. Tamar Complex). Dr I Maclean. 07966 693 552; e-mail: i.m.d.maclean@exeter.ac.uk

TAMAR COMPLEX. Gladys Grant, 18 Orchard Crescent, Oreston, Plymouth, PL9 7NF. 01752 406 287; e-mail: gladysgrant@talktalk.net

Wildlife Hospital
MOUSEHOLE WILD BIRD HOSPITAL & SANCTUARY ASSOCIATION LTD. Raginnis Hill, Mousehole, Penzance, Cornwall, TR19 6SR. 01736 731 386. All species. No ringing.

Wildlife Trust
CORNWALL WILDLIFE TRUST. (1962; 14,000). Five Acres, Allet, Truro, Cornwall, TR4 9DJ. 01872 273 939; e-mail: info@cornwallwildlifetrust.org.uk www.cornwallwildlifetrust.org.uk

THE ISLES OF SCILLY WILDLIFE TRUST. (1984: 324) Carn Thomas, Hugh Town, St Marys, Isles of Scilly TR21 0PT.01720 422 153; e-mail: enquiries@ios-wildlifetrust.org.uk www.www.ios-wildlifetrust.org.uk

CUMBRIA

BirdAtlas/Avifauna
The Breeding Birds of Cumbria by Stott, Callion, Kinley, Raven and Roberts (Cumbria Bird Club, 2002).

Bird Recorders
CUMBRIA. Colin Raven, 18 Seathwaite Road, Barrow-in-Furness, Cumbria, LA14 4LX. E-mail: colin@walneyobs.fsnet.co.uk

NORTH WEST (Allerdale & Copeland). Derek McAlone, 88 Whinlatter Road, Mirehouse, Whitehaven, Cumbria CA28 8DQ. 01946 691 370; e-mail: derekmcalone@hotmail.co.uk

SOUTH (South Lakeland & Furness). Ronnie Irving. 24 Birchwood Close, Vicarage Park, Kendal, Cumbria LA9 5BJ. E-mail: ronnie@fenella.fslife.co.uk

Bird Reports
BIRDS AND WILDLIFE IN CUMBRIA (1970-), from Dave Piercy, Secretary, Derwentwater Youth Hostel, Borrowdale, Keswick CA12 5UR. 01768 777 909;

e-mail: daveandkathypiercy@tiscali.co.uk www.cumbriabirdclub.org.uk

WALNEY BIRD OBSERVATORY REPORT, membership secretary; keith.parkes5@btopenworld.com

BTO Regional Representative
CUMBRIA. Clive Hartley, Undercragg, Charney Well La, Grange Over Sands, LA11 6DB. 01539 536 824; e-mail: clive.hartley304@btinternet.com

Clubs
ARNSIDE & DISTRICT NATURAL HISTORY SOCIETY. (1967; 221). Roger Spooner. 01524 701 619;
Meetings: 7.30pm, 2nd Tuesday of the month (Sept-Apr). WI Hall, Orchard Road, Arnside. (Also summer walks).

CUMBRIA BIRD CLUB. (1989; 330). Dave Piercy, Secretary, Derwentwater Youth Hostel, Borrowdale, Keswick CA12 5UR. 01768 777 909; e-mail: daveandkathypiercy@tiscali.co.uk www.cumbriabirdclub.org.uk
Meetings: Various evenings and venues (Oct-Mar) check on website for further details.

Ringing Groups
EDEN RG. G Longrigg, 1 Spring Cottage, Heights, Appleby-in-Westmorland, Cumbria CA16 6EP.

MORECAMBE BAY WADER RG. J Sheldon, 140 Oxford Street, Barrow-in-Furness, Cumbria LA14 5PJ.

WALNEY BIRD OBSERVATORY. K Parkes, 176 Harrogate Street, Barrow-in-Furness , Cumbria, LA14 5NA. 01229 824 219.

RSPB Local Groups
CARLISLE. (1974; 400). Bob Jones, 130 Greenacres, Wetheral, Carlisle, 01225 561 684; e-mail: bob@onethirty.force9.co.uk www.rspb.org.uk/groups/carlisle
Meetings: 7.30pm, Wednesday monthly (Sep-Mar), Tithe Barn, (Behind Marks And Spencer's), West Walls, CARLISLE, Cumbria, CA3. Also monthly field trips except August.

SOUTH LAKELAND. (1973; 305). Mr Martin Baines, 101 Serpentine Road, Kendal, Cumbria, LA9 4PD. 01539 732 214; e-mail: SlRSPB@marshallecology.co.uk www.rspb.org.uk/groups/southlakeland/
Meetings: Contact above.

WEST CUMBRIA. (1986; 270). Marjorie Hutchin, 3 Camerton Road, Gt Broughton, Cockermouth, Cumbria CA13 0YR. 01900 825 231; e-mail: majorie.hutchin@btinternet.com www.rspb.org.uk/groups/westcumbria
Meetings: 7.30pm, 1st Tuesday (Sept-Apr), United Reformed Church, Main St, Cockermouth.

Wetland Bird Survey Organisers
CUMBRIA (excluding estuaries). Dave Shackleton, e-mail: dave.shack@care4free.net

239

ENGLAND

DUDDON ESTUARY. Rosalyn Gay, 01229 773 820; e-mail: Rosaatmillom@aol.com

IRT, MITE AND ESK ESTUARIES. Peter Jones, e-mail: webs@bto.org

MORECAMBE BAY (NORTH). Clive Hartley, 015395 36824; e-mail: clive.hartley304@btinternet.com

SOLWAY ESTUARY (SOUTH). Norman Holton, 016973 51330; e-mail: norman.holton@rspb.org.uk

Wildlife Trust
CUMBRIA WILDLIFE TRUST. (1962; 15,000). Plumgarths, Crook Road, Kendal, Cumbria LA8 8LX. 01539 816 300; www.cumbriawildlifetrust.org.uk e-mail: mail@cumbriawildlifetrust.org.uk

DERBYSHIRE

BirdAtlas/Avifauna
The Birds of Derbyshire, ed. RA Frost (in preparation)

Bird Recorders
1. JOINT RECORDER. Roy A Frost, 66 St Lawrence Road, North Wingfield, Chesterfield, Derbyshire S42 5LL. 01246 850037; e-mail: frostra66@btinternet.com

2. Records Committee & rarity records. Rodney W Key, 3 Farningham Close, Spondon, Derby, DE21 7DZ. 01332 678571; e-mail: r_key@sky.com

3. JOINT RECORDER. Richard M R James, 10 Eastbrae Road, Littleover, Derby, DE23 1WA. 01332 771787; e-mail: rmrjames@yahoo.co.uk

Bird Reports
CARSINGTON BIRD CLUB ANNUAL REPORT, from The Secretary.

DERBYSHIRE BIRD REPORT (1954-), from Bryan Barnacle, Mays, Malthouse Lane, Froggatt, Hope Valley, Derbyshire S32 3ZA. 01433 630 726; e-mail: barney@mays1.demon.co.uk

OGSTON BIRD CLUB REPORT (1970-), from see contact for Ogston Bird Club below.

BTO Regional Representative
NORTH AND SOUTH. Dave Budworth, 121 Wood Lane, Newhall, Swadlincote, Derbys DE11 0LX. 01283 215 188; e-mail: dbud01@aol.com

Clubs
BAKEWELL BIRD STUDY GROUP. (1987; 80).Ken Rome, View Cottage, Wensley, Matlock, Derbys DE4 2LH. E-mail: viewcottage@lineone.net www.bakewellbirdstudygroup.co.uk
Meetings: 7.30pm, 2nd Monday of the month, Friends Meeting House, Bakewell.

BUXTON FIELD CLUB. (1946; 68). B Aries, 1 Horsefair Avenue, Chapel-en-le-Frith, High Peak, Derbys SK23 9SQ. 01298 815 291; e-mail: brian.aries@btinternet.com

Meetings: 7.30pm, Saturdays fortnightly (Oct-Mar), Methodist Church Hall, Buxton.

CARSINGTON BIRD CLUB. (1992; 257). Paul Hicking (Secretary), 12 Beaurepaire Crescent, Belper, DerbyshireDE5 1HR. 01773 827 727; e-mail: membership@carsingtonbirdclub.co.uk www.carsingtonbirdclub.co.uk
Meetings: 3rd Tuesday of the month (Sep-Mar), Hognaston Village Hall, (Apr-Aug), outdoors.

DERBYSHIRE ORNITHOLOGICAL SOCIETY. (1954; 550). Steve Shaw, 84 Moorland View Road, Walton, Chesterfield, Derbys S40 3DF. 01246 236 090; e-mail: steveshaw84mvr@btinternet.com www.derbyshireOS.org.uk
Meetings: 7.30pm, last Friday of the winter months, various venues.

OGSTON BIRD CLUB. (1969; 1,126). Peter Birley, 35 Rosemary Drive, Alvaston, Derby, DE24 0TA. 01332 753 078; e-mail: peter.birley@sky.com www.ogstonbirdclub.co.uk

SOUTH PEAK RAPTOR STUDY GROUP. (1998; 12). M E Taylor, 76 Hawksley Avenue, Newbold, Chesterfield, Derbys S40 4TL. 01246 277 749.

Ringing Groups
DARK PEAK RG. W M Underwood, Ivy Cottage, 15 Broadbottom Road, Mottram-in-Longdendale, Hyde, Cheshire SK14 6JB.
E-mail: w.m.underwood@talk21.com

SORBY-BRECK RG. Dr Geoff P Mawson, Moonpenny Farm, Farwater Lane, Dronfield, Sheffield S18 1RA. E-mail: moonpenny@talktalk.net www.sorbybreckringinggroup.co.uk

SOUDER RG. Dave Budworth, 121 Wood Lane, Newhall, Swadlincote, Derbys DE11 0LX. E-mail: dbud01@aol.com

RSPB Local Groups
CHESTERFIELD. (1987; 274). Alan Goddard. 01246 230 244; e-mail: alandgoddard10@btinternet.com www.rspb.org.uk/groups/chesterfield
Meetings: 7.15pm, usually 3rd Monday of the month, Winding Wheel, New Exhibition Centre, 13 Holywell Street, Chesterfield.

DERBY LOCAL GROUP. (1973; 500). Chris Hunt, 38 Spenbeck Drive, Allestree, Derby, DE22 2UH. 01332 551 701; e-mail: chris.hunt42@ntlworld.com www.rspb.org.uk/groups/derby
Meetings: 7.30pm, 2nd Wednesday of the month (Sep-Apr), Broughton Suite, Grange Banqueting Suite, 457 Burton Road, Littleover, Derby DE23 6FL.

HIGH PEAK. (1974; 160). Jim Jeffery. 0161 494 5367; e-mail: henrygordon@live.co.uk www.rspb.org.uk/groups/highpeak
Meetings: 7.30pm, 3rd Monday of the month (Sep-May), Marple Senior Citizens Hall, Memorial Park, Marple, STOCKPORT SK6 6BA.

ENGLAND

Wetland Bird Survey Organiser
DERBYSHIRE. Position Vacant.

Wildlife Trust
DERBYSHIRE WILDLIFE TRUST. (1962; 14,000). East Mill, Bridge Foot, Belper, Derbyshire DE56 1XH. 01773 881 188; e-mail: enquiries@derbyshirewt.co.uk www.derbyshirewildlifetrust.org.uk

DEVON

BirdAtlas/Avifauna
BIRDS of DEVON by Michael Tyler (Devon Birdwatching & Preservation Society, 2010).

Tetrad Atlas of Breeding Birds of Devon by H P Sitters (Devon Birdwatching & Preservation Society, 1988).

The Birds of Lundy by Tim Davis and Tim Jones 2007. Available from R M Young (Bookseller) on 01769 573350 (see www.birdsoflundy.org.uk for further details)

Bird Recorder
Steve Waite, 38 Durley Road, Seaton, Devon EX12 2HW. 01297 20326; e-mail: recorder@devonbirds.org www.devonbirds.org/

Bird Reports
DEVON BIRD REPORT (1929-) from Mrs Joy Vaughan, 28 Fern Meadow, Okehampton, Devon, EX20 1PB. 01837 53360; e-mail: joy@vaughan411.freeserve.co.uk www.devonbirds.org

LUNDY FIELD SOCIETY ANNUAL REPORT (1947-). £3 each inc postage, check website for availability, from Frances Stuart, 3 Lower Linden Road, Clevedon, North Somerset BS21 7SU; E-mail: lfssec@hotmail.co.uk

BTO Regional Representative
Stella Beavan. 07710 879 277; e-mail: stella@treedown.eclipse.co.uk

BTO Garden BirdWatch Ambassadors
NORTH. David Gayton;
e-mail: gayton881@btinternet.com
SOUTH. Martin Overy;
e-mail: martin@martin-overy.co.uk

Clubs
DEVON BIRD WATCHING & PRESERVATION SOCIETY. (1928; 1200). Mrs Joy Vaughan, 28 Fern Meadow, Okehampton, Devon, EX20 1PB. 01837 53360; www.devonbirds.org e-mail: joy@vaughan411.freeserve.co.uk

KINGSBRIDGE & DISTRICT NATURAL HISTORY SOCIETY. (1989; 130). Martin Catt, Migrants Rest, East Prawle, Kingsbridge, Devon TQ7 2DB. 01548 511 443;

e-mail: martin.catt@btinternet.com
Meeting: 4th Monday of Sept-Apr, 7.30pm phone for venue.

LUNDY FIELD SOCIETY. (1946; 450). Mr Paul James,Hibernia,New Road,Pamber Green,TadleyRG26 3AG. E-mail: lfssec@hotmail.co.uk - www.lundy.org.uk
Meeting: AGM 1st Saturday in March, 1.45pm, Exeter University.

TOPSHAM BIRDWATCHING & NATURALISTS' SOCIETY. (1969; 140). Keith Chester (Membership Secretary). 01392 877 817; e-mail: tbnsociety@hotmail.com http://topshambns.blogspot.com
Meetings: 7.30pm, 2nd Friday of the month (Sep-May), Matthews Hall, Topsham.

Ringing Groups
DEVON & CORNWALL WADER RG. R C Swinfen, 72 Dunraven Drive, Derriford, Plymouth, PL6 6AT. 01752 704 184.

LUNDY FIELD SOCIETY. A M Taylor, 26 High Street, Spetisbury, Blandford, Dorset DT11 9DJ. 01258 857336; e-mail: ammataylor@yahoo.co.uk

SLAPTON BIRD OBSERVATORY. R C Swinfen, 72 Dunraven Drive, Derriford, Plymouth, PL6 6AT. 01752 704 184.

RSPB Local Groups
EXETER & DISTRICT. (1974; 466). Roger Tucker. 01392 860518; e-mail: parrog@aol.com www.exeter-rspb.org.uk
Meetings: 7.30p, various evenings, Southernhay United Reformed Church Rooms, Dix's Field, EXETER

PLYMOUTH. (1974; 600). Mrs Eileen Willey, 11 Beverstone Way, Roborough, Plymouth, PL6 7DY. 01752 208996; e-mail: edward.willey@sky.com

TORBAY AND SOUTH DEVON TEAM. John Allan. 01626 821 344; e-mail: john@morsey.f2s.com www.rspb.org.uk/groups/torbayandsouthdevon

Wetland Bird Survey Organisers
DEVON other sites. Peter Reay, Crooked Fir, Moorland Park, South Brent, Devon TQ10 9AS. 01364 73293; e-mail: peter.p.j.reay@btinternet.com

TAMAR COMPLEX. Gladys Grant, 18 Orchard Crescent, Oreston, Plymouth, PL9 7NF. 01752 406 287; e-mail: gladysgrant@talktalk.net

TAW/TORRIDGE ESTUARY. Terry Chaplin. 01271 342 590; e-mail: terry@chaplin.eclipse.co.uk

Wildlife Hospital
BIRD OF PREY CASUALTY CENTRE. Mrs J E L Vinson, Crooked Meadow, Stidston Lane, South Brent, Devon, TQ10 9JS. 01364 72174. Birds of prey, with emergency advice on other species. Aviaries, rehabilitation facilities. Veterinary support.

ENGLAND

Wildlife Trust
DEVON WILDLIFE TRUST. (1962; 33,000). Cricklepit, Commercial Road, Exeter, EX2 4AB. 01392 279244 (fax) 01392 433221; e-mail: contactus@devonwildlifetrust.org www.devonwildlifetrust.org

DORSET

BirdAtlas/Avifauna
Dorset Breeding Bird Atlas (working title). In preparation.

The Birds of Dorset by Dr George Green (Christopher Helm 2004).

Bird Recorder
Kevin Lane. E-mail: kevin@broadstoneheath.co.uk

Bird Reports
DORSET BIRDS (1977-), from Neil Gartshore, Moor Edge, 2 Bere Road, Wareham, Dorset BH20 4DD. 01929 552 560; e-mail: enquiries@callunabooks.co.uk

THE BIRDS OF CHRISTCHURCH HARBOUR (1956-), from Ian Southworth, 1 Bodowen Road, Burton, Christchurch, Dorset BH23 7JL.
E-mail: ianbirder@aol.com

PORTLAND BIRD OBSERVATORY REPORT, from Warden, see Reserves.

BTO Regional Representative
DORSET. Ieuan Evans (temporary). 01842 750 050; e-mail: ieuan.evans@bto.org

Clubs
CHRISTCHURCH HARBOUR ORNITHOLOGICAL GROUP. (1956; 275). Mr. I.H. Southworth, Membership Secretary, 1 Bodowen Road, Burton, Christchurch, Dorset BH23 7JL. 01202 478 093. www.chog.org.uk

DORSET BIRD CLUB. (1987; 525). Mrs Diana Dyer, The Cedars, 30 Osmay Road, Swanage, Dorset BH19 2JQ. 01929 421 402; e-mail: membership@ dorsetbirds.org.uk www.dorsetbirds.org.uk

DORSET NATURAL HISTORY & ARCHAEOLOGICAL SOCIETY. (1845; 2188). Dorset County Museum. High West Street, Dorchester, Dorset DT1 1XA. 01305 262 735; e-mail: secretary@dorsetcountymuseum.org www.dorsetcountymuseum.org

Ringing Groups
CHRISTCHURCH HARBOUR RS. E C Brett, 3 Whitfield Park, St Ives, Ringwood, Hants, BH24 2DX. E-mail: ed_brett@lineone.net

PORTLAND BIRD OBSERVATORY. Martin Cade, Old Lower Light, Portland Bill, Dorset, DT5 2JT. 01305

820553; e-mail: obs@btinternet.com www.portlandbirdobs.org.uk

STOUR RG. R Gifford, 62 Beacon Park Road, Upton, Poole, Dorset BH16 5PE.

RSPB Local Groups
BLACKMOOR VALE. (1981; 130). Alison Rymell, Group Leader. 01985 844 819; e-mail: alisonrymell@yahoo.co.uk www.rspb.org.uk/groups/blackmoorvale
Meetings: 7.30pm, 3rd Friday in the month, Gillingham Primary School.

EAST DORSET. (1974; 435). Hugh Clark. 01202 532595; e-mail: hugh.clark@hotmail.co.uk www.rspb.org.uk/groups/eastdorset
Meetings: 7.30pm, 2nd Wednesday of the month, St Mark's Church Hall, Talbot Village, Wallisdown, Bournemouth.

POOLE. (1982; 305). John Derricott, 49 Medbourne Close, Blandford, Dorset DT11 7UA. 01258 450 927; e-mail: derricott1969@sky.com www.rspb.org.uk/groups/poole
Meetings: 7.30pm, Upton Community Centre, Poole Road, Upton.

SOUTH DORSET. (1976; 422). Andrew Parsons. 01305 772 678; e-mail: andrew_parsons_141@yahoo.co.uk www.rspb.org.uk/groups/southdorset
Meetings: 3rd Thursday of each month (Sep-April), St. Georges Church Hall, Fordington, DORCHESTER, Dorset, DT1 1LB.

Wetland Bird Survey Organisers
DORSET (excl estuaries). John Jones. E-mail: blackbirdcott@tiscali.co.uk

THE FLEET & PORTLAND HARBOUR. Steve Groves, Abbotsbury Swannery, New Barn Road, Abbotsbury, Dorset DT3 4JG. (W)01305 871 684; e-mail: swannery@gotadsl.co.uk

POOLE HARBOUR. Harold Lilley. 01202 889 633; e-mail: halilley@tiscali.co.uk

RADIPOLE & LODMOOR. Nick Tomlinson, e-mail: webs@bto.org

Wildlife Hospital
SWAN RESCUE SANCTUARY. Ken and Judy Merriman, The Wigeon, Crooked Withies, Holt, Wimborne, Dorset BH21 7LB. 01202 828 166. www.swan.jowebdesign.co.uk
24 hr rescue service for swans. Large sanctuary of 40 ponds and lakes. Hospital and intensive care. Veterinary support. Free advice and help line. Three fully equipped rescue ambulances. Rescue water craft for all emergencies. Viewing by appointment only.

Wildlife Trust
DORSET WILDLIFE TRUST. (1961; 25,000). Brooklands Farm, Forston, Dorchester, Dorset, DT2 7AA. 01305 264 620; e-mail: enquiries@dorsetwildlifetrust.org.uk www.dorsetwildlife.org.uk

ENGLAND

DURHAM

BirdAtlas/Avifauna
A Summer Atlas of Breeding Birds of County Durham by Stephen Westerberg/Kieth Bowey. (Durham Bird Club, 2000).

Bird Recorder
Mark Newsome, 69 Cedar Drive, Jarrow, NE32 4BF. E-mail: mvnewsome@hotmail.com

Bird Reports
BIRDS IN DURHAM (1971-), from D Sowerbutts, 9 Prebends Fields, Gilesgate, Durham, DH1 1HH. H:0191 386 7201; e-mail: d16lst@tiscali.co.uk

BTO Regional Representative
David L Sowerbutts, 9 Prebends Field, Gilesgate Moor, Durham, DH1 1HH. H:0191 386 7201; e-mail: david.sowerbutts@dunelm.org.uk

Club
DURHAM BIRD CLUB. (1975; 320). Paul Anderson, Chairman, 2 Hawsker Close, Tunstall Village, Sunderland SR3 2YD. E-mail: paulandcath29@aol.com
www.durhambirdclub.org
Meetings: Monthly indoor meetings (Sept-Apr), Durham Wildlife Trust HQ at Rainton Meadows, Houghton le Spring.

Ringing Groups
DURHAM DALES RG. J R Hawes, Fairways, 5 Raby Terrace, Willington, Crook, Durham DL15 0HR.

RSPB Local Groups
DARLINGTON. (2005). Clifford Evans. 01325 466 471; e-mail: cgevans@talktalk.net
www.communigate.co.uk/ne/darlingtonrspbgroup
Meetings: 1st Thursday of the month (Sept-July), Cockerton Methodist Church, Cockerton Green, Darlington.

DURHAM. (1974; 125). Richard Cowen. 0191 377 2061; e-mail: richardcowen2002@yahoo.co.uk
www.durham-rspb.org.uk
Meetings: 7.30pm, 2nd Tuesday of the month (Oct-Mar), Room CG83, adjacent to Scarborough Lecture Theatre, University Science Site, Stockton Road entrance.

Wetland Bird Survey Organiser
DURHAM. Position vacant.

Wildlife Trust
DURHAM WILDLIFE TRUST. (1971; 4,000). Rainton Meadows, Chilton Moor, Houghton-le-Spring, Tyne & Wear, DH4 6PU. 0191 584 3112; e-mail: mail@durhamwt.co.uk
www.durhamwt.co.uk

ESSEX

Bird Atlas/Avifauna
Tetrad Atlas of Breeding Birds of Essex by M K Dennis (Essex Birdwatching Society, 1996).

The Birds of Essex by Simon Wood (A&C Black, August 2007).

Bird Recorder
Les Steward, 6 Creek View, Basildon, Essex SS16 4RU. 01268 551 464, E-mail: les.steward@btinternet.com

Bird Report
ESSEX BIRD REPORT (inc Bradwell Bird Obs records) (1950-), from Peter Dwyer, Sales Officer, 48 Churchill Avenue, Halstead, Essex, CO9 2BE. 01787 476 524; e-mail: petedwyer@petedwyer.plus.com

BTO Regional Representatives
NORTH-EAST. Matthew Shuter. 01255 424 076; e-mail: btoexne@gmail.co.uk

NORTH-WEST. Graham Smith. 01277 354 034; e-mail: silaum.silaus@tiscali.co.uk

SOUTH. Position vacant.

Club
ESSEX BIRDWATCHING SOCIETY. (1949; 700). John and Louise Sykes, Joint General Secretary, 14 Acres End, Chelmsford, Essex CM1 2XR.
E-mail: john.sykes@btinternet.com
www.essexbirdwatchsoc.co.uk
Meetings: 1st Friday of the month (Oct-Mar), Friends' Meeting House, Rainsford Road, Chelmsford.

Ringing Groups
ABBERTON RG. C P Harris, Wyandotte, Seamer Road, Southminster, Essex, CM0 7BX.

BRADWELL BIRD OBSERVATORY. C P Harris, Wyandotte, Seamer Road, Southminster, Essex, CM0 7BX.

RSPB Local Groups
CHELMSFORD AND CENTRAL ESSEX. (1976; 1200). Graham Webster. 01621 843 799; e-mail: gjwebster123@aol.com
www.rspb.org.uk/groups/chelmsford
Meetings: 8pm, Thursdays, eight times a year. The Cramphorn Theatre, Chelmsford.

COLCHESTER. (1981; 220). Mr Russell Leavett, 10 Grove Road, Brantham, Manningtree, Essex CO11 1TX. 01206 399 059; e-mail: rleavett@btinternet.com
www.rspb.org.uk/groups/colchester
Meetings: 7.45pm, 2nd Thursday of the month (Sep-Apr), Shrub End Community Hall, Shrub End Road, Colchester. Regular coach and car trips to local birding sites and those further afield.

SOUTH EAST ESSEX. (1983; 200). Graham Mee, 34 Park View Drive, Leigh on Sea, Essex SS9 4TU. 01702 525 152; e-mail: grahamm@southendrspb.co.uk

243

www.southeastrspb.org.uk
Meetings: 7.30pm, usually 1st Tuesday of the month (Sep-May), Belfairs School Hall, School Way, Leigh-on-Sea SS9 4HX.

Wetland Bird Survey Organisers
CROUCH/ROACH ESTUARY and SOUTH DENGIE. Peter Mason, e-mail: Petermason32@waitrose.com

HAMFORD WATER. Julian Novorol, e-mail: webs@bto.org

LEE VALLEY. Cath Patrick. 01992 709 882; e-mail: cpatrick@leevalleypark.org.uk

NORTH BLACKWATER. John Thorogood. 01206 768 771, e-mail: webs@bto.org

SOUTH BLACKWATER AND NORTH DENGIE. Anthony Harbott. 01992 575 213; e-mail: anthonyharbott@talktalk.net

STOUR ESTUARY. Rick Vonk, 01473 328 006; e-mail: rick.vonk@rspb.org.uk

THAMES ESTUARY — Foulness. Chris Lewis, e-mail: cpm.lewis@ukonline.co.uk

Wildlife Trust
ESSEX WILDLIFE TRUST. (1959; 36,000). The Joan Elliot Visitor Centre, Abbots Hall Farm, Great Wigborough, Colchester, CO5 7RZ. 01621 862 960; e-mail: admin@essexwt.org.uk
www.essexwt.org.uk

GLOUCESTERSHIRE

Bird Atlas/Avifauna
Atlas of Breeding Birds of the North Cotswolds. (North Cotswold Ornithological Society, 1990)

Birds of The Cotswolds. A New Breeding Atlas, by I.Main, D.Pearce et al. for NCOS (Liverpool University Press 2009).

Bird Recorder
GLOUCESTERSHIRE EXCLUDING S.GLOS (AVON). Richard Baatsen. E-mail: baatsen@surfbirder.com

Bird Reports
CHELTENHAM BIRD CLUB BIRD REPORT (1998-2001) - no longer published.

GLOUCESTERSHIRE BIRD REPORT (1963-). £7.50 including postage, from David Cramp, 2 Ellenor Drive, Alderton, Tewkesbury, GL20 8NZ.
E-mail: djcramp@btinternet.com

NORTH COTSWOLD ORNITHOLOGICAL SOCIETY ANNUAL REPORT (1983-), from T Hutton, 15 Green Close, Childswickham, Broadway, Worcs, WR12 7JJ. 01386 858 511.

BTO Regional Representative
Mike Smart, 01452 421 131; e-mail: smartmike@btinternet.com

Clubs
CHELTENHAM BIRD CLUB. (1976; 94). Membership Secretary. 01451 850 385.
www.cheltenhambirdclub.org.uk
Meetings: 7.15pm, Mondays (Oct-Mar), Bournside School, Warden Hill Road, Cheltenham.

DURSLEY BIRDWATCHING & PRESERVATION SOCIETY. (1953; 350). Jennifer Rogers, 15 Shadwell, Uley, Dursley, Glos GL11 5BW. 01453 860 128; e-mail: j.rogers1@btinternet.com
www.dursleybirdwatchers.btik.co.uk
Meetings: 7.45pm, 2nd and 4th Monday (Sept-Mar), Dursley Community Centre.

GLOUCESTERSHIRE NATURALISTS' SOCIETY. (1948; 500). Mike Smart, 143 Cheltenham Road, Gloucester, GL2 0JH. 01452 421 131; e-mail: smartmike@btinternet.com
www.glosnats.org.uk

NORTH COTSWOLD ORNITHOLOGICAL SOCIETY. (1982; 70). T Hutton, 15 Green Close, Childswickham, Broadway, Worcs WR12 7JJ. 01386 858 511.
Meetings: Monthly field meetings, usually Sunday 9.30pm.

Ringing Groups
COTSWOLD WATER PARK RG. John Wells, 25 Pipers Grove, Highnam, Glos, GL2 8NJ.
E-mail: john.wells2@btinternet.com

SEVERN ESTUARY GULL GROUP. M E Durham, 6 Glebe Close, Frampton-on-Severn, Glos, GL2 7EL. 01452 741 312.

WILDFOWL & WETLANDS TRUST. Richard Hearn, Wildfowl & Wetlands Trust, Slimbridge, Glos, GL2 7BT. E-mail: richard.hearn@wwt.org.uk

RSPB Local Group
GLOUCESTERSHIRE. (1972; 600). David Cramp, 2 Ellenor Drive, Alderton, Tewkesbury, GL20 8NZ. 01242 620 281; e-mail: djcramp@btinternet.com
www.rspbgloucestershire.co.uk
Meetings: 7.30pm, 3rd Tuesday of the month, Gala Club, Longford, Gloucester.

Wildlife Hospital
VALE WILDLIFE RESCUE - WILDLIFE HOSPITAL + REHABILITATION CENTRE. Any staff member, Station Road, Beckford, Tewkesbury, Glos GL20 7AN. 01386 882 288; e-mail: info@valewildlife.org.uk
www.valewildlife.org.uk All wild birds. Intensive care. Registered charity. Veterinary support.

Wetland Bird Survey Organisers
GLOUCESTERSHIRE (Inland). Mike Smart. 01452 421 131; e-mail: smartmike@btinternet.com

COTSWOLD WATER PARK. Gareth Harris, Cotswold Water Park Society, www.waterpark.org
e-mail: gareth.harris@waterpark.org

ENGLAND

Wildlife Trust
GLOUCESTERSHIRE WILDLIFE TRUST. (1961; 23,000).
Conservation Centre, Robinswood Hill Country Park,
Reservoir Road, Gloucester, GL4 6SX. 01452 383 333;
e-mail: info@gloucestershirewildlifetrust.co.uk
www.gloucestershirewildlifetrust.co.uk

HAMPSHIRE

Bird Atlas/Avifauna
Birds of Hampshire by J M Clark and J A Eyre
(Hampshire Ornithological Society, 1993).

Bird Recorder
RECORDER. Keith Betton, 8 Dukes Close, Folly Hill,
Farnham, Surrey GU9 0DR. 01252 724 068;
e-mail: keithbetton@hotmail.com

Bird Reports
HAMPSHIRE BIRD REPORT (1955-). 2008 edition
£12.10 inc postage, from Mrs Margaret Boswell, 5
Clarence Road, Lyndhurst, Hants, SO43 7AL. 023 8028
2105; e-mail: mag_bos@btinternet.com
www.hos.org.uk

BTO Regional Representative
Glynne C Evans, Waverley, Station Road, Chilbolton,
Stockbridge, Hants SO20 6AL. H:01264 860 697;
e-mail: hantsbto@hotmail.com

BTO Garden BirdWatch Ambassador
Alick Jones; e-mail: gbwhants@btinternet.com

Clubs

HAMPSHIRE
ORNITHOLOGICAL
SOCIETY. (1979; 1,500).
John Shillitoe, Honarary
Secretary, Westerly,
Hundred Acres Road,
Wickham, Hampshire PO17
6HY. 01329 833 086;
www.hos.org.uk
e-mail: john@shillitoe.freeserve.co.uk

SOUTHAMPTON & DISTRICT BIRD GROUP. (1994;
52). Dave Holloway, 73 Ampthill Road, Freemantle,
Southampton, SO15 8LN.
E-mail: david.holloway@solent.ac.uk
Meetings: Programme available.

Ringing Groups
FARLINGTON RG. D A Bell, 38 Holly Grove, Fareham,
Hants, PO16 7UP.

ITCHEN RG. W F Simcox, 10 Holdaway Close,
Kingsworthy, Winchester, SO23 7QH.
E-mail: wilfsimcox@gmx.com

RSPB Local Groups
BASINGSTOKE. (1979; 90). Peter Hutchins, 35
Woodlands, Overton, Whitchurch, RG25 3HN. 01256
770 831; (M)07895 388 378;

e-mail: fieldfare@jaybry.gotadsl.co.uk
www.rspb.org.uk/groups/basingstoke
Meetings: 7.30pm 3rd Wednesday of the month
(Sept-May), The Barn, Church Cottage, St Michael's
Church, Church Square, Basingstoke.

NEW FOREST. Dane Thomas. 01452 615 171;
e-mail: RSPB@newmilton.org
www.rspb.org.uk/groups/newforest
Meetings: 7.30pm 2nd Wednesday of the month
(Sept-June) Lyndhurst Community Centre, High
Street, LYNDHURST SO43 7NY

NORTH EAST HAMPSHIRE. (1976; 215). Sue
Radbourne. 01276 29 434;
e-mail: Mailto@northeasthantsRSPB.org.uk
www.northeasthantsrspb.org.uk
Meetings: See website.

PORTSMOUTH. (1974; 210). Gordon Humby, 19
Charlesworth Gardens, Waterlooville, Hants, PO7
6AU. 02392 353 949;
e-mail: PortsmouthRSPB@googlemail.com
www.rspb.org.uk/groups/portsmouth
Meetings: 7.30pm, 4th Saturday of every month.
St Andrews Church Hall, Havant Road, Farlington,
PORTSMOUTH, PO6 1AA

WINCHESTER & DISTRICT LOCAL GROUP. (1974;
120). Pam Symes, 29A Maytree Close, Badger Farm,
Winchester, SO22 4JE. 01962 851 821;
e-mail: psymes033@gmail.com
www.rspb.org.uk/groups/winchester
Meetings: 7.30pm, 1st Wednesday of the month (not
Jan or Aug), Shawford Parish Hall, Pearson Lane,
Shawford.

Wetland Bird Survey Organisers
AVON VALLEY. John Clark, 01252 623 397;
e-mail: johnclark50@sky.com

HAMPSHIRE (estuaries/coastal). John Shillitoe. 01329
833 086; e-mail: john@shillitoe.freeserve.co.uk

HAMPSHIRE (Inland - excluding Avon Valley). Keith
Wills, 01252 525 218;
e-mail: keithb.wills@ukgateway.net

ISLE OF WIGHT. Jim Baldwin. 01983 721 137;
e-mail: jimr.baldwin@tiscali.co.uk

Wildlife Trust
HAMPSHIRE & ISLE OF WIGHT WILDLIFE TRUST.
(1960; 28,000). Beechcroft House, Vicarage Lane,
Curdridge, Hampshire SO32 2DP. 01489 774 400;
e-mail: info@hmwt.org.uk - www.hwt.org.uk

HEREFORDSHIRE

Bird Recorder
Steve Coney, 5 Springfield Road, Withington,
Hereford, HR1 3RU. 01432 850 068;
e-mail: coney@bluecarrots.com

ENGLAND

Bird Report
THE BIRDS OF HEREFORDSHIRE (2004 -), from
Jim Wilkinson, Hon. Treasurer, Coughton Forge,
Coughton, Ross-on-Wye HR9 5SF.
www.herefordshirebirds.org

BTO Regional Representative
Chris Robinson, 01981 510 360;
e-mail: herefordbtorep@btinternet.com

Club
HEREFORDSHIRE ORNITHOLOGICAL CLUB. (1950; 439).
TM Weale, Foxholes, Bringsty Common, Worcester,
WR6 5UN. 01886 821 368;
e-mail: weale@tinyworld.co.uk
www.herefordshirebirds.org
Meetings: 7.30pm, 2nd Thursday of the month
(Autumn/winter), Holmer Parish Centre, Holmer,
Hereford.

Ringing Group
LLANCILLO RG. Dr G R Geen, Little Langthorns, High
Cross Lane, Little Canfield, Dunmow, Essex CM6 1TD.
01371 878 095; e-mail: grahamgeen@btinternet.com

Wildlife Hospital
HEREFORDSHIRE. Chris Robinson, 01981 510 360;
e-mail: herefordbtorep@btinternet.com

Wildlife Trust
HEREFORDSHIRE NATURE TRUST. (1962; 2,535). Lower
House Farm, Ledbury Road, Tupsley, Hereford, HR1
1UT. 01432 356 872;
e-mail: enquiries@herefordshirewt.co.uk
www.herefordshirewt.org

HERTFORDSHIRE

Bird Atlas/Avifauna
Birds at Tring Reservoirs by R Young et al
(Hertfordshire Natural History Society, 1996).

Mammals, Amphibians and Reptiles of Hertfordshire
by Hertfordshire NHS in association with Training
Publications Ltd, 3 Finway Court, Whippendell Road,
Watford WD18 7EN, (2001).

The Breeding Birds of Hertfordshire by K W Smith et
al (Herts NHS, 1993). Purchase from HNHS at £5 plus
postage. E-mail: herts.naturalhistorysociety@aol.com

Bird Recorder
David Bilcock. E-mail: birdrecorder@hnhs.org
www.hnhs.org/birds

Bird Report
HERTFORDSHIRE BIRD REPORT (1880-2006), from
Linda Smith, 24 Mandeville Road, Welwyn Garden
City, Herts AL8 7JU.
E-mail: herts.naturalhistorysociety@ntlworld.com
www.hnhs.org and www.hertsbirdclub.org.uk

BTO Regional Representative
Chris Dee, 26 Broadleaf Avenue, Thorley Park,
Bishop's Stortford, Herts, CM23 4JY. H:01279 755 637;

e-mail: hertsbto@hotmail.com
http://hertsbto.blogspot.com

BTO Garden BirdWatch Ambassador
Jean Crystal; e-mail: jeanlcrystal@aol.com
Simon Jones; e-mail: simon.l.jones@ntlworld.com
Myra Campbell;
e-mail: myra42campbell@googlemail.com

Clubs
FRIENDS OF TRING RESERVOIRS.
(1993; 400). Membership
Secretary, PO Box 1083, Tring
HP23 5WU. 01442 822 471; e-mail:
keith@fotr.org.uk
www.fotr.org.uk
Meetings: See website.

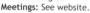

HERTFORDSHIRE BIRD CLUB. (1971; 330) Part of
Hertfordshire Natural History Society. Linda Smith, 24
Mandeville Rise,, Welwyn Garden City, Herts AL8 7JU.
01707 330 405;
e-mail: secretary@hnhs.org
www.hertsbirdclub.org.uk

HERTFORDSHIRE NATURAL HISTORY SOCIETY AND
HERTS BIRD CLUB. (1875; 320). Linda Smith, 24
Mandeville Rise, Welwyn Garden City, Herts, AL8 7JU.
01707 330 405; e-mail: secretary@hnhs.org
www.hnhs.org and www.hertsbirdclub.org.uk
Meetings: Saturday afternoon, Nov and Mar (date and
venue varies).

Ringing Groups
MAPLE CROSS RG. P Delaloye. E-mail: pdelaloye@
tiscali.co.uk

RYE MEADS RG. Chris Dee, 26 Broadleaf Avenue,
Thorley Park, Bishop's Stortford, Herts CM23 4JY.
H:01279 755637; e-mail: hertsbto@hotmail.com
www.rmrg.org.uk

TRING RG. Mick A'Court, 6 Chalkshire Cottages,
Chalkshire road, Butlers Cross, Bucks HP17 0TW.
01296 623 610; e-mail: mick_acourt@o2.co.uk

RSPB Local Groups
CHORLEYWOOD & DISTRICT. (1977; 142). Carol Smith,
24 Beacon Way, Rickmansworth, Herts WD3 7PE.
01923 897 885; e-mail: carolsmithuk@hotmail.com
www.rspb.org.uk/groups/chorleywood
Meetings: 8pm, 3rd Thursday of the month (Sept-
Nov, Jan-May), 2nd Thursday (Dec), Russell School,
Brushwood Drive, Chorleywood.

HARPENDEN. (1974; 1000). Geoff Horn, 41 Ridgewood
Drive, Harpenden, Herts AL5 3LJ. 01582 765 443;
e-mail: geoffrhorn@yahoo.co.uk
www.rspb.org.uk/groups/harpenden
Meetings: 8pm, 2nd Thursday of the month (Sept-
June), All Saint's Church Hall, Station Road,
Harpenden.

HEMEL HEMPSTEAD. (1972; 150). Ian Wilson, 15
Seymour Crescent, Hemel Hempstead, Herts, HP2
5DS. 07929 997 759; www.hemelrspb.org.uk

ENGLAND

e-mail: ian.aeronautics@gmail.com
Meetings: 8pm, 1st Monday of the month (Sep-Jun),The Cavendish School, Warners End, Hemel Hempstead.

HITCHIN & LETCHWORTH. (1973; 100). Dr Martin Johnson, 1 Cartwright Road, Royston, Herts SG8 9ET. 01763 249459; e-mail: martinrjspc@hotmail.com
Meetings: 7.30pm, 1st Friday of the month, The Settlement, Nevells Road, Letchworth SG6 4UB.

POTTERS BAR & BARNET. (1977; 1400). Lesley Causton, 57 Lakeside Crescent, East Barnet, Herts EN4 8QH. 0208 440 2038; www.pottersbar-rspb.org.uk
e-mail: lesleycauston@talktalk.net
Meetings: 2.00pm, 2nd Wednesday of the month, St Johns URC Hall, Mowbray Road, Barnet. Evening meetings, 3rd Friday of the month (not Jul, Aug or Dec) 7.45pm, Potters Bar United Reform Church, Tilbury Hall, Darkes Lane, Potters Bar, EN6 1BZ.

ST ALBANS. (1979; 1550 in catchment area). Peter Antram, 6 Yule Close, Bricket Wood, St Albans, Herts AL2 3XZ. 01923 678 534;
e-mail: peter@antram.demon.co.uk
www.rspb.org.uk/groups/stalbans
Meetings: 7.30pm, 2nd Tuesday of the month (Sep-May), St Saviours Church Hall, Sandpit Lane, St Albans.

SOUTH EAST HERTS. (1971; 2,400 in catchment area). Terry Smith, 31 Marle Gardens, Waltham Abbey, Essex, EN9 2DZ. 01992 715 634;
e-mail: se_herts_rspb@yahoo.co.uk
www.rspb.org.uk/groups/southeasthertfordshire
Meetings: 7.30pm, usually last Tuesday of the month (Sept-June), URC Church Hall, Mill Lane, Broxbourne EN10 7BQ.

STEVENAGE. (1982; 1300 in the catchment area). Mrs Ann Collis, 16 Stevenage Road, Walkern, Herts, 01483 861 547; e-mail: p.collis672@btinternet.com
www.rspb.org.uk/groups/stevenage
Meetings: 7.30pm, 3rd Tuesday of the month, Friends Meeting House, Cuttys Lane, Stevenage.

WATFORD. (1974; 590). Janet Reynolds. 01923 249 647; e-mail: janet.reynolds@whht.nhs.uk
www.rspb.org.uk/groups/watford
Meetings: 7.30pm, 2nd Wednesday of the month (Sep-Jun), St Thomas' Church Hall, Langley Road, Watford.

Wetland Bird Survey Organiser
HERTFORDSHIRE (excl. Lee Valley). Jim Terry. E-mail: jimjoypaddy@virginmedia.com

LEE VALLEY. Cath Patrick. 01992 709 882;
e-mail: cpatrick@leevalleypark.org.uk

Wildlife Trust
HERTS & MIDDLESEX WILDLIFE TRUST. (1964; 18,500). Grebe House, St Michael's Street, St Albans, Herts, AL3 4SN. 01727 858 901; e-mail: info@hmwt.org
www.wildlifetrust.org.uk/herts/

ISLE OF WIGHT

Bird Recorder
Robin Attrill, 17 Waterhouse Moor, Harlow, Essex CM18 6BA. E-mail: robin@rpattrill.freeserve.co.uk

Bird Reports
ISLE OF WIGHT BIRD REPORT (1953-) (Pre-1986 not available), from Mr DJ Hunnybun, 40 Churchill Road, Cowes, Isle of Wight, PO31 8HH. 01983 292 880;
e-mail: davehunnybun@hotmail.com

BTO Regional Representative
James C Gloyn, 3 School Close, Newchurch, Isle of Wight, PO36 0NL. 01983 865 567;
e-mail: gloynjc@yahoo.com

Clubs
ISLE OF WIGHT NATURAL HISTORY & ARCHAEOLOGICAL SOCIETY. (1919; 500). The Secretary, Unit 16, Prospect Business Centre, Prospect Business Centre, West Cowes, Isle of Wight PO31 7HD. 01983 823 855; www.iwnhas.org
e-mail: iwnhas@btconnect.com

ISLE OF WIGHT ORNITHOLOGICAL GROUP. (1986; 155). Mr DJ Hunnybun, 40 Churchill Road, Cowes, Isle of Wight, PO31 8HH. 01983 292 880;
e-mail: davehunnybun@hotmail.com

Wetland Bird Survey Organiser
ISLE OF WIGHT. Jim Baldwin. 01983 721 137;
e-mail: jimr.baldwin@tiscali.co.uk

Wildlife Trust
Director, See Hampshire,

KENT

Bird Atlas/Avifauna
The Birds of Kent by Taylor et al. Kent OS, 1981.

Bird Recorder
Barry Wright, 6 Hatton Close, Northfleet, Kent DA11 8SD. 01474 320 918 (M)07789 710 555;
e-mail: barrybirding@tiscali.co.uk

Bird Reports
DUNGENESS BIRD OBSERVATORY REPORT (1989-), from Warden, see Reserves.

KENT BIRD REPORT (1952-), from Chris Roome, Rowland House, Station Road, Staplehurst, KentTN12 0PY. 01580 891 686;
e-mail: chris.roome@zulogic.co.uk

SANDWICH BAY BIRD OBSERVATORY REPORT, from Warden, see Reserves,

BTO Regional Representative
Chris Robinson, 01981 510 360;
e-mail: herefordbtorep@btinternet.com

ENGLAND

Club

KENT ORNITHOLOGICAL SOCIETY. (1952; 650). Mr Martin Coath, 14A Mount Harry Road, Sevenoaks, Kent TN13 3JH. 01732 460 710; www. kentos.org.uk - e-mail: crag_martixn2000@yahoo.co.uk Meetings: Indoor: October-April at various venues; the AGM in April is at Grove Green community Hall, Grovewood Drive, Maidstone ME14 5TQ. See website for details: www.kentos.org.uk

Ringing Groups

DUNGENESS BIRD OBSERVATORY. David Walker, 01797 321 309; e-mail: dungeness.obs@tinyonline.co.uk www.dungenessbirdobs.org.uk

RECULVER RG. Chris Hindle, 42 Glenbervie Drive, Herne Bay, Kent, CT6 6QL. 01227 373 070; e-mail: christopherhindle@hotmail.com

SANDWICH BAY BIRD OBSERVATORY. Mr KB Ellis, 6 Alderney Gardens, St Peters, Broadstairs, Kent CT10 2TN. 01304 617 341; e-mail: keithjulie@talktalk.net

SWALE WADER GROUP. Rod Smith, 67 York Avenue, Chatham, Kent, ME5 9ES. 01634 865 836. www.swalewaders.co.uk

RSPB Local Groups

CANTERBURY. (1973; 216). Chris Sproul. 01227 450 655; e-mail: cyasproul@yahoo.co.uk www.rspb.org.uk/groups/canterbury Meetings: 8.00pm, 2nd Tuesday of the month (Sept-Apr), Chaucer Social Club, Off Chaucer Drive, Canterbury, CT1 1YW.

GRAVESEND & DISTRICT. (1977; 278). Jeffrey Kirk. 01474 365 757; www.rspbgravesend.org.uk e-mail: jeffandwendy28@btopenworld.com Meetings: 7.45pm, 2nd Wednesday of the month (Sep-May), St Botolph's Hall, North Fleet, Gravesend.

MAIDSTONE. (1973; 250). Dick Marchese, 11 Bathurst Road, Staplehurst, Tonbridge, Kent TN12 0LG. 01580 892 458; e-mail: marchese8@aol.com http://maidstone.localrspb.org.uk/ Meetings: 7.30pm, 3rd Thursday of the month, Grove Green Community Hall, Penhurst Close, Grove Green, opposite Tesco's.

MEDWAY. (1974; 230). Marie Tilley. 01634 387 431; e-mail: marie.tilley@btinternet.com www.medway-rspb.pwp.blueyonder.co.uk Meetings: 7.45pm 3rd Tuesday of the month (except Aug),Parkwood Community Centre, Parkwood Green, GILLINGHAM ME8 9PN

SEVENOAKS. (1974; 265). Anne Chapman. 01732 456 459; e-mail: anneanddave.chapman@virgin.net www.rspb.org.uk/groups/sevenoaks Meetings: 7.45pm 1st Thursday of the month, Otford Memorial Hall.

THANET. (1975; 119). Peter Radclyffe, Cottage of St John, Caterbury Road, Sarre, Kent CT7 0JY. 01843

847 345; e-mail: Hazel.johnson1@sky.com www.rspb.org.uk/groups/thanet Meetings: 7.30pm last Tuesday of the month (Jan-Nov), Portland Centre.

TONBRIDGE. (1975; 150 reg attendees/1700 in catchment). Gabrielle Sutcliffe. 01732 365 583; e-mail: martin@ellismp.plus.com www.rspb.org.uk/groups/tonbridge Meetings: 7.45pm 3rd Wednesday of the month (Sept-Apr), St Phillips Church, Salisbury Road.

Wetland Bird Survey Organisers

DUNGENESS AREA. David Walker, Dungeness Bird Observatory, 01797 321 309; e-mail: dungeness.obs@tinyonline.co.uk www.dungenessbirdobs.org.uk

EAST KENT. Ken Lodge, 01843 843 105; e-mail: lodge9pa@btinternet.com

PEGWELL BAY. Pete Findley, c/o Sandwich Bay Bird Observatory, 01304 379 074; e-mail: pwjfindley@hotmail.com

SWALE, MEADWAY & NORTH KENT MARSHES. Gordon Allison, e-mail: gordon.allison@rspb.org.uk

Wildlife Hospital

RAPTOR CENTRE. Eddie Hare, Ivy Cottage, Groombridge Place, Groombridge, Tunbridge Wells, Kent TN3 9QG. 01892 861 175; e-mail: raptorcentre@btconnect.com www.raptorcentre.co.uk Birds of prey. Veterinary support. 24hr rescue service for sick and injured birds of prey that covers the South-East.

Wildlife Trust

KENT WILDLIFE TRUST. (1958; 10500). Tyland Barn, Sandling, Maidstone, Kent, ME14 3BD. 01622 662 012; e-mail: info@kentwildlife.org.uk www.kentwildlifetrust.org.uk

LANCASHIRE

Bird Atlas/Avifauna

An Atlas of Breeding Birds of Lancaster and District by Ken Harrison (Lancaster & District Birdwatching Society, 1995).

Atlas of Breeding Birds of Lancashire and North Merseyside (2001), sponsored by North West Water. Contact: Bob Pyefinch, 12 Bannistre Court, Tarleton, Preston PR4 6HA.

Birds of Lancashire and North Merseyside by White, McCarthy and Jones (Hobby Publications 2008).

Bird Recorder

(See also Manchester).

LANCASHIRE (Inc North Merseyside). Steve White, 102 Minster Court, Crown Street, Liverpool, L7 3QD. 0151 707 2744; e-mail: stevewhite102@btinternet.com

ENGLAND

Bird Reports
BIRDS OF LANCASTER & DISTRICT (1959-), from
RSPB Leighton Moss shop and Lambert's, Rosemary
Lane, Lancaster (£8).,The Bramblings,1 Washington
Drive,WartonLA5 9RA. E-mail: ldbws@yahoo.co.uk
www.lancasterbirdwatching.org.uk

EAST LANCASHIRE ORNITHOLOGISTS' CLUB BIRD
REPORT (1982-) Members £2.50, Non-members £5.50,
from Tony Cooper, 28 Peel Park Ave, Clitheroe BB7
1ET; www.eastlancashireornithologists.org.uk

CHORLEY AND DISTRICT NATURAL HISTORY SOCIETY
ANNUAL REPORT (1979 -), published on website
www.chorleynats.org.uk

BLACKBURN & DISTRICT BIRD CLUB ANNUAL REPORT
(1992-), from Doreen Bonner, 6 Winston Road,
Blackburn, BB1 8BJ. 01254 261 480;
e-mail: webmaster@blackburnbirdclub.co.uk
www.blackburnbirdclub.co.uk

FYLDE BIRD REPORT (1983-), from Paul Ellis, 18
Staining Rise, Blackpool, FY3 0BU.
www.fyldebirdclub.org

LANCASHIRE BIRD REPORT (1914-), from Secretary,
Lancs & Cheshire Fauna Soc.

ROSSENDALE ORNITHOLOGISTS' CLUB BIRD REPORT
(1977-), from Secretary, Rossendale Ornithologists
Club, 25 Church St, Newchurch, Rossendale, Lancs
BB4 9EX. E-mail: info@rossendalebird.freeuk.com
www.rossendalebird.freeuk.com

BTO Regional Representatives
EAST. Tony Cooper, 28 Peel Park Avenue, Clitheroe,
Lancs, BB7 1ET. 01200 424 577;
e-mail: anthony.cooper@talktalk.net

NORTH & WEST. Jean Roberts. 01524 770 295;
e-mail: JeanRbrts6@aol.com

SOUTH. Stephen Dunstan.
E-mail: stephen-dunstan@tiscali.co.uk

Clubs
BLACKBURN & DISTRICT BIRD CLUB. (1991; 134). Jim
Bonner, 6 Winston Road, Blackburn, BB1 8BJ. 01254
261 480; e-mail: webmaster@blackburnbirdclub.co.uk
www.blackburnbirdclub.co.uk
Meetings: Normally 7.30pm, 1st Monday of the
month, (Sept-Apr), Church Hall, Preston New Road.
Check website for all indoor and outdoor meetings.

CHORLEY & DISTRICT NATURAL HISTORY SOCIETY.
(1979; 170). Phil Kirk, Millend, Dawbers Lane, Euxton,
Chorley, Lancs PR7 6EB. 01257 266783;
e-mail: secretary@chorleynats.org.uk
www.chorleynats.org.uk
Meetings: 7.30pm, 3rd Thursday of the month (Sept-
Apr), St Mary's Parish Centre, Chorley

EAST LANCASHIRE ORNITHOLOGISTS' CLUB. (1955;
45). Dr J Plackett, 71 Walton Lane, Nelson, Lancs BB9
8BG. 01282 612 870;

e-mail: j.plackett@eastlancsornithologists.org.uk
www.eastlancsornithologists.org.uk
Meetings: 7.30pm, 1st Monday of the month (Check
website or local press), St Anne's Church Hall, Fence,
Nr Burnley.

FYLDE BIRD CLUB (Registered
charity number 1102961). (1982;
110). Paul Ellis, 18 Staining Rise,
Blackpool, FY3 0BU. 01253 891281;
e-mail: paul.ellis24@btopenworld.
com or KBeaver@uclan.ac.uk
www.fyldebirdclub.org
Meetings: 7.45pm, 4th Tuesday of the month, River
Wyre Hotel, Breck Road, Poulton le Fylde.

FYLDE NATURALISTS' SOCIETY. (1946; 140). Julie
Clarke, 7 Cedar Avenue, Poulton-le-Fylde, Blackpool,
FY6 8DQ. 01253 883 785;
e-mail: secretary@fyldenaturalists.co.uk
www.fyldenaturalists.co.uk
Meetings: 7.30pm, fortnightly (Sep-Mar), Fylde Coast
Alive, Church Hall, Raikes Parade, Blackpool unless
otherwise stated in the Programme.

LANCASHIRE & CHESHIRE FAUNA SOCIETY. (1914;
150). Dave Bickerton, 64 Petre Crescent, Rishton,
Lancs, BB1 4RB. 01254 886257; www.lacfs.org.uk
e-mail: bickertond@aol.com

LANCASTER & DISTRICT BIRD WATCHING SOCIETY.
(1959; 200). Pete Marsh (Acting Secretary),Leck View
Cottage,Ashley's Farm,High TathamLA2 8PH. 01524
264 944; (M)0798 866 487; e-mail: PMrsh123@aol.com
www.lancasterbirdwatching.org.uk
Meetings: 7.30pm, last Monday of the month
(Sep-Nov, Feb-Mar), Bare Methodist Church Hall,
St Margarets Road, Morecambe; (Jan and Apr) the
Hornby Institute, Hornby.

PRESTON BIRD WATCHING & NATURAL HISTORY
SOCIETY. (1876 as the Preston Scientific Society;
140). Stephen R. Halliwell, 3 Baillie Street, Williams
Lane, Fulwood Park, Preston. 01772 705 468;
e-mail: stephenhalliwell@supanet.com
www.prestonsociety.co.uk
Meetings: Check website for details.

ROSSENDALE ORNITHOLOGISTS' CLUB. (1976; 35). Ian
Brady, 25 Church St, Newchurch, Rossendale, Lancs
BB4 9EX. 01706 222 120;
e-mail: info@rossendalebird.freeuk.com
www.rossendalebird.freeuk.com
Meetings: 7.30pm, 3rd Monday of the month,
Weavers Cottage, Bacup Road, Rawtenstall.

Ringing Groups
FYLDE RG. S. Eaves.

NORTH LANCS RG. John Wilson BEM, 40 Church Hill
Avenue, Warton, Carnforth, Lancs LA5 9NU.
E-mail: johnwilson711@btinternet.com

SOUTH WEST LANCASHIRE RG. I H Wolfenden,
01519 311 232.

RSPB Local Groups

BLACKPOOL. (1983; 170). Alan Stamford, 6 Kensington Road, Cleveleys, FY5 1ER. 01253 859 662; e-mail: alanstamford140@msn.com
Meetings: 7.30pm, 2nd Friday of the month (Sept-June), Frank Townend Centre, Beach Road, Cleveleys.

LANCASTER. (1972; 176). Michael Gardner. 01524 65211; e-mail: mgardner511@googlemail.com www.rspb.org.uk/localgroups/lancaster

Wetland Bird Survey Organisers

ALT ESTUARY. Steve White; e-mail: lwildlife@cix.co.uk

EAST LANCASHIRE AND FYLDE. Position vacant.

MORECAMBE BAY (SOUTH) & RIVER LUNE. Jean Roberts, 01524 770 295; e-mail: JeanRbrts6@aol.com

NORTH LANCASHIRE (INLAND). Peter Marsh, 7989 866 487; e-mail: pbmarsh@btopenworld.com

RIBBLE ESTUARY. Temporary LO Ken Abram; e-mail: k.abram@btinternet.com

WEST LANCASHIRE (INLAND). Tom Clare; e-mail: tom.clare@wwt.org.uk

Wildlife Trust

THE WILDLIFE TRUST FOR LANCASHIRE, MANCHESTER AND NORTH MERSEYSIDE. (1962; 18,000). Mr James Ellaby, Communications Officer, The Barn, Berkeley Drive, Bamber Bridge, Preston PR5 6BY. 01772 324 129; e-mail: info@lancswt.org.uk www.lancswt.org.uk

LEICESTERSHIRE & RUTLAND

The Birds of Leicestershire and Rutland by Rob Fray et al. (A&C Black, 2009)

Bird Recorder

Steve Lister, 6 Albert Promenade, Loughborough, Leicestershire LE11 1RE. 01509 829 495; e-mail: stevelister@surfbirder.com

Bird Reports

LEICESTERSHIRE & RUTLAND BIRD REPORT (1941-), from Mrs S Graham, 5 Lychgate Close, Cropston, Leicestershire LE7 7HU. 0116 236 6474; e-mail: JSGraham83@aol.com

RUTLAND NAT HIST SOC ANNUAL REPORT (1965-), from Secretary. 01572 747302.

BTO Regional Representative

LEICESTER & RUTLAND. David Wright, 01530 231 102; e-mail: wrig361@aol.com

Clubs

BIRSTALL BIRDWATCHING CLUB. (1976; 50). Mr KJ Goodrich, 6 Riversdale Close, Birstall, Leicester, LE4

4EH. 0116 267 4813; e-mail: kjgood1532@aol.com
Meetings: 7.30pm, 2nd Tuesday of the month (Oct-Apr), The Rothley Centre, Mountsorrel Lane, Rothley, Leics LE7 7PR.

LEICESTERSHIRE & RUTLAND ORNITHOLOGICAL SOCIETY. (1941; 580). Mrs Rosemary Rowley, 4 Orchard View, Mountsorrel, Leicester, LE12 7HW. 0116 230 2747; e-mail: rowleyrosemary@hotmail.com www.lros.org.uk
Meetings: 7.30pm, 1st Friday of the month (Oct-May), Oadby Methodist Church, off Central Car Park, alternating with The Rothley Centre, Mountsorrel Lane, Rothley. Additional meeting at Rutland Water Birdwatching Cntr.

SOUTH LEICESTER BIRDWATCHERS. (2006; 60). Paul Seaton, 76 Roehampton Drive, Wigston, Leics, LE18 1HU. 07973 156 060; e-mail: paul.lseaton@btinternet. com
Meetings: 7.30 pm, 2nd Wednesday of the month (Sep-Jun), County Scout Centre, Winchester Road, Blaby, Leicester LE8 4HN.

RUTLAND NATURAL HISTORY SOCIETY. (1964; 256). Mrs L Worrall, 6 Redland Close, Barrowden, Oakham, Rutland, LE15 8ES. 01572 747 302; e-mail: contactrnhs@btinternet.com - www.rnhs.org.uk
Meetings: 7.30pm, 1st Tuesday of the month (Oct-Apr), Oakham CofE School, Burley Road, Oakham.

Ringing Groups

RUTLAND WATER RG. Tim Appleton, Reserve Manager, Egleton, Oakham, Rutland LE15 8BT; e-mail: awbc@rutland water.org.uk

STANFORD RG. John Cranfield, 41 Main Street, Fleckney, Leicester, LE8 8AP. 0116 240 4385; e-mail: JacanaJohn@talktalk.net www.stanfordrg.org.uk

RSPB Local Groups

LEICESTER. (1969; 1600 in catchment area). Chris Woolass, 136 Braunstone Lane, Leicester, LE3 2RW. 0116 299 0078; e-mail: j.woolass1@ntlworld.com www.rspb.org.uk/groups/leicester
Meetings: 7.30pm, 3rd Friday of the month (Sep-May), Trinity Methodist Hall, Harborough Road, Oadby, LEICESTER, LE2 4LA

LOUGHBOROUGH. (1970; 300). Robert Orton. 01509 413 936; e-mail: Lboro.RSPB@virgin.net www.rspb.org.uk/groups/loughborough
Meetings: Monthly Friday nights, Loughborough University.

Wetland Bird Survey Organisers

LEICESTERSHIRE & RUTLAND (excl Rutland Water). Brian Moore, 01162 910 411 (afternoons only); e-mail: b_moore@ntlworld.com

RUTLAND WATER. Tim Appleton, Reserve Manager, 01572 770 651; e-mail: tim@rutlandwater.org.uk

ENGLAND

Wildlife Trust
LEICESTERSHIRE & RUTLAND WILDLIFE TRUST. (1956;
14,000). Brocks Hill Environment Centre, Washbrook
Lane, Oadby, Leicestershire LE2 5JJ. 0116 272 0444
(fax) 0116 272 0404; e-mail: info@lrwt.org.uk
www.lrwt.org.uk

LINCOLNSHIRE

Bird Recorders
JOINT RECORDER: John Clarkson.
E-mail: recorder_north@lincsbirdclub.co.uk

JOINT RECORDER: John Badley.
E-mail: recorder_south@lincsbirdclub.co.uk

Bird Reports

*LINCOLNSHIRE BIRD REPORT (1964-
), 1990 is now sold out, 2008 is
the latest report, £13.75 including
postage,* from Bill Sterling,
Newlyn, 5 Carlton Avenue,
Healing, NE Lincs DN41 7PW.
E-mail: wbsterling@hotmail.com

*LINCOLNSHIRE RARE AND SCARCE BIRD REPORTS
(1997-1999) & (2000-2002), £13.75 each including
postage.* Bill Sterling, Newlyn, 5 Carlton Avenue,
Healing, NE Lincs DN41 7PW.
E-mail: wbsterling@hotmail.com

*SCUNTHORPE & NORTH WEST LINCOLNSHIRE BIRD
REPORT (1973-),* from Secretary, Scunthorpe Museum
Society, Ornithological Section, (Day)01724 402 871
(Eve)01724 734 261.

BTO Regional Representatives
EAST. Philip Espin. 01507 605 448;
e-mail: philespin@live.co.uk

NORTH. Chris Gunn. 01777 707 888;
e-mail: donandchris@hotmail.co.uk

SOUTH. Hugh Dorrington. 01778 440 716;
e-mail: hdorrington@btconnect.com

WEST. Peter Overton, Hilltop Farm, Welbourn,
Lincoln, LN5 0QH. 01400 273 003;
e-mail: bto@hilltopfarmholidays.co.uk
Sponsoring the Kestrel in the Bird Atlas through
Biosearch Expeditions www.biosearch.org.uk

Club
LINCOLNSHIRE BIRD CLUB. (1979; 304). Robert Carr,
35 St Leonard's Close, Woodhall Spa, Lincs LN10 6SX.
E-mail: secretary@lincsbirdclub.co.uk
www.lincsbirdclub.co.uk
Meetings: Local groups hold winter evening meetings
(contact Secretary for details).

SCUNTHORPE MUSEUM SOCIETY (Ornithological
Section). (1973; 50). Keith Parker, 7 Ryedale Avenue,
Winterton, Scunthorpe, Lincs DN15 9BJ.
Meetings: 7.15pm, 3rd Monday of the month (Sep-
Apr), Scunthorpe Museum, Oswald Road.

Ringing Groups
GIBRALTAR POINT BIRD OBSERVATORY. Mr M.R.
Briggs. E-mail: mbriggs@gibobs.fsworld.co.uk

WASH WADER RG. P L Ireland, 27 Hainfield Drive,
Solihull, W Midlands, B91 2PL. 0121 704 1168;
e-mail: pli@blueyonder.co.uk

RSPB Local Groups
GRIMSBY AND CLEETHORPES. (1986; 2200 in
catchment area). Jenny Curtis. 014772 232 632;
e-mail: grimsbyRSPB@gmail.com
www.rspb.org.uk/groups/grimsby
Meetings: 7.30pm, 1st Monday of the month (Sept-
May), Corpus Christi Church Hall, Grimsby Road,
Cleethorpes, DN35 7LJ.

LINCOLN. (1974; 250). Peter Skelson, 26 Parksgate
Avenue, Lincoln, LN6 7HP. 01522 695747;
e-mail: peter.skelson@lincolnrspb.org.uk
www.lincolnrspb.org.uk
Meetings: 7.30pm, 2nd Thursday of the month (not
Jun, Jul, Aug, Dec), The Robert Hardy Centre, Bishop
Grosseteste College, Longdales Road, Lincoln.

SOUTH LINCOLNSHIRE. (1987; 350). Robert Townhill.
01400 230 445; www.southlincsrspb.org.uk
e-mail: robert.townhill@btinternet.com
Meetings: Contact group.

Wetland Bird Survey Organisers
HUMBER ESTUARY (INNER SOUTH). Keith Parker,
e-mail: webs@bto.org

HUMBER ESTUARY (MID SOUTH). Harriet Billanie,
01904 613 121; e-mail: harriet.billanie@rspb.org.uk

HUMBER ESTUARY (OUTER SOUTH). John Walker,
01507 338 038; (M) 07970 838421;
e-mail: webs@bto.org

NORTH LINCOLNSHIRE (INLAND). Position vacant.

SOUTH LINCOLNSHIRE/PETERBOROUGH (INLAND). Bob
Titman; e-mail: titman@nildram.co.uk

WASH - LINCOLNSHIRE. Jim Scott, 01485 542 689 ;
e-mail: jim.scott@rspb.org.uk

Wildlife Trust
LINCOLNSHIRE WILDLIFE TRUST. (1948; 26,000).
Banovallum House, Manor House Street, Horncastle,
Lincs, LN9 5HF. 01507 526 667; www.lincstrust.org.uk
e-mail: info@lincstrust.co.uk

LONDON, GREATER

Bird Atlas/Avifauna
The Breeding Birds of the London Area, 2002. ISBN
0901009 121 ed Jan Hewlett (LNHS, 2002).

Two Centuries of Croydon's Birds by John Birkett
(RSPB Croydon Local Group 2007). £10 plus p&p.

ENGLAND

Bird Recorder (see also Surrey)
Andrew Self, 16 Harp Island Close, Neasden, London, NW10 0DF. 07889 761 828; e-mail: a-self@sky.com http://londonbirders.wikia.com

Bird Report
CROYDON BIRD SURVEY (1995), from Secretary, Croydon RSPB Group, 020 8640 4578; e-mail: johndavis.wine@care4free.net www.croydon-rspb.org.uk

LONDON BIRD REPORT (20-mile radius of St Paul's Cath) (1936-), from Catherine Schmitt, Publications Sales, London Natural History Society, 4 Falkland Avenue, London N3 1QR. 020 8346 4359.

BTO Regional Representatives
LONDON, NORTH. Ian Woodward, 245 Larkshall Road, Chingford, London, E4 9HY. 07947 321 889; e-mail: ianw_bto_nlon@hotmail.co.uk

LONDON, SOUTH. Richard Arnold. 020 8224 1135; e-mail: bto@thomsonecology.com

Clubs
THE LONDON BIRD CLUB (formerly the Ornithological Section of the London Natural History Society). (1858; 1000). Mrs Angela Linnell, 20 Eleven Acre Rise, Loughton, Essex, IG10 1AN. 020 8508 2932; e-mail: angela.linnell@phonecoop.coop www.lnhs.org.uk
Meetings: See website.

MARYLEBONE BIRDWATCHING SOCIETY. (1981; 110). Marion Hill, 20 Howitt Close, Howitt Road, London NW3 4LX. E-mail: birdsmbs@yahoo.com www.birdsmbs.org.uk Meeting:2nd Friday of month (Sept-May), 7.15pm Gospel Oak Methodist Church, Lisburne Road, London NW3 2NT. Also programme of Saturday local and coach outings and weekly walks on Hampstead Heath.

Ringing Groups
LONDON GULL STUDY GROUP - (SE including Hampshire, Surrey, Susex, Berkshire and Oxfordshire). This group is no longer active but still receiving sightings/recoveries of ringed birds.. (Also includes Hampshire, Surrey, Sussex, Berkshire and Oxfordshire). No longer in operation but able to give information on gulls. Mark Fletcher, 24 The Gowans, Sutton-on-the-Forest, York, YO61 1DJ. E-mail: fletcher548@btinternet.com

RUNNYMEDE RG. D G Harris, 22 Blossom Waye, Hounslow, TW5 9HD; http://rmxrg.org.uk E-mail: daveharris@tinyonline.co.uk

RSPB Local Groups
BEXLEY. (1979; 180). Tony Banks, 15 Boundary Road, Sidcup, Kent DA15 8SS. 020 8859 3518; e-mail: tonybanks@fsmail.net

www.bexleyrspb.org.uk
Meetings: 7.30pm, 3rd Friday of the month, Hurstmere School Hall, Hurst Road, Sidcup.

BROMLEY. (1972; 285). Val Bryant, 11 Hastings Road, Bromley, Kent BR2 8NZ. 0208 462 6330; e-mail: valbryant5@gmail.com www.rspb.org.uk/groups/bromley Meetings: 2nd Wednesday of the month (Sep-Jun), 4th floor, Central Library Building, Bromley High Street.

CENTRAL LONDON. (1974; 250). Margaret Blackburn. 0208 866 5853; e-mail: mblackburn@tesco.net www.janja.dircon.co.uk/rspb Meetings: (Indoor) 2nd Thursday of the month (Sep-May), St Columba's Church Hall, Pont St, London SW1. See website for details of field meetings.

CROYDON. (1973; 4000 in catchment area). John Davis, 9 Cricket Green, Mitcham, CR4 4LB. 020 8640 4578; e-mail: johndavis.wine@care4free.net www.croydon-rspb.org.uk Meetings: 2nd Monday of each month at 2pm-4pm and again at 8pm-10pm at Old Whitgiftian Clubhouse, Croham Manor Road, South Croydon.

ENFIELD. (1971; 2700). Norman G Hudson, 125 Morley Hill, Enfield, Middx, EN2 0BQ. 020 8363 1431; e-mail: dorandnor@tiscali.co.uk www.rspb.org.uk/groups/enfield Meetings: 8pm, 1st Thursday of the month, St Andrews Hall, Enfield Town.

HAVERING. (1972; 270). Martin Runchman. 01767 690 093; e-mail: mrunchman@yahoo.com www.rspb.org.uk/groups/havering/ Meetings: 8pm, 2nd Friday of the month, Hornchurch Library, North Street, Hornchurch.

NORTH EAST LONDON. David Littlejohns. 0208 989 4746; e-mail: NelondonRSPB@yahoo.co.uk www.rspb.org.uk/groups/northeastlondon Meetings: 7.30pm, 2nd Tuesday of every month, Snaresbrook Primary School, Meadow Walk, South Woodford, LONDON, E18 2EN.

NW LONDON RSPB GROUP. (1983; 2000 in catchment area). Bob Husband, The Firs, 49 Carson Road, Cockfosters, Barnet, Herts EN4 9EN. 020 8441 8742. www.rspb.org.uk/groups/nwlondon Meetings: 8pm, Usually last Tuesday of the month, (Sep-Mar), Wilberforce Centre, St Paul's Church, The Ridgeway, Mill Hill, London, NW7 1QU.

PINNER & DISTRICT. (1972; 300). Ian Jackson, 6 Oakfield Avenue, Kenton, Harrow, Middx HA3 8TH. 020 8907 3513; e-mail: imnme@btinternet.com www.rspb.org.uk/groups/pinner/ Meetings: 8pm, 2nd Thursday of the month (Sept-May), Church Hall, St John The Baptist Parish Church, Pinner HA5 3AS.

RICHMOND & TWICKENHAM. (1979; 285). Roger Theobald. 0208 977 6343;

e-mail: RichmondRSPB@yahoo.co.uk
www.rspb.org.uk/groups/richmond
Meetings: 8.00pm, 1st Wednesday of the month, York
House, Twickenham.

Wetland Bird Survey Organiser
GREATER LONDON (EXCLUDING THE THAMES
ESTUARY). Helen Baker;
e-mail: helen.baker60@tiscali.co.uk

LEE VALLEY. Cath Patrick, 01992 709 882;
e-mail: cpatrick@leevalleypark.org.uk

SWALE, MEDWAY AND NORTH KENT MARSHES. Gordon
Allison; e-mail: Gordon.Allison@rspb.org.uk
THAMES ESTUARY - FOULNESS. Chris Lewis;
e-mail: cpm.lewis@ukonline.co.uk

Wildlife Trust
LONDON WILDLIFE TRUST. (1981; 7500). Skyline
House, 200 Union Street, London, SE1 0LX. 0207 261
0447; e-mail: enquiries@wildlondon.org.uk
www.wildlondon.org.uk

MANCHESTER, GREATER

Bird Atlas/Avifauna
Breeding Birds in Greater Manchester by Philip
Holland et al (1984).

Bird Recorder
RECORDER. Ian McKerchar, 42 Green Ave, Astley,
Manchester, M29 7EH. 01942 701 758;
e-mail: ianmckerchar1@gmail.com
www.manchesterbirding.com

Bird Reports
LEIGH ORNITHOLOGICAL SOCIETY BIRD REPORT
(1971-), from Mr D Shallcross, 28 Surrey Avenue,
Leigh, Lancs, WN7 2NN; www.leighos.org.uk
e-mail: chairman@leighos.org.uk

BTO Regional Representative
MANCHESTER. Steve Suttill, 94 Manchester Road,
Mossley, Ashton-under-Lyne, Lancashire OL5 9AY.
01457 836 360; e-mail: ianmckerchar1@gmail.com
www.manchesterbirding.com

Clubs
ALTRINGHAM AND DISTRICT NATURAL HISTORY
SOCIETY. Claire Joures (Secretary). 0161 928 4513.
Meetings: 7:30pm, Tuesdays, Hale Methodist Church
Hall, Oak Road, off Hale Road, Hale. 50p charge
includes refreshments.

GREATER MANCHESTER BIRD RECORDING GROUP.
(2002: 40) Restricted to contributors of the county
bird report. Ian McKerchar.
E-mail: ianmckerchar1@gmail.com
www.manchesterbirding.com

LEIGH ORNITHOLOGICAL
SOCIETY. (1971; 118). Mr D
Shallcross, 28 Surrey Avenue,
Leigh, Lancs, WN7 2NN.

E-mail: chairman@leighos.org.uk
www.leighos.org.uk
Meetings: 7.15pm, Fridays, Leigh Library (check
website for details).

ROCHDALE FIELD NATURALISTS' SOCIETY. (1970; 90).
Mrs D Francis, 20 Hillside Avenue, Shaw, Oldham OL2
8HR. 01706 843 685; e-mail:
secretary@rochdalefieldnaturalistssociety.co.uk
www.rochdalefieldnaturalistssociety.co.uk
Meetings: 7.30pm (Sept-Apr) at Cutgate Baptist
Church, Edenfield Rd, Rochdale. Yearly syllabus
(out after AGM in Sept) states dates of lectures and
outings.

STOCKPORT BIRDWATCHING SOCIETY. (1972; 80).
Dave Evans, 36 Tatton Road South, Stockport,
Cheshire, SK4 4LU. 0161 432 9513;
e-mail: windhover@ntlworld.com
Meetings: 7.30pm, last Wednesday of the month
(Sep-Apr), The Heatons Sports Club, Heaton Moor
Stockport.

Ringing Groups
LEIGH RG. A J Gramauskas, 21 Elliot Avenue,
Golborne, Warrington, WA3 3DU. 0151 929 215.

SOUTH MANCHESTER RG. Mr KR Grant.

RSPB Local Groups
BOLTON. (1978; 320). Barrie Shore.
E-mail: b.shore@sky.com
http://boltonrspb.users.btopenworld.com
Meetings: 7.30pm, Thursdays (dates vary),Canon
Slade School, Bradshaw Brow, BOLTON, BL2 3BP.

MANCHESTER. (1972;3600 in catchment area). Peter
Wolstenholme, 31 South Park Road, Gatley, Cheshire,
SK8 4AL. 0161 428 2175;
e-mail: Conservation@RSPBmanchester.org.uk
http://johnfair.brinkster.net/rspb/default.asp
Meetings: 7.30 pm, St James Parish Hall, Gatley
Green, Church Road, Gatley, Cheadle.

STOCKPORT LOCAL GROUP. (1979; 120). Gay Crossley,
5 Broadhill Close, Bramhall, Stockport, Cheshire
SK7 3BY. 0161 439 3210; e-mail: StockportRSPB@
googlemail.com - www.rspb.org.uk/groups/stockport
Meetings: 7.30pm, 2nd Monday of the month (Sep-
Apr), Stockport College of Technology, Lecture
Theatre B.

WIGAN. (1973; 80). Neil Martin. 01695 624 860;
e-mail: neimaz07@yahoo.co.uk
www.rspb.org.uk/groups/wigan
Meetings: 7.45pm. St Anne's Parish Hall, Church
Lane, Shevington, Wigan, Lancashire, WN6 8BD.

Wetland Bird Survey Organiser
GREATER MANCHESTER. Adrian Dancy. 0161 278 5381;
e-mail: webs@bto.org

Wildlife Trust
See Lancashire.

ENGLAND

MERSEYSIDE & WIRRAL

Bird Atlas see Cheshire

Bird Recorders see Cheshire; Lancashire

Bird Reports see also Cheshire
HILBRE BIRD OBSERVATORY REPORT, from Warden, see Reserves,

BTO Regional Representatives
MERSEYSIDE RR and RDO. Bob Harris, 3 Mossleigh, Whixalll, Whitchurch, Shropshire SY13 2SA. Work 0151 706 4311; e-mail: harris@liv.ac.uk

WIRRAL. Paul Miller. 01928 787 535; e-mail: paulandhilarymiller@live.co.uk

Clubs
MERSEYSIDE NATURALISTS' ASSOCIATION. (1938; 150). David Bryant, Chairman, 13, Strafford Drive, Bootle, Merseyside L20 9JN. 0151 523 5240; e-mail: chairman@mnapage.info www.mnapage.info
Meetings: 2-4pm, Saturday afternoons (Feb, Oct and Nov), Bootle Cricket Club, check website for details. 7-8 coach outings per year.

WIRRAL BIRD CLUB. (1977; 150). The Secretary. E-mail: wirralbirdclub@gmail.com www.wirralbirdclub.com

Ringing Groups
MERSEYSIDE RG. Bob Harris, 3 Mossleigh, Whixalll, Whitchurch, Shropshire SY13 2SA. Work 0151 706 4311; e-mail: harris@liv.ac.uk

SOUTH WEST LANCASHIRE RG. I H Wolfenden, 35 Hartdale Road, Thornton, Liverpool, Merseyside L23 1TA. 01519 311 232.

RSPB Local Groups
LIVERPOOL. (1966; 162). Chris Tynan, 10 Barker Close, Huyton, Liverpool, L36 0XU. 0151 480 7938 (M)07831 352 870; e-mail: christtynan@aol.com www.rspbliverpool.org.uk
Meetings: Indoor meetings, 7 for 7.30pm, 3rd Monday of the month (Sep-Apr), Mossley Hill Parish Church, Junc. Rose Lane and Elmswood Rd. Outdoor meetings visiting sites acress the north west.

SOUTHPORT. (1974; 300). Alan Toms. 01704 871 540; e-mail: tomsrspb@talktalk.net www.rspb.org.uk/groups/southport
Meetings: 7.45pm, 3rd Friday of the month, Lord Street West Church Hall, Duke Street, SOUTHPORT.

WIRRAL. (1982; 120). Jeremy Bradshaw. 0151 632 2364; e-mail: Info@wirralRSPB.org.uk www.rspb.org.uk/groups/wirral
Meetings: 7.30pm, 1st Thursday of the month,

Bromborough Civic Centre, 2 Bromborough Village Road, WIRRAL.

Wetland Bird Survey Organiser
MERSEY ESTUARY. Graham Thomason, e-mail: webs@bto.org

MERSEYSIDE (inland). Stephen Birch. 07779 862 821; e-mail: stevebirch1@live.co.uk

Wildlife Trust
See Lancashire.

NORFOLK

Bird Atlas/Avifauna
The Birds of Norfolk by Moss Taylor, Michael Seago, Peter Allard & Don Dorling (Pica Press, 1999, reprinted 2007).

The Norfolk Bird Atlas, Summer and Winter Distributions 1999-2007. M Taylor and JH Marchant. (BTO, 2011).

Bird Recorders
JOINT COUNTY RECORDERS. Dave and Jacquie Bridges, 27 Swann Close, Hempstead Road, Holt, Norfolk NR25 6DP. 01263 713 249; e-mail: dnjnorfolkrec@aol.com

Bird Reports
NAR VALLEY ORNITHOLOGICAL SOCIETY ANNUAL REPORT (1977-), from The Chairman, Ian Black.

NORFOLK BIRD & MAMMAL REPORT (1953-), from DL Paull, 8 Lindford Drive, Eaton, Norwich NR4 6LT. E-mail: info@nnns.org.uk - www.NNNS.org.uk

NORFOLK ORNITHOLOGISTS' ASSOCN ANNUAL REPORT (1961-), from Holme Bird Observatory, 01485 525 406, or NOA, Broadwater Road, Holme Next the Sea, Hunstanton, Norfolk, PE36 6LQ. E-mail: info@noa.org.uk

WENSUM VALLEY BIRDWATCHING SOCIETY (2003-), e-mail: admin@wvbs.co.uk www.wvbs.co.uk

BTO Regional Representatives
NORTH-EAST. Chris Hudson, Cornerstones, 5 Ringland Road, Taverham, Norwich, NR8 6TG. 01603 868 805 (M)07771 635 844; e-mail: Chris697@btinternet.com

NORTH-WEST. Bob Osborne. 01553 670 430; e-mail: rtoclass40@yahoo.co.uk

SOUTH-EAST. Rachel Warren. 01603 593 912; e-mail: campephilus@btinternet.com

SOUTH-WEST. Vince Matthews, Rose's Cottage, The Green, Merton, Thetford, Norfolk IP25 6QU. 01953 884 125; e-mail: norfolksouthwest@tiscali.co.uk

Clubs
CLEY BIRD CLUB. (1986; 500). Peter Gooden, 45 Charles Road, Holt NR25 6DA. 01263 712 368.

ENGLAND

Meetings: 8.00pm, Wednesdays, monthly (Dec-Feb), White Horse Hotel, Blakeney.

GREAT YARMOUTH BIRD CLUB. (1989; 30). Keith R Dye, 104 Wolseley Road, Great Yarmouth, Norfolk, NR31 0EJ. 01493 600 705.www.gybc.org.uk
Meetings: 7.45pm, 4th Monday of the month, Rumbold Arms, Southtown Road.

NAR VALLEY ORNITHOLOGICAL SOCIETY. (1976; 125). Ian Black, Three Chimneys, Tumbler Hill, Swaffham, Norfolk, PE37 7JG. 01760 724 092; e-mail: ian_a_black@hotmail.com www.accessbs.com/narvos - plus Facebook page and email group - narvalleyornithologicalsociety@yahoogroups.com
Meetings: 7.30pm, last Tuesday of the month (Jul-Nov and Jan-May), Barn Theatre, Convent of The Sacred Heart, Mangate Street, Swaffham, PE37 7QW.

NORFOLK & NORWICH NATURALISTS' SOCIETY. (1869; 630). The Secretary, Woodhouse, Free Lane, Ditchingham, Bungay NR35 2DW. www.NNNS.org.uk
Meetings: 7.30pm, 3rd Tuesday of the month (Oct-Mar), St Andrew's Church Hall, Church Lane, Norwich

NORFOLK ORNITHOLOGISTS' ASSOCIATION. (1962; 1100). Sophie Barker, Broadwater Road, Holme-next-Sea, Hunstanton, Norfolk PE36 6LQ. 01485 525 406; e-mail: info@noa.org.uk www.noa.org.uk

WENSUM VALLEY BIRDWATCHING SOCIETY. (2003; 125). Colin Wright, 7 Hinshalwood Way, Old Costessey, Norwich, Norfolk NR8 5BN. 01603 740 548; e-mail: admin@wvbs.co.uk - www.wvbs.co.uk
Meetings: 7.30pm, 3rd Thursday of the month, Weston Longville village hall.

Ringing Groups
BTO NUNNERY RG. Kate Risely, c/o BTO, The Nunnery, Thetford, Norfolk IP24 2PU. E-mail: kate.risely@bto.org

HOLME BIRD OBSERVATORY. Miss SA Barker. E-mail: info@noa.org.uk

NORTH NORFOLK FARMLAND STUDY & RINGING GROUP. Keith Herber, Laleham, 60 Dale End, Brancaster Staithe, Kings Lynn PE31 8DA. 01485 210 980; e-mail: keith.herber@btinternet.com
NORTH WEST NORFOLK RG. Mr J L Middleton, 8 Back Lane, Burnham Market, Norfolk PE31 8EY. E-mail: johnmiddleton@bmarket.freeserve.co.uk

SHERINGHAM RG. D Sadler, 26 Abbey Road, Sheringham, Norfolk, NR26 8NN. 01263 821 904.

WASH WADER RG. P L Ireland, 27 Hainfield Drive, Solihull, W Midlands, B91 2PL. 0121 704 1168; e-mail: pli@blueyonder.co.uk

RSPB Local Groups
NORWICH. (1971; 360). David Porter. 01603 745 310; e-mail: RSPBnorwichgroup@virginmedia.com www.rspb.org.uk/groups/norwich
Meetings: 7.30pm, 2nd Monday of the month (except Aug), Hellesdon Community Centre, Middletons Lane, Hellesdon, Norwich (entrance of Woodview Road).

WEST NORFOLK. (1977; 247). Neil Stephenson. 01553 828 752; e-mail: neilstephenson@onetel.com http://rspb-westnorfolk.org
Meetings: 7.15pm, 3rd Wednesday of the month (Sep-Apr), South Wootton Village Hall, Church Lane, South Wootton, King's Lynn.

Wetland Bird Survey Organisers
BREYDON WATER. Jim Rowe, 01493 700 645; e-mail: jim.rowe@rspb.org.uk

NORFOLK (OTHER SITES). Tim Strudwick, 01603 462 128 ; e-mail: strumpshaw@rspb.org.uk

NORTH NORFOLK COAST. Michael Rooney; e-mail: michael.rooney@naturalengland.org.uk

OUSE WASHES. Paul Harrington, 01354 680 212; e-mail: paul.harrington@rspb.org.uk

THE WASH. Jim Scott, 01485 542 689; e-mail: jim.scott@rspb.org.uk

Wildlife Trust
NORFOLK WILDLIFE TRUST. (1926; 35,000). Bewick House, 22 Thorpe Road, Norwich, Norfolk NR1 1RY. 01603 625 540; www.norfolkwildlifetrust.org.uk e-mail: info@norfolkwildlifetrust.org.uk

NORTHAMPTONSHIRE

Bird Atlas/Avifauna
The Birds of Northamptonshire. J.Blincow (privately published, 1990).

Bird Recorder
Position vacant, Enquiries to Mike Alibone, E-mail: northantsbirds@ntlworld.com

Bird Report
NORTHANTS BIRDS (1969-), from Mr John Coleman, 2 Marsons Drive, Crick, Northants NN6 7TD. 01788 822 905.

BTO Regional Representative
Barrie Galpin. 01780 444 351; e-mail: barrie.galpin@zen.co.uk

BTO Garden BirdWatch Ambassador
John Woollett; e-mail: jcwoollett@btinternet.com

Clubs
NORTHAMPTONSHIRE BIRD CLUB. (1973; 100). http://sites.google.com/site/northantsbirdclub/
Meetings: 7.30pm, 1st Wednesday of the month.

ENGLAND

Moulton Community Sports Centre, Pound Lane, Moulton, Northants.

Ringing Group
NORTHANTS RG. D M Francis, 2 Brittons Drive, Billing Lane, Northampton, NN3 5DP.

STANFORD RG. John Cranfield, 41 Main Street, Fleckney, Leicester, LE8 8AP. 0116 240 4385; e-mail: JacanaJohn@talktalk.net

RSPB Local Groups
MID NENE. (1975; 350). Hilary Guy. 01536 516 422; e-mail: hilary@snowdrop.demon.co.uk
www.rspb.org.uk/groups/midnene
Meetings: 7.30pm, 2nd or 3rd Thursday of the month (Sep-Apr), The Saxon Hall, Thorpe Street/Brook Street, Raunds.

NORTHAMPTON. (1978; 3000). Liz Wicks, 6 Waypost Court, Lings, Northampton, NN3 8LN. 01604 513 991; e-mail: lizydrip@ntlworld.com
Meetings: 7.30pm, 2nd Thursday of the month, Northants County Council staff sports and social club (Wootton Hall Pavilion), Wootton Hall Park, Wootton NN4 0JA

Wetland Bird Survey Organiser
Jim Williams, 01203 402 121; e-mail: jim.williams4@btinternet.com

Wildlife Trust
See Cambridgeshire.

NORTHUMBERLAND

Bird Atlas/Avifauna
Northumbrian Birds. Thieir History and Status up to the 21st Century. I Kerr et al. (N&TBC, 2001).

The Atlas of Breeding Birds in Northumbria edited by J C Day et al (Northumberland and Tyneside Bird Club, 1995).

The Atlas of Wintering Birds in Northumbria. J Day & M Hodgson. (N&TBC, 2003).

Bird Recorder
Tim Dean, 2 Knocklaw Park, Rothbury, Northumberland NE65 7PW. 01669 621460 (M)07766 263167; e-mail: t.r.dean@btopenworld.com

Bird Reports
BIRDS IN NORTHUMBRIA (1970-), from Trevor Blake, 6 Glenside, Ellington, Morpeth, Northumberland NE61 5LS. 01670 862 635; e-mail: trevor.1958@live.co.uk

BIRDS ON THE FARNE ISLANDS (1971-), from Secretary, Natural History Society of Northumbria. 0191 2326386; e-mail: nhsn@ncl.ac.uk
www.nhsn.ncl.ac.uk

BTO Regional Representative & Regional Development Officer
Tom Cadwallender, 22 South View, Lesbury, Alnwick, Northumberland NE66 3PZ. H:01665 830 884 M: 07980 341 9412; e-mail: tomandmurielcadwallender@hotmail.com

RDO. Muriel Cadwallender, 22 South View, Lesbury, Alnwick, Northumberland NE66 3PZ. 01665 830 884; e-mail: tomandmurielcadwallender@hotmail.com

BTO Garden BirdWatch Ambassador
Val Tuck; e-mail: V.L.Tuck@newcastle.ac.uk

Clubs
NATURAL HISTORY SOCIETY OF NORTHUMBRIA. (1829; about 950). John Littlewood, NHS of Northumbria, Great North Museum, Hancock, Barras Bridge, Newcastle upon Tyne NE2 4PT. 0191 232 6386; e-mail: nhsn@ncl.ac.uk - www.nhsn.ncl.ac.uk
Meetings: Weekly indoor and outdoor meetings throughout the year, details can be found at www.nhsn.ncl.ac.uk

NORTH NORTHUMBERLAND BIRD CLUB. (1984; 210). Richard Narraway, Workshop Cottage, The Friary, Bamburgh, NE69 7AE. 01668 214 759; e-mail: ringouzel@northnorthumberlandbirdclub.co.uk
www.northnorthumberlandbirdclub.co.uk
Meetings: 7.30pm, 1st Friday of the month(Sept), 2nd Friday (Oct-Jun), Bamburgh Pavilion (below castle).

NORTHUMBERLAND & TYNESIDE BIRD CLUB. (1958; 270). Alan Tilmouth, 12 Stowe Gardens, Pegsworth, Morpeth, NE61 6TH. 01670 512 013; e-mail: ntbcorg@gmail.com - www.ntbc.org.uk
Meetings: 7.00pm, 2nd Thursday of the month (Sep-Apr), Newcastle Falcons Rugby Club, Brunton Road, Kenton Bank Foot, Newcastle upon Tyne NE13 8AF.

Ringing Groups
NORTHUMBRIA RG. Secretary. B Galloway, 34 West Meadows, Stamfordham Road, Westerhope, Newcastle upon Tyne NE5 1LS. 0191 286 4850.

Wetland Bird Survey Organisers
LINDISFARNE. Andrew Craggs, Lindisfarne NNR, 01289 381 470; e-mail: webs@bto.org

NORTHUMBERLAND COAST. Daniel M Turner, 0191 257 6680; e-mail: dan.m.turner@btopenworld.com

NORTHUMBERLAND (Inland). Steve Holliday; e-mail: steveholliday@hotmail.co.uk

Wildlife Hospitals
BERWICK SWAN & WILDLIFE TRUST. The Honorary Secretary, Windmill Way East, Ramparts Business Park, Berwick-upon-Tweed TD15 1TU. 01289 302 882; e-mail: swan-trust@hotmail.co.uk
www.swan-trust.org Registered charity. All categories of wildlife. Pools for swans and other waterfowl. Veterinary support.

Wildlife Trust
NORTHUMBERLAND WILDLIFE TRUST. (1962; 13,000).

The Garden House, St Nicholas Park, Jubilee Road, Gosforth, Newcastle upon Tyne, NE3 3XT. 0191 284 6884; e-mail: mail@northwt.org.uk
www.nwt.org.uk

NOTTINGHAMSHIRE

Bird Recorders
Andy Hall. E-mail: andy.h11@ntlworld.com

Bird Reports
LOUND BIRD REPORT (1990-) latest 2007 report £4, from Gary Hobson, 18 Barnes Avenue, Wrenthorpe, Wakefield, WF1 2BH. 01924 384 419; e-mail: gary.lbc1@tiscali.co.uk

BIRDS OF NOTTINGHAMSHIRE (1943-) - £8 for 2009, £3 for previous issues, plus p&p, from Ms Jenny Swindells, 21 Chaworth Road, West Bridgford, Nottingham NG2 7AE. 0115 9812 432; e-mail: j.swindells@btinternet.com
www.nottsbirders.net

NETHERFIELD WILDLIFE GROUP ANNUAL REPORT (1990-). £5 inc postage, from Mr N Matthews, 4 Shelburne Close, Heronridge, Nottingham, NG5 9LL. www.netherfieldwildlife.org.uk

BTO Regional Representative
Mrs Lynda Milner, 6 Kirton Park, Kirton, Newark, Notts NG22 9LR. 01623 862 025; e-mail: milner.lynda@googlemail.com

BTO Garden BirdWatch Ambassador
Colin Harwood; e-mail: C.Harwood1@btinternet.com

Clubs
LOUND BIRD CLUB. (1991; 50). Gary Hobson, 18 Barnes Avenue, Wrenthorpe, Wakefield, WF1 2BH. 01924 384 419; e-mail: loundbirdclub@btinternet.com
http://loundbirdclub.webs.com
Meetings: Various walks and talks throughout the year, see website for details.

NETHERFIELD WILDLIFE GROUP. (1999; 130). Philip Burnham, 57 Tilford Road, Newstead Village, Nottingham, NG15 0BU. 01623 401 980 (M)07765 369 590; e-mail: philb50@fastmail.fm
www.netherfieldwildlife.org.uk

NOTTINGHAMSHIRE BIRDWATCHERS. (1935; 360). Ms Jenny Swindells, 21 Chaworth Road, West Bridgford, Nottingham, NG2 7AE. 0115 9812 432; www.nottsbirders.net
e-mail: j.swindells@btinternet.com
Meetings and events: Please see website for details.

WOLLATON NATURAL HISTORY SOCIETY. (1976; 86). Mrs P Price, 33 Coatsby Road, Hollycroft, Kimberley, Nottingham NG16 2TH. 0115 938 4965.
Meetings: 7.30pm, 3rd Wednesday of the month, St

Leonards Community Centre, Wollaton Village, HG8 2ND.

Integrated Population Monitoring Group
TRESWELL WOOD INTEGRATED POPULATION MONITORING GROUP. Chris du Feu, 66 High Street, Beckingham, Notts, DN10 4PF.
E-mail: chris@chrisdufeu.force9.co.uk

Ringing Groups
BIRKLANDS RG. A Ashley, 39 Winkburn Road, Mansfield, Notts NG19 6SJ. 07794 179 494; e-mail: alowe@nottswt.co.uk

NORTH NOTTS RG. Adrian Blackburn, Willows End, 27 Palmer Road, Retford, Notts DN22 6SS. 01777 706516 (M)07718 766873:; e-mail: adrian.blackburn@sky.com

SOUTH NOTTINGHAMSHIRE RG. K J Hemsley, 8 Grange Farm Close, Toton, Beeston, Notts NG9 6EB.
E-mail: k.hemsley@ntlworld.com

RSPB Local Groups
MANSFIELD LOCAL GROUP. (1986; 200). John Barlow, 240 Southwell Road West, Mansfield, NG18 4LB. 01623 626 647; e-mail: Terri-Cumberland@supanet.com
www.rspb.org.uk/groups/mansfield
Meetings: 7pm, 1st Wednesday of the month (Sep-Jun), Bridge St Methodist Church, Rock Valley, Mansfield.

NOTTINGHAM. (1974; 290). Penny Cross, 93 Hilton Road, Nottingham, NG3 6AQ. 0115 960 4205; e-mail: pennyguilbert@hotmail.com
www.notts-rspb.org.uk
Meetings: 7.30pm, 1st Wed of month (Sept - May). Nottingham Mechanics, North Sherwood St. Nottingham, NG1 4EZ.

Wetland Bird Survey Organiser
Gary Hobson, e-mail: webs@bto.org

Wildlife Trust
NOTTINGHAMSHIRE WILDLIFE TRUST. (1963; 4,300). The Old Ragged School, Brook Street, Nottingham, NG1 1EA. 0115 958 8242; e-mail: info@nottswt.co.uk
www.nottinghamshirewildlife.org.uk

OXFORDSHIRE

Bird Atlas/Avifauna
Birds of Oxfordshire by J W Brucker et al (Oxford, Pisces, 1992).

The New Birds of the Banbury Area by T G Easterbrook (Banbury Ornithological Society, 1995).

Bird Recorder
Ian Lewington, 119 Brasenose Road, Didcot, Oxon, OX11 7BP. 01235 819 792; e-mail: ian@recorder.fsnet.co.uk

Bird Reports
BIRDS OF OXFORDSHIRE (1921-), from Barry Hudson,

ENGLAND

Pinfold, 4 Bushy Row, Bampton, Oxon OX18 2JU. 01865 775 632.

BANBURY ORNITHOLOGICAL SOCIETY ANNUAL REPORT (1966-). £5 each including postage, from MJ Lewis, Old Mill Cottage, Avon Dassett, Southam, Warwickshire, CV47 2AE. 01295 690 643; e-mail: mikelewisad@hotmail.com

BTO Regional Representatives
NORTH. Frances Buckel, Witts End, Radbones Hill, Over Norton, Chipping Norton, Oxon OX7 5RA. 01608 644 425; e-mail: fran.buckel@btinternet.com

SOUTH. Mr John Melling, 17 Lime Grove, Southmoor, Nr Abingdon, Oxon OX13 5DN. E-mail: bto-rep@oos.org.uk

Clubs
BANBURY ORNITHOLOGICAL SOCIETY (includes parts of Northamptonshire, Oxfordshire and Warwickshire). (1952; 100). Frances Buckel, Witts End, Radbones Hill, Over Norton, Chipping Norton, Oxon OX7 5RA. 01608 644 425; e-mail: fran.buckel@btinternet.com www.banburyornithologicalsociety.org.uk **Meetings:** 7.30pm, 2nd Monday of the month,The Banbury Cricket Club, White Post Road, Bodicote OX15 4BN.

OXFORD ORNITHOLOGICAL SOCIETY. (1921; 330). Barry Hudson, Pinfold, 4 Bushy Row, Bampton, Oxon OX18 2JU. 01993 852 028; www.oos.org.uk e-mail: secretary@oos.org.uk **Meetings:** 7.45pm, various dates, Stratfield Brake, Kidlington.

Ringing Group
EDWARD GREY INSTITUTE. Dr A G Gosler, c/o Edward Grey Institute, Department of Zoology, South Parks Road, Oxford OX1 3PS. 01865 271 158; e-mail: andrew.gosler@zoo.ox.ac.uk

RSPB Local Groups
OXFORD. (1977; 100). Roy Grant, 23 St Christopher's Place, Cowley, Oxford OX4 2HS. 08865 774 659; www.rspb-oxford.org.uk **Meetings:** 7.45pm, normally 1st Thursday of the month, Sandhills Primary School, Terret Avenue, Headington, Oxford (opposite Thornhill park and ride).

VALE OF WHITE HORSE. (1977; 330). Philip Morris. 01367 710 285; www.rspb-vwh.org.uk **Meetings:** 7.45pm, 3rd Monday of the month (Sep-May). Steventon Village Hall, The Green, Steventon, ABINGDON OX13 3RR

Wetland Bird Survey Organiser
OXFORDSHIRE (North). Sandra Bletchly. E-mail: sandra.banornsoc@btinternet.com

OXFORDSHIRE (South). Ian Lees. 01865 311 104; e-mail: ianlees@me.com

Wildlife Trust
BBOWT. (1959; 24,000). The Lodge, 1 Armstrong Road, Littlemore, Oxford, OX4 4XT. 01865 775 476; e-mail: info@bbowt.org.uk - www.bbowt.org.uk

SHROPSHIRE

Bird Atlas/Avifauna
Atlas of the Breeding Birds of Shropshire (Shropshire Ornithological Society, 1992).
Bird Recorder
Geoff Holmes, 22 Tenbury Drive, Telford Estate, Shrewsbury, SY2 5YF. 01743 364 621; e-mail: geoff.holmes.4@btinternet.com

Bird Report
SHROPSHIRE BIRD REPORT (1956-) no recent editions. From Helen Griffiths (Hon Secretary), 104 Noel Hill Road, Cross Houses, Shrewsbury SY5 6LD. 01743 761 507; www.shropshirebirds.com

BTO Regional Representative
Allan Dawes, 01691 654 245; e-mail: allandawes@btinternet.com

BTO Garden BirdWatch Ambassadors
Cath Price; e-mail: Cath_Price@btinternet.com
John Arnfield; e-mail: arnfield.2@osu.edu
Trevor Blackshaw; e-mail: trevor.blackshaw@ssesurf.co.uk

Club
SHROPSHIRE ORNITHOLOGICAL SOCIETY. (1955; 800). Helen Griffiths, 104 Noel Hill Road, Cross Houses, Shrewsbury, SY5 6LD. 01743 761 507; e-mail: helen.griffiths@naturalengland.org.uk www.shropshirebirds.com **Meetings:** 7.15pm, 1st Thursday of month (Oct-Apr), Shirehall, Shrewsbury.

RSPB Local Group
SHROPSHIRE. (1992; 320). Roger M Evans. 01295 253 330; www.rspb.org.uk/groups/shropshire **Meetings:** 7.30pm, 4th Wednesday of the month (Sep-Apr), Council Chamber, Shirehall, Shrewsbury. Also field trip year round. 3rd Wednesday in the month (Oct-March) Secret Hills Centre Craven Arms.

SOUTH SHROPSHIRE Sub Group - CRAVEN ARMS. (1992; 320). Alvin Botting. 01547 540 176; e-mail: Christinelbateman@yahoo.com www.rspbsouthshropshire.co.uk **Meetings:** 7.30pm, 2nd Tuesday of the month (Sep-Apr), The Secret Hills Centre, School Road, CRAVEN ARMS SY7 9RS.

Wetland Bird Survey Organiser
SHROPSHIRE. Michael Wallace. 01743 369 035; e-mail: michaelwallace47@gmail.com

Wildlife Trust
SHROPSHIRE WILDLIFE TRUST. (1962; 10,000). 193

ENGLAND

Abbey Foregate, Shrewsbury SY2 6AH. 01743 284 280;
e-mail: enquiries@shropshirewildlifetrust.org.uk
www.shropshirewildlifetrust.org.uk

SOMERSET & BRISTOL

Bird Atlas/Avifauna
Atlas of Breeding Birds in Avon 1988-91 by R L Bland
and John Tully (out of print).

Bristol Ornithology no. 29, by Robin Prytherch (Bristol
Ornithological Club 2008).

The Birds of Exmoor and the Quantocks by D.K.
Ballance and B.D. Gibbs, 2003. (Isabelline Books,
2 Highbury House, 8 Woodland Crescent, Falmouth
TR11 4QS or or mikann@beakbool.demon.co.uk).

A History of The Birds of Somerset, by D.K.Ballance,
2006 (Isabelline Books as above).

Bird Recorders
SOMERSET. Brian D Gibbs, 23 Lyngford Road,
Taunton, Somerset, TA2 7EE. 01823 274 887; www.
somersetbirds.net
e-mail: brian.gibbs@virgin.net

BRISTOL, S GLOUCESTERSHIRE, BATH AND NE
SOMERSET, NORTH SOMERSET. John Martin, 34
Cranmoor Green, Pilning, Bristol BS35 4QF. 01454 633
040; (M)07767 867 341; www.boc-bristol.org.uk
e-mail: avonbirdrecorder@googlemail.com

Bird Reports
AVON BIRD REPORT (1977-), £8 plus postage, from
Harvey Rose, 01275 873 407;
e-mail: h.e.rose@bris.ac.uk

EXMOOR NATURALIST (1974-), from Secretary, Exmoor
Natural History Society. E-mail: carol.enhs@virgin.net

SOMERSET BIRDS (1912-) £7.50 inc p&p,, from
Somerset Ornithological Society, c/o Flat 2,
Dunboyne, Bratton Lane, Minehead, Somerset TA24
8SQ. 01643 706 820.

BTO Regional Representatives
AVON. Richard L Bland, 11 Percival Road, Bristol, BS8
3LN. Home/W:01179 734 828; e-mail: richardbland@
blueyonder.co.uk

AVON ASSISTANT REGIONAL REPRESENTATIVE. John
Tully, 6 Falcondale Walk, Westbury-on-Trym, Bristol,
BS9 3JG. 0117 950 0992; e-mail: johntully4@aol.com

SOMERSET. Eve Tigwell, Hawthorne Cottage, 3 Friggle
Street, Frome, Somerset BA11 5LP. 01373 451630;
e-mail: eve.tigwell@zen.co.uk

Clubs
BRISTOL NATURALISTS' SOCIETY
(Ornithological Section). (1862;
550). Hon. Secretary, 20 Harcourt
Hill, Redland, Bristol BS6 7RB.
01179 243 352. E-mail:

sec-brisnats@blueyonder.co.uk
www.bristolnats.org.uk
Meetings: 7.30pm, 2nd Wednesday in the mohth
(check for dates, Oct-Mar), Westmorland Hall,
Westmorland Road, Bristol

BRISTOL ORNITHOLOGICAL CLUB. (1966; 670). Mrs
Judy Copeland, 19 St George's Hill, Easton-in-
Gordano, North Somerset, BS20 0PS. 01275 373 554;
e-mail: judy.copeland@tiscali.co.uk
www.bristolornithologicalclub.co.uk
Meetings: 7.30pm, 3rd Thursday of the month,
Newman Hall, Grange Court Road, Westbury-on-Trym.

CAM VALLEY WILDLIFE GROUP. (1994: 356). André
Fournier, 1 Boomfield Lane, Paulton, Bristol BS39
7QU. 01761 148 153; e-mail: enquiries@cvwg.org.uk
www.somersetmade.co.uk/cvwg/

EXMOOR NATURAL HISTORY SOCIETY. (1974; 480). The
Secretary, 12 King George Road, Minehead, Somerset,
TA24 5JD. 01643 707 624; www.enhs.org.uk
e-mail: carol.enhs@virgin.net
Meetings: 7.30pm, 1st Wednesday of the month (Oct-
Mar), Methodist Church Hall, The Avenue, Minehead.

SOMERSET ORNITHOLOGICAL SOCIETY. (1974; 350).
Mr JA Hazell, Membership Secretary, 9 Hooper Road,
Street, Somerset BA16 0NP. 01458 443 780;
e-mail: jeff.hazell@somersetbirds.net
www.somersetbirds.net
Meetings: 7.30pm, various Thursdays (Oct-Apr),
Ruishton Village Hall, Taunton.

Ringing Groups
CHEW VALLEY RS. Mr A Ashman.
E-mail: alan.ashman@talktalk.net

GORDANO VALLEY RG. Lyndon Roberts, 20 Glebe
Road, Long Ashton, Bristol, BS41 9LH. 01275 392722;
e-mail: mail@lyndonroberts.com

RSPCA. Mr K Leighton. E-mail: kleighton@rspca.org.uk

RSPB Local Groups
BATH AND DISTRICT. (1989; 220). Alan Barrett. 01225
310 905; e-mail: alan_w_h_barrett@yahoo.co.uk
www.rspb.org.uk/groups/bath
Meetings: 7.30pm, 3rd Wednesday of the month (Sep-
Mar), First Floor, Green Park Station, BATH, BA1 2DR.

SOUTH SOMERSET. (1979; 300). Denise Chamings,
Daniels Farm, Lower Stratton, South Petherton,
Somerset TA13 5LP. 01460 240 740;
e-mail: denise.chamings@talktalk.net
www.rspb.org.uk/groups/southsomerset
Meetings: 7.30pm, 3rd Thursday of the month (Sep-
May), The Millennium Hall, Seavington St. Mary,
Ilminster, TA19 0QH.

TAUNTON. (1975; 148). Eric Luxton. 01823 283 033;
e-mail: eric.luxton@btinternet.com
www.rspb.org.uk/groups/taunton
Meetings: 7.30pm, last Friday of the month, Trull
Memorial Hall, Church Road, Trull, TAUNTON TA3
7JZ.

ENGLAND

WESTON-SUPER-MARE (N SOMERSET). (1976; 215). Eric Allcock. 01934 418 162;
e-mail: ericallcock50@yahoo.com
www.rspb.org.uk/groups/westonsupermare
Meetings: 7.45pm, 1st Thursday of the month (Sep-Apr), St Pauls Church Hall, Walliscote Road, Weston-Super-Mare.

Wetland Bird Survey Organisers
SEVERN ESTUARY - SOUTHERN COAST. Harvey Rose, e-mail: webs@bto.org

SOMERSET (other sites) and SOUTH AVON (inland). Keith Fox, 01275 854 678;
e-mail: keith@kfox.wanadoo.co.uk

SOMERSET LEVELS. Steve Meen;
e-mail: steve.meen@rspb.org.uk
Wildlife Trusts
AVON WILDLIFE TRUST. (1980; 17,000). 32 Jacobs Wells Road, Bristol, BS8 1DR. 0117 917 7270;
e-mail: mail@avonwildlifetrust.org.uk
www.avonwildlifetrust.org.uk

SOMERSET WILDLIFE TRUST. (1964; 21,000). Tonedale Mill,Tonedale,Wellington,Somerset TA21 0AW. 01823 652 40; e-mail: enquiries@somersetwildlife.org
www.somersetwildlife.org

STAFFORDSHIRE

Bird Atlas/Avifauna
See West Midlands.

Bird Recorder
Nick Pomiankowski,22 The Villas, West End, Stoke ST4 5AQ. 01782 849 682;
e-mail: staffs-recorder@westmidlandbirdclub.com

Bird Report
See West Midlands.

BTO Regional Representatives
NORTH EAST. Martin Godfrey. 01785 229 713;
e-mail: martinandrosie@aol.com

SOUTH & CENTRAL. Martin Godfrey. 01785 229 713;
e-mail: martinandrosie@aol.com

WEST. Martin Godfrey. 01785 229 713;
e-mail: martinandrosie@aol.com

Clubs
SOUTH PEAK RAPTOR STUDY GROUP. (1998; 12). M E Taylor, 76 Hawksley Avenue, Newbold, Chesterfield, Derbys S40 4TL. 01246 277 749.

WEST MIDLAND BIRD CLUB (STAFFORD BRANCH). Scott Petrek (Branch Secretary). E-mail:
stafford-secretary@westmidlandbirdclub.com
www.westmidlandbirdclub.com/stafford
Meetings: 7.30pm, 2nd Friday of the month (Oct-Mar), at Perkins Engines Sports & Social Club, Tixall Road, Stafford.

WEST MIDLAND BIRD CLUB (TAMWORTH BRANCH). (1992). Barbara Stubbs, 19 Alfred Street, Tamworth, Staffs, B79 7RL. 01827 57865;
e-mail: tamworth@westmidlandbirdclub
www.westmidlandbirdclub.com/tamworth
Meetings: 7.30pm, 3rd Friday of the month (Sep-Apr), Phil Dix Centre, Corporation Street, Tamworth.

RSPB Local Groups
BURTON-ON-TRENT AND SOUTH DERBYSHIRE. (1973; 50). Dave Lummis, 121 Wilmot Road, Swadlincote, Derbys, DE11 9BN. 01283 219 902;
e-mail: davelummis@hotmail.co.uk
www.basd-rspb.co.uk
Meetings: 7.30pm 1st Wednesday of the month, All Saint's Church, Branston Road, Burton.

LICHFIELD & DISTRICT. (1977; 1150). Bob Russon, 108 Walsall Road, Lichfield, Staffs, WS13 8AF. 01543 252 547; e-mail: LichfieldRSPB@hotmail.co.uk
www.rspb.org.uk/groups/lichfield
Meetings: 7.30pm, 2nd Tuesday of the month (Jan-May, Sept-Dec), St Mary's Centre, Lichfield.

NORTH STAFFS. (1982; 221). John Booth, 32 St Margaret Drive, Sneyd Green, Stoke-on-Trent, ST1 6EW. 01782 262 082; e-mail: daylateuk@yahoo.co.uk
www.rspb.org.uk/groups/northstaffordshire
Meetings: 7.30pm, normally 3rd Wednesday of the month, North Staffs Conference Centre (Medical Institute).

SOUTH WEST STAFFORDSHIRE. (1972; 192). Mrs Theresa Dorrance, 39 Wilkes Road, Codsall, Wolverhampton, WV8 1RZ. 01902 847 041;
e-mail: stevedorrance@googlemail.com
Meetings: 8.00pm, 2nd Tuesday of the month (Sep-May), Codsall Village Hall.

Wetland Bird Survey Organisers
STAFFORDSHIRE. Steven Turner;
e-mail: webs@bto.org

Wildlife Hospitals
BRITISH WILDLIFE RESCUE CENTRE. Alfred Hardy, Amerton Working Farm, Stowe-by-Chartley, Stafford, ST18 0LA. 01889 271 308; e-mail: joyce.hardy351@ntlworld.com
www.britishwildliferescue.co.uk
On A518 Stafford/Uttoxeter road. All species, including imprints and permanently injured. Hospital, large aviaries and caging. Open to the public every day. Veterinary support.

GENTLESHAW BIRD OF PREY HOSPITAL. Jenny Smith, Gentleshaw Wildlife Centre, Fletcher's Country Garden Centre, Stone Road, Eccleshall, Staffs ST21 6JY. 01785 850 379; www.gentleshawwildlife.co.uk
e-mail: info@gentleshawwildlife.co.uk
Registered charity. All birds of prey (inc. owls).

ENGLAND

Hospital cages and aviaries; release sites. Veterinary support.
Also GENTLESHAW BIRD OF PREY AND WILDLIFE CENTRE, Fletchers Country Garden Centre, Stone Road, Eccleshall, Stafford. 01785 850 379.

Wildlife Trust
STAFFORDSHIRE WILDLIFE TRUST. (1969; 14,000). The Wolseley Centre, Wolseley Bridge, Stafford, ST17 0WT. 01889 880 100; www.staffs-wildlife.org.uk
e-mail: info@staffs-wildlife.org.uk

SUFFOLK

Bird Atlas/Avifauna
Birds of Suffolk by S H Piotrowski, (Helm 2003).

Bird Recorders
NORTH EAST. David Fairhurst.
E-mail: davidfairhurst@lycos.com

SOUTH EAST (inc. coastal region from Slaughden Quay southwards). Scott Mayson;
e-mail: s.mayson@fsmail.net

WEST (whole of Suffolk W of Stowmarket, inc. Breckland). Colin Jakes, 7 Maltward Avenue, Bury St Edmunds, Suffolk IP33 3XN. 01284 702 215;
e-mail: colin.jakes@stedsbc.gov.uk

Bird Report
SUFFOLK BIRDS (inc Landguard Bird Observatory Report) (1950-), from Ipswich Museum, High Street, Ipswich, Suffolk.

BTO Regional Representative
Mick T Wright, 15 Avondale Road, Ipswich, IP3 9JT. 01473 710 032; e-mail: micktwright@btinternet.com

BTO Garden BirdWatch Ambassador
Mr C R Powell. E-mail: carlann.powell@tiscali.co.uk

Clubs
LAVENHAM BIRD CLUB. (1972; 54). Mr G Pattrick, Brights Farmhouse, Brights Lane, Lavenham, Suffolk CO10 9PH. 01787 248 128.
Meetings: 7.30pm, normally 3rd Saturday (Sep-Mar, except Dec), Lavenham Guildhall.

SUFFOLK ORNITHOLOGISTS' GROUP. (1973; 650). Phil Whittaker, Oak Barn, Pipps Ford, Needham Market, Ipswich, Suffolk IP6 8LJ. 01449 76 0353; e-mail: info@sogonline.org.uk
www.sogonline.org.uk
Meetings: Last Thursday of the month (Jan-Mar, Oct-Nov), London Road Holiday Inn (IP2 0UA) on the SW side of Ipswich near the A14/A12 Copdock roundabout.

Ringing Groups
DINGLE BIRD CLUB. Dr D Pearson, 4 Lupin Close, Reydon, Southwold, Suffolk IP18 6NW. 01502 722 348.

LACKFORD RG. Dr Peter Lack, 11 Holden Road, Lackford, Bury St Edmunds, Suffolk IP28 6HZ.
E-mail: bee.eaters@btinternet.com

LANDGUARD RG. Landguard Ringing Group, Landguard Bird Observatory, View Point Road, Felixstowe, Suffolk, IP11 3TW. 01394 673782;
e-mail: landguardbo@yahoo.co.uk
www.lbo.co.uk

RSPB Local Groups
BURY ST EDMUNDS. (1982; 150). Dan Brawn. 0845 393 2011; e-mail: danbrawn@mathematics.fsnet.co.uk
www.rspb.org.uk/groups/burystedmunds
Meetings: 7.30pm, 3rd Tuesday of the month (Sep-May), County Upper School, Beetons Way, Bury St Edmunds.

IPSWICH. (1975; 230). Mr Chris Courtney, St Elmo, 19 Marlborough Road, Ipswich, Suffolk IP4 5AT. 01473 423 213; e-mail: chrisc.courtney@yahoo.co.uk
www.rspb.org.uk/groups/ipswich
Meetings: 7.30pm, 2nd Thursday of the month (Sep-Apr), Sidegate Lane Primary School, Sidegate Lane, Ipswich.

LOWESTOFT & DISTRICT. (1976; 130). Howard Bayliss. 01502 539 030; e-mail: leader.group@tesco.net
www.rspb.org.uk/groups/lowestoft
Meetings: 7.15pm 1st Monday in the month, St Marks Church Centre, Oulton Broad.

WOODBRIDGE. (1987; 400). Malcolm Key, Riverside, Parham, Suffolk, IP13 9LZ. 01728 723 155;
e-mail: malcolm.key@btopenworld.com
Meetings: 7.30pm, 1st Thursday of the month (Oct-May), Woodbridge Community Hall.

Wetland Bird Survey Organisers
ALDE COMPLEX. Ian Castle,
e-mail: ic.pda@the-pda.com

ALTON WATER. John Glazebrook,
e-mail: johnglazebrook@btopenworld.com

BLYTH ESTUARY (SUFFOLK). Adam Burrows, 01502 676 171; e-mail: adam.burrows@naturalengland.org.uk

DEBEN ESTUARY. Nick Mason, 7876 086 039;
e-mail: nick.mason4@btinternet.com

ORWELL ESTUARY. Mick Wright, 01473 710 032;
e-mail: micktwright@btinternet.com

SUFFOLK (OTHER SITES). Alan Miller, 01728 833 405;
e-mail: alan.miller@suffolkwildlifetrust.org

Wildlife Trust
SUFFOLK WILDLIFE TRUST. (1961; 25,000). Brooke House, The Green, Ashbocking, Ipswich, IP6 9JY. 01473 890 089; e-mail: info@suffolkwildlifetrust.org
www.suffolkwildlifetrust.org

SURREY

Bird Atlas/Avifauna
Birds of Surrey by Jeffery Wheatley (Surrey Bird Club 2007).

Bird Recorder (inc London S of Thames & E to Surrey Docks)
SURREY (includes Greater London south of the Thames and east to the Surrey Docks, excludes Spellthorne). Eric Soden, Ceres, Moushill Lane, Milford, Surrey GU8 5BQ. 01483 429 799; e-mail: eric.soden@talktalk.net

Bird Report
SURBITON AND DISTRICT BIRD WATCHING SOCIETY (1972-), from Thelma Caine, 21 More Lane, Esher, Surrey KT10 8AJ. E-mail: sdbws@encief.co.uk www.encief.co.uk/sdbws

SURREY BIRD REPORT (1953-), from J Gates, 5 Hillside Road, Weybourne, Farnham, Surrey GU9 9DW. 01252 315 047; e-mail: jeremygates@live.com

BTO Regional Representative
Penny Williams, Bournbrook House, Sandpit Hall Lane, Chobham Surrey GU24 8HA. 01276 857 736; e-mail: penny@waxwing.plus.com

Clubs
SURBITON & DISTRICT BIRDWATCHING SOCIETY. (1954; 140). Gary Caine, 21 More Lane, Esher, Surrey, KT10 8AJ. 01372 468 432; e-mail: sdbws@encief.co.uk www.encief.co.uk/sdbws
Meetings: 7.30pm, 3rd Tuesday of the month, Surbiton Library Annex.

SURREY BIRD CLUB. (1957; 340). Penny Williams, Bournbrook House, Sandpit Hall Lane, Chobham Surrey GU24 8HA. 01276 857 736; e-mail: penny@waxwing. plus.com www.surreybirdclub.org.uk **Meetings:** See website for details.

Ringing Groups
HERSHAM RG. A J Beasley, 29 Selbourne Avenue, New Haw, Weybridge, Surrey KT15 3RB. E-mail: abeasley00@hotmail.com

RUNNYMEDE RG. D G Harris, 22 Blossom Waye, Hounslow, TW5 9HD; http://rmxrg.org.uk E-mail: daveharris@tinyonline.co.uk

RSPB Local Groups
DORKING & DISTRICT. (1982; 230). John Burge, Broughton Norrels Drive, East Horsley, Leatherhead, KT24 5DR. 01483 283 803; e-mail: burgejs@gmail.com www.rspb.org.uk/groups/dorkinganddistrict
Meetings: 8.00pm, Fridays once a month (Sep-Apr), Christian Centre, next to St Martin's Church, Dorking.

EAST SURREY. (1984; 2800 plus in catchment area). John Lawrence, 123 Chaldon Way, Coulsdon, Surrey CR5 1DN. 01737 553 316; www.eastsurreyrspb.co.uk e-mail: jfjlawrence@gmail.com
Meetings: 8.00pm, 2nd Wednesday of the month (except August), White Hart Barn, Godstone, RH9 8DT.

EPSOM & EWELL. (1974; 168). Janet Gilbert, 78 Fairfax Avenue, Ewell, Epsom, Surrey KT17 2QQ. 0208 394 0405; e-mail: janetegilbert@btinternet.com www.rspb.org.uk/groups/epsom
Meetings: 7.45pm, 2nd Friday of the month, All Saints Church Hall, Fulford Road, West Ewell.

GUILDFORD AND DISTRICT. (1974; 550). Michael Grimshaw. 01483 467 074; e-mail: michaelgrimshaw@btinternet.com www.rspb.org.uk/groups/guildford

Meetings: 2.15pm 2nd Thursday and 7.45pm 4th Wednesday (Oct-Apr), Onslow Village Hall, Guildford.

NORTH WEST SURREY. (1973; 150). Dave Braddock, 20 Meadway Drive, New Haw, Surrey, KT15 2DT. 01932 858 692; e-mail: dave@utter-chaos.co.uk www.rspb.org.uk/groups/nwsurrey
Meetings: 7.45pm, 4th Wednesday of the month (not Dec, Jul, Aug), Sir William Perkin's School, Chertsey KT16 9BN.

Wetland Bird Survey Organiser
SURREY. Penny Williams; e-mail: webs@bto.org

Wildlife Hospitals
THE SWAN SANCTUARY. See National Directory.

THE WILDLIFE AID FOUNDATION. Randalls FarmHouse, Randalls Road, Leatherhead, Surrey, KT22 0AL. 01372 377 332, 24-hr emergency line 09061 800 132 (50p/ min) (fax) 01372 375 183; e-mail: mail@wildlifeaid.org.uk www.wildlifeaid.org.uk Registered charity. Wildlife hospital and rehabilitation centre helping all native British species. Special housing for birds of prey. Membership scheme and fund raising activities. Veterinary support.

Wildlife Trust
SURREY WILDLIFE TRUST. (1959; 25,700). School Lane, Pirbright, Woking, Surrey, GU24 0JN. 01483 795 440; e-mail: info@surreywt.org.uk www.surreywildlifetrust.org

SUSSEX

Bird Atlas/Avifauna
Birds of Selsey and Pagham, 2003.

Birds of Sussex ed by Paul James (Sussex Ornithological Society, 1996).

Fifty Years of Birdwatching, a celebration of the acheivements of the Shoreham District OS from 1953

onwards, 2003. £5 + P&P at current rates. Mrs Sue Miles, SDOS Hon.Secretary, 24 Chancellors Park, Hassocks, West Sussex BN6 8EZ; e-mail: secretary@sdos.org or through website www.sdos.org

Henfield Birdwatch 2010 ed Mike Russell et al, Henfield Birdwatch. Contact Val Bentley, 01273 4947 23 or e-mail chetsford@talk21.com for further details.

Bird Recorder
Mr Nick Paul, Old Durfold, Warnham, Horsham, West Sussex RH15 3RY. 01403 264 762;
e-mail: recorder@sos.org
www.sos.org

Bird Reports
BIRDS OF RYE HARBOUR NR ANNUAL REPORT (1977-published every 5 years), from Dr Barry Yates, see Clubs.

PAGHAM HARBOUR LOCAL NATURE RESERVE ANNUAL REPORT, from Warden, see Reserves.

SHOREHAM DISTRICT ORNITHOLOGICAL SOCIETY ANNUAL REPORT (1952-) - back issues available at £3.50 + P&P at current rates, from Mrs Sue Miles, 24 Chancellors Park,Hassocks, West Sussex BN6 8EZ. E-mail: secretary@sdos.orgor through website - www.sdos.org

SUSSEX BIRD REPORT (1963-), from J E Trowell, Lorrimer, Main Road, Icklesham, Winchelsea, E Sussex, TN36 4BS. E-mail: membership@sos.org.uk www.sos.org.uk

BTO Regional Representative
Dr Helen Crabtree. 01444 441 687;
e-mail: hcrabtree@gmail.com

Clubs
FRIENDS OF RYE HARBOUR NATURE RESERVE. (1973; 1800). Friends of Rye Harbour, 2 Watch Cottages, Nook Beach, Winchelsea, E Sussex TN36 4LU. 01797 223862; e-mail: rhnr.office@eastsussex.gov.uk
www.wildrye.info
Meetings: Monthly talks in winter, monthly walks all year.

HENFIELD BIRDWATCH. (1999; 135). Mike Russell, 31 Downsview, Small Dole, Henfield, West Sussex BN5 9YB. 01273 494311;
e-mail: mikerussell@sussexwt.org.uk

SHOREHAM DISTRICT ORNITHOLOGICAL SOCIETY. (1953; 200). Mrs. Shena Maskell, SDOS Membership Secretary, 41 St. Lawrence Avenue, Worthing, West Sussex BN14 7JJ. E-mail: membership@sdos.org or through website - www.sdos.org
Meetings: 7.30pm, 2nd Tuesday of the month (Oct-Apr), St Peter's Church Hall, Shoreham-by-Sea. (7 indoor meetings, 18+ field outings).

**S
D
O
S**

SUSSEX ORNITHOLOGICAL SOCIETY. (1962; 1600). Val Bentley, Chetsford, London Road, Henfield, West Sussex BN5 9JJ. 01273 494 723;
e-mail: secretary@sos.org.uk - www.sos.org.uk
Meetings: Annual conference in January (Haywards Heath), AGM in April, field outings throughout year.

Ringing Groups
BEACHY HEAD RS. R D M Edgar, 32 Hartfield Road, Seaford, E Sussex BN25 4PW.

CUCKMERE RG. Tim Parmenter, 18 Chapel Road, Plumpton Green, East Sussex, BN7 3DD. 01273 891 881.

RYE BAY RG. P Jones; e-mail: philjones@beamingbroadband.com

STEYNING RINGING GROUP. B R Clay, Meghana, Honeysuckle Lane, High Salvington, Worthing, West Sussex BN13 3BT. E-mail: brian.clay@ntlworld.com

RSPB Local Groups
BATTLE. (1973; 80). David Yates. 01424 773 826;
e-mail: familyatbattle@yahoo.co.uk
www.battlerspb.org.uk
Meetings: 7.30pm, 4th Tuesday of the month, Battle and Langton Primary School, Battle.

BRIGHTON & DISTRICT. (1974; 260). Mark Weston. 07802 293 417; e-mail: mark.weston@rspb.org.uk
www.rspb.org.uk/groups/brighton
Meetings: 7.30pm, 4th Thursday of the month, All Saints Church Hall, Eaton Road, Hove. Anyone is welcome, non-members should phone first as dates can vary.

CHICHESTER & SW SUSSEX. (1979; 245). Kerry Jackson. 01243 265 783;
e-mail: chichesterRSPB@aol.com
www.rspb.org.uk/groups/chichester
Meetings: 7.30 pm 2nd Thursday of each month, Newell Centre, Newell Centre, Tozer Way, St Pancras, Chichester.

CRAWLEY & HORSHAM. (1978; 148). Andrea Saxton, 104 Heath Way, Horsham, W Sussex, RH12 5XS. 01403 242 218; e-mail: Andrea.saxton@sky.com
www.rspb.org.uk/groups/crawley
Meetings: 8.00pm, 3rd Wednesday of the month (Sept-Apr), The Friary Hall, Crawley.

EAST GRINSTEAD. (1998; 185). Nick Walker, 14 York Avenue, East Grinstead, W Sussex RH19 4TL. 01342 315 825; e-mail: nickwalker55@btinternet.com
www.rspb.org.uk/groups/egrinstead
Meetings: 8.00pm, last Wednesday of the month, Large Parish Hall, De La Warr Road, East Grinstead.

EASTBOURNE & DISTRICT. (1993; 320). Ian Muldoon. 01273 476852; e-mail: ian1muldoon@yahoo.co.uk
www.rspb.org.uk/groups/eastbourne
Meetings: 2.15 pm and 7.30 pm,1st Wednesday of the month (Sep-Jun), St. Wilfrid's Church Hall, Eastbourne Road, Pevensey Bay.

ENGLAND

HASTINGS & ST LEONARDS. (1983; 110). Richard Prebble.. 01424 751 790;
e-mail: Lynn.jenkins98@gmail.com
www.rspb.org.uk/groups/hastings
Meetings: 7.30pm, 3rd Friday of the month, Taplin Centre, Upper Maze Hill.

Wetland Bird Survey Organiser
CHICHESTER HARBOUR. Mr E Rowsell. 01243 510 985;
e-mail: edward@conservancy.co.uk

OTHER SITES. Richard Bown. 01323 479 569;
e-mail: hr.bown@btinternet.com

Wildlife Hospital
BRENT LODGE BIRD & WILDLIFE TRUST. Penny Cooper, Brent Lodge, Cow Lane, Sidlesham, Chichester, West Sussex, PO20 7LN; www.brentlodge.org
01243 641 672 (emergency number).
All species of wild birds and small mammals. Full surgical and medical facilities (inc. X-ray) in conjunction with veterinary support. Purpose-built oiled bird washing unit. Veterinary support.

Wildlife Trust
SUSSEX WILDLIFE TRUST. (1961; 26,000). Woods Mill, Shoreham Road, Henfield, W Sussex, BN5 9SD. 01273 492 630; e-mail: enquiries@sussexwt.org.uk
www.sussexwt.org.uk

TYNE & WEAR

Bird Recorders
See Durham; Northumberland.

Bird Report
See Durham; Northumberland.

Clubs
NATURAL HISTORY SOCIETY OF NORTHUMBRIA. (1829; 900). The Natural History Society of Northumbria, Great North Museum: Hancock, Newcastle upon Tyne, NE2 4PT. 0191 232 6386; e-mail: nhsn@ncl.ac.uk
www.NHSN.ncl.ac.uk
Meetings: Weekly indoor and outdoor meetings throughout the year, details can be found at www.nhsn.ncl.ac.uk

NORTHUMBERLAND & TYNESIDE BIRD CLUB. (1958; 250). Alan Tilmouth, 12 Stowe Gardens, Pegswood, Morpeth, Northumberland NE61 6TH. 07807 507 182;
e-mail: ntbcorg@gmail.com
www.ntbc.org.uk

RSPB Local Groups
NEWCASTLE UPON TYNE. (1969; 250). Marie Ollerenshaw. E-mail: NewcastleRSPBgroup@gmail.com
www.rspb.org.uk/groups/newcastle
Meetings: 7pm, (Mar, Jun, Sep, Nov), Northumbria University, Ellison Place, Newcastle upon Tyne.

WARWICKSHIRE

Bird Atlas/Avifauna
See West Midlands.

Bird Recorder
Jonathan Bowley, 17 Meadow Way, Fenny Compton, Southam, Warks, CV47 2WD. 01295 770069;
e-mail: warks-recorder@westmidlandbirdclub.com

Bird Report
See West Midlands.

BTO Regional Representatives
Mark Smith. 01926 735 398;
e-mail: mark.smith36@ntlworld.com

Clubs
NUNEATON & DISTRICT BIRDWATCHERS' CLUB. (1950; 78). Alvin K Burton, 23 Redruth Close, Horeston Grange, Nuneaton, Warwicks CV11 6FG. 024 7664 1591; http://ndbwc.webs.com/
Meetings: 7.30pm, 3rd Thursday of the month (Sep-Jun), Hatters Space Community Centre, Upper Abbey Street, Nuneaton.

Ringing Groups
ARDEN RG. Roger J Juckes, 24 Croft Lane, Temple Grafton, Alcester, Warks B49 6PA. 01789 778 748.

BRANDON RG. David Stone, Overbury, Wolverton, Stratford-on-Avon, Warks CV37 0HG. 01789 731 488.

RSPB Local Group
See West Midlands.

Wildlife Trust
WARWICKSHIRE WILDLIFE TRUST. (1970; 13,000). Brandon Marsh Nature Centre, Brandon Lane, Coventry, CV3 3GW. 024 7630 2912;
e-mail: enquiries@wkwt.org.uk
www.warwickshire-wildlife-trust.org.uk

WEST MIDLANDS

Bird Atlas/Avifauna
The New Birds of the West Midlands (covering Staffordshire, Warwickshire, Worcestershire, and the former West Midlands County), edited by Graham and Janet Harrison (West Midland Bird Club, 2005). Available from 147 Worlds End Lane, Quinton, Birmingham B32 1JX.

Bird Recorder
Kevin Clements, 26 Hambrook Close, Dunstall Park, Wolverhampton, West Midlands WV6 0XA. 01902 568 997; e-mail: west-mids-recorder@westmidlandbirdclub.com

Bird Reports
THE BIRDS OF SMESTOW VALLEY AND DUNSTALL PARK (1988-), from Secretary, Smestow Valley Bird Group.

ENGLAND

THE BIRDS OF STAFFORDSHIRE, WARWICKSHIRE, WORCESTERSHIRE AND THE WEST MIDLANDS (1934-), from Barbara Oakley, 147 Worlds End, Quinton, Birmingham B32 1JX. E-mail: secretary@westmidlandbirdclub.com www.westmidlandbirdclub.com

BTO Regional Representative
BIRMINGHAM & WEST MIDLANDS. Steve Davies. 07882 891 726; e-mail: stevedaviesbtorep@hotmail.co.uk

BTO Garden BirdWatch Ambassador
Mr M Hope-Urwin. E-mail: mandm@greenbee.net

Clubs
SMESTOW VALLEY BIRD GROUP. (1988; 46). Frank Dickson, 11 Bow Street, Bilston, Wolverhampton, WV14 7NB. 01902 493 733.
WEST MIDLAND BIRD CLUB - serving Ornithologists in Staffs, Warks, Worcs and the West Midlands County. (1929; 2000). Barbara Oakley. E-mail: secretary@westmidlandbirdclub.com - www.westmidlandbirdclub.com
Meetings: Check website for details of the different branches and their events.

WEST MIDLAND BIRD CLUB (BIRMINGHAM BRANCH). (1995; 800). Andy Mabbett. E-mail: birmingham@westmidlandbirdclub.com www.westmidlandbirdclub.com/birmingham
Meetings: 7.30pm, usually last Tuesday (Oct-Apr), Birmingham Medical Institute, in Harborne Road, Edgbaston, near Five Ways.

WEST MIDLAND BIRD CLUB (SOLIHULL BRANCH). (1973). Raymond Brown, The Spinney, 63 Grange Road, Dorridge, Solihull B93 8QS. 01564 772 550; e-mail: solihull@westmidlandbirdclub www.westmidlandbirdclub.com/solihull
Meetings: 7.30 pm, Fridays (usually 1st of month), Guild House, Knowle, Solihull, West Midlands B93 0LN.

Ringing Groups
MERCIAN RG (Sutton Coldfield). Mr DJ Clifton. 59 Daisybank Crescent, Walsall, WS5 3BH. 01922 628 572.

RSPB Local Groups
BIRMINGHAM. (1975; 100). John Bailey, 52 Gresham Road, Hall Green, Birmingham, B28 0HY. 0121 777 4389; e-mail: jvbailey@btinternet.com www.rspb-birmingham.org.uk
Meetings: 7.30pm, 3rd Thursday of the month (Sep-Jun), Salvation Army Citadel, St Chads, Queensway, Birmingham.

COVENTRY & WARWICKSHIRE. (1969; 130). Ron Speddings.01926 428 365; e-mail: Ron@speddings.spacomputers.com

www.rspb.org.uk/groups/coventryandwarwickshire
Meetings: 7.30pm, 4th Friday of the month, (Sep-May unless otherwise stated), Warwick Arts Centre And Baginton Village Hall.

SOLIHULL. (1983; 2600). John Roberts, 115 Dovehouse Lane, Solihull, West Midlands, B91 2EQ. 0121 707 3101; e-mail: johnbirder@care4free.net www.rspb.org.uk/groups/solihull
Meetings: 7.30pm, usually 2nd Tuesday of the month (Sep-Apr), Oliver Bird Hall, Church Hill Road, Solihull.

STOURBRIDGE. (1978; 150). David Ackland. 01384 293 090; e-mail: davidackland@blueyonder.co.uk www.rspb.org.uk/groups/stourbridge
Meetings: 2nd Wednesday of the month (Sep-May), Wollaston Suite, Stourbridge Town Hall, Crown Centre, STOURBRIDGE, West Midlands, DY8 1YE.

SUTTON COLDFIELD. (1986; 250). Martin Fisher. 0121 308 4400; e-mail: martinjfisher@care4free.net www.rspb.org.uk/groups/suttoncoldfield
Meetings: 7.30pm, 1st Monday of the month, Bishop Vesey's Grammer School.

WALSALL. (1970). Mike Pittaway, 2 Kedleston Close, Bloxwich, Walsall, WS3 3TW. 01922 710 568; e-mail: chair@rspb-walsall.org.uk www.rspb-walsall.org.uk
Meetings: 7.30pm, 3rd Wednesday of the month, St Marys School, Jesson Road, Walsall.

WOLVERHAMPTON. (1974; 100). Barry Proffitt. 07900 431 820; e-mail: RSPBwolverhampton@hotmail.co.uk www.rspb.org.uk/groups/wolverhampton
Meetings: 7.30pm, 2nd Wednesday of the month (Sept-Apr), The Newman Centre, Haywood Drive, Tettenhall, Wolverhampton. Also monthly field-trips (Sep-Jun).

Wetland Bird Survey Organiser
WEST MIDLANDS. Position vacant.

Wildlife Trust
THE WILDLIFE TRUST FOR BIRMINGHAM AND THE BLACK COUNTRY. (1980; 5,500). 28 Harborne Road, Edgbaston, Birmingham, B15 3AA. 0121 454 1199e-mail: info@bbcwildlife.org.uk www.bbcwildlife.org.uk

WILTSHIRE

Bird Atlas/Avifauna
Birds of Wiltshire, by James Ferguson-Lees et al, 2007, Wiltshire Ornithological Society.

Bird Recorder
Rob Turner, 14 Ethendun, Bratton, Westbury, Wilts, BA13 4RX. 01380 830 862; e-mail: robt14@btopenworld.com

Bird Report
HOBBY (journal of the Wiltshire OS) (1975-), from John Osborne, 4 Fairdown Avenue, Westbury,

Wiltshire BA13 3HS. 01373 8645 98;
e-mail: josb@talktalk.net
www.wiltshirebirds.co.uk

BTO Regional Representatives
NORTH. Bill Quantrill. 01225 866 245;
e-mail: william.quantrill@btinternet.com

SOUTH. Bill Quantrill. 01225 866 245;
e-mail: william.quantrill@btinternet.com

Clubs
SALISBURY & DISTRICT NATURAL HISTORY SOCIETY.
(1952; 146). Elisabeth Richmond, 15 Chantry Road,
Wilton, Salisbury, SP2 0LT. 01722 742 755;
e-mail: erichmond@madasafish.com
Meetings: 7.30pm, 3rd Thursday of the month (Sept-
Apr), Lecture Hall, Salisbury Museum, Kings House,
The Close, Salisbury.
WILTSHIRE ORNITHOLOGICAL SOCIETY. (1974; 450).
Phil Deacon, 12 Rawston Close, Nythe, Swindon, Wilts
SN3 3PW. 01793 528 930; www.wiltshirebirds.co.uk
e-mail: phil.deacon@ntlworld.com
Meetings: See website for details.

Ringing Group
COTSWOLD WATER PARK RG. John Wells, 25 Pipers
Grove, Highnam, Glos, GL2 8NJ.
E-mail: john.wells2@btinternet.com

WEST WILTSHIRE RG. Mr M.J. Hamzij, 13 Halfway
Close, Trowbridge, Wilts BA14 7HQ.
E-mail: m.hamzij@btinternet.com

RSPB Local Groups
NORTH WILTSHIRE. (1973; 115). 01793 349 262;
e-mail: Raymond.thatcher@ntlworld.com
www.rspb.org.uk/groups/northwiltshire
Meetings: 7.30pm, 1st Tuesday of the month (Sep-
Jun), Even Swindon Community Centre, Jennings St,
Swindon SU 137 849.

SOUTH WILTSHIRE. (1986; 720). Tony Goddard,
Clovelly, Lower Road, Charlton All Saints, Salisbury,
SP5 4HQ. 01725 510 309;
e-mail: goddard543@hotmail.com
www.rspb.org.uk/groups/southwiltshire
Meetings: 7.30pm, Tuesday evenings (monthly),
Salisbury Arts Centre, Salisbury.

Wetland Birds Survey Organiser
COTSWOLD WATER PARK. Gareth Harris;
e-mail: gareth.harris@waterpark.org
www.waterpark.org

WILTSHIRE. Julian Rolls, e-mail: webs@bto.org

Wildlife Trust
WILTSHIRE WILDLIFE TRUST.
(1962; 18,500). Elm Tree Court,
Long Street, Devizes, Wilts, SN10
1NJ. 01380 725 670; e-mail:
info@wiltshirewildlife.org
www.wiltshirewildlife.org

Wiltshire Wildlife Trust

Bird Atlas/Avifauna
See West Midlands

Bird Recorder
Steven Payne, 6 Norbury Close, Redditch B98
8RP. 01527 60169; e-mail: worcs-recorder@
westmidlandbirdclub.com
www.westmidlandbirdclub.com

Bird Report
See West Midlands.

BTO Regional Representative
G Harry Green MBE, Windy Ridge, Pershore Road,
Little Comberton, Pershore, Worcs, WR10 3EW. 01386
710 377; e-mail: zen130501@zen.co.uk

Ringing Group
WYCHAVON RG. J R Hodson, 15 High Green, Severn
Stoke, Worcester, WR8 9JS. 01905 371 333;
e-mail: hodson77@btinternet.com

Club
WEST MIDLAND BIRD CLUB (KIDDERMINSTER BRANCH).
Celia Barton, 28A Albert Street, Wall Heath,
Kingswinford, DY6 0NA. 01384 839 838;
e-mail: kidderminster@westmidlandbirdclub.com
www.westmidlandbirdclub.com
Meetings: 7.30pm, 4th Wednesday of the month
(Sep-Apr), St Oswalds Church Centre, Broadwaters,
Kidderminster.

RSPB Local Group
WORCESTER & MALVERN. (1980; 300). Frances Evans,
120 Bath Road, Worcester WR5 3EP. 01905 359 132;
e-mail: francesevans@gmail.com
www.rspb.org.uk/groups/worcester
Meetings: 7.30pm, 2nd Wednesday in month (Sept-
May), Powick Village Hall.

Wetland Birds Survey Organiser
WORCESTERSHIRE. Andrew Warr;
e-mail: andrew.warr3@btopenworld.com

Wildlife Hospital
VALE WILDLIFE RESCUE - WILDLIFE HOSPITAL +
REHABILITATION CENTRE. Any staff member, Station
Road, Beckford, Tewkesbury, Glos GL20 7AN. 01386
882 288; e-mail: info@valewildlife.org.uk
www.valewildlife.org.uk All wild birds. Intensive
care. Registered charity. Veterinary support.

Wildlife Trust
WORCESTERSHIRE WILDLIFE TRUST. (1968; 9,000).
Lower Smite Farm, Smite Hill, Hindlip, Worcester,
WR3 8SZ. 01905 754 919;
e-mail: enquiries@worcestershirewildlifetrust.org
www.worcswildlifetrust.co.uk

ENGLAND

YORKSHIRE

Bird Atlas/Avifauna
Atlas of Breeding Birds in the Leeds Area 1987-1991
by Richard Fuller et al (Leeds Birdwatchers' Club, 1994).

*An Atlas of the Breeding Birds of the Huddersfield Area, 1987-1992.*by Brian Armitage et al (2000) - very few copies left.

Birds of Barnsley by Nick Addey (Pub by author, 114 Everill Gate Lane, Broomhill, Barnsley S73 0YJ, 1998).

Birds of The Huddersfield Area by Paul and Betty Bray (Huddersfield Birdwatchers Club 2008).

Birds of the Lower Derwent Valley: A Histoical Review 1850-2002, by CS Ralston, English Nature, 2005.

Breeding Bird Atlas for Barnsley in preparation.
The Birds of Halifax, by Nick Dawtrey (only 20 left), 14 Moorend Gardens, Pellon, Halifax, W Yorks, HX2 0SD.

The Birds of Spurn, by G Neal. (2nd edition, Spurn BO Trust, 2007).

The Birds of Wintersett, by S Denny. (Published by author, 2003).

The Birds of Yorkshire by John Mather (Croom Helm, 1986).

County Bird Recorder
Craig Thomas, Sunnybank, Church Lane, Flamborough YO15 1PG. 01262 851 677;
e-mail: craigcthomas@yahoo.co.uk

Vice County Bird Recorders
VC61 (Yorkshire Naturalist's Union, Bird Section - East Yorkshire). Geoff Dobbs, 1 Priory Road, Beverley, East Yorkshire HU17 0EG. 07778 559 763;
e-mail: geoffdobbs@aol.com

VC62 (West Yorkshire)/HARROGATE & CRAVEN. Phil Bone, 11 Dorrington Close, Pocklington, York, YO42 2GS. 0788 084 6905; e-mail: philsarab@aol.co.uk

VC63 (South & West Yorkshire). Covering all bird study groups and South and West Yorkshire and three reserves – Fairburn Ings, Old Moor (both RSPB) and Potteric Carr (Yorkshire Wildlife Trust), John Wint, 9 Yew Tree Park, Whitley, Goole, East Yorkshire DN14 0NZ. 01977 662 826;
e-mail: j.wint114@btinternet.com

VC64 (Mid-West Yorkshire). Ian Court, 2 Burley Mews, Steeton, Keighley BT20 6TX. 01535 658 582;
e-mail: ian.court@mypostoffice.co.uk

VC65 (North Yorkshire West). Steve Worwood, 18 Coltsgate Hill, Ripon, HG4 2AB;
e-mail: steve@worwood.entadsl.com

Bird Reports
BARNSLEY & DISTRICT BIRD STUDY GROUP REPORT (1971-), from Waxwing Books, Sunnybank Cottage, Ruston Parva, Driffield YO25 4DG.

BRADFORD NATURALISTS' SOCIETY ANNUAL REPORT, from Mr I Hogg, 23 St Matthews Road, Bankfoot, Bradford, BD5 9AB. 01274 727902.

BRADFORD ORNITHOLOGICAL GROUP REPORT (1987-)
- after the 2008 issue, this report will only be available to paid up members of the group., from Jenny Barker, 3 Chapel Fold, Slack Lane, Oakworth, Keighley, BD22 0RQ.

DONCASTER BIRD REPORT (1955-), from Mr M Roberts, 8 Sandbeck court, Rossington, Doncaster, DN11 0FN. 01302 326 265.

FILEY BRIGG BIRD REPORT (1976-), from Colin and Rose Court. 01723 515 925;
e-mail: recorder@fbog.co.uk
www.fbog.co.uk

HARROGATE & DISTRICT NATURALISTS' ORNITHOLOGY REPORT (1996-), from Jill Warwick, Sharow Grange, Sharow, Ripon, HG4 5BN. 01765 602 832;
e-mail: jill@swland.co.uk

HULL VALLEY WILDLIFE GROUP REPORT (2000-) covering Hull Valley. from Roy Lyon, 670 Hotham Road South, Hull, HU5 5LE. 07754 439 496.
www.hullvalleywildlifegroup.co.uk

BIRDS IN HUDDERSFIELD (1966-), from Mr M Wainman, 2 Bankfield Avenue, Taylor Hill, Huddersfield HD4 7QY. 01484 305 054;
e-mail: brian.armitage@ntlworld.com

LEEDS BIRDWATCHERS' CLUB ANNUAL REPORT (1949-), from Peter Murphy, 12 West End Lane, Horsforth, Leeds LS18 5JP.

BIRDS OF ROTHERHAM (1975-) - cost £2.50 inc p&p, cheque payable to R.D.O.S., from The Secretary, Rotherham & District Bird Club.;
e-mail: rdos@hotmail.co.uk
www.rotherhambirds.co.uk

BIRDS IN THE SHEFFIELD AREA (1973-), from Richard Hill, Honorary Secretary, 22 Ansell Road, Sheffield, South Yorkshire S11 7PE. E-mail: Secretary@sbsg.org
www.sbsg.org

THE BIRDS OF SK58 (1993-1999), from Secretary, SK58 Birders. E-mail: recorder@sk58birders.com
www.sk58birders.com

SORBY RECORD (1962-), from Ken Dorning, Sorby NHSoc, c/o Room C12i, Dainton Building, Brook Hill, Sheffield S3 7HF.

SPURN BIRD OBSERVATORY ANNUAL REPORT, from Warden, see Reserves.

SWILLINGTON INGS BIRD GROUP - ANNUAL REPORT AND TWENTY YEAR REVIEW - 2008, from Chris Robinson, 43 Northfield Road, Sprotbrough, Doncaster, DN5 8AY. 07534 271 254; e-mail: GBFShrike@hotmail.com http://sibg1.wordpress.com

YORKSHIRE BIRD REPORT -Yorkshire Naturalists Union (1940-). 2009 edition £12 including postage, from Jill Warwick, Sharow Grange, Sharow, Ripon, HG4 5BN. 01765 602 832; e-mail: jill@swland.co.uk

YORK ORNITHOLOGICAL CLUB REPORT (1970-) 2008 edition now available, from Linda Newton 5 Fairfields Drive, Skelton, York YO30 1YP. 01904 471 446; E-mail: secretary@yorkbirding.org.uk

WINTERSETT AREA ANNUAL REPORT (1988-), from Steve Denny, 13 Rutland Drive, Crofton, Wakefield, WF4 1SA. 01924 864487.

BTO Regional Representatives
NORTH-EAST. Mick Carroll, 10 Cross Avenue, Pickering, North Yorkshire YO18 7HP. 01751 476 550.

NORTH-WEST. Gerald Light. 01756 753 720; e-mail: gerald@uwlig.plus.com

SOUTH-EAST AND SOUTH-WEST. Position vacant.

EAST. Position vacant.

BRADFORD RR & RDO. Mike L Denton, 77 Hawthorne Terrace, Crosland Moor, Huddersfield, HD4 5RP. 01484 646 990.

YORKSHIRE (HARROGATE). Mike Brown, 48 Pannal Ash Drive, Harrogate, N Yorks, HG2 0HU. 01423 567 382; e-mail: mike@thebrownsathome.plus.com

HULL. Geoff Dobbs, 1 Priory Road, Beverley, East Yorkshire HU17 0EG. 07778 559 763; e-mail: geoffdobbs@aol.com

LEEDS & WAKEFIELD RR & RDO. Position vacant.

RICHMOND. John Edwards, 7 Church Garth, Great Smeaton, Northallerton, N Yorks DL6 2HW. H:01609 881 476; e-mail: john@jhedwards.plus.com

YORK. Rob Chapman, 12 Moorland Road, York, YO10 4HF. 01904 633 558; e-mail: robert.chapman@tinyworld.co.uk

BTO Garden BirdWatch Ambassadors
John Preston; e-mail: j.preston@btcv.org.uk
Liz Clinton; e-mail: liztomclinton@aol.com
Tim Godson; e-mail: tim.godson@btinternet.com

Clubs
BARNSLEY BIRD STUDY GROUP. (1970; 35). Graham Speight, 58 Locke Avenue, Barnsley, South Yorkshire S70 1QH. 01226 321 300.
Meetings: 7.15pm, 1st Thursday in the month (Nov-

Mar), RSPB Old Moor, Barnsley.
BRADFORD ORNITHOLOGICAL GROUP. (1987; 160). Shaun Radcliffe, 8 Longwood Avenue, Bingley, W Yorks, BD16 2RX. 01274 770 960.
www.bradfordbirding.org
Meetings: 1st Tuesday of the month - see website for details.

CASTLEFORD & DISTRICT NATURALISTS' SOCIETY. (1956; 16). Michael J Warrington, 31 Mount Avenue, Hemsworth, Pontefract, W Yorks WF9 4QE. 01977 614 954; e-mail: michaelwarrington@talktalk.net
Meetings: 7.30pm, Tuesdays monthly (Sep-Mar), SkillsXchange Campus, Castleford. Check contact name for dates.

DONCASTER & DISTRICT ORNITHOLOGICAL SOCIETY. (1955; 40). Dave Ward, Membership Secretary, 11 Newstead Road, Scawthorpe, Doncaster DN5 9JS.
www.birdingdoncaster.org.uk
Meetings: 7.15pm, last Thursday of the month (Jan-May and Sep-Nov), Parklands Sports and social club, Wheatley Hall Road.

FILEY BRIGG ORNITHOLOGICAL GROUP. (1977; 100). Dr Sue Hull, 32 West Road, Filey, N Yorkshire YO14 9LP. 01723 515 042; e-mail: secretary@fbog.co.uk
www.fbog.co.uk

HARROGATE & DISTRICT NATURALISTS' SOCIETY. (1947; 350). Ms Sue Coldwell, General Secretary, 4 Abbotts Way, Knaresborough, North Yorkshire HG5 8EU. E-mail: gen.sechdns@yahoo.com
www.knaresborough.co.uk/hdns/index.html
Meetings: 7.30pm, St. Roberts Centre, 2/3 Robert Street, Harrogate. The programme of meetings is sent out to members in September.

HORNSEA BIRD CLUB. (1967; 35). John Eldret, 44 Rolston Road, Hornsea, HU18 1UH. 01964 532 854.
Meetings: 7.30pm, 3rd Friday of the month (Sep-Mar), Hornsea Library. Monthly visits to local bird reserves.

HUDDERSFIELD BIRDWATCHERS' CLUB. (1966; 90). Chris Abell, 57 Butterley Lane, New Mill, Holmfirth, HD9 7EZ. 01484 681 499; e-mail: cdabell@gmail.com
www.huddersfieldbirdwatchersclub.co.uk
Meetings: 7.30pm, Tuesday's fortnightly (Sep-May), The Old Court Room, Town Hall, Ramsden St, Huddersfield HD1 2TA.

HULL VALLEY WILDLIFE GROUP. (1997; 175). The Secretary, 29 Beech View, Cranswick, East Yorkshire YO25 9QQ. 01377 270 957. 01377 270 957.
www.hullvalleywildlifegroup.co.uk

LEEDS BIRDWATCHERS' CLUB. (1949; 60). Peter Murphy, 12 West End lane, Horsforth, Leeds, LS18 5JP. 0113 293 0188;
e-mail: pandbmurphy@ntlworld.com
Meetings: 7.15pm Monday fortnightly, Quaker Meeting House, Woodhouse Lane, Leeds.

ROTHERHAM & DISTRICT ORNITHOLOGICAL SOCIETY. (1974; 80). Malcolm Taylor, 18 Maple Place, Chapeltown, Sheffield, S35 1QW. 0114 246 1848;

ENGLAND

e-mail: rdos@hotmail.co.uk
www.rotherhambirds.co.uk
Meetings: 7.30pm, 2nd Friday of the month, United
Reform church hall, Herringthorpe.

SCARBOROUGH BIRDERS. (1993;
25). R.N.Hopper (Membership
Secretary), 10A Ramshill Road,
Scarborough, N Yorkshire YO11
2QE. 01723 369 537.
www.scarboroughbirding.co.uk
Meetings: 3rd Thursday of the
month (Sep-Nov) and (Jan-Apr).
Check website for details.

SHEFFIELD BIRD STUDY GROUP. (1972; 160). Richard
Hill, Honorary Secretary, 22 Ansell Road, Sheffield,
South Yorkshire S11 7PE.
E-mail: Secretary@sbsg.org - www.sbsg.org
Meetings: 7.15pm, 2nd Wednesday of the month
(Sep-May), Lecture Theatre 5, Sheffield University
Arts Tower.

SK58 BIRDERS. (1993; 66). Andy Hirst, 15 Hunters
Drive, Dinnington, Sheffield, S25 2TG. 07947 068 125;
e-mail: contact@sk58birders.com
www.sk58birders.com
Chair: Mick Clay, 2 High St, S.Anston, Sheffield. 01909
566 000.
Meetings: 7.30pm, last Wednesday of the month
(except July, Aug & Dec (Christmas social), Upstairs
Room, Loyal Trooper pub, South Anston.

SORBY NHS (ORNITHOLOGICAL SECTION). (1918; 400).
The Secretary, C/O 100 Bole Hill Lane, Sheffield S10
1SD, E-mail: ornithology@sorby.org.uk
www.sorby.org.uk**Meetings:** Indoor and field meetings
held regularly as advertised on the website and in the
newsletter.

SOUTH PEAK RAPTOR STUDY GROUP. (1998; 12). M E
Taylor, 76 Hawksley Avenue, Newbold, Chesterfield,
Derbys S40 4TL. 01246 277 749.

SOUTH RYEDALE AND EAST YORKSHIRE RAPTOR
GROUP. Mick Carroll. 10 Cross Avenue, Pickering,
North Yorkshire YO18 7HP. 01751 476 550.

SWILLINGTON INGS BIRD GROUP. (1989; 83).
Chris Robinson, 43 Northfield Road, Sprotbrough,
Doncaster, DN5 8AY. 07534 271 254.
http://sibg1.wordpress.com
Meetings: 7.30pm, 1st Thursday of even months with
informal evening evenings 1st Thursday of odd months
(please phone for details of venue).

WAKEFIELD NATURALISTS' SOCIETY. (1851; 32).
Michael Warrington, 31 Mount Avenue, Hemsworth,
Pontefract, W Yorks WF9 4QE. 01977 614 954;
e-mail: michaelwarrington@talktalk.net
Meetings: 7.30pm, 2nd Tuesday of the month
(Sep-Apr), Friends Meeting House, Thornhill Street,
Wakefield.

YORK ORNITHOLOGICAL CLUB. (1967; 80). Linda
Newton, 5 Fairfields Drive, Skelton, York YO30 1YP,
01904 471 446; e-mail: secretary@yorkbirding.org.uk
www.yorkbirding.org.uk
Meetings: 7.30pm, 1st Tuesday of the month,
Friends' Meeting House, Friargate, York (see
website).

YORKSHIRE NATURALISTS' UNION (Bird Section).
(1875; 500). Mr John Wint (Vice Chairman). 01977 662
826; e-mail: j.wint114@btinternet.com
www.ynu.org.uk

Ringing Groups
BARNSLEY RG. M C Wells, 715 Manchester Road,
Stocksbridge, Sheffield, S36 1DQ. 0114 288 4211;
e-mail: martinwells@barnsleybsg.plus.com

DONCASTER RG. D Hazard, 41 Jossey Lane,
Scawthorpe, Doncaster, S Yorks DN5 9DB. 01302 788
044; e-mail: dave.hazard@tiscali.co.uk

EAST DALES RG. P. Bone, 11 Dorrington Close,
Pocklington, York, YO42 2GS.
E-mail: philsarab@aol.co.uk

SORBY-BRECK RG. Geoff P Mawson, Moonpenny Farm,
Farwater Lane, Dronfield, Sheffield S18 1RA.
E-mail: moonpenny@talktalk.net

SPURN BIRD OBSERVATORY. Paul Collins, Kew Villa,
Seaside Road, Kilnsea, Hull HU12 0UB. 01964 650 479;
e-mail: pcnfa@hotmail.com

WINTERSETT RG. P Smith, 16 Templar Street,
Wakefield, W Yorks, WF1 5HB. 01924 375 082.

RSPB Local Groups
AIREDALE AND BRADFORD. (1972; 3500 in catchment
area). Paul Barrett. 01274 582 078;
e-mail: AbRSPB@blueyonder.co.uk
www.rspb.org.uk/groups/airedaleandbradford
Meetings: 7.30pm, monthly on Fridays, Room 3,
Shipley Library.

CRAVEN & PENDLE. (1986; 300). Colin Straker. 01756
751 888; e-mail: colin.straker@btinternet.com
www.cravenandpendlerspb.org
Meetings: 7.30pm 2nd Wednesday of the month (Sep-
May), St Andrews Church Hall, Newmarket Street,
Skipton.

DONCASTER. (1984; 105). Sue Clifton, West Lodge,
Wadworth Hall Lane, Wadworth, Doncaster, DN11
9BH. Tel/(fax) 01302 854 956;
e-mail: sue.cl@waitrose.com
www.rspb.org.uk/groups/doncaster
Meetings: 7.30pm 2nd Wednesday of the month
(Sept-May), Salvation Army Community Church,
Lakeside.

EAST YORKSHIRE. (1986;120). Trevor Malkin, 9 Angus
Drive, Driffield, E Yorks, YO25 5BQ. 01377 257 325;
e-mail: eastyorksrspb@yahoo.co.uk

ENGLAND

www.rspb.org.uk/groups/eastyorkshire
Meetings: 7.30pm, North Bridlington Library, Martongate, BRIDLINGTON (check website for details).

HARROGATE DISTRICT. (2005). Bob Orange. E-mail: robert_orange@btinternet.com www.harrogaterspb.com **Meetings:** 7.50pm, 3rd Monday of the month (Oct-Mar). Christ Church Parish Centre, The Stray, Harrogate HG1 4SW.

HUDDERSFIELD & HALIFAX. (1981; 120). David Hemingway, 267 Long Lane, Dalton, Huddersfield, HD5 9SH. 01484 301 920; e-mail: d.hemingway@ntlworld.com www.rspb.org.uk/groups/huddersfieldand halifax **Meetings:** 7.30pm, Huddersfield Methodist Mission, 3-13 Lord Street, HUDDERSFIELD, HD1 1QA.

HULL & DISTRICT. (1983; 334). Betty Hilton. 01482 849 503; e-mail: betty9hilton@gmail.com www.rspb.org.uk/groups/hull **Meetings:** 7.30pm, Tuesdays (Sept-Apr), Christchurch United Reformed Church, South Ella Way, Kirk Ella, HULL. (£2 for Local Group Members and £2.50 for Non Members).

LEEDS. (1974; 560). Ian Willoughby. 0113 258 6555. www.rspb.org.uk/groups/leeds **Meetings:** 7.30pm, 3rd Wednesday of the month (Sep-Apr), Friends Meeting House, 188 Woodhouse Lane, LEEDS, Yorkshire, LS2 9DX.

RICHMONDSHIRE & HAMBLETON. (2005). Jim Brettell. 01748 850 272; e-mail: jgb@barneyschool.org.uk www.rspb.org.uk/groups/ richmondshireandhambleton **Meetings:** Check website.

SHEFFIELD. (1981; 500). Susan Bradshaw. 0114 239 9072;E-mail: s.bradshaw@sheffield.ac.uk www.rspb-sheffield.org.uk **Meetings:** 7.30pm 1st Thursday of the month (Sept-May), Central United Reformed Church, Norfolk St, Sheffield.

WAKEFIELD. (1987; 130). Duncan Stokoe, 12 New Road, Horbury, Wakefield, West Yorkshire WF4 5LR. E-mail: duncanstokoe@talktalk.net www.rspb.org.uk/groups/wakefield **Meetings:** 7.30pm, 4th Thursday of the month (Sep-Apr), Ossett War Memorial Community Centre, Prospect Road, Ossett, WF5 8AN.

YORK. (1972; 600). Chris Lloyd, 7 School Lane, Upper Poppleton, York, YO26 6JS. 01904 794865; e-mail: rspb.calyork@btinternet.com www.yorkrspb.org.uk **Meetings:** 7.30pm, Tues, Wed or Thurs, Temple Hall, York St John University, Lord Mayors Walk, York.

Wetland Bird Survey Organiser
EAST YORKSHIRE & SCARBOROUGH (EXCLUDING THE HUMBER). Shirley Pashby; e-mail: webs@bto.org

HARROGATE AND YORKSHIRE DALES. William Haines, 07870 828 9788; e-mail: bill.haines@tiscali.co.uk HUDDERSFIELD/HALIFAX AREA. Position vacant. HUMBER ESTUARY (NORTH). Nick Cutts, 01430 423515; e-mail: N.D.Cutts@hull.ac.uk

LEEDS AREA. Paul Morris; e-mail: pmorris@wyjs.org.uk

SOUTH YORKSHIRE. Position vacant.

WAKEFIELD AREA. Peter Smith; e-mail: webs@bto.org

Wildlife Hospital
ANIMAL HOUSE WILDLIFE WELFARE. Mrs C Buckroyd, 14 Victoria Street, Scarborough, YO12 7SS. 01723 371 256 (please leave a message on the answer machine and callers will be contacted as soon as possible); e-mail: cynthiabuckroyd@talktalk.net or cindybuckroyd@hotmail.com All species of wild birds. Oiled birds given treatment before forwarding to cleaning stations. Incubators, hospital cages, heat pads, release sites. Birds ringed before release. Prior telephone call requested. Collection if required. Veterinary support. Charity shop at 127 Victoria Road.

Wildlife Trusts
SHEFFIELD WILDLIFE TRUST. (1985; 4,450). 37 Stafford Road, Sheffield, S2 2SF. 0114 263 4335 (fax) 0114 263 4345; e-mail: mail@wildsheffield.com www.wildsheffield.com

YORKSHIRE WILDLIFE TRUST. (1946; 21,500). 1 St George's Place, Tadcaster Road,YorkYO24 1GN. 01904 659 570; e-mail: info@ywt.org.uk www.ywt.org.uk

SCOTLAND

Bird Report
SCOTTISH BIRD REPORT from The SOC, The Scottish Birdwatching Resource Centre, Waterston House, Aberlady, East Lothian, EH32 0PY.

Club
See Scottish Ornithologists' Club in National Directory.

ANGUS & DUNDEE

Bird Recorder
ANGUS & DUNDEE. Jon Cook, 76 Torridon Road, Broughty Ferry, Dundee, DD5 3JH. 01382 738 495; e-mail: 1301midget@tiscali.co.uk

Bird Report
ANGUS & DUNDEE BIRD REPORT (1974-), from the County Recorder, 01382 738 495; e-mail: 1301midget@tiscali.co.uk

BTO Regional Representative
ANGUS. Bruce Lynch, 01382 737 528; e-mail: b_lynch1@sky.com

Clubs
ANGUS & DUNDEE BIRD CLUB. (1997; 220). Dorothy Fyffe, 33 Ireland Street, Carnoustie, Angus DD7 6AS. 01241 853 053; www.angusbirding.com **Meetings:** 7.30pm, Tuesdays, Montrose Basin Wildlife Centre.

ADBC

SOC TAYSIDE BRANCH. (145). Brian Boag, Birch Brae, Knapp, Inchture, Perthshire PH14 9SW. 01828 686 669; www.the-soc.org.uk

Ringing Group
TAY RG. Ms S Millar; e-mail: shirley@edenecology.co.uk

RSPB Members' Groups
DUNDEE. (1972;110). Graham Smith, 01382 532 461; e-mail: grahamnjen@hotmail.com www.RSPB.org.uk/groups/dundee **Meetings:** 7.30 pm, monthly on a Wednesday (Sep-Mar), Methodist Church, 20, West Marketgait, Dundee. Admission £1.00 for all, including refreshments.

Wetland Bird Survey Organisers
ANGUS (excl Montrose Basin). Dr BM Lynch, 27 Luke Place, Broughty Ferry, Dundee DD5 3BN. e-mail: b_lynch1@sky.com

MONTROSE BASIN. Adam McClure, 01674 676 336; e-mail: amcclure@swt.org.uk

ARGYLL

Birds of Argyll (Argyll Bird Club 2007, £45 inc postage), available from Bob Furness, The Cnoc, Tarbert, Arrochar, Dunbartonshire G83 7DG. 01301 702 603.

Bird Recorder
ARGYLL. Paul Daw, Tigh-na-Tulloch, Tullochgorm, Minard, Argyll, PA32 8YQ. 01546 886 260; e-mail: monedula@globalnet.co.uk

Bird Reports
ARGYLL BIRD REPORT (1984-), From Dr Bob Furness, The Cnoc, Tarbet, Dunbartonshire G83 7DG.01301 702 603; e-mail: r.furness@bio.gla.ac.uk

ISLE OF MULL BIRD REPORT (2004-), From Mr Alan Spellman, Maridon, Lochdon, Isle of Mull, Argyll. PA64 6AP. 01680 812 448; e-mail: mullbirds@btinternet.com www.mullbirds.com

BTO Regional Representatives
ARGYLL (MULL, COLL, TIREE AND MORVERN). Arthur Brown/ Rod Little, 01688 400 415/01688 400 315; e-mail: pamartbrown@btinternet.com or e-mail: rltt@aol.com

ARGYLL MAINLAND, BUTE AND GIGHA. Richard Allan, 01852 300 359; e-mail: r.allan13@btinternet.com

ISLAY, JURA, COLONSAY. John S Armitage, Airigh Sgallaidh, Portnahaven, Isle of Islay, PA47 7SZ. 01496 860 396; e-mail: jsa@ornquest.plus.com www.islaybirder.blogspot.com

Clubs
ARGYLL BIRD CLUB. (1983;270). Katie Pendreigh, The Whins, Farry Road, Tayinloan, Argyll PA37 1PT. 01631 710 630; www.argyllbirdclub.org **Meetings:** All-day Indoor Meetings are held on a Saturday in early March and early November each year, see website for details.

ISLE OF MULL BIRD CLUB. (2001;160), Mrs Janet T Hall, Membership Secretary, Druim Mhor, Craignure, Isle of Mull, Argyll PA65 6AY. 01680 812 441; e-mail: oystercatcher@dee-emm.co.uk www.mullbirdclub.org.uk **Meetings:** 7 for 7.30pm start, 3rd Friday of the month (Oct-Apr), Craignure Village Hall.

SCOTLAND

Ringing Group
TRESHNISH ISLES AUK RG. Robin Ward,
e-mail: robin.ward2@virginmedia.com

RSPB Local Group
HELENSBURGH. (1975; 62). Steve Chadwin, 01436
670 158.
Meetings: The Guide Halls, Lower John Street,

Wildlife Hospital
WINGS OVER MULL. Richard and Sue Dewar,
Auchnacroish House, Torosay, Craignure, Isle of
Mull PA65 6AY. Tel/fax: 01680 812 594;
email: dewars@wingsovermull.com
www.wingsovermull.com

Wetland Bird Survey Organisers
ARGYLL MAINLAND. Paul Daw, 01546 886 260;
e-mail: monedula@globalnet.co.uk

ARRAN. J Cassels, e-mail: james.cassels@virgin.net

BUTE. Ian Hopkins;
e-mail: ian@hopkins0079.freeserve.co.uk

ISLAY, JURA, COLONSAY. John S Armitage;
e-mail: jsa@ornquest.plus.com

TIREE & COLL. John Bowler,
e-mail: john.bowler@rspb.org.uk

AYRSHIRE

Bird Recorder
AYRSHIRE. Fraser Simpson, 4 Inchmurrin Drive,
Kilmarnock, Ayrshire KA3 2JD.
e-mail: recorder@ayrshire-birding.org.uk
www.ayrshire-birding.org.uk

Bird Report
AYRSHIRE BIRD REPORT (1976-), from
Dr RG Vernon, 29 Knoll Park, Ayr KA7
4RH. 01292 442 195; e-mail: rgv_mcv@
tiscali.co.uk

BTO Regional Representative
AYRSHIRE. Brian Broadley, 01290
424 241; e-mail: brianbroadley@
onegreendoor.com

Club
SOC AYRSHIRE. (1962; 154). Anne Dick, Rowanmyle
House, Tarbolton, Mauchline KA5 5LU. 01292 541
981. www.ayrshire-birding.org.uk
www.the-soc.org.uk
Meetings: 7.30pm, Tuesdays monthly, Monkton
Community Church, Monkton by Prestwick.

RSPB Members' Groups
CENTRAL AYRSHIRE LOCAL GROUP. (1978; 85).
Ronnie Coombes (Group Leader), 01292 265 891;
e-mail: ronnie.coombes@tesco.net
www.ayrshire-birding.org.uk

Meetings: 7.30pm 3rd Monday of the month (Sep-
Apr), Newton Wallacetown Church Hall, 60 Main
Street, Ayr.

NORTH AYRSHIRE. (1976; 180). John Tedd, 01294
823 434; e-mail: john.tedd@virgin.net
www.narspb.org.uk
Meetings: 7.30pm, various Fridays (Sep-Apr), Argyll
Centre, Donaldson Avenue, SALTCOATS, Ayrshire,
KA21 5AG.

Wetland Bird Survey Organiser
AYRSHIRE (excluding Isle Of Cumbrae). Mr David
Grant, e-mail: david.grant@sac.ac.uk

Wildlife Hospital
HESSILHEAD WILDLIFE RESCUE CENTRE. Gay & Andy
Christie, Gateside, Beith, Ayrshire, KA15 1HT.
01505 502 415; e-mail: info@hessilhead.org.uk
www.hessilhead.org.uk All species. Releasing
aviaries. Veterinary support. Visits only on open
days please.

THE SCOTTISH BORDERS

Bird Atlas/Avifauna
*The Breeding Birds of South-east Scotland, a tetrad
atlas 1988-1994* by R D Murray et al. (Scottish
Ornithologists' Club, 1998).

Bird Recorder
Ray Murray, 4 Bellfield Crescent, Eddleston,
Peebles, EH45 8RQ. 01721 730 677;
e-mail: raymurray1@tiscali.co.uk

Bird Report
BORDERS BIRD REPORT (1979-), From Malcolm Ross,
Westfield Cottage, Smailholm, Kelso TD5 7PN.01573
460 699; e-mail: eliseandmalcolm@btinternet.com

BTO Regional Representative
Graham Pyatt, The Schoolhouse, Manor, Peebles
EH45 9JN. 01721 740 319;
e-mail: d.g.pyatt@btinternet.com

Club
SOC BORDERS BRANCH. (100). Graham Pyatt, The
Schoolhouse, Manor, Peebles EH45 9JN. 01721 740
319; www.the-soc.org.uk
Meetings: 7.30pm, 2nd Monday of the month,
George & Abbotsford Hotel, Melrose.

Ringing Group
BORDERS RG. (1991; 10). Dr T W Dougall, 38
Leamington Terrace, Edinburgh EH10 4JL. (Office)
0131 344 2600.

RSPB Members' Group
BORDERS. (1995; 94). John Marshall, 01896 850
564; e-mail: ncmandjrm@btinternet.com
Meetings: 7.30pm, 3rd Wednesday of the month,
The Corn Exchange, Market Square, MELROSE

Wetland Bird Survey Organiser
BORDERS. Andrew Bramhall; e-mail: webs@bto.org

CAITHNESS

Bird Atlas/Avifauna
A History of Caithness Birds 1769 to 2001, by
S.A.M. Manson. (Published by author, 2002).

Bird Recorder
CAITHNESS. Stan Laybourne, Old Schoolhouse,
Harpsdale, Halkirk, Caithness, KW12 6UN. 01847
841244; e-mail: stanlaybourne@talk21.com

BTO Regional Representative
CAITHNESS. Donald Omand, 9 Skiall, Shebster,
Thurso, Caithness KW14 7YD. 01847 811 403;
e-mail: achreamie@yahoo.co.uk

Clubs
SOC CAITHNESS BRANCH. (51). Stan Laybourne, Old
Schoolhouse, Harpsdale, Halkirk, Caithness, KW12
6UN. 01847 841 244; www.the-soc.org.uk
e-mail: stanlaybourne@talk21.com

Wetland Bird Survey Organiser
CAITHNESS. Stan Laybourne; e-mail: webs@bto.org

CLYDE

Bird Atlas/Avifauna
*A Guide to Birdwatching in the Clyde Area
(2001)*by Cliff Baister and Marin Osler (Scottish
Ornithologists' Club, Clyde branch).

Bird Recorders
CLYDE ISLANDS (ARRAN, BUTE & CUMBRAES).
Bernard Zonfrillo, 28 Brodie Road, Glasgow G21
3SB;
e-mail: b.zonfrillo@bio.gla.ac.uk

CLYDE. Iain P Gibson, 8 Kenmure View, Howwood,
Johnstone, Renfrewshire, PA9 1DR. 01505 705 874;
e-mail: iaingibson.soc@btinternet.com

Bird Report
CLYDE BIRDS (1973-), From Valerie
Wilson, 76 Laigh Road, Newton
Mearns, Glasgow, G77 5EQ. e-mail:
wilsonval@btinternet.com

Clyde Birds

Clyde Bird Report 2005
Clyde Islands Bird Report 2005

BTO Regional Representative
LANARK, RENFREW, DUMBARTON.
John Knowler, 0141 584 9117;
e-mail: john.knowler@ntlworld.com

Club
SOC CLYDE BRANCH. (300). Hayley Douglas, Top
Right, 35 Church Street, Lochwinnoch PA12 4AE.
07715 634 079; www.the-soc.org.uk

Ringing Group
CLYDE RG. (1979; 18). I Livingstone, 01698 749 844;
e-mail: iainlivcrg@googlemail.com

RSPB Members' Groups
GLASGOW. (1972;141). Roger Adams. 0141 942
6920; e-mail: Rogerlpadams7@aol.com
www.rspb.org.uk/groups/glasgow
Meetings: 7.30pm, monthly on a Thursday (Sep-
Apr), Adelaides, 209 Bath Street, GLASGOW G2
4HZ.

HAMILTON. (1976;90). Jim Lynch, 0141 583 1044;
e-mail: birder45a@yahoo.co.uk
www.baronshaugh.co.uk
Meetings: 7.30pm, 3rd Thursday of the month
(Sept-May), Watersports Centre, Motherwell (next
to Strathclyde Loch).

RENFREWSHIRE. (1986; 200). Iain Smeaton, e-mail:
RenfrewRSPB@hotmail.co.uk
www.rspb.org.uk/groups/renfrewshire
Meetings: 1st Friday of the month (Sep-Apr), The
McMaster Centre, 2a Donaldson Drive, RENFREW

Wetland Bird Survey Organisers
GLASGOW/RENFREWSHIRE/LANARKSHIRE & CLYDE
ESTUARY. John Clark;
e-mail: johnclark@jcmc.demon.co.uk

BUTE. Ian Leslie Hopkins, 01700 504 042;
e-mail: ian@hopkins0079.freeserve.co.uk

DUMFRIES & GALLOWAY

Bird Recorder
Paul Collin, Gairland, Old Edinburgh Road,
Minnigaff, Newton Stewart, DG8 6PL. 01671 402
861; e-mail: pncollin@live.co.uk

Bird Report
*DUMFRIES & GALLOWAY REGION BIRD REPORT
(1985-)*, From Peter Swan, 3 Castle View, Castle
Douglas, DG7 1BG. 01556 502 144.

BTO Regional Representatives
DUMFRIES. Edmund Fellowes, 01387 262 094;
e-mail: edmundfellowes@aol.com

KIRKCUDBRIGHT. Andrew Bielinski, 41 Main
Street, St Johns Town of Dalry, Castle Douglas,
Kirkcudbright, DG7 3UP. 01644 430 418 (evening);
e-mail: andrewb@bielinski.fsnet.co.uk

WIGTOWN. Geoff Sheppard, The Roddens, Leswalt,
Stranraer, Wigtownshire, DG9 0QR. 01776 870 685;
e-mail: geoff.roddens@btinternet.com

Clubs
SOC DUMFRIES BRANCH. (1961; 105). Mrs Pat Abery,
East Daylesford, Colvend, Dalbeattie, Dumfries,
DG5 4QA. 01556 630 483; www.the-soc.org.uk

SCOTLAND

Meetings: 7.30pm, 2nd Wednesday of the month (Sept-Apr), Cumberland St Day Centre.

SOC STEWARTRY BRANCH. (1976; 80). Miss Joan Howie, 60 Main Street, St Johns Town of Dalry, Castle Douglas, Kirkcudbrightshire, DG7 3UW. 01644 430 226.
www.the-soc.org.uk
Meetings: 7.30pm, usually 2nd Thursday of the month (Sep-Apr), Kells School, New Galloway.

SOC WEST GALLOWAY BRANCH. (1975; 50). Geoff Sheppard, The Roddens, Leswalt, Stranraer, Wigtownshire, DG9 0QR. 01776 870 685; e-mail: geoff.roddens@btinternet.com
www.the-soc.org.uk
Meetings: 7.30pm, 2nd Tuesday of the month (Oct-Mar), Stranraer Library.

Ringing Group
NORTH SOLWAY RG. Geoff Sheppard, 01776 870 685; e-mail: geoff.roddens@btinternet.com

RSPB Members' Group
GALLOWAY. (1985;150). Cynthia Douglas, Midpark, Balmaclellan, Castle Douglas, DG7 3PX. 01644 420 605; e-mail: cynthia@cdouglas.plus.com
www.rspb.org.uk/groups/galloway
Meetings: 7.30pm 3rd Tuesday in the month (Sep-May),Parish Church Hall, Queen Street, Castle Douglas.

Wetland Bird Survey Organisers
AUCHENCAIRN AND ORCHARDTON BAYS. Euan MacAlpine, 01556 640 244; e-mail: js.eamm@sky.com

DUMFRIES & GALLOWAY. Andy Riches, 07792 142 446; e-mail: slioch69@aol.com

FLEET BAY. David Hawker. 01556 610 086; e-mail: dheco@dsl.pipex.com

LOCH RYAN. Geoff Shepherd, 01776 870 685; e-mail: geoff.roddens@btinternet.com

ROUGH FIRTH. Judy Baxter, 01556 630 262; e-mail: Jbaxter@nts.org.uk

WIGTOWN BAY. Paul Collin, 01671 402 861; e-mail: pncollin@live.co.uk

FIFE

Bird Atlas/Avifauna
The Birds of Fife by Anne-Marie Smout. Donald 1983.

The Fife Bird Atlas 2003 by Norman Elkins, Jim Reid, Allan Brown, Derek Robertson & Anne-Marie Smout. Available from Allan W. Brown (FOAG), 61 Watts Gardens, Cupar, Fife KY15 4UG, Tel. 01334 656804, email: swans@allanwbrown.co.uk

Bird Recorders
FIFE REGION INC OFFSHORE ISLANDS (NORTH FORTH). Mr Malcolm Ware, 15a King Street, Inverkeithing, Fife, KY11 1NB; e-mail: mw160598@hotmail.co.uk

ISLE OF MAY BIRD OBSERVATORY. Iain English, 19 Nethan Gate, Hamilton, S Lanarks, ML3 8NH. e-mail: i.english@talk21.com

Bird Reports
FIFE BIRD REPORT (1988-) (FIFE & KINROSS BR 1980-87), From Mr Malcolm Ware, 15a King Street, Inverkeithing, Fife, KY11 1NB. e-mail: mw160598@hotmail.co.uk

ISLE OF MAY BIRD OBSERVATORY REPORT (1985-), From Iain English, 19 Nethan Gate, Hamilton, S Lanarks, ML3 8NH. e-mail: i.english@talk21.com

BTO Regional Representative
FIFE & KINROSS. Norman Elkins, 18 Scotstarvit View, Cupar, Fife, KY15 5DX. 01334 654 348; e-mail: jandnelkins@btinternet.com

Clubs
FIFE BIRD CLUB. (1985; 200). Mr Drew Crosbie (Membership Secretary), 14 Dunvegan Drive, Falkirk, Central Scotland FK2 7UG. www.fifebirdclub.org
Meetings: 7.30pm, (various evenings), Dean Park Hotel, Chapel Level, Kirkcaldy.

LOTHIANS AND FIFE SWAN & GOOSE STUDY GROUP. (1978)Allan & Lyndesay Brown, 61 Watts Gardens, Cupar, Fife, KY15 4UG; e-mail: swans@allanwbrown.co.uk

SOC FIFE BRANCH. (1950;170). Karen Dick,South Lodge,St Michaels,St AndrewsKY16 0DU. 01334 848 278; (M)7825 786 165; e-mail: fifesoc@sky.com www.the-soc.org.uk
Meetings: 7.30pm, 2nd Wednesday of the month (Sep-Apr), Venue details available at www.the-soc.org.uk/branch-meetings.htm#fife

Ringing Groups
ISLE OF MAY BIRD OBSERVATORY. David Grieve. 01899 309 176.

TAY RG. Ms S Millar, e-mail: shirley@edenecology.co.uk

Wetland Bird Survey Organisers
FIFE (excluding estuaries). Allan Brown; e-mail: swans@allanwbrown.co.uk

FORTH ESTUARY (North). Alastair Inglis, e-mail: aandjinglis@hotmail.com

TAY AND EDEN ESTUARIES. Norman Elkins, 01334 654 348; e-mail: jandnelkins@btinternet.com

Wildlife Hospital
SCOTTISH SPCA WILD LIFE REHABILITATION CENTRE. Middlebank Farm, Masterton Road, Dunfermline, Fife, KY11 8QN. 01383 412 520 All species. Open to visitors, groups and school parties. Illustrated talk on oiled bird cleaning and other aspects of wildlife rehabilitation available. Veterinary support.

FORTH

Bird Recorder
UPPER FORTH (Does not include parts of Stirling in Loch Lomondside/Clyde Basin). Chris Pendlebury, 3 Sinclair Street, Dunblane, FK5 0AH. 07798 711 134; e-mail: chris@upperforthbirds.co.uk

Bird Report
FORTH AREA BIRD REPORT (1975-) - enlarged report published annually in The Forth Naturalist and Historian, University of Stirling, From Dr Roy Sexton, Asst. Editor, Forth Naturalist and Historian, 22 Alexander Drive, Bridge of Allan, FK9 4QB.01786 833 409; e-mail: RoyGravedigger@AOL.com www.fnh.stir.ac.uk

BTO Regional Representative
CENTRAL. Neil Bielby, 56 Ochiltree, Dunblane, Perthshire, FK15 0DF. 01786 823 830; e-mail: n.bielby@sky.com

Club
SOC CENTRAL SCOTLAND BRANCH. (1968; 101). Mr RL Gooch, The Red House, Dollarfield, Dollar, Clacks FK14 7LX. 01259 742 326; www.the-soc.org.uk
Meetings: 7.30pm, 1st Thursday of the month (Sep-Apr), The Smith Art Gallery and Museum, Dumbarton Road, Stirling.

RSPB Members' Group
CENTRAL, FORTH VALLEY. (1995; 150). Jenni Fulton, 0790 153 8078; e-mail: jennifultonRSPB@yahoo.co.uk www.rspb.org.uk/groups/forthvalley
Meetings: 7.30pm, 3rd Thursday of the month (Sept-Apr), Hillpark Centre, Stirling.

Wetland Bird Survey Organisers
INNER FORTH ESTUARY. Michael Bell, Contact via WeBS Office; e-mail: mvbell34@tiscali.co.uk

NORTH FORTH ESTUARY. Alistair Inglis, 01383 822 115; e-mail: aandjinglis@hotmail.com

OUTER SOUTH ESTUARY. Duncan Priddle, 01620 827 459; e-mail: dpriddle@eastlothian.gov.uk

TYNINGHAM ESTUARY. Bobby Anderson, 01620 827318; e-mail: randerson@eastlothian.gov.uk

HIGHLAND

Bird Atlas/Avifauna
The Birds of Sutherland by Alan Vittery (Colin Baxter Photography Ltd, 1997).

Skye Birds, by RL McMillan. (Published by the author, 2005).

Bird Recorders
ROSS-Shire, INVERNESS-SHIRE, SUTHERLAND, BADENOCH & STRATHSPEY, LOCHABER, LOCHALSH and SKYE. Hugh Insley, 1 Drummond Place, Inverness,IV2 4JT. 01463 230 652; (M)07831 479 804; e-mail: hugh.insley@btinternet.com

Bird Reports
HIGHLAND BIRD REPORT (1991-). 2008 edition £9.50 inc p&p, From Alistair F McNee, Liathach, 4 Balnafettack Place, Inverness, IV3 8TQ. 01463 220 493; e-mail: aj.mcnee@care4free.net

BTO Regional Representatives
INVERNESS & SPEYSIDE. Hugh Insley, 1 Drummond Place, Inverness,IV2 4JT. 01463 230 652; e-mail: hugh.insley@btinternet.com

RUM, EIGG, CANNA & MUCK. Bob Swann, 14 St Vincent Road, Tain, Ross-shire, IV19 1JR. 01862 894 329; e-mail: robert.swann@homecall.co.uk

ROSS-SHIRE. Simon Cohen, e-mail: saraandsimon@hotmail.com

SUTHERLAND. Position vacant.

SKYE. Position vacant.

Clubs
EAST SUTHERLAND BIRD GROUP. (1976; 120). Tony Mainwood, 13 Ben Bhraggie Drive, Golspie, Sutherland KW10 6SX. 01408 633 247; e-mail: tony.mainwood@ btinternet.com
Meetings: 7.30pm, Last Monday of the month (Oct, Nov, Jan, Feb, Mar), Golspie Community Centre.

SOC HIGHLAND BRANCH. (1955; 151). Kathy Bonniface, Alt Dubh, North End, Tomatin, IV13 7YP. 01808 511 740.e-mail: kathybonniface@aol.com www.the-soc.org.uk
Meetings: 7.45pm, 1st Tuesday of the month (Sep-Mar), Culloden Library.

Ringing Group
HIGHLAND RG. Bob Swann, e-mail: robert.swann@homecall.co.uk

SCOTLAND

RSPB Members' Group
HIGHLAND. (1987; 214). Doreen Manson, Muirton Lodge, Urray, Muir of Ord, Ross-shire IV6. 01997 433 283; e-mail: john@jmanson2.wanadoo.co.uk
www.rspb.org.uk/groups/highland
Meetings: 7.30pm, last Thursday of the month (Sep-Apr), Kingsmill Hotel, Culcabock Road, Inverness.

Wetland Bird Survey Organisers
MORAY BASIN COAST. Bob Swann;
e-mail: robert.swann@homecall.co.uk

SKYE AND LOCHALSH. Robert McMillan;
e-mail: bob@skye-birds.com

SUTHERLAND (EXLUDING THE MORAY BASIN).
Position vacant

BADENOCH AND STRATHSPEY. Keith Duncan;
e-mail: webs@bto.org

CAITHNESS. Stan Laybourne; e-mail: webs@bto.org

LOCHABER. John Dye; e-mail: john.dye@virgin.net

WEST INVERNESS AND WESTER ROSS. Position vacant

LOTHIAN

Bird Atlas/Avifauna
The Breeding Birds of South-east Scotland, a tetrad atlas 1988-1994 by R D Murray et al. (Scottish Ornithologists' Club, 1998).

Bird Recorder
Stephen Welch, 25 Douglas Road, Longniddry, EH32 0LQ; 01875 852 802;(M) 07931 524 963; e-mail: lothianrecorder@the-soc.org.uk

Bird Reports
LOTHIAN BIRD REPORT (1979-), from the Lothian SOC Branch Secretary.

BTO Regional Representative
Alan Heavisides, 9 Addiston Crescent, Balerno, Edinburgh, EH14 7DB. 0131 449 3816; e-mail: alanheavisides@yahoo.com

BTO Garden BirdWatch Ambassador
Prof J I B Wilson, e-mail: jib4wilson@o2.co.uk

Clubs
EDINBURGH NATURAL HISTORY SOCIETY. (1869; 200). The Secretary, e-mail: enquiries@edinburghnaturalhistorysociety.org.uk
www.edinburghnaturalhistorysociety.org.uk
Meetings: 7.30pm, 4th Wednesday of the month The Guide Hall, 33 Melville Street, Edinburgh.

LOTHIANS AND FIFE MUTE SWAN STUDY GROUP. (1978; 12). Allan & Lyndesay Brown, 61 Watts Gardens, Cupar, Fife, KY15 4UG.
e-mail: swans@allanwbrown.co.uk

LOTHIAN SOC. (1936; 570). Doreen Main, Seatoller, Gullane, East Lothian EH31 2DH.
e-mail: doreen.main@yahoo.com
www.the-soc.org.uk
Meetings: 7.30pm, 2nd Tuesday (Sep-Dec and Jan-Apr), Lounge 2, Meadowbank Sports Stadium - Oct & Mar), Waterston House, Aberlady.

RSPB Members' Group
EDINBURGH. (1974;480). Mark Stephen, 25 Newcroft Drive, Glasgow G44 5RT.
e-mail: markbirder@googlemail.com
www.rspb.org.uk/groups/edinburgh/
Meetings: 7.30pm, 3rd Tuesday or Wednesday of the month (Sep-Apr), Napier University, Craiglockhart Campus, Edinburgh.

Wetland Bird Survey Organisers
FORTH ESTUARY (Outer South). Duncan Priddle, 01620 827 459;
e-mail: dpriddle@eastlothian.gov.uk

LOTHIAN (excl estuaries). Joan Wilcox,0131 664 8893; e-mail: webs@bto.org

TYNINGHAME ESTUARY. Mr R Anderson, John Muir Country Park, 01620 827 318;
e-mail: randerson@eastlothian.gov.uk

MORAY & NAIRN

Bird Atlas/Avifauna
The Birds of Moray and Nairn by Martin Cook (Mercat Press, 1992).

Bird Recorders
MORAY AND NAIRN. Martin J H Cook, Rowanbrae, Clochan, Buckie, Banffshire, AB56 5EQ. 01542 850 296; e-mail: martin.cook99@btinternet.com

Bird Reports
BIRDS IN MORAY AND NAIRN (1988-), From The Moray & Nairn Recorder, 01542 850 296;
e-mail: martin.cook99@btinternet.com

BTO Regional Representatives
MORAY & NAIRN. Bob Proctor, 78 Marleon Field, Elgin, Moray, IV30 4GE.
e-mail: bobandlouise@proctor8246.fsnet.co.uk

Wetland Bird Survey Organisers
LOSSIE ESTUARY. Bob Proctor;
e-mail: bobandlouise@proctor8246.fsnet.co.uk

MORAY & NAIRN (Inland). David Law, 01463 725 200; e-mail: jdavidlaw@btinternet.com

SCOTLAND

MORAY BASIN COAST. Bob Swann, 01862 894 329;
e-mail: robert.swann@homecall.co.uk

NORTH EAST SCOTLAND

Bird Atlas/Avifauna
The Birds of North East Scotland by S T Buckland,
M V Bell & N Picozzi (North East Scotland Bird Club,
1990).

Bird Recorder
NORTH-EAST SCOTLAND. Hywel Maggs, 4 Merlin
Terrace, Newburgh, Ellon, Aberdeenshire AB41
6FA.01358 788 106;
e-mail: hywelmaggs@hotmail.com

Bird Reports
NORTH-EAST SCOTLAND BIRD REPORT (1974-), From
Dave Gill, Drakemyre Croft, Cairnorrie, Methlick,
Aberdeenshire, AB41 7JN. 01651 806 252;
e-mail: david@gilldavid1.orangehome.co.uk

NORTH SEA BIRD CLUB ANNUAL REPORT (1979-),
From Andrew Thorpe, Ocean Laboratory and Centre
for Ecology, Aberdeen University, Newburgh, Ellon,
Aberdeenshire, AB41 6AA. 01224 274 428;
e-mail: nsbc@abdn.ac.uk

BTO Regional Representatives
ABERDEEN. Paul Doyle, 01358 751 384;
e-mail: paul@albaecology.co.uk

KINCARDINE & DEESIDE. Graham Cooper, Westbank,
Beltie Road, Torphins, Banchory, Aberdeen, AB31
4JT. 01339 882 706;
e-mail: grm.cooper@btinternet.com

Club
SOC GRAMPIAN BRANCH. (1956; 110). Graham
Cooper, Westbank, 72 Beltie Road, Torphins,
Banchory, Aberdeen, AB31 4JT. 01339 882 706;
www.the-soc.org.uk
Meetings: 7.30pm, usually 1st Monday of the month
(Sep-Apr), Sportsmans's Club, 11 Queens Road,
Aberdeen.

Ringing Group
GRAMPIAN RG. R Duncan,
e-mail: Raymond@waxwing.fsnet.co.uk

RSPB Members' Group
ABERDEEN. (1975; 210). Mark Sutherland
(Chairman), 29 Earlswells Road, Cults,AB15 9NY.
01224 861 446;
e-mail: rodney_payne@btopenworld.com
www.rspb.org.uk/groups/aberdeen
Meetings: 7.30pm, monthly in the winter, Lecture
Theatre, Zoology Dept, Tillydrone Av, Aberdeen.
Two birding trips monthly throughout the year.

Wildlife Hospital
GRAMPIAN WILDLIFE REHABILITATION TRUST. 40
High Street, New Deer, Turriff, Aberdeenshire,
AB53 6SX. 01771 644 489; (M)07803 235 383;
e-mail: laurence.brain@btconnect.com Veterinary
surgeon. Access to full practice facilities. Will care
for all species of birds.

ORKNEY

Bird Atlas/Avifauna
The Birds of Orkney by CJ Booth et al (The Orkney
Press, 1984).

Bird Recorder
Mr EJ Williams, Fairholm, Finstown, Orkney, KW17
2EQ. e-mail: jim@geniefea.freeserve.co.uk

Bird Report
*ORKNEY BIRD REPORT (inc North
Ronaldsay Bird Report) (1974-)*,
From Mr EJ Williams, Fairholm,
Finstown, Orkney, KW17 2EQ.
e-mail: jim@geniefea.freeserve.
co.uk

ORKNEY
BIRD REPORT
2009

BTO Regional Representative
Colin Corse, Garrisdale, Lynn
Park, Kirkwall, Orkney, KW15 1SL. 01856 874 484;
e-mail: ccorse@aol.com

Club
SOC ORKNEY BRANCH. (1993; 15). Colin Corse,
Garrisdale, Lynnpark Road, Kirkwall, Orkney, KW15
1SL. H: 01856 874 484; e-mail: ccorse@aol.com
www.the-soc.org.uk

Ringing Groups
NORTH RONALDSAY BIRD OBSERVATORY. Ms A E
Duncan, e-mail: alison@nrbo.prestel.co.uk
www.nrbo.co.uk

ORKNEY RG. Colin Corse, H: 01856 874 484;
e-mail: ccorse@aol.com

SULE SKERRY RG. Dave Budworth, 01283 215 188.

RSPB Members' Group
ORKNEY. (1985;300 in catchment area). Dick
Matson. 01856 751 426; e-mail: p.wilson410@
btinternet.com
Meetings: Meetings advertised in newsletter and
local press, held at St Magnus Centre, Kirkwall.

Wetland Bird Survey Organiser
ORKNEY. Eric Meek, 01856 850 176;
e-mail: eric.meek@rspb.org.uk

SCOTLAND

OUTER HEBRIDES

Atlas/Avifauna
The Birds of the Outer Hebrides by P.Cunningham, (Mercat Press, 1990).

Bird Recorder
OUTER HEBRIDES. Brian Rabbitts, 6 Carinish, Isle of North Uist HS6 5HL. 01876 580 328; e-mail: rabbitts@hebrides.net

Bird Report
OUTER HEBRIDES BIRD REPORT (1989-), From The Recorder. 6 Carinish, Isle of North Uist HS6 5HL. 01876 580 328; e-mail: rabbitts@hebrides.net

BTO Regional Representatives
BENBECULA & THE UISTS. Yvonne Benting, 07837 253 698; e-mail: yvonne-birder@live.com

LEWIS & HARRIS. Chris Reynolds, 11 Reef, Isle of Lewis, HS2 9HU. 01851 672 376; e-mail: cmreynolds@btinternet.com

Ringing Group
SHIANTS AUK RG. Mr J.J. Lennon, Group Secretary, 01636 525 963.

Wetland Bird Survey Organisers
UISTS AND BENBECULA. Yvonne Benting; e-mail: yvonne-birder@live.com

ISLAY, JURA AND COLONSAY. John Armitage, 01496 860 396; e-mail: jsa@ornquest.plus.com www.islaybirder.blogspot.com

LEWIS & HARRIS. Position vacant.

PERTH & KINROSS

Bird Recorder
PERTH & KINROSS. Scott Paterson, 12 Ochil View, Kinross, KY13 8TN. 01577 864 248, e-mail: scottpaterson12@yahoo.co.uk

BTO Regional Representative
PERTHSHIRE. Richard Paul. 01882 632 212; e-mail: richard@rannoch.net

Club
PERTHSHIRE SOCIETY OF NATURAL SCIENCE (Ornithological Section). (1964; 29). Miss Esther Taylor, 23 Verena Terrace, Perth,PH2 0BZ. 01738 621 986; e-mail: birdsatpsns@btinternet.com www.psns.org.uk
Meetings: 7.30pm, Wednesdays monthly (Oct-Mar), Perth Museum. Summer outings.

Wetland Bird Survey Organisers
LOCH LEVEN. Jeremy Squire, e-mail: webs@bto.org

PERTH & KINROSS (inland). Michael Bell. e-mail: mvbell34@tiscali.co.uk

TAY AND EDEN ESTUARIES. Norman Elkins, 01334 654 348; e-mail: jandnelkins@btinternet.com

SHETLAND

Bird Recorders
FAIR ISLE. David Parnaby, e-mail: fibo@btconnect.com

SHETLAND. Mark Chapman, 55 Leaside, Firth, Mossbank, ShetlandZE2 9TF. 01806 242 401; e-mail: msc.1@btinternet.com

Bird Reports
FAIR ISLE BIRD OBSERVATORY REPORT (1949-), From Scottish Ornithologists' Club, 21 Regent Terrace, Edinburgh, EH7 5BT. 0131 556 6042

SHETLAND BIRD REPORT (1969-) £10 inc p&p, no pre 1973 available, From Martin Huebeck, Shetland Bird Club, Sumburgh Lighthouse, Virkie, Shetland ZE3 9JN; e-mail: martinheubeck@btinternet.com

BTO Regional Representative
Dave Okill, Heilinabretta, Trondra, Shetland, ZE1 0XL. 01595 880 450; e-mail: david@auroradesign.plus.com

Club
SHETLAND BIRD CLUB. (1973; 200). Russ Haywood, Lamnaberg, Wester Quarff, Shetland ZE2 9EZ. 01950 477 471; e-mail: haywood712@btinternet.com www.nature-shetland.co.uk

Ringing Groups
FAIR ISLE BIRD OBSERVATORY. Deryk Shaw, Bird Observatory, Fair Isle, Shetland, ZE2 9JU. e-mail: ffibo@btconnect.com

SHETLAND RG. Dave Okill, Heilinabretta, Trondra, Shetland, ZE1 0XL. 01595 880 450

Wetland Bird Survey Organiser
SHETLAND. Paul Harvey, Shetland Biological Records Centre, Shetland Amenity Trust, (Day)01595 694 688; e-mail: sbrc@shetlandamenity.org

WALES

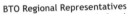

Bird Report
See Welsh Ornithological Society in National Directory.

BTO Honorary Wales Officer
BTO WALES OFFICER. John Lloyd, Cynghordy Hall, Cynghordy, Llandovery, Carms SA20 0LN. e-mail: the_lloyds@dsl.pipex.com

Club
See Welsh Ornithological Society in National Directory.

EAST WALES

Bird Atlas/Avifauna
Birds of Breconshire, by M.Peers and M.Shrubb. (Brecknock WT, 1990).

The Birds of Gwent by Venables et al, published by Helm on behalf of Gwent Ornithological Society, 2008.

The Birds of Montgomeryshire, by B.Holt and G. Williams. (Published by authors, 2008).

The Birds of Radnorshire in preparation, due 2012.

The Gwent Atlas of Breeding Birds by Tyler, Lewis, Venables & Walton (Gwent Ornithological Society, 1987).

Bird Recorders
BRECONSHIRE. Andrew King, Heddfan, Pennorth, Brecon, Powys LD3 7EX. 01874 658 351; e-mail: andrew.king53@virgin.net

GWENT. Chris Jones, 22 Walnut Drive, Caerleon, Newport, South Wales NP18 3SB. e-mail: countyrecorder@gwentbirds.org.uk

MONTGOMERYSHIRE. Brayton Holt, Scops Cottage, Pentrebeirdd, Welshpool, Powys SY21 9DL. 01938 500 266; e-mail: brayton.wanda@virgin.net

RADNORSHIRE (VC43). Pete Jennings, 01597 811 522; e-mail: radnorshirebirds@hotmail.com

Bird Reports
BRECONSHIRE BIRDS (1962-), from Brecknock Wildlife Trust.

GWENT BIRD REPORT (1964-), from Jerry Lewis, Y Bwthyn Gwyn, Coldbrook, Abergavenny, Monmouthshire NP7 9TD. (H)01873 855 091; (W)01633 644 856

MONTGOMERYSHIRE BIRD REPORT (1981-82-), no longer produced, back issues from Montgomeryshire Wildlife Trust.

BTO Regional Representatives
BRECKNOCK. John Lloyd, Cynghordy Hall, Cynghordy, Llandovery, Carms, SA20 0LN. 01550 750 202; e-mail: the_lloyds@dsl.pipex.com

GWENT. Jerry Lewis, Y Bwthyn Gwyn, Coldbrook, Abergavenny, Monmouthshire NP7 9TD. 01873 855 091; e-mail: jerryLewis@monmouthshire.gov.uk

MONTGOMERY. Jane Kelsall, 01970 872 019; e-mail: janekelsall@phonecoop.coop

RADNORSHIRE. Position vacant.

Clubs
THE GWENT ORNITHOLOGICAL SOCIETY. (1964; 420). T J Russell. 01600 716 266; www. gwentbirds.org.uk e-mail: secretary@GwentBirds.org.uk
Meetings: 7.30pm, alternate Saturdays (Sept-Apr), Goytre Village Hall.

MONTGOMERYSHIRE WILDLIFE TRUST BIRD GROUP. (1997; 110). A M Puzey, Four Seasons, Arddleen, Llanymynech, Powys SY22 6RU. 01938 590 578. www.montwt.co.uk/bird_group.html
Meetings: 7.30pm, 3rd Wednesday of the month (Jan-Mar) and (Sep-Dec), Welshpool Methodist Hall.

RADNORSHIRE BIRD GROUP. Pete Jennings, Penbont House, Elan Valley, Rhayader, Powys LD6 5HS. 01597 811 522; e-mail: radnorshirebirds@hotmail. com
Co-ordinates bird recording and surveys in the county through the county recorder

Ringing Groups
GOLDCLIFF RG. Mr RM Clarke; e-mail: chykembro2@aol.com

LLANGORSE RG. (1987; 15). Jerry Lewis, H:01873 855 091; W:01633 644 856

Wetland Bird Survey Organisers
RADNORSHIRE. Peter Jennings, 01597 811 522; e-mail: radnorshirebirds@hotmail.com

BRECONSHIRE. Andrew King, 01874 658 351; e-mail: andrew.king53@virgin.net

MONTGOMERYSHIRE. Jane Kelsall, 01970 832 625; e-mail: janekelsall@phonecoop.coop

Wildlife Trusts
BRECKNOCK WILDLIFE TRUST. (1963; 650). Lion House, Bethel Square, Brecon, Powys LD3 7AY. 01874 625 708; www.brecknockwildlifetrust.org.uk e-mail: enquiries@brecknockwildlifetrust.org.uk

WALES

GWENT WILDLIFE TRUST. (1963; 9,950). Seddon House, Dingestow, Monmouth, NP25 4DY. 01600 740 600; e-mail: info@gwentwildlife.org www.gwentwildlife.org

MONTGOMERYSHIRE WILDLIFE TRUST. (1982; 1000). 42 Broad Street, Welshpool, Powys, SY21 7RR. 01938 555 654; e-mail: info@montwt.co.uk www.montwt.co.uk

RADNORSHIRE WILDLIFE TRUST. (1987; 878). Warwick House, High Street, Llandrindod Wells, Powys LD1 6AG. 01597 823 298; e-mail:info@rwtwales.org www.radnorshirewildlifetrust.org.uk

NORTH WALES

Bird Atlas/Avifauna
The Birds of Anglesey/Adar Môn by P.Hope Jones and P.Whalley. (Menter Môn, 2004).

The Birds of Caernarfonshire by John Barnes (1997, from Lionel Pilling, 51 Brighton Close, Rhyl LL18 3HL).

Bird Recorders
ANGLESEY. Stephen Culley, 22 Cae Derwydd, Cemaes Bay, Anglesey, LL67 0LP. 01407 710 542; e-mail: SteCul10@aol.com

CAERNARFONSHIRE. John Barnes, Fach Goch, Waunfawr, Caernarfon, LL55 4YS. 01286 650 362.

DENBIGHSHIRE & FLINTSHIRE. Ian Spence, 43 Blackbrook, Sychdyn, Mold, Flintshire CH7 6LT. 01352 750 118; e-mail: ianspence.cr@btinternet.com www.cbrg.org.uk

MEIRIONNYDD. Jim Dustow, Lake Vyrnwy; e-mail: Jim.Dustow@rspb.org.uk

Bird Reports
BARDSEY BIRD OBSERVATORY ANNUAL REPORT, from the Warden, see Reserves.

CAMBRIAN BIRD REPORT (Anglesey, Meirionnydd and Caernarfon) (1953-), from Geoff Gibbs. 01248 681 936; e-mail: geoffkate.gibbs@care4free.net www.welshos.org.uk/cambrian/

NORTH-EAST WALES BIRD REPORT (2004-), formerly CLWYD BIRD REPORT (2002-2003), from Ian M Spence, 43 Blackbrook, Sychdyn, Mold, Flintshire CH7 6LT. 01352 750 118; www.cbrg.org.uk e-mail: ianspence.cr@btinternet.com

WREXHAM BIRDWATCHERS' SOCIETY ANNUAL REPORT (1982-), from The Secretary, Wrexham Birdwatchers' Society.

BTO Regional Representatives
ANGLESEY. Tony White. 01407 710 137; e-mail: wylfor@treg5360.freeserve.co.uk

CAERNARFON. Geoff Gibbs. 01248 681 936; e-mail: geoffkate.gibbs@care4free.net

CLWYD EAST. Dr Anne Brenchley, Ty'r Fawnog, 43 Black Brook, Sychdyn, Mold, Flints CH7 6LT. 01352 750 118; e-mail: anne.brenchley@btinternet.com

CLWYD WEST. Mel ab Owain, 31 Coed Bedw, Abergele, Conwy, LL22 7EH. 01745 826 528; e-mail: melabowain@btinternet.com

MEIRIONNYDD. David Anning. 01654 761 481; e-mail: anning.ecology@tiscali.co.uk

Clubs
BANGOR BIRD GROUP. (1947; 100). Jane Prosser, 15 Victoria Street, Bangor, Gwynedd LL57 2HD. 01248 364 632.
Meetings: 7.30pm every Wednesday, Semester terms, Bramble Building, University of Bangor.

CAMBRIAN ORNITHOLOGICAL SOCIETY. (1952; 190). Geoff Gibbs. 01248 681 936; e-mail: geoffkate.gibbs@care4free.net www.welshos.org.uk/cambrian/
Meetings: 7.30pm, 1st Friday of the month, Pensychnant Centre, Sychnant Pass.

CLWYD BIRD RECORDING GROUP (committee that produces the Bird Report). Ian Spence, Tel/fax 01352 750118; e-mail: ianspence.cr@btinternet.com www.cbrg.org.uk

CLWYD ORNITHOLOGICAL SOCIETY. (1956; 45). Ms J Irving, 45, Plas Uchaf Avenue, Prestatyn, Denbighshire LL19 9NR01745 854 132; e-mail: jacqui970irving@btinternet.com
Meetings: 7.30pm (Sep-Apr), Farmers Arms, Waen, St. Asaph.

DEE ESTUARY CONSERVATION GROUP. (1973; 25 grps). Richard Smith, Secretary, e-mail: decg@deeestuary.co.uk www.deeestuary.co.uk/decg.htm

DEESIDE NATURALISTS' SOCIETY. (1973; 1,000). Secretary, 21 Woodlands Court, Hawarden, Deeside, Flints CH5 3NB. 01244 537 440; e-mail: deenaturalists@btinternet.com www.deesidenaturalists.org.uk

WREXHAM BIRDWATCHERS' SOCIETY. (1974; 90). Miss Marian Williams, 10 Lake View, Gresford, Wrexham, Clwyd LL12 8PU. 01978 854 633.

WALES

Meetings: 7.30pm, 1st Friday of the month (Sep-Apr), Gresford Memorial Hall, Gresford.

Ringing Groups
BARDSEY BIRD OBSERVATORY. Steven Stansfield, Bardsey Island, 07855 264 151; e-mail: wildlifeimagesuk@gmail.com

CHESHIRE SWAN GROUP. David Cookson, 01270 567 526; E-mail: Cheshireswans@aol.com www.record-lrc.co.uk (then follow link to Cheshire Swans Group).

MERSEYSIDE RG. Bob Harris, 0151 706 4311; e-mail: harris@liv.ac.uk

SCAN RG. Dr D. Moss. e-mail: dorian@dorianmoss.com

RSPB Local Group
NORTH WALES. (1986; 80). Maureen Douglas, 57 Penrhyn Beach East, Penrhyn Bay, Llandudno, Conwy LL30 3RW. 01492 547 768; e-mail: Mary.clarke@clarren.freeserve.co.uk www.rspb.org.uk/groups/northwales
Meetings: 7.30pm, 3rd Friday of the month (Sep-Apr), St Davids Church Hall, Penrhyn Bay, LLANDUDNO, Gwynedd, LL30 3EJ.

Wetland Bird Survey Organisers
ANGLESEY (other sites). Ian Sims, RSPB Malltraeth Marsh; e-mail: ian.sims@rspb.org.uk

CAERNARFONSHIRE. Rhion Pritchard, 01248 679 462; e-mail: rhion678pritchard@btinternet.com

CLWYD (Coastal). Position vacant.

ARTRO/MAWDDACH/TRAETH BACH/DYSYNNI ESTUARY. Jim Dustow, Lake Vyrnwy, 01766 830 976; Jim.Dustow@rspb.org.uk

MEIRIONNYDD (other sites). Trefor Owen, 01766 590 302; e-mail: webs@bto.org

DEE ESTUARY. Colin Wells, Burton Point Farm, 0151 336 7681; e-mail: colin.wells@rspb.org.uk

FORYD BAY. Simon Hugheston-Roberts, 01248 672 507; e-mail: sm.roberts@ccw.gov.uk

Wildlife Trust
NORTH WALES WILDLIFE TRUST. (1963; 6,450). 376 High Street, Bangor, Gwynedd, LL57 1YE. 01248 351 541; e-mail: nwwt@wildlifetrustswales.org www.northwaleswildlifetrust.org.uk

SOUTH WALES

Bird Atlas/Avifauna
An Atlas of Breeding Birds in West Glamorgan by David M Hanford et al (Gower Ornithological Society, 1992).

Birds of Glamorgan by Clive Hurford and Peter Lansdown (Published by the authors, c/o National Museum of Wales, Cardiff, 1995)

Bird Recorders
GLAMORGAN (EAST). David RW Gilmore, 116, Donald Street, Roath, Cardiff, Glamorgan CF24 4TN. 7779 176 766; e-mail: d.gilmore2@ntlworld.com

GOWER (WEST GLAMORGAN). Robert Taylor, 285 Llangyfelach Road, Brynhyfryd, Swansea, SA5 9LB. 01792 464 780; (M) 07970 567 007; e-mail: rob@birding.freeserve.co.uk

Bird Reports
EAST GLAMORGAN BIRD REPORT (title varies 1963-95) 1996-2009, from Mr John D Wilson, 122 Westbourne Road, Penarth, Vale of Glamorgan, CF64 3HH. 029 2033 9424; www.glamorganbirds.org.uk e-mail: john.wilson@glamorganbirds.org.uk

GOWER BIRDS (1965-) - covers Swansea, Neath and Port Talbot counties, from Barry Stewart, 36 Pencaecrwn Road, Gorseinon, Swansea SA4 4FU; e-mail: gowerbirdsf@hotmail.co.uk www.glamorganbirds.org.uk

BTO Regional Representatives
EAST GLAMORGAN (former Mid & South Glam) RR. Wayne Morris, 8 Hughes Street, Penygraig, Tonypandy, Rhondda Cynon Taf CF40 1LX. 01443 430 284; e-mail: eastglambto@gmail.com- http://eastglambto.wordpress.com

GLAMORGAN (WEST) Alistair Flannagan, 01792 537 439; e-mail: alastair.flannagan@ntlworld.com

BTO Garden BirdWatch Ambassadors
Mr M Bailey, e-mail: mick@mickbailey.fsnet.co.uk
Miss A Skull, e-mail: gbw@hiafi.co.uk

Clubs
CARDIFF NATURALISTS' SOCIETY. (1867; 200). Stephen R Howe, National Museum of Wales, Cardiff, CF10 3NP. e-mail: steve.howe@museumwales.ac.uk www.cardiffnaturalists.org.uk
Meetings: 7.30pm, various evenings, Llandaff Campus Uwic, Western Avenue, Cardiff.

GLAMORGAN BIRD CLUB. (1990; 290). Alan Rosney, 10 Park-y-Nant, Nantgarw, CF15 7TJ. 01443 841 555; e-mail: alan.rosney@glamorganbirds.org.uk www.glamorganbirds.org.uk
Meetings: 7.30pm, 2nd Tuesday of winter months, Kenfig Reserve Centre.

GOWER ORNITHOLOGICAL SOCIETY. (1956; 120). Peter Douglas-Jones, 28 Brynfield Road, Langland,

WALES

Swansea, SA3 4SX. 01792 360 287;
www.glamorganbirds.org.uk
e-mail: gowerbirds@hotmail.co.uk
Meetings: 7.15pm, last Friday of the month
(Sep-Mar), The Environment Centre, Pier Street,
Swansea.

Ringing Groups
FLAT HOLM RG. Brian Bailey, Tamarisk House,
Wards Court, Frampton-on-Severn, Glos, GL2 7DY.
e-mail: brian.bailey@sandbservices.eclipse.co.uk

KENFIG RG. Mr D.G. Carrington, Kenfig NNR, Ton
Kenfig, Bridgend, CF33 4PT.

RSPB Local Groups
CARDIFF & DISTRICT. (1973:). Huw Moody-Jones.
01446 760 757;
e-mail: huwmoodyjones@hotmail.com
www.RSPB.org.uk/groups/cardiff
Meetings: 7.30pm, various Fridays (Sept-May),
Llandaff Parish Hall, Llandaff, Cardiff.

WEST GLAMORGAN. (1985; 346). Maggie Cornelius.
01792 229 244;
e-mail: RSPBwglamgrp@googlemail.com
www.rspb.org.uk/groups/westglamorgan
Meetings: 7.30pm, Environment Centre, Pier
Street, SWANSEA, SA1 1RY

Wetland Bird Survey Organisers
EAST GLAMORGAN. Daniel Jenkins-Jones, (H)0292
062 1394; (M)07828 093 613; e-mail: webs@bto.org

SEVERN ESTUARY. Niall Burton, c/o BTO, The
Nunnery, Thetford, Norfolk, IP24 2PU.
e-mail: niall.burton@bto.org

WEST GLAMORGAN. Alistair Flannagan, 01792 537
439; e-mail: alastair.flannagan@ntlworld.com

Wildlife Hospital
GOWER BIRD HOSPITAL. Karen Kingsnorth and
Simon Allen, Valetta, Sandy Lane, Pennard,
Swansea, SA3 2EW. 01792 371 630; e-mail: admin@
gowerbirdhospital.org.uk
www.gowerbirdhospital.org.uk

All species of wild birds, also
hedgehogs and small mammals.
Prior phone call essential.
Gower Bird Hospital cares for
sick, injured and orphaned wild
birds and animals with the sole
intention of returning them
to the wild. Post release radio tracking projects,
ringing scheme. Contact us for more information.

Wildlife Trust
WILDLIFE TRUST OF SOUTH AND WEST WALES.
(2002; 4,000). Nature Centre, Parc Slip, Fountain
Road, Tondu, Bridgend CF32 0EH. 01656 724 100;
e-mail: info@welshwildlife.org
www.welshwildlife.org

WEST WALES

Bird Atlas/Avifauna
Birds of Ceredigion by (the late) Hywel Roderick
and Peter Davis (The WT of South & West Wales,
2010).

The Birds of Carmarthenshire by John Lloyd (in
preparation)

Birds of Pembrokeshire by Jack Donovan and
Graham Rees (Dyfed Wildlife Trust, 1994).

Bird Recorders
CARMARTHENSHIRE. Owen Harris, 5 William
Terrace, Burry Port, Carmarthenshire SA16 0PG.
e-mail: Owenharris@aol.com

CEREDIGION. Russell Jones, Bron y Gan, Talybont,
Ceredigion, SY24 5ER. 07753 774 891;
e-mail: russell.jones@rspb.org.uk

PEMBROKESHIRE (Joint). Stephen Berry, Teifi
House, Dolbadau Road, Cilgerran, Pembrokeshire
SA43 2SS. 0123 614 258; (M)07772 869 730;
e-mail: stephen.berry16@btinternet.com

PEMBROKESHIRE (Joint). Jon Green, Crud Yr Awel,
Bowls Road, Blaenporth, Ceredigion SA43 2AR.
01239 811 561; e-mail: jonrg@tiscali.co.uk

Bird Reports
*CARMARTHENSHIRE BIRD
REPORT (1982-) £6.80 by
post or £6.30 online,* From:
Available online at www.
carmarthenshirebirds.co.uk
or from Wendell Thomas,
48 Glebe Road, Loughor,
Swansea, SA4 6QD

CEREDIGION BIRD REPORT
(biennial 1982-87; annual
1988-2010) - £7 inc postage, cheques payable to
South and West Wildlife Trust, from John Davis,
Pantllidiart, Tristant, ABERYSTWYTH, SY23 4RQ

PEMBROKESHIRE BIRD REPORT (1981-), from Ms
Barbara Priest, The Pines, Templeton, Pembs, SA67
8RT. e-mail: bpriest175@btinternet.com

BTO Regional Representatives
CARDIGAN. Moira Convery, 41 Danycoed,
Aberystwyth, SY23 2HD. 01970 612 998;
e-mail: moira.convery@gmail.com

CARMARTHEN. Terry Wells, 01267 238836;
e-mail: bto@twells.me.uk

PEMBROKE. Annie and Bob Haycock, 1 Rushmoor,
Martletwy, Narberth,Pembrokeshire SA67 8BB.
01834 891 667; e-mail: rushmoor1@tiscali.co.uk

WALES

Clubs
CARMARTHENSHIRE BIRD CLUB. (2003; 120).
Owen Harris, 5 William Terrace, Burry Port,
Carmarthenshire SA16 0PG.
e-mail: Owenharris@aol.com
www.carmarthenshirebirds.co.uk
Meetings: Winter evenings at WWT Penclacwydd
(check website for details).

PEMBROKESHIRE BIRD GROUP. (1993; 60). Ms
Barbara Priest, The Pines, Templeton, Pembs, SA67
8RT. e-mail: bpriest175@btinternet.com
Meetings: 7.30pm, 1st Monday of the month (Oct-
Apr), The Patch, Furzy Park, Haverfordwest.

Ringing Group
PEMBROKESHIRE RG. J Hayes, 3 Wades Close,
Holyland Road, Pembroke, SA71 4BN. 01646 687
036; e-mail: hayes313@btinternet.com

Wetland Bird Survey Organisers
CARDIGAN (incl Dyfi Estuary). Dick Squires;
e-mail: webs@bto.org

CARMARTHEN, BAY AND INLAND. Ian Hainsworth,
01792 205 693; e-mail: ian.hains@ntlworld.com

GWENT (excl. Severn Estuary). Chris Jones, 22
Walnut Drive, Caerleon, Newport, Gwent NP18 3SB;
e-mail: chrisj22@talktalk.net

PEMBROKESHIRE. Annie Haycock;
e-mail: rushmoor1@tiscali.co.uk

Wildlife Hospital
NEW QUAY BIRD HOSPITAL. Jean Bryant, Penfoel,
Cross Inn, Llandysul, Ceredigion, SA44 6NR. 01545
560 462. All species of birds. Fully equipped for
cleansing oiled seabirds. Veterinary support.

Wildlife Trust
WILDLIFE TRUST OF SOUTH AND WEST WALES.
(2002; 4,000). Nature Centre, Parc Slip, Fountain
Road, Tondu, Bridgend CF32 0EH. 01656 724 100;
e-mail: info@welshwildlife.org
www.welshwildlife.org

ISLE OF MAN

Manx Bird Atlas
An Atlas of Breeding and Wintering Birds on the Isle of Man
Principal Editor: Chris Sharpe

Bird Atlas/Avifauna
Manx Bird Atlas.
5-yr BBS and Winter
Atlas research
completed.
(Liverpool University
Press, 2007).
Contact: Chris
Sharpe (see below,
BTO)

Bird Recorder
Chris Sharpe. E-mail:chris@manxbirdlife.im

Bird Reports
MANX BIRD REPORT (1947-), published in Peregrine.
From Mrs A C Kaye, Cronk Ny Ollee, Glen Chass, Port
St Mary, Isle of Man IM9 5PL. 01624 834 015.

CALF OF MAN BIRD OBSERVATORY ANNUAL REPORT,
from Secretary, Manx National Heritage, Manx
Museum, Douglas, Isle of Man, IM1 3LY.

BTO Regional Representatives
Dr Pat Cullen, as above. 01624 623 308 ;
E-mail:bridgeen@mcb.net

Club
MANX ORNITHOLOGICAL SOCIETY. (1967; 150). Mrs A
C Kaye, Cronk Ny Ollee, Glen Chass, Port St Mary, Isle
of Man IM9 5PL. 01624 834 015 .
Meetings: 1st Tues in month, 7.30pm, Union Mills
Hall.

Ringing Group
MANX RINGING GROUP. Mr Kevin Scott; E-mail:
manxrg@gmail.com
www.manxringer.blogspot.com

Wetland Bird Survey Organiser
Dr Pat Cullen, Troutbeck, Cronkbourne, Braddan, Isle
of Man, IM4 4QA. Home: 01624 623308 Work 01624
676774; E-mail:bridgeen@mcb.net

Wildlife Trust
MANX WILDLIFE TRUST. (1973; 900). 7-8 Market
Place, Peel, Isle of Man IM5 1AB. 01624 844 432;
E-mail:enquiries@manxwt.org.uk
www.manxwt.org.uk

CHANNEL ISLANDS

Wetland Bird Survey Organisers
CHANNEL ISLANDS (inland). Glyn Young. 01534 860 000; e-mail:glyn.young@durrell.org

ALDERNEY

Atlas/Avifauna
The Birds of Alderney, by JG Sanders. (The Press at St Anne, 2007).

Bird Recorder
Mark Atkinson; e-mail:atkinson@cwgsy.net

Bird Report
ALDERNEY SOCIETY AND COUNTY ORNITHOLOGICAL REPORT (1992-), from Recorder;
e-mail: atkinson@cwgsy.net

BTO Regional Representative
Philip Alexander. 01481 726 173;
e-mail:alybru@cwgsy.net

Wetland Birds Survey Organiser
Trust Ecologist, Alderney Wildlife Trust Office, 51 Victoria Street, St Anne Alderney GY9 3TA. 01481 822 935; e-mail:info@alderneywildlife.org

Wildlife Trust
ALDERNEY WILDLIFE TRUST. (2002; 460). Alderney Wildlife Trust Office, 51 Victoria Street, St Anne Alderney GY9 3TA. 01481 822 935;
e-mail:info@alderneywildlife.org
www.alderneywildlife.org

GUERNSEY

Bird Atlas/Avifauna
Birds of the Bailiwick: Guernsey, Alderney, Sark and Herm by Duncan Spencer & Paul Hillion, 2010, Jill Vaudin Publishing.

Bird Recorder
Mark Lawlor; e-mail:mplawlor@cwgsy.net

Bird Report
REPORT & TRANSACTIONS OF LA SOCIETE GUERNESIAISE (1882-), from Recorder.

BTO Regional Representative
Philip Alexander. 01481 726 173;
e-mail:alybru@cwgsy.net

Clubs
LA SOCIÉTÉ GUERNESIAISE (Ornithological Section). (1882; 1,400). Secretary, La Société Guernesiaise, Candie Gardens, St Peter Port, Port Guernsey GY1 1UG. 01481 725 093; e-mail:societe@cwgsy.net
www.societe.org.gg
Meetings: First Thurs of month, 8pm, Candie Gardens lecture theatre.

RSPB Local Group
GUERNSEY BAILIWICK. (1975; 350+). Donna Francis. 01481 232 632; e-mail:donna@cwgsy.net
www.rspbguernsey.co.uk
Meetings: 8pm, La Villette Hotel, St Martins, GUERNSEY, GY4 6QG.

Wetland Bird Survey Organiser
GUERNSEY COAST. Mary Simmons, Les Maeures, Mont d'Aval, Castel, Guernsey GY5 7UQ. 01481 256 016; e-mail:msim@cwgsy.net

Wildlife Hospital
GUERNSEY. GSPCA ANIMAL SHELTER. Mrs Jayne Le Cras, Les Fiers Moutons, St Andrews, Guernsey, Channel Islands GY6 8UD. 01481 257 261; (emergency number 07781 104 082); e-mail:admin@gspca.org.gg
www.gspca.org.gg All species. Modern cleansing unit for oiled seabirds. 24-hour emergency service. Veterinary support.

JERSEY

Bird Recorder
Tony Paintin, Cavok, 16 Quennevais Gardens, St Brelade, Jersey, Channel Islands, JE3 8FQ. 01534 741 928; e-mail:cavokjersey@hotmail.com

Bird Report
JERSEY BIRD REPORT (1991-), from La Société Jersiaise, 7 Pier Road, St Helier, Jersey JE2 4XW; e-mail:societe@societe-jersiaise.org

BTO Regional Representative
Tony Paintin, Cavok, 16 Quennevais Gardens, St Brelade, Jersey, Channel Islands, JE3 8FQ. 01534 741 928; e-mail:cavokjersey@hotmail.com

Club
SOCIÉTIÉ JERSIAISE (Ornithological Section). (1948; 40). C/O La Société Jersiaise, 7 Pier Road, St Helier, Jersey JE2 4XW. 01534 758 314;
e-mail:societe@societe-jersiaise.org
www.societe-jersiaise.org
Meetings: 8.00pm, alternate Thursdays throughout the year, Museum in St.Helier.

Wetland Bird Survey Organiser
JERSEY COAST. Roger Noel.
e-mail:rogernoel1@googlemail.com

Wildlife Hospital
JERSEY. JSPCA ANIMALS' SHELTER. The Manager, 89 St Saviour's Road, St Helier, Jersey, JE2 4GJ. 01534 724 331; e-mail:info@jspca.org.je
www.jspca.org.je All species. Expert outside support for owls and raptors. Oiled seabird unit. Veterinary surgeon on site. Educational Centre.

NORTHERN IRELAND

Bird Recorder
George Gordon, 2 Brooklyn Avenue, Bangor, Co
Down, BT20 5RB. 028 9145 5763;
e-mail: gordon@ballyholme2.freeserve.co.uk

Bird Reports
NORTHERN IRELAND BIRD REPORT, from Secretary,
Northern Ireland, Birdwatchers' Association (see
National Directory).

IRISH BIRD REPORT, Included in Irish Birds,
BirdWatch Ireland in National Directory.

BTO Regional Representatives
BTO IRELAND OFFICER. Shane Wolsey. 028 9146
7947; e-mail: shane@swolsey.biz

ANTRIM & BELFAST. David Galbraith. 028 9338
2539; e-mail: davidgalbraith903@btinternet.com

ARMAGH. Stephen Hewitt;
e-mail: sjameshewitt@hotmail.com

DOWN. Kerry Leonard. 028 9145 2602;
e-mail: kerrysleonard@hotmail.com

FERMANAGH. Michael Stinson. 07890 358 239;
e-mail: mick.stinston@hotmail.com

LONDONDERRY. Charles Stewart, 028 7775 0468;
e-mail: charles.stewart2@btinternet.com

TYRONE. Michael Stinson. 07890 358 239;
e-mail: mick.stinston@hotmail.com

BTO Garden BirdWatch Ambassadors
Ms P A Flowerday.
e-mail: pflowerday@utvinternet.com

Clubs
NORTHERN IRELAND BIRDWATCHERS' ASSOCIATION
See National Directory.

NORTHERN IRELAND ORNITHOLOGISTS' CLUB See
National Directory.

CASTLE ESPIE BIRDWATCHING CLUB (COMBER).
(1995; 60). Dot Blakely, 8 Rosemary Park, Bangor,
Co Down, BT20 3EX. 028 9145 0784;
e-mail: dot.blakely@tesco.net

Ringing Groups
BELFAST & DOWN RINGING GROUP. Mr D C Clarke.
07774 780 750;
e-mail: declan.clarke@homecall.co.uk

COPELAND BIRD OBSERVATORY. C W Acheson, 28
Church Avenue, Dunmurry, Belfast BT17 9RS.

RSPB Local Groups
ANTRIM. (1977; 23). Brenda Campbell . 02893 323
657; e-mail: brendacampbell@supanet.com
www.rspb.org.uk/groups/antrim
Meetings: 8pm, 2nd Monday of the month,
College of Agriculture Food & Rural Enterprise, 22
Greenmount Road, ANTRIM.

BANGOR. (1973; 25). Fulton Somerville;
e-mail: fultonsomerville@yahoo.co.uk
Meetings: Trinity Presbyterian Church Hall, Main
Street, BANGOR, County Down.

BELFAST. (1970; 130). Ian Jackson. 028 9756
2661;e-mail: ian686jackson@btinternet.com
Meetings: Cooke Centenary Church Hall, Cooke
Centenary Church Hall, Ormeau Rd, BELFAST.

COLERAINE. (1978; 45). Peter Robinson, 34
Blackthorn Court, Coleraine, Co Londonderry, BT52
2EX. 028 7034 4361;
e-mail: robinson493@btinternet.com
Meetings: 7.30pm, third Monday of the month
(Sept-Apr), St Patricks Church, Minor Church Hall,
Corner of Brook St and Circular Road, Coleraine.

FERMANAGH. (1977; 28). Doreen Brown. 028 6632
2479; e-mail: dbrown498@btinternet.com
Meetings: 8pm, Cathedral Hall, Halls Lane,
ENNISKILLEN BT74 7DR.

LARNE. (1974; 35). Jimmy Christie, 314 Coast Road,
Ballygally, Co Antrim, BT40 2QZ. 028 2858 3223;
e-mail: candjchristie@btinternet.com
Meetings: 7.30pm, 1st Wednesday of the month,
Larne Grammar School.

LISBURN. (1978; 30). Peter Galloway. 028 9266
1982; e-mail: pgalloway56@o2.co.uk
www.rspblisburn.com
Meetings: 7.30pm, 4th Monday of the month,
Friends Meeting House, 4 Magheralave Road,
LISBURN.

Wetland Bird Survey Organisers
BANN ESTUARY. Hill Dick. 02870 329 720;
e-mail: webs@bto.org

BELFAST LOUGH. Shane Wolsey, 07831 697 371;
e-mail: shane@swolsey.biz

DUNDRUM BAY. Malachy Martin, Murlough NNR,
BT33 0NQ. 028 4375 1467;
e-mail: Malachy.Martin@nationaltrust.org.uk

LOUGH FOYLE. Matthew Tickner. 028 491 547;
e-mail: matthew.tickner@rspb.org.uk

STRANGFORD LOUGH. Kerry Mackie, WWT Castle Espie; 028 9187 4146; e-mail: kerry.mackie@wwt.org.uk

Wildlife Hospital
TACT WILDLIFE CENTRE. Mrs Patricia Nevines, 2 Crumlin Road, Crumlin, Co Antrim, BT29 4AD. 028 9442 2900; e-mail: tactwildlife@btinternet.com www.tactwildlifecentre.org.uk All categories of birds treated and rehabilitated; released where practicable, otherwise given a home. Visitors (inc. school groups and organisations) welcome by prior arrangement. Veterinary support.

Wildlife Trust
ULSTER WILDLIFE TRUST. (1978; 7.500). 3 New Line, Crossgar, Co Down, BT30 9EP. 028 4483 0282; e-mail: info@ulsterwildlifetrust.org www.ulsterwildlifetrust.org

REPUBLIC OF IRELAND

BirdWatch Ireland, Unit 20, Block D, Bullford Business Campus, Kilcoole, Co. Wicklow, Ireland 353 (0)1 281 9878 E-mail: info@ birdwatchireland.ie www.birdwatchireland.ie

Rarities. Paul Milne, 100 Dublin Road, Sutton, Dublin 13, +353 (0)1 832 5653; e-mail: paul.milne@oceanfree.net

CLARE. John Murphy, e-mail: jemurphy@esatclear.ie

CORK. Mark Shorten, e-mail: mshorten@indigo.ie

DONEGAL. Ralph Sheppard, e-mail: rsheppard@eircom.net

DUBLIN, LOUTH, MEATH AND WICKLOW. Declan Murphy & Dick Coombes, e-mail: dmurphy@birdwatchireland.ie or e-mail: rcoombes@birdwatchireland.ie

GALWAY. Chris Peppiatt, e-mail: chris.peppiatt@iol.ie

KERRY. Michael O'Clery & Jill Crosher, e-mail: moclery@tinet.ie

LIMERICK. Tony Mee, Ballyorgan, Kilfinane, Co. Limerick.

MAYO. Tony Murray, National Parks and Wildlife, Lagduff More, Ballycroy, Westport; e-mail: murraytony@hotmail.com

MID-SHANNON. Stephen Heery, e-mail: sheery@eircom.net

MONAGHAN. Joe Shannon, e-mail: joeshan@eircom.net

WATERFORD. Paul Walsh, 16 Castlepoint, Crosshaven, Co. Cork; e-mail: pmwalsh@waterfordbirds.com

WEXFORD. Tony Murray, Wexford Wildfowl Reserve, North Slob; e-mail: murraytony@hotmail.com

Bird Reports
IRISH BIRD REPORT, contact BirdWatch Ireland in National, Directory).

CAPE CLEAR BIRD OBSERVATORY ANNUAL REPORT, from the observatory.

CORK BIRD REPORT (1963-71; 1976-), Cork Bird Report Editorial Team, Long Strand, Castlefreke, Clonakilty, Co. Cork; e-mail: cbr@corkecology.net

EAST COAST BIRD REPORT (1980-), Contact BirdWatch Ireland.

BirdWatch Ireland Branches
Branches may be contacted in writing via BirdWatch Ireland HQ (see entry in National Directory).

Ringing Groups
CAPE CLEAR B.O, Steve Wing, e-mail: steve.ccbo@gmail.com

GREAT SALTEE RINGING STATION, Mr O J Merne, 20 Cuala Road, Bray, Co Wicklow, Ireland; e-mail: omerne@eircom.net

MUNSTER RG, Mr K.P.C. Collins, Ballygambon, Lisronagh, Clonmel, County Tipperary, e-mail: kcsk@eircom.net

NATIONAL DIRECTORY

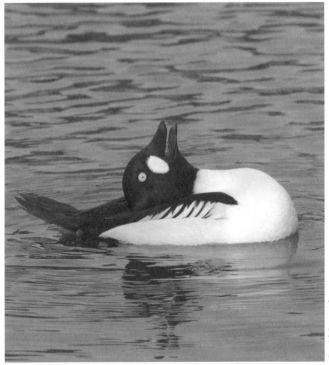

David Cromack

The Wildfowl & Wetlands Trust operates nine centres which are internationally important for wintering species such as Goldeneye, but the Trust works hard to promote greater biodiversity in all wetland habitats..

287

NATIONAL ORGANISATIONS

After the title of each organisation you will see (in brackets) the year the
group was founded and, where known, the current membership figure.

ARMY ORNITHOLOGICAL SOCIETY (1960; 200)

Open to serving and retired
MoD employees who have
an interest in their local
MoD estate. Activities
include field meetings,
expeditions, the preparation
of checklists of birds on
Ministry of Defence property,
conservation advice and an
annual journal *Adjutant*.
Contact: www.aos-uk.com
e-mail: secretary@aos.org.uk

ASSOCIATION OF COUNTY RECORDERS AND EDITORS (1993; 120)

The basic aim of ACRE is to promote best practice
in the business of producing county bird reports,
in the work of Recorders and in problems arising in
managing record systems and archives. Organises
periodic conferences and publishes *newsACRE*.
Contact: The Secretary; e-mail: countyrec@cawos.org

ASSOCIATION FOR THE PROTECTION OF RURAL SCOTLAND (1926)

Works to protect Scotland's countryside from
unnecessary or inappropriate development,
recognising the needs of those who live and work
there and the necessity of reconciling these with the
sometimes competing requirements of recreational
use.
Contact: Association for the Protection of Rural
Scotland, Gladstone's Land, 3rd Floor, 483
Lawnmarket, Edinburgh EH1 2NT. 0131 225 7012;
e-mail: info@ruralscotland.org
www.ruralscotland.btik.com

BARN OWL TRUST (1988)

A registered charity dedicated to conserving the Barn
Owl and its environment and is
the main source of Barn Owl
information in the UK. The
Trust's educational work
began in 1989 and it now
runs training courses for
ecological consultants and
planning officers. It carries
out surveys of old buildings
due for development,
and advises on Barn Owl
mitigation measures. A booklet *Barn Owls on Site*,
a guide for developers and planners, published by
English Nature, is widely used by local authorities and
other official bodies.
Published research projects cover subjects such
as the effect of barn conversions on Barn Owls,
road mortality, the survival of released Barn Owls,
rehabilitation and release methods, as well as county

surveys. The Trust has erected over 2,000 nestboxes
is are closely involved in habitat creation both on its
own land and through farm visits.
Contact: Barn Owl Trust, Waterleat, Ashburton,
Devon TQ13 7HU. 01364 653 026;
e-mail: info@barnowltrust.org.uk
www.barnowltrust.org.uk

BIRDING FOR ALL (2000; 700)

(Formerly the Disabled
Birders Association)
The DBA is a registered
charity and international
movement, which aims to
promote access to reserves
and other birding places and
to a range of services, so
that people with different
needs can follow the birding
obsession as freely as able-
bodied people. Membership is currently free and new
members are needed to help give a stronger message
across to those who own and manage nature reserves
to improve access when they are planning and
improving facilities. DBA also seeks to influence those
who provide birdwatching services and equipment.
The DBA also runs overseas trips. Chairman, Bo
Beolens.
Contact: Birding For All, 18 St Mildreds Road,
Cliftonville, Margate,
Kent CT9 2LT; e-mail: bo@birdingforall.com
www.birdingforall.com

BIRD OBSERVATORIES COUNCIL (1970)

Aims to provide a forum for establishing closer links
and co-operation between individual observatories
and to help co-ordinate the work carried out by
them. All accredited bird observatories affiliated
to the Council undertake a ringing programme and
provide ringing experience to those interested, most
also provide accommodation for visiting birdwatchers.
Contact: Peter Howlett, Bird Observatories Council,
c/o Dept of Biodiversity, National Museum Wales,
Cardiff CF10 3NP. 0292 057 3233;
e-mail: info@birdobscouncil.org.uk
www.birdobscouncil.org.uk

BIRD STAMP SOCIETY (1986; 220)

Quarterly journal *Flight* contains philatelic and
ornithological articles. Lists all new issues and
identifies species. Runs a quarterly Postal Auction;
number of lots range from 400 to 800 per auction.
UK subs £14 per annum from 1st August. Under-16s
half price.
Contact: Mrs R Bradley, Bird Stamp Society, 31 Park
View, Crossway Green, Chepstow NP16 5NA. 01291
625412; e-mail: bradley666@lycos.co.uk
www.birdstampsociety.org

NATIONAL ORGANISATIONS

BIRDWATCH IRELAND (1968; 14,000 with a network of 20 branches)

The largest independent conservation organisation in Ireland. Its primary objective is the protection of wild birds and their habitats in Ireland through the efforts of their staff, members a nd volunteers alike. It carries out extensive research and survey work, operates applied conservation projects and manages a network of reserves nationwide. It prepares and advocates policies and recruits, retains and services a growing membership base. It publishes *Wings* magazine and an annual journal *Irish Birds*.
Contact: BirdWatch Ireland, Unit 20, Block D, Bullford Business Campus, Kilcoole, Co. Wicklow, Ireland. 353 (0)1 281 9878
E-mail: info@birdwatchireland.ie
www.birdwatchireland.ie

BRITISH BIRDS RARITIES COMMITTEE (1959)

The Committee adjudicates records of species of rare occurrence in Britain (marked `R' in the Log Charts) and publishes its annual report in *British Birds*. The BBRC also assesses records from the Channel Islands. In the case of rarities trapped for ringing, records should be sent to the Ringing Office of the British Trust for Ornithology, who will in turn forward them to the BBRC.
Contact: The Hon Secretary, British Birds Rarities Committee, e-mail: secretary@bbrc.org.uk
www.bbrc.org.uk

BRITISH DRAGONFLY SOCIETY (1983; 1,604)

The BDS aims to promote the conservation and study of dragonflies. Members receive two issues of *Dragonfly News* and *BDS Journal* each year in spring and autumn. There are countrywide field trips, an annual members day and training is available on aspects of dragonfly ecology. The BDS has published a booklet, *Dig a Pond for Dragonflies* containing advice on pond creation and maintenance to attract dragonflies, also *Managing Habitats for Dragonflies* which is aimed at countryside managers.
Contact: Mr H Curry, Hon Secretary, British Dragonfly Society, 23 Bowker Way, Whittlesey, Cambs PE7 1PY.
e-mail: bdssecretary@dragonflysoc.org.uk
www.dragonflysoc.org.uk

BRITISH FALCONERS' CLUB (1927; 1,200)

Largest falconry club in Europe, with regional branches. Its aim is to encourage responsible falconers and conserve birds of prey by breeding, holding educational meetings and providing facilities, guidance and advice to those wishing to take up the sport. Publishes *The Falconer* annually and newsletter twice yearly.
Contact: British Falconers' Club, Westfield, Meeting Hill, Worstead, North Walsham, Norfolk NR28 9LS. 01692 404 057;
e-mail: admin@britishfalconersclub.co.uk
www.britishfalconersclub.co.uk

BRITISH NATURALISTS ASSOCIATION (1905)

The association, a registered charity, was founded to promote the interests of nature lovers and bring them together. Today, it encourages and supports schemes and legislation for the protection of the country's natural resources. It organises meetings, field weeks, lectures and exhibitions to help popularise the study of nature. BNA publishes two magazines and copies of *Country-Side* are available to non-members at some libraries.
Contact: General Secretary, BNA, PO Box 5682, Corby, Northants NN17 2ZW. 0844 892 1817;
e-mail: info@bna-naturalists.org
www.bna-naturalists.org

BRITISH ORNITHOLOGISTS' CLUB (1892; 450)

A registered charity, the Club's objects are 'the promotion of scientific discussion between those interested in ornithology, and to facilitate the publication of scientific information in connection with ornithology'. The Club maintains a special interest in avian systematics, taxonomy and distribution. Publishes the *Bulletin of the British Ornithologists' Club* quarterly, also (since 1992) a continuing series of occasional publications. About eight lecture dinner meetings are held each year.
Contact: BOC Office, British Ornithologists' Club, PO Box 417, Peterborough, PE7 3FX. (Tel/Fax) 01733 844 820; e-mail: boc@bou.org.uk
www.boc-online.org

BRITISH ORNITHOLOGISTS' UNION (1858; 1,250)

The BOU is one of the world's oldest and most respected ornithological societies. It aims to promote ornithology within the scientific and birdwatching communities, both in Britain and around the world. This is largely achieved by the publication of its quarterly international journal, *Ibis* (1859-), featuring work at the cutting edge of our understanding of the world's birdlife. It also publishes an ongoing series of country/island group 'checklists' (24 titles to date - see BOU website for details) and operates an active programme of meetings, seminars and conferences. Work being undertaken around the world can include research projects that have received financial assistance from the BOU's ongoing programme of Ornithological Research Grants. Copies of journals and offprints received and books reviewed in *Ibis* are held as part of the Alexander Library in the Zoology Department of the University of Oxford (see Edward Grey Institute). The BOU Records Committee maintains the official British List (see below)
Contact: Steve Dudley, British Ornithologists' Union, PO Box 417, Peterborough, PE7 3FX. (Tel/Fax) 01733 844 820; e-mail: bou@bou.org.uk
www.bou.org.uk, www.ibis.ac.uk and
www.bouproc.net

BOU

NATIONAL ORGANISATIONS

BRITISH ORNITHOLOGISTS' UNION RECORDS COMMITTEE

A standing committee of the British Ornithologists' Union (BOU), the BOURC's function is to maintain the British List, the official list of birds recorded in Great Britain. The up-to-date list can be viewed on the BOU website. Where vagrants are involved it is concerned only with those which relate to potential additions to the British List (ie first records). In this it differs from the British Birds Rarities Committee (qv) in maintaining the British List, it also differs from the BBRC in that it examines, where necessary, important pre-1950 records, monitors introduced species for possible admission to or deletion from the List, and reviews taxonomy and nomenclature relating to the List. BOURC reports are published in *Ibis* and are also available via the BOU website. Decisions which affect the List are also announced direct to the birdwatching public via e-groups, web forums and the popular birdwatching press.
Contact: Steve Dudley, BOURC, PO Box 417, Peterborough, PE7 3FX. (Tel/Fax) 01733 844 820; e-mail: bourc@bou.org
www.bou.org.uk

BRITISH TRUST FOR ORNITHOLOGY (1933; 13,500)

A registered charity governed by an elected Council, BTO has a rapidly growing membership and enjoys the support of a large number of county and local birdwatching clubs and societies through the BTO/Bird Clubs Partnership. Its aims are: `To promote and encourage the wider understanding, appreciation and conservation of birds through scientific studies using the combined skills and enthusiasm of its members, other birdwatchers and staff.' Through the fieldwork of its members and other birdwatchers, the BTO is responsible for the majority of the monitoring of British birds, British bird population and their habitats. BTO surveys include the National Ringing Scheme, the Nest Record Scheme, the Breeding Bird Survey (in collaboration with JNCC and RSPB), and the Waterways Breeding Bird Survey, which all contribute to an integrated programme of population monitoring. The BTO also runs projects on the birds of farmland and woodland, also (in collaboration with WWT, RSPB and JNCC) the Wetland Bird Survey, in particular Low Tide Counts. Garden BirdWatch, which started in 1995, now has more than 15,000 participants. The Trust has 140 voluntary regional representatives (see County Directory) who organise fieldworkers for the BTO's programme of national surveys in which members participate. The results of these co-operative efforts are communicated to government departments, local authorities, industry and conservation bodies for effective action. For details of current activities see National Projects. Members receive *BTO News* six times a year and have the option of subscribing to the thrice-yearly journal, *Bird Study* and twice yearly *Ringing & Migration*. Local meetings are held in conjunction with bird clubs and societies; there are regional and national

birdwatchers' conferences, and specialist courses in bird identification and modern censusing techniques. Grants are made for research, and members have the use of a lending and reference library at Thetford and the Alexander Library at the Edward Grey Institute of Field Ornithology (qv)
Contact: British Trust for Ornithology, The Nunnery, Thetford, Norfolk IP24 2PU. 01842 750 050; e-mail: info@bto.org - www.bto.org

BTO SCOTLAND (2000; 989)

BTO Scotland's main functions are to promote the work of the Trust and develop wider coverage for surveys in Scotland, by encouraging greater participation in survey work. It also seeks to develop contract research income within Scotland. BTO Scotland ensures that the Trust's work is not just related to the priorities of the UK as a whole but is also focused on the priorities of Scotland, with a landscape and wildlife so different from the rest of the UK.
Contact: BTO Scotland, British Trust for Ornithology, School of Biological and Environmental Sciences, Cottrell Building, University of Stirling, Stirling FK9 4LA. 01786 466 560; www.bto.org
e-mail: scot.info@bto.org

BRITISH LIBRARY SOUND ARCHIVE - WILDLIFE SOUNDS (1969)

(Formerly BLOWS - British Library of Wildlife Sounds) The most comprehensive collection of bird sound recordings in existence: over 150,000 recordings of more than 8,000 species of birds worldwide, available for free listening. Copies or sonograms of most recordings can be supplied for private study or research and, subject to copyright clearance, for commercial uses. Contribution of new material and enquiries on all aspects of wildlife sounds and recording techniques are welcome. Publishes *Bioacoustics* journal, CD guides to bird songs and other wildlife, including ambience titles. Comprehensive catalogue available on-line at http://cadensa.bl.uk/uhtbin/cgisirsi/x/x/0/49/
Contact: Cheryl Tipp, Curator, Wildlife Sounds, The British Library Sound Archive, 96 Euston Road, London NW1 2DB. 020 7412 7403; e-mail: wildlifesound@bl.uk
www.bl.uk/reshelp/findhelprestype/sound/wildsounds/wildlife.html

BRITISH WATERFOWL ASSOCIATION

The BWA is an association of enthusiasts interested in keeping, breeding and conserving all types of waterfowl, including wildfowl and domestic ducks and geese. It is a registered charity, without trade affiliations, dedicated to educating the public about waterfowl and the need

NATIONAL ORGANISATIONS

for conservation as well as to raising the standards of keeping and breeding ducks, geese and swans in captivity.
Contact: Mrs Sue Schubert, British Waterfowl Association, PO Box 163, Oxted, RH8 0WP. 01892 740 212; e-mail: info@waterfowl.org.uk
www.waterfowl.org.uk

BRITISH WILDLIFE REHABILITATION COUNCIL (1987)

Promoting the care and rehabilitation of wildlife casualties through the exchange of information between people such as rehabilitators, zoologists and veterinary surgeons who are active in this field. Organises an annual symposium or workshop. Publishes a regular newsletter. Supported by many national bodies including the Zoological Society of London, the British Veterinary Zoological Society, the RSPCA, the SSPCA, and the Vincent Wildlife Trust.
Contact: To make a contribution - Janet Peto, BWRC, PO Box 8686, Grantham, Lincolnshire NG31 0AG; e-mail: janet@bwrc.org.uk - www.bwrc.org.uk

BTCV (formerly British Trust for Conservation Volunteers) (1959)

BTCV's mission is to create a more sustainable future by inspiring people and improving places. It aims to enrich the lives of people, through volunteering opportunities, employment, improved health, and life skills development; to improve the biodiversity and local environment of 75,000 places and to support active citizenship in 5,000 community-based groups. BTCV currently supports 300,000 volunteers to take practical action to improve their urban and rural environments. Publishes a quarterly magazine, *Roots*, a series of practical handbooks and a wide range of other publications.
Contact: BTCV, Sedum House, Mallard Way, Doncaster DN4 8DB. 01302 388 883; e-mail: Information@btcv.org.uk - www.btcv.org.uk

BTCV CYMRU
Contact: The Conservation Centre, BTCV Cymru, Forest Farm Road, Whitchurch, Cardiff, CF14 7JJ. 029 2052 0990; e-mail: wales@btcv.org.uk
www.btcvcymru.org

BTCV SCOTLAND
Runs 7-14 day Action Breaks in Scotland during which participants undertake conservation projects; weekend training courses in environmental skills; midweek projects in Edinburgh, Glasgow, Aberdeen, Stirling and Inverness.
Contact: BTCV Scotland, Balallan House, 24 Allan Park, Stirling FK8 2QG. 01786 479 697; e-mail: scotland@btcv.org.uk
www2.btcv.org.uk/display/btcv_scotland

BTCV NORTHERN IRELAND (1983)
Contact: Conservation Volunteers Northern Ireland, Beech House, 159 Ravenhill Road, Belfast BT6 0BP. 028 9064 5169; e-mail: CVNI@btcv.org.uk
www.cvni.org

BUGLIFE – THE INVERTEBRATE CONSERVATION TRUST (2000)

The first organisation in Europe devoted to the conservation of all invertebrates, actively engaged in halting the extinction of Britain's rarest slugs, snails, bees, wasps, ants, spiders, beetles and many more. It is working to achieve this through practical conservation projects; promoting the environmental importance of invertebrates and raising awareness about the challenges to their survival; assisting in the development of helpful legislation and policy and encouraging and supporting invertebrate conservation initiatives by other organisations in the UK, Europe and worldwide.
Contact: Buglife (ICT), 1st Floor, 90 Bridge Street, Peterborough PE1 1DY. 01733 201 210; www.buglife.org.uk
e-mail: info@buglife.org.uk

CAMPAIGN FOR THE PROTECTION OF RURAL WALES (1928; 2,800)
Its aims are to help the conservation and enhancement of the landscape, environment and amenities of the countryside, towns and villages of rural Wales and to form and educate opinion to ensure the promotion of its objectives. It gives advice and information upon matters affecting protection, conservation and improvement of the visual environment.
Contact: Ty Gwyn, 31 High Street, Welshpool, Powys SY21 7YD. 01938 552 525 or 01938 556 212; e-mail: info@cprwmail.org.uk - www.cprw.org.uk

CENTRE FOR ECOLOGY & HYDROLOGY (CEH)
The work of the CEH, a component body of the Natural Environment Research Council, includes a range of ornithological research, covering population studies, habitat management and work on the effects of pollution. The CEH has a long-term programme to monitor pesticide and pollutant residues in the corpses of predatory birds sent in by birdwatchers, and carries out detailed studies on affected species. The Biological Records Centre (BRC), part of the CEH, is responsible for the national biological data bank on plant and animal distributions (except birds).
Contact: Centre for Ecology & Hydrology, Maclean Building, Crowmarsh Gifford, Wallingford, Oxfordshire OX10 8BB. (01491 838 800.
E-mail: enquiries@ceh.ac.uk - www.ceh.ac.uk

CONSERVATION FOUNDATION (1982)
Created by David Bellamy and David Shreeve to provide a means for people in public, private and

NATIONAL ORGANISATIONS

not-for-profit sectors to collaborate on environmental causes. Over the years its programme has included award schemes, conferences, promotions, special events, field studies, school programmes, media work, seminars and workshops etc. The Conservation Foundation has created and managed environmental award schemes of all kinds including the Ford European Awards, The Trust House Forte Community Chest, The PA Golden Leaf Awards, The Co-op Save Our Species Awards, the Pollution Abatement Technology Awards and many others. For information about how to apply for current award schemes visit the website.
Contact: Conservation Foundation, 1 Kensington Gore, London SW7 2AR. 020 7591 3111; e-mail: info@conservationfoundation.co.uk www.conservationfoundation.co.uk

COUNTRY LAND AND BUSINESS ASSOCIATION (1907; 36,000)
The CLA is at the heart of rural life and is the voice of the countryside for England and Wales, campaigning on issues which directly affect those who live and work in rural communities. Its members, ranging from some of the largest landowners, with interests in forest, moorland, water and agriculture, to some with little more than a paddock or garden, together manage 50% of the countryside.
Contact: Country Land and Business Association, 16 Belgrave Square, London, SW1X 8PQ. 020 7235 0511; e-mail: mail@cla.org.uk www.cla.org.uk

COUNTRYSIDE COUNCIL FOR WALES
The Government's statutory adviser on wildlife, countryside and maritime conservation matters in Wales and the executive authority for the conservation of habitats and wildlife. CCW champions the environment and landscapes of Wales and its coastal waters as sources of natural and cultural riches, as a foundation for economic and social activity, and as a place for leisure and learning opportunities.
Contact: Countryside Council for Wales, Maes-y-Ffynnon, Penrhosgarnedd, Bangor, Gwynedd LL57 2DL, 0845 1306 229; e-mail: enquiries@ccw.gov.uk www.ccw.gov.uk

CPRE (formerly Council for the Protection of Rural
 England) (1926; 60,000)
Patron HM The Queen. CPRE now has 43 county branches and 200 local groups. It highlights threats to the countryside and promotes positive solutions. In-depth research supports active campaigning, and through reasoned argument and lobbying, CPRE seeks to influence public opinion and decision-makers at every level. Membership open to all.
Contact: CPRE National Office, 128 Southwark Street, London SE1 0SW. 020 7981 2800; e-mail: info@cpre.org.uk www.cpre.org.uk

DEPARTMENT OF THE ENVIRONMENT FOR NORTHERN IRELAND
Responsible for the declaration and management of National Nature Reserves, the declaration of Areas of Special Scientific Interest, the administration of Wildlife Refuges, the classification of Special Protection Areas under the EC Birds Directive, the designation of Special Areas of Conservation under the EC Habitats Directive and the designation of Ramsar sites under the Ramsar Convention. It administers the Nature Conservation and Amenity Lands (Northern Ireland) Order 1985, the Wildlife (Northern Ireland) Order 1985, the Game Acts and the Conservation (Natural Habitats, etc) Regulations (NI) 1995 and the Environment (Northern Ireland) Order 2002.
Contact: Department of Environment Headquarters, Clarence Court, 10 - 18 Adelaide Street, Belfast BT2 8GB. 028 9054 0540; e-mail: enquiries@doeni.gov.uk www.doeni.gov.uk

EARTHWATCH INSTITUTE (1971)
Earthwatch developed the innovative idea of engaging the general public into the scientific process by bringing together individual volunteers and scientists on field research projects, thereby providing an alternative means of funding, as well as a dedicated labour force for field scientists. Last year, more than 3,500 volunteers had worked on Earthwatch projects, which have grown to 140 projects in over 50 countries around the world.
Contact: Earthwatch Institute (Europe), Mayfield House, 256 Banbury Road, Oxford OX2 7DE. 01864 318 838; e-mail: info@earthwatch.co.uk www.earthwatch.org/europe

EDWARD GREY INSTITUTE OF FIELD ORNITHOLOGY (1938)
The EGI takes its name from Edward Grey, first Viscount Grey of Fallodon, a life-long lover of birds and former Chancellor of the University of Oxford, who gave his support to an appeal for its foundation capital. The Institute now has a permanent research staff; it usually houses some 12-15 research students, five or six senior visitors and post-doctoral research workers. Field research is carried out mainly in Wytham Woods near Oxford and on the island of Skomer in West Wales. In addition there are laboratory facilities and aviary space for experimental work. The Institute houses the Alexander Library, one of the largest collections of 20th Century material on birds in the world and which is supported by the British Ornithologists Union which provides much of the material. The Library is open to members of the BOU and Oxford Ornithological Society; other bona fide ornithologists may use the library by prior arrangement.
Contact: Claire Harvey, PA to Professor Sheldon, The EGI, Department of Zoology, South Parks Road, Oxford OX1 3PS; +44(0)1865 271 275; e-mail: claire.harvey@zoo.ox.ac.uk www.zoo.ox.ac.uk/egi/

NATIONAL ORGANISATIONS

ENVIRONMENT AGENCY
A non-departmental body that aims to protect and improve the environment and to contribute towards the delivery of sustainable development through the integrated management of air, land and water. Functions include pollution prevention and control, waste minimisation, management of water resources, flood defence, improvement of salmon and freshwater fisheries, conservation of aquatic species, navigation and use of inland and coastal waters for recreation. Sponsored by the Department of the Environment, Transport and the Regions, MAFF and the Welsh Office.
Contact: Environment Agency, National Customer Contact Centre, PO Box 544, Rotherham S60 1BY. General enquiries; 08708 506 506 (Mon-Fri, 8am - 6pm); pollution hotline 0800 807 060; floodline 0845 988 1188; www.environment-agency.gov.uk e-mail: enquiries@environment-agency.gov.uk

FARMING AND WILDLIFE ADVISORY GROUP (FWAG) (1969)

An independent UK-registered charity led by farmers and supported by government and leading countryside organisations. Its aim is to unite farming and forestry with wildlife and landscape conservation. Active in most UK counties. There are 120 Farm Conservation Advisers who give practical advice to farmers and landowners to help them integrate environmental objectives with commercial farming practices.
Contact: *English Head Office*, FWAG, National Agricultural Centre, Stoneleigh, Kenilworth, Warwickshire CV8 2RX. 02476 696 699; e-mail: info@fwag.org.uk www.fwag.org.uk

Northern Ireland, FWAG, National Agricultural Centre, 46b Rainey Street, Magherafelt, Co. Derry BT45 5AH. 028 7930 0606; e-mail: n.ireland@fwag.org.uk

Scottish Head Office, FWAG Scotland, 024 7669 6699; e-mail: info@fwag.org.uk

Mid-Wales Office. The Arches, West Street, Rhayader, Powys LD6 5AB; 01597 811 826; e-mail: helen.barnes@fwag.org.uk

FIELD STUDIES COUNCIL (1943)
Manages Centres where students from schools, universities and colleges, as well as individuals of all ages, can stay to study various aspects of the environment under expert guidance. Courses include many for birdwatchers, providing opportunities to study birdlife on coasts, estuaries, mountains and islands. Others demonstrate bird ringing and others are for members of the BTO. Research workers and naturalists wishing to use the records and resources are welcome.
There are centres in England, Scotland, Wales and Northern Ireland, see website for contact details and courses available.
Contact: Field Studies Council, Preston Montford, Montford Bridge, Shrewsbury SY4 1HW. 0845 345 4071; www.field-studies-council.org e-mail: enquiries@field-studies-council.org

FIELDFARE TRUST
A registered charity, Fieldfare works with people with disabilities and countryside managers to improve access to the countryside for everyone. It provides advice and training services to countryside management teams, supported by its research into national standards for accessibility under the BT Countryside for All Project. For members of the public it runs projects which can enable them to take action locally, provide information on accessible places to visit and run events like the Fieldfare Kielder Challenge which encourages young people to get active in the countryside.
Fieldfare have recently created a new website www.phototrails.org that allows users to view countryside routes through a series of photographs and descriptions of the path features.
Contact: Fieldfare Trust, Volunteer House, 69 Crossgate, Cupar, Fife KY15 5AS. 01334 657 708; e-mail: info@fieldfare.org.uk - www.fieldfare.org.uk

FORESTRY COMMISSION OF GREAT BRITAIN
The government department responsible for the protection and expansion of Britain's forests and woodlands, it runs from national offices in England, Wales and Scotland, working to targets set by Commissioners and Ministers in each of the three countries. Its objectives are to protect Britain's forests and resources, conserve and improve the biodiversity, landscape and cultural heritage of forests and woodlands, develop opportunities for woodland recreation and increase public understanding and community participation in forestry.
Contact: *Forestry Commission GB Functions*, 231 Corstorphine Road, Edinburgh EH12 7AT. 0131 334 0303; e-mail: enquiries@forestry.gsi.gov.uk www.forestry.gov.uk
Forestry Commission England, England National Office, 620 Bristol Business Park, Coldharbour Lane, Bristol BS16 1EJ. 0117 906 6000; e-mail: fcengland@forestry.gsi.gov.uk

Forestry Commission Scotland, 231 Corstorphine Road, Edinburgh EH12 7AT. 0131 334 0303, (Fax) 0131 314 6152; e-mail: fcscotland@forestry.gsi.gov.uk

Forestry Commission Wales, Welsh Assembly Government, Rhodfa Padarn, Llanbadarn Fawr, Aberystwyth, Ceredigion SY23 3UR. 0300 068 0300.e-mail: fcwenquiries@forestry.gsi.gov.uk

FRIENDS OF THE EARTH (1971; 100,000)
The largest international network of environmental groups in the world, represented in 68 countries. In the UK it has a unique network of campaigning local groups, working in 200 communities in England,

Wales and Northern Ireland. It is largely funded by supporters with more than 90% of income coming from individual donations, the rest from special fundraising events, grants and trading.
Contact: Friends of the Earth, 26-28 Underwood Street, London, N1 7JQ. 020 7490 1555; e-mail: info@foe.co.uk - www.foe.co.uk

GAME CONSERVANCY TRUST (1933; 22,000)

A registered charity which researches the conservation of game and other wildlife in the British countryside. More than 60 scientists are engaged in detailed work on insects, pesticides, birds (30 species inc. raptors) mammals (inc. foxes), and habitats. The results are used to advise government, landowners, farmers and conservationists on practical management techniques which will benefit game species, their habitats, and wildlife. Each June the *Annual Review* lists about 50 papers published in the peer-reviewed scientific press.
Contact: Game Conservancy Trust, Burgate Manor, Fordingbridge, Hampshire, SP6 1EF. 01425 652 381; e-mail: info@gct.org.uk - www.gct.org.uk

GAY BIRDERS CLUB (1994; 300+)

A voluntary society for lesbian, gay and bisexual birdwatchers, their friends and supporters, over the age of consent, in the UK and worldwide. The club has a network of regional contacts and organises day trips, weekends and longer events at notable birding locations in the UK and abroad; about 200+ events in a year. Members receive a quarterly newletter *Out Birding* with details of all events. There is a Grand Get-Together every 18 months. Membership £12 waged and £5 unwaged.
Contact: Gay Birders Club, GeeBeeCee, BCM-Mono, London WC1N 3XX. e-mail: contact@gbc-online.org.uk www.gbc-online.org.uk

HAWK AND OWL TRUST (1969)

Registered charity dedicated to the conservation and appreciation of wild birds of prey and their habitats. Publishes a newsletter *Peregrine* and educational materials for all ages.The Trust achieves its major aim of creating and enhancing nesting, roosting and feeding habitats for birds of prey through projects which involve practical research, creative conservation and education, both on its own reserves and in partnership with landowners, farmers and others. Members are invited to take part in fieldwork, population studies, surveys, etc. The Trust manages three main reserves: Sculthorpe Moor in Norfolk; Shapwick Moor on the Somerset Levels; and Fylingdales Moor conservation area in North Yorkshire. Its Sculthorpe reserve near Fakenham, Norfolk and National Conservation and

Education Centre at Chiltern Open Air Museum near Chalfont St Giles, Buckinghamshire, offer schools and other groups cross-curricular environmental activities
Contact: Hawk and Owl Trust, PO Box 400, Bishops Lydeard, Taunton TA4 3WH.
Tel: 0844 984 2824; www.hawkandowl.org e-mail: enquiries@hawkandowl.org

INTERNATIONAL CENTRE FOR BIRDS OF PREY (1967)

The ICBP works for the conservation of birds of prey and their habitats through public education, captive breeding, treatment and rehabilitation of injured wild birds of prey. Conducts research for understanding health and the conservation of all birds of prey. The Centre is open to the general public for 10 months of the year. It also undertakes more in-depth education to specific groups and parties, from first schools to universities and offers off-site lectures and teaching. The Centre continues its captive breeding aims; to research species; breed from species not previously understood; provide teaching and written information for captive breeding programmes at home and abroad; maintain the Collection and provide birds for demonstrations, both in the UK and further afield. It undertakes and encourages non-invasive research with the Collection, working with colleges and universities to provide access to the birds for projects and papers. The Centre also works with the National Birds of Prey Trust and the National Aviary Pittsburgh, BNHS and many other groups and facilities to continue to support worldwide field research projects, undertakes international conservation programmes and accepts and treats and rehabilitates injured wild birds of prey. Open all year 10.30am-5.30pm (or dusk if earlier) Closed Christmas Day and Boxing Day.
Contact: International Birds of Prey Centre, Boulsdon House, Newent, Gloucestershire, GL18 1JJ. 01531 820 286 or 01531 821 581; e-mail: jpj@icbp.org www.nbpc.co.uk

IRISH RARE BIRDS COMMITTEE (1985)

Assesses records of species of rare occurrence in the Republic of Ireland. Details of records accepted and rejected are incorporated in the *Irish Bird Report*, published annually in *Irish Birds*. In the case of rarities trapped for ringing, ringers in the Republic of Ireland are required to send their schedules initially to the National Parks and Wildlife Service, 51 St Stephen's Green, Dublin 2. A copy is then taken before the schedules are sent to the British Trust for Ornithology.
Contact: Secretary: Kieran Fahy, Silveracre, Yoletown, Tacumshin, County Wexford; e-mail: secretary@irbc.ie www.irbc.ie

JOINT NATURE CONSERVATION COMMITTEE (1990)

A committee of the three country agencies (Natural England, Scottish Natural Heritage and the Countryside Council for Wales), together with

NATIONAL ORGANISATIONS

independent members and representatives from Northern Ireland and the Countryside Agency. Supported by specialist staff, its statutory responsibilities include the establishment of common standards for monitoring, the analysis of information and research; advising Ministers on the development and implementation of policies for or affecting nature conservation; and the undertaking and commissioning of research relevant to these functions. JNCC additionally has the UK responsibility for relevant European and wider international matters. The Species Team, located at the HQ address, is responsible for terrestrial bird conservation.
Contact: Joint Nature Conservation Committee, Monkstone House, City Road, Peterborough PE1 1JY. 01733 562 626; e-mail: comment@jncc.gov.uk
www.jncc.gov.uk

LINNEAN SOCIETY OF LONDON (1788, 2,000)
Named after Carl Linnaeus, the 18th Century Swedish biologist who created the modern system of scientific biological nomenclature, the Society promotes all aspects of pure and applied biology. It houses Linnaeus' collection of plants, insects and fishes, library and correspondence. The Society has a major reference library of some 100,000 volumes. Publishes the *Biological, Botanical* and *Zoological Journals*, and the *Synopses of the British Fauna*.
Contact: Linnean Society of London, Burlington House, Piccadilly, London W1J 0BF. 020 7434 4479; e-mail: info@linnean.org
www.linnean.org

MAMMAL SOCIETY (1954; 2,500)
The Mammal Society is the only organisation solely dedicated to the study and conservation of all British mammals. It seeks to raise awareness of mammal

ecology and conservation needs, to survey British mammals and their habitats to identify the threats they face and to to promote mammal studies in the UK and overseas.
Contact: The Mammal Society, 3 The Carronades, New Road, Southampton SO14 0AA. 0238 0237 874; e-mail: enquiries@mammal.org.uk
www.mammal.org.uk

MARINE CONSERVATION SOCIETY (1983)
MCS is the UK charity that campaigns for clean seas and beaches around the British coastline, sustainable fisheries, and protection for all marine life. MCS is consulted on a wide range of marine issues and provides advice primarily to government. but also to industry, on topics ranging from offshore wind and oil and gas to marine strategies and fisheries reform. It provides advice to ensure that further action is taken to conserve our seas and reduce the effect of marine activities on marine habitats and species. It has an extensive programme for volunteers, ranging from fund-raising and an annual clean-up of UK beaches to surveys of species such as basking shark.

Contact: Marine Conservation Society, Unit 3 Wolf Business Park, Alton Road, Ross-on-Wye, Herefordshire HR9 5NB. 01989 566 017.
www.mcsuk.org

NATIONAL TRUST (1895; 3.5 Million)
Charity that works for the preservation of places of historic interest or natural beauty in England, Wales and Northern Ireland. It relies on 3.5 million members, 49,000 volunteers, 500,000 schoolchildren and millions of visitors, donors and supporters. The Trust protects and opens to the public more than 300 historic houses and gardens, 49 industrial monuments and mills, plus more than 617,500 acres of land and 700 miles of coast. About 10% of SSSIs and ASSIs in England, Wales and Northern Ireland are wholly or partially owned by the Trust, as are 63 NNRs (e.g. Blakeney Point, Wicken Fen, Murlough and Dinefwr Estate), 33% of Ramsar sites include Trust land as do 45% of SPAs.
Contact: Central Office: Heelis, Kemble Drive, Swindon, Wiltshire SN2 2NA. Tel: 01793 817 400. Membership enquiries: National Trust, PO Box 39, Warrington, WA5 7WD. 0844 800 1895; e-mail: enquiries@thenationaltrust.org.uk
www.thenationaltrust.org.uk

NATIONAL TRUST FOR SCOTLAND (1931; 310,000)
The conservation charity that protects and promotes Scotland's natural and cultural heritage for present and future generations to enjoy. Its 128 properties open to the public are described in its annual *Scotland For You* guide.
Contact: National Trust for Scotland, Wemyss House, 28 Charlotte Square, Edinburgh, EH2 4ET. 0844 493 2100; e-mail: information@nts.org.uk
www.nts.org.uk

NATURAL ENGLAND
Natural England has been formed by bringing together English Nature, the landscape, access and recreation elements of the Countryside Agency and the environmental land management functions of the Rural Development Service.
Natural England is working towards the delivery of four strategic outcomes:
• A healthy natural environment through conservation and enhancement.
• Encouraging more people to enjoy, understand and act to improve the natural environment, more often.
• Ensure the use and management of the natural environment is more sustainable.
• A secure environmental future.
Contact: Natural England, Northminster House, Peterborough, PE1 1UA. 0845 600 3078; e-mail: enquiries@naturalengland.org.uk
www.naturalengland.org.uk

NATURAL HISTORY MUSEUM AT TRING (1937)
Founded by Lionel Walter (later Lord) Rothschild, the Museum displays British and exotic birds (1,500

species) including many rarities and extinct species. Galleries open all year except 24-26 Dec. Adjacent to the Bird Group of the Natural History Museum — with over a million specimens and an extensive ornithological library, an internationally important centre for bird research.

Contact: The Natural History Museum at Tring, Akeman Street, Tring, Herts HP23 6AP. 020 7942 6171; e-mail: tring-enquiries@nhm.ac.uk www.nhm.ac.uk/tring

NATURE PHOTOGRAPHERS' PORTFOLIO (1944; 74)

A society for photographers of wildlife, especially birds. Circulates postal portfolios of prints and transparencies and an on-line folio.

Contact: A Winspear-Cundall, Hon Secretary, Nature Photographers' Portfolio, 8 Gig Bridge Lane, Pershore, Worcs WR10 1NH. 01386 552 103; e-mail: arthurcundall@hotmail.co.uk www.nature-photographers-portfolio.co.uk

NORTHERN IRELAND BIRDWATCHERS' ASSOCIATION (1991; 120)

The NIBA Records Committee, established in 1997, has full responsibility for the assessment of records in N Ireland. NIBA also publishes the *Northern Ireland Bird Report* and is responsible for Flightline, a local rate telephone hotline for rare bird sightings.

Contact: The Membership Secretary, Northern Ireland Birdwatchers' Assoc, 9 Ballymacash Rd, Lisburn, Co. Antrim, N Ireland BT28 3DX . 01247 467 408; e-mail: andrew.crory@gmail.com http://nibirds.blogspot.com

NORTHERN IRELAND ORNITHOLOGISTS' CLUB (1965; 150)

Formed to focus the interests of active birdwatchers in Northern Ireland, it operates Tree Sparrow and Barn Owl nestbox schemes and a winter feeding programme for Yellowhammers. Has a regular programme of lectures and field trips for members and organises a high quality annual photographic competition. Publishes *The Harrier* quarterly.

Contact: The Honorary Secretary, C Gillespie, Northern Ireland Ornithologists Club, 4 Demesne Gate, Saintfield, Co. Down, BT24 7BE. 02897 519 371; e-mail: carolgillespie@btinternet.com - www.nioc.co.uk

NORTH SEA BIRD CLUB (1979; 200)

The stated aims of the Club are to: provide a recreational pursuit for people employed offshore; obtain, collate and analyse observations of all birds seen offshore; produce reports of observations, including an annual report; promote the collection of data on other wildlife offshore. Currently it holds in excess of 100,000 records of birds, cetaceans and insects reported since 1979.

Contact: The North Sea Bird Club, Ocean Laboratory and Culterty Field Station, University of Aberdeen, Newburgh, Aberdeenshire AB41 6AA. 01224 274 428; e-mail: nsbc@abdn.ac.uk - www.abdn.ac.uk/nsbc

PEOPLE'S DISPENSARY FOR SICK ANIMALS (1917)

Registered charity. Provides free veterinary treatment for sick and injured animals whose owners qualify for this charitable service.

Contact: PDSA, Whitechapel Way, Priorslee, Telford, Shropshire TF2 9PQ. 01952 290 999; e-mail: pr@pdsa.org.uk www.pdsa.org.uk

POND CONSERVATION

Pond Conservation is the national charity dedicated to creating and protecting ponds and the wildlife they support. It carries out research, surveys and practical conservation, working in partnership with others, and also works to protect the wildlife of other freshwaters. Key projects include: Million Ponds Project, an ambitious scheme to dig half a million new high-quality potential ponds in the UK that will be good for biodiversity; Garden ponds survey to find out what really lives in the UK's garden ponds; Pond Habitat Action Plan, in conjunction with the Environment Agency.

Contact: Pond Conservation,01865 483 249; e-mail: info@pondconservation.org.uk www.pondconservation.org.uk

RAPTOR FOUNDATION (1989)

Involved in the care of wild disabled birds of prey, as well as raptors rescued from breeders. The foundation is involved in research into raptor ailments and assists veterinary schools with placement of student vets at the centre. A full 24 hour rescue service is available for injured raptors and owls and the centre assists in breed-and-release schemes to rebuild populations across Europe. Centre is open to the public (200 birds of 40 different species on display) 10am to 5pm each day apart from Jan 1 and Dec 25/26.

Contact: The Raptor Foundation, The Heath, St Ives Road, Woodhurst, Cambs PE28 3BT. 01487 741 140; e-mail: heleowl@aol.com www.raptorfoundation.org.uk

RAPTOR RESCUE (1978)

Since inauguration, Raptor Rescue has evolved into one of the UK's foremost organisations dedicated to ensuring all sick and injured birds of prey are cared for in heated hospital units by suitably qualified people, and wherever possible, released back into the wild. Facilities include secluded aviaries, rehabilitation aviaries/flights, foster birds for rearing young to avoid imprinting. Veterinary support. Reg charity.

Contact: Raptor Rescue, Bird of Prey Rehabilitation, 0870 241 0609; www.raptorrescue.org.uk e-mail: secretary@raptorrescue.org.uk

RARE BREEDING BIRDS PANEL (1973; 7)

An independent body funded by the JNCC and RSPB. Both bodies are represented on the panel, as are BTO and ACRE. It collects all information on rare breeding birds in the United Kingdom, so that changes in status can be monitored as an aid to conservation and stored for posterity. Special forms are used

Rare Breeding Birds Panel

(obtainable free from the secretary and the website) and records should be submitted via the county and regional recorders. Since 1996 the Panel also monitors breeding by scarcer non-native species and seeks records of these in the same way. Annual report is published in *British Birds*. For details of species covered by the Panel see Log Charts and the websites.

Contact: The Secretary, Rare Breeding Birds Panel, The Old Orchard, Grange Road, North Berwick, East Lothian EH39 4QT. 01620 894 037; e-mail: secretary@rbbp.org.uk - www.rbbp.org.uk

ROYAL AIR FORCE ORNITHOLOGICAL SOCIETY (1965; 250)

RAFOS organises regular field meetings for members, carries out ornithological census work on MoD properties and mounts major expeditions annually to various UK and overseas locations. Publishes a Newsletter twice a year, a Journal annually, and reports on its expeditions and surveys.

Contact: General Secretary; www.rafos.org.uk e-mail: rafos_secretary@hotmail.com

ROYAL NAVAL BIRDWATCHING SOCIETY (1946; 250 approx)

Covering all main ocean routes, the Society has a system for reporting the positions and identity of seabirds and landbirds at sea by means of standard sea report forms. Maintains an extensive worldwide seabird database. Members are encouraged to photograph birds and a library of images is maintained. Publishes a Bulletin and an annual report entitled *The Sea Swallow*. The Simpson Scholarship provides assistance to embryonic ornithologists for studies regarding seabirds and landbirds at sea.

Contact: General Secretary, CPO Steve Copsey (temporary position); by e-mail: copsey@tesco.net www.rnbws.org.uk

ROYAL PIGEON RACING ASSOCIATION (1897; 39,000)

Exists to promote the sport of pigeon racing and controls pigeon racing within the Association. Organises liberation sites, issues rings, calculates distances between liberation sites and home lofts, and assists in the return of strays. May be able to assist in identifying owners of ringed birds caught or found.

Contact: Royal Pigeon Racing Association, The Reddings, Cheltenham, GL51 6RN. 01452 713 529; www.rpra.org

ROYAL SOCIETY FOR THE PREVENTION OF CRUELTY TO ANIMALS (1824; 43,690)

In addition to its animal centres, the Society also runs a woodland study centre and nature reserve at Mallydams Wood in East Sussex and specialist wildlife rehabilitation centres at West Hatch, Taunton, Somerset TA3 5RT (0870 0101847), at Station Road, East Winch, King's Lynn, Norfolk PE32 1NR (0870 9061420), and London Road, Stapeley, Nantwich,

Cheshire CW5 7JW (not open to the public). Inspectors are contacted through their National Communication Centre, which can be reached via the Society's 24-hour national cruelty and advice line: 08705 555 999.

Contact: RSPCA Headquarters, Willberforce Way, Horsham, West Sussex RH13 9RS. 0300 1234 555; 24-hour cruelty and advice line: 0300 1234 999. www.rspca.org.uk

ROYAL SOCIETY FOR THE PROTECTION OF BIRDS (1899 1,000,000+)

UK Partner of BirdLife International, and Europe's largest voluntary wildlife conservation body. The RSPB, a registered charity, is governed by an elected body (see also RSPB Phoenix and RSPB Wildlife Explorers) Its work in the conservation of wild birds and habitats covers the acquisition and management of nature reserves; research and surveys; monitoring and responding to development proposals, land use practices and pollution which threaten wild birds and biodiversity; and the provision of an advisory service on wildlife law enforcement.

The RSPB currently manages 200 nature reserves in the UK, covering almost 130,00 hectares and home to 80% of Britain's rarest or most threatened bird species. The aim is to conserve a countrywide network of reserves with all examples of the main bird communities and with due regard to the conservation of plants and other animals.

Current national projects include extensive work on agriculture, and conservation and campaigning for the conservation of the marine environment and to halt the illegal persecution of birds of prey. Increasingly, there is involvement with broader environmental concerns such as climate change and transport.

The RSPB's International Dept works closely with Birdlife International and its partners in other countries and is involved with numerous projects overseas, especially in Europe and Asia.

Contact: RSPB, The Lodge, Sandy, Beds SG19 2DL. Membership enquiries: 01767 693 680. Wildlife enquiries: 01767 693 690; www.rspb.org.uk e-mail: (firstname.name)@rspb.org.uk

Regional Offices:
ENGLAND
Eastern England, Stalham House, 65 Thorpe Road, Norwich NR1 1UD. 01603 661 662.
Covers: Beds, Cambs, Essex, Herts, Lincs, Norfolk, Suffolk.

London Office, RSPB London Office, 2nd Floor, 65 Petty France, London, SW1H 9EU. 0207 808 1240.

Midlands, 46 The Green, South Bar, Banbury, Oxfordshire, OX16 9AB. 01295 253 330.
Covers: Bucks, Derbys, Herefordshire, Leicestershire, Northants, Notts, Oxon, Rutland, Shropshire, Staffs, Warwickshire, West Midlands, Worcestershire.

Northern England, Denby Dale Office, Westleigh Mews, Wakefield Road, Denby Dale, Huddersfield,

HD8 8QD. 01484 861 148.

Covers: Cheshire, Cleveland, Cumbria, East Riding of Yorkshire, Greater Manchester, Lancashire, Merseyside, Middlesbrough, North, South and West Yorkshire, North East and North Lincolnshire, Northumberland, Tyne and Wear.

South East, 2nd Floor, 42 Frederick Place, Brighton, East Sussex, BN1 4EA. 01273 775 333.

Covers: East Sussex, Hampshire, Isle of Wight, Kent, Surrey, West Berkshire, West Sussex.

South West, Keble House, Southernhay Gardens, Exeter EX1 1NT. 01392 432 691.

Covers: Bristol, Cornwall, Devon, Dorset, Somerset, Gloucs, Wiltshire.

SCOTLAND

Scotland Headquarters, Dunedin House, 25 Ravelston Terrace, Edinburgh, EH4 3TP. 0131 311 6500.
e-mail: rspb.scotland@rspb.org.uk

East Scotland, 10 Albyn Terrace, Aberdeen, Aberdeenshire, AB10 1YP. 01224 624 824.

Covers: Aberdeen, Aberdeenshire, Angus, Moray, Perth and Kinross.

North Scotland, Etive House, Beechwood Park, Inverness, IV2 3BW. 01463 715 000;
e-mail: nsro@rspb.org.uk

Covers: Eilean Siar, Highland.

South and West Scotland, 10 Park Quadrant, Glasgow, G3 6BS. 0141 331 0993;
e-mail: glasgow@rspb.org.uk

Covers: Argyll and Bute, Clackmannanshire, Dumfries and Galloway, East Ayrshire, East Lothian, East Dunbartonshire, East Renfrewshire, Midlothian, North Ayrshire, North Lanarkshire, Renfrewshire, Scottish borders, South Ayrshire, South Lanarkshire, Stirling, West Dunbartonshire, West Lothian.

WALES

RSPB Wales, Sutherland House, Castlebridge, Cowbridge Road East, Cardiff CF11 9AB. 029 2035 3000.

NORTHERN IRELAND

Northern Ireland Headquarters, Belvoir Park Forest, Belfast, BT8 7QT. 028 9049 1547.

Covers: County Antrim, County Armagh, County Down, County Fermanagh, County Londonderry, County Tyrone.

RSPB WILDLIFE EXPLORERS and RSPB PHOENIX (formerly YOC) (1965; 168,000)

Junior section of the RSPB. There are more than 100 groups run by 300 volunteers. Activities include projects, holidays, roadshows, competitions, and local events for children, families and teenagers. Phoenix members (13 years and over) receive *BirdLife* magazine every two months, plus *Wingbeat* – the only environmental magazine written by teenagers for teenagers – four times a year.

Contact: The Youth Manager, RSPB Youth and Education Dept, The Lodge, Sandy, Beds SG19 2DL. 01767 680 551; e-mail: explorers@rspb.org.uk and phoenix@rspb.org.uk www.rspb.org.uk/youth

SAVE OUR SEABIRDS CHARITABLE TRUST (1988)

Founded following an oil spill which resulted in oiled birds being washed ashore in SE England, it now has two functions:1) to rescue and support the rescue of seabirds injured by pollution and 2) to raise awareness of the pollution that damages them. The Trust has built up a network of concerned people and carers along the South-East coast organised in five geographical areas: Medway to Folkestone; Rye to Bexhill; Pevensey Bay to Cuckmere; Newhaven to Hove; and Shoreham to Chichester. In practical terms, its members act to get injured seabirds to carers as quickly as possible; advise people who report casualties how best to help; keep carers in touch with each other and up-to date with the best methods of care for various injuries; and run money-raising events.

Contact: Save Our Seabirds Charitable Trust, 22 Pearl Court, Courtfield Terrace, Eastbourne, East Sussex BN21 4AA. e-mail: stanleysec@aol.com www.saveourseabirdscharitabletrust.org.uk

SCOTTISH BIRDS RECORDS COMMITTEE (1984; 7 members, plus secretary)

Set up by the Scottish Ornithologists' Club to ensure that records of species not deemed rare enough to be considered by the British Birds Rarities Committee, but which are rare in Scotland, are fully assessed; also maintains the official list of Scottish birds.

Contact: Angus Hogg, Secretary, Scottish Birds Records Committee, 11 Kirkmichael Road, Crosshill, Maybole, Ayrshire KA19 7RJ; www.the-soc.org.uk e-mail: dcgos@globalnet.co.uk

SCOTTISH ORNITHOLOGISTS' CLUB (1936; 2,250)

The Club has 14 branches (see County Directory), each with a programme of winter meetings and field trips throughout the year. The SOC organises an annual weekend conference in the autumn and a joint SOC/BTO one-day birdwatchers' conference in spring. In August 2009 it re-launched its magazine, *Scottish Birds*, which is now published quarterly and incorporates the *Scottish Bird News* and the scarce sightings journal *Birding Scotland*. The SOC is based in a large resource centre which offers panoramic views of Aberlady Bay and houses the George Waterston Library. Details can be found on the website.

Contact: The Scottish Birdwatching Resource Centre, The SOC, Waterston House, Aberlady, East Lothian EH32 0PY. 01875 871 330; (Fax) 01875 871 035; e-mail: mail@the-soc.org.uk www.the-soc.org.uk

SCOTTISH NATURAL HERITAGE (1991)

SNH is the Scottish Executive's statutory advisor in respect to the conservation, enhancement, enjoyment, understanding and sustainable use of the natural heritage.

Contact: Scottish Natural Heritage, Great Glen House, Leachkin Road, Inverness IV3 8NW. 01463 725 000; e-mail: enquiries@snh.gov.uk www.snh.org.uk

NATIONAL ORGANISATIONS

SCOTTISH SOCIETY FOR THE PREVENTION OF CRUELTY TO ANIMALS (1839; 45,000 supporters)

Represents animal welfare interests to Government, local authorities and others. Educates young people to realise their responsibilities. Maintains an inspectorate to patrol and investigate and to advise owners about the welfare of animals and birds in their care. Maintains welfare centres, two of which include oiled bird cleaning centres. Bird species, including birds of prey, are rehabilitated and where possible released back into the wild.
Contact: Scottish SPCA, Braehead Mains, 603 Queensferry Road, Edinburgh EH4 6EA. 03000 999 999; e-mail: enquiries@scottishspca.org www.scottishspca.org

SCOTTISH WILDLIFE TRUST (1964; 35,000)

The Trust aims to re-establish: a network of healthy and resilient ecosystems supporting expanding communities of native species across large areas of Scotland's land, water and seas. Its main activities focus on managing 123 wildlife reserves and undertaking practical conservation tasks; influencing and campaigning for better wildlife-related policy and action; and inspiring people to enjoy and find out more about wildlife. Member of The Wildlife Trusts partnership and organises Scottish Wildlife Week. Publishes *Scottish Wildlife* three times a year.
Contact: Scottish Wildlife Trust, Cramond House, Cramond Glebe Road, Edinburgh EH4 6NS. 0131 312 7765; e-mail: enquiries@swt.org.uk www.swt.org.uk

SEABIRD GROUP (1966; 350)

Concerned with conservation issues affecting seabirds. Co-ordinates census and monitoring work on breeding seabirds; has established and maintains the Seabird Colony Register in collaboration with the JNCC; organises triennial conferences on seabird biology and conservation topics. Small grants available to assist with research and survey work on seabirds. Publishes the *Seabird Group Newsletter* every four months and the journal *Atlantic Seabirds* quarterly, in association with the Dutch Seabird Group.
Contact: Linda Wilson, JNCC, Dunnet House, 7 Thistle Place, Aberdeen, AB10 1UZ; e-mail: linda.wilson@jncc.gov.uk www.seabirdgroup.org.uk

SOCIETY OF WILDLIFE ARTISTS (1964; 69 Members, 68 Associates)

Registered charity that seeks to generate an appreciation of the natural world through all forms of fine art. Annual exhibition held in October at the Mall Galleries, London. Through bursary schemes the Society has been able to help young artists with awards of up to £750 towards travel, education or the cost of materials.
Contact: The Secretary, Society of Wildlife Artists, Federation of British Artists, 17 Carlton House Terrace, London SW1Y 5BD. 020 7930 6844; e-mail: info@mallgalleries.com www.swla.co.uk

SWAN SANCTUARY (2005)

Founded by Dorothy Beeson BEM. A registered charity which operates nationally. Has a fully equipped swan hospital with an operating theatre, X-ray facilities and a veterinary surgeon. New site has several nursing ponds and a four acre rehabilitation lake where around 4,000 swans and the same number of other forms of wildlife are treated. 24-hour service operated, with volunteer rescuers on hand to recover victims of oil spills, vandalism etc. Reg. charity number 1002582.
Contact: The Swan Sanctuary, Felix Lane, Shepperton, Middlesex TW17 8NN. Emergency number: 01932 240 790; www.swanuk.org.uk e-mail: swans@swanuk.org.uk

UK400 CLUB (1981)

Serves to monitor the nation's leading twitchers and their life lists, and to keep under review contentious species occurrences. Publishes a bi-monthly magazine *Rare Birds*. Membership open to all.
Contact: LGR Evans, UK400 Club; e-mail: lgreuk400@aol.com www.uk400clubonline.co.uk

WADER STUDY GROUP (INTERNATIONAL) (1970; 500)

An association of wader enthusiasts, both amateur and professional, from all parts of the world. The Group aims to maintain contact between them, to help in the organisation of co-operative studies, and to provide a vehicle for the exchange of information. Publishes the *Wader Study Group Bulletin* three times a year and holds annual meetings throughout Europe.
Contact: The General Secretary, International Wader Study Group, The British Trust for Ornithology, The Nunnery, Thetford, Norfolk IP24 2PU. www.waderstudygroup.org

WELSH KITE TRUST (1996; 1,200)

A registered charity that undertakes the conservation and annual monitoring of Red Kites in Wales. It attempts to locate all the breeding birds, to compile data on population growth, productivity, range expansion etc. The Trust liaises with landowners, acts as consultant on planning issues and with regard to filming and photography, and represents Welsh interests on the UK Kite Steering Group. Provides a limited rescue service for injured kites and eggs or chicks at risk of desertion or starvation. Publishes a newsletter *Boda Wennol* twice a year, sent free to subscribing Friends of the Welsh Kite and to all landowners with nesting kites.
Contact: Tony Cross, Project Officer, Welsh Kite Trust, Samaria, Nantmel, Llandrindod Wells, Powys LD1 6EN. 01597 825 981; www.welshkitetrust.orge-mail: info@welshkitetrust.org

WELSH ORNITHOLOGICAL SOCIETY (1988; 250)

Promotes the study, conservation and enjoyment of birds throughout Wales. Runs the Welsh Records

NATIONAL ORGANISATIONS

Panel which adjudicates records of scarce species in Wales. Publishes the journal *Welsh Birds* twice a year, along with newsletters, and organises an annual conference.
Contact: Membership details from Welsh Ornithological Society, Alan Williams, Membership Secretary, 30 Fairfield, Penperlleni, Pontypool, NP4 0AQ; e-mail: mochdreboy@waitrose.com
www.welshos.org.uk

WETLAND TRUST
Set up to encourage conservation of wetlands and develop study of migratory birds, and to foster international relations in these fields. Destinations for recent expeditions inc. Brazil, Senegal, The Gambia, Guinea-Bissau, Nigeria, Kuwait, Thailand, Greece and Jordan. Large numbers of birds are ringed each year in Sussex and applications are invited from individuals to train in bird ringing or extend their experience.
Contact: Phil Jones, Wetland Trust, Elms Farm, Pett Lane, Icklesham, Winchelsea, E Sussex TN36 4AH. 01797 226374; e-mail: phil@wetlandtrust.org

WILDFOWL & WETLANDS TRUST (1946; 130,000 members and 4,700 bird adopters)
Registered charity founded by the late Sir Peter Scott to conserve wetlands and their biodiversity. WWT has nine centres with reserves (see Arundel, Caerlaverock, Castle Espie, Llanelli, Martin Mere, Slimbridge, Washington, Welney, and The London Wetland Centre in Reserves and Observatories section). The centres are nationally or internationally important for wintering wildfowl. Programmes of walks and talks are available for visitors with varied interests – resources and programmes are provided for school groups. Research Department works on population dynamics, species management plans and wetland ecology. The Wetland Advisory Service (WAS) undertakes contracts, and Wetland Link International promotes the role of wetland centres for education and public awareness.
Contact: Wildfowl and Wetlands Trust, Slimbridge, Glos, GL2 7BT. 01453 891 900; www.wwt.org.uk
e-mail: enquiries@wwt.org.uk

WILDLIFE SOUND RECORDING SOCIETY (1968; 327)
Works closely with the Wildlife Section of the National Sound Archive. Members carry out recording work for scientific purposes as well as for pleasure. A field weekend is held each spring, and members organise meetings locally. Four CD sound magazines of members' recordings are produced for members each year, and a journal, *Wildlife Sound*, is published twice a year.
Contact: Hon Membership Secretary, WSRS, Wildlife Sound Recording Society, www.wildlife-sound.org
e-mail: enquiries@wildlife-sound.org

WILDLIFE TRUSTS (1995; 791,000)
Originally the Society of the Promotion of Nature Reserves, founded in 1912, now the largest UK charity exclusively dedicated to conserving all habitats and species, with a membership of more than 791,000 people including 108,000 junior members in 47 individual county trusts. Collectively, they manage more than 2,200 nature reserves spanning over 80,000 hectares. The Wildlife Trusts also lobby for better protection of the UK's natural heritage and are dedicated to protecting wildlife for the future. Members receive *Natural World* magazine three times a year. See also Wildlife Watch.

Contact: The Wildlife Trusts, The Kiln, Waterside, Mather Road, Newark NG24 1WT. 01636 677 711; e-mail: enquiry@wildlifetrusts.org
www.wildlifetrusts.org

WILDLIFE WATCH (1977; 108.000)
The junior branch of The Wildlife Trusts (see previous entry) It supports 1,500 registered volunteer leaders running Watch groups across the UK. Publishes *Watchword* and *Wildlife Extra* for children and activity books for adults working with young people.
Contact: Wildlife Watch, The Wildlife Trusts, The Kiln, Waterside, Mather Road, Newark NG24 1WT. 01636 677 711; e-mail: watch@wildlifetrusts.org
www.wildlifewatch.org.uk

WWF-UK (1961)
WWF is the world's largest independent conservation organisation, comprising 27 national organisations. It works to conserve and protect endangered species and address global threats to nature by seeking long-term solutions with people in government and industry, education and civil society. Publishes *WWF News* (quarterly magazine)
Contact: WWF-UK (World Wide Fund for Nature), Panda House, Weyside Park, Catteshall Lane, Godalming, Surrey GU7 1XR. 01483 426 444;
www.wwf.org.uk

ZOOLOGICAL PHOTOGRAPHIC CLUB (1899)
Circulates black and white and colour prints of zoological interest via a series of postal portfolios.
Contact: Martin B Withers, Hon Secretary, Zoological Photographic Club, 93 Cross Lane, Mountsorrel, Loughborough, Leics LE12 7BX. 0116 229 6080.

ZOOLOGICAL SOCIETY OF LONDON (1826)
Carries out research, organises symposia and holds scientific meetings. Manages the Zoological Gardens in Regent's Park (first opened in 1828) and Whipsnade Wild Animal Park near Dunstable, Beds, each with extensive collections of birds. The Society's library has a large collection of ornithological books and journals. Publications include *the Journal of Zoology, Animal Conservation, Conservation Biology* book series, *The Symposia* and *The International Zoo Yearbook.*
Contact: Zoological Society of London, Regent's Park, London, NW1 4RY. 020 7722 3333; www.zsl.org

NATIONAL PROJECTS

National ornithological projects depend for their success on the active participation of amateur birdwatchers. In return they provide birdwatchers with an excellent opportunity to contribute in a positive and worthwhile way to the scientific study of birds and their habitats, which is the vital basis of all conservation programmes. The following entries provide a description of each particular project and a note of whom to contact for further information (full address details of project organisers are in the previous section).

BIRD ATLAS 2007-11
BTO, run in partnership with BirdWatch Ireland and the Scottish Ornithologists' Club
Atlases have provided a periodic stock-take of the birds of Britain and Ireland, and this latest Atlas will do just that, only this time in both the breeding season and in winter. It will generate range and

abundance maps for all species while giving the opportunity to contrast past and present distributions and assess changes, for better or worse. Fieldwork was completed at the end of the 2-2011 breeding season, though around 20 counties undertaking local atlases will continue for another year or more. Look online to see if your county is continuing fieldwork and please submit you records. National results and statistics continue to be updated daily.
Contact: e-mail: birdatlas@bto.org
www.birdatlas.net

BirdTrack
Organised by BTO on behalf of BTO, RSPB and BirdWatch Ireland.
BirdTrack is a free, online bird recording system for birdwatchers to store and manage bird records from anywhere in Britain and Ireland.
The idea is simple — just make a note of the birds seen or heard at each site visited then enter the observations on an easy-to-use web page (www. birdtrack.net). Exciting real-time outputs are generated by BirdTrack, including species reporting rate graphs and animated maps of sightings, all freely-available online. The data collected are used by researchers to investigate migration movements and the distribution of scarce birds, and to support species conservation at local, national and international scales. **Contact:** Nick Moran, BTO.
E-mail: birdtrack@bto.org

BREEDING BIRD SURVEY
Supported by the BTO, JNCC and the RSPB.
Begun in 1994, the BBS is designed to keep track of

the changes in populations of our common breeding birds. It is dependent on volunteer birdwatchers throughout the country who can spare about five hours a year to cover a 1x1km survey square. There are just two morning visits to survey the breeding birds each year.

Survey squares are picked at random by computer to ensure that all habitats and regions are covered. Since its inception it has been a tremendous success, with more than 3,000 squares covered and more than 200 species recorded each year.
Contact: Kate Risely, e-mail: bbs@bto.org, or your local BTO Regional Representative (see County Directory).

CONSTANT EFFORT SITES (CES) SCHEME
The CES scheme, run since 1983, coordinates standardised summer ringing at 120 sites across Britain and Ireland. This allows the BTO to monitor trends in the numbers of adults at breeding sites, annual breeding productivity and survival rates of adults for 25 common songbirds. Information from CES complements demographic information from other surveys and feeds into the BTO's Integrated Population Monitoring, highlighting the causes of changes in bird populations.
The scheme is funded by a partnership between BTO, JNCC, The National Parks & Wildlife Service (Ireland) and ringers themselves.
Contact: Greg Conway, BTO, e-mail: ces@bto.org

GARDEN BIRD FEEDING SURVEY
A BTO project.
The Garden Bird Feeding Survey is the longest-running study of garden birds in Britain. Each year approximately 250 householders record the numbers and variety of birds using food supplements and water that they have provided in their garden. Observations are made on a weekly basis from October to March inclusive. Gardens are selected by region and type; from city flats, suburban semis, rural houses to outlying farms.
Contact: Tim Harrison, BTO.
E-mail: tim.harrison@bto.org

BTO GARDEN BIRDWATCH
A BTO project.
Started in January 1995, this project is a year-round survey that monitors the use that birds and other

NATIONAL PROJECTS

types of wildlife make of gardens. Approximately 15,000 participants from all over the UK and Ireland keep a weekly log of species using their gardens. The data collected are used to monitor regional, seasonal and year-to-year changes in the garden populations of our commoner birds, mammals, butterflies, reptiles and amphibians. To cover running costs there is an annual subscription of £15. Participants receive a quarterly colour magazine *The Bird Table* and all new joiners receive a full-colour, garden bird handbook. Results and more information are available online:
www.bto.org/gbw
Contact: Garden Ecology Team, BTO.
E-mail: gbw@bto.org

GOOSE CENSUSES
A WWT project
Britain and Ireland support internationally important goose populations. During the day, many of these feed away from wetlands and are not adequately censused by the Wetland Bird Survey. Additional surveys are therefore undertaken to provide estimates of population size. These primarily involve roost counts, supplemented by further counts of feeding birds.

Most populations are censused up to three times a year, typically during the autumn, midwinter, and spring. In addition, counts of the proportion of juveniles in goose flocks are undertaken to provide estimates of annual productivity. Further volunteers are always needed. In particular, counters in Scotland, Lancashire and Norfolk are sought. For more information
Contact: Richard Hearn, Programme Manager.
E-mail: richard.hearn@wwt.org.uk
T: +44 (0)1453 891 185;
e-mail: monitoring@wwt.org.uk

HERONRIES CENSUS
A BTO project.
This survey started in 1928 and has been carried out under the auspices of the BTO since 1934. It represents the longest continuous series of population data for any European breeding bird (Grey Heron). Counts of apparently occupied nests are made at as many heronries as possible each year, throughout the UK, to provide an index of current population levels; data from Scotland and Northern Ireland are scant and more contributions from these countries would be especially welcomed. Herons may be hit hard during periods of severe weather and are vulnerable to pesticides and pollution. Currently, however, population levels are relatively high. Little Egret and other incoming species of colonial waterbird such as Cattle Egret are now fully included, whether nesting with Grey Herons or on their own; counts of Cormorant nests at heronries are also encouraged.
Contact: John Marchant, BTO

IRISH WETLAND BIRD SURVEY (I-WebS)
A joint project of BirdWatch Ireland, the National Parks & Wildlife Service of the Dept of Arts, Culture & the Gaeltacht, and WWT, and supported by the Heritage Council and WWF-UK.
Established in 1994, I-WebS aims to monitor the numbers and distribution of waterfowl populations wintering in Ireland in the long term, enabling the population size and spatial and temporal trends in numbers to be identified and described for each species.

Methods are compatible with existing schemes in the UK and Europe, and I-WebS collaborates closely with the Wetland Bird Survey (WeBS) in the UK. Synchronised monthly counts are undertaken at wetland sites of all habitats during the winter.

Counts are straightforward and counters receive a newsletter and full report annually. Additional help is always welcome, especially during these initial years as the scheme continues to grow.
Contact: BirdWatch Ireland;
www.birdwatchireland.ie

NEST BOX CHALLENGE
A BTO project
A popular survey designed to monitor the breeding success of birds in Britain's green spaces. All you need to do is register one or more nest boxes in your garden or local green space and then observe what birds nest in them and how they get on. Since the project was launched in 2007, 20,000 nest boxes have been registered across the UK and participants have been recording whether or not these boxes are occupied, how many eggs have been laid in them and how many chicks have hatched and flown. Since 2010, the survey has been extended to include open nests, so if you find a Blackbird nesting in your privet hedge or a Collared Dove in your cherry tree, you can register it and report on its progress too. This survey is 'paperless', so participants must be able to report their findings via the BTO website. For information on taking part, please visit www.bto.org/nbc
Contact: Carl Barimore, BTO
E-mail: nest.records@bto.org

NEST RECORD SCHEME
A BTO Project forming part of the BTO's Integrated Population Monitoring programme carried out under contract with the JNCC.
The NRS monitors changes in the nesting success and the timing of breeding of Britain's bird species by gathering information on nests found anywhere in the country, from a Blackbird in a garden to an Oystercatcher on a Scottish loch. Participants locate nests and then carefully monitor their progress over several visits, making counts of the number of eggs and/or chicks and recording whether they are successful. Over 30,000 nest records are submitted to the BTO each year by volunteer surveyors and the

results are updated annually and published on-line as part of the BirdTrends Report (www.bto.org/birdtrends). Guidance on how to become a BTO nest recorder, including best practice guidelines on minimising disturbance while visiting nests, is available at www. bto.org/nrs and a free starter pack available on request.
Contact: Carl Barimore, BTO
E-mail: nrs@bto.org

RAPTOR AND OWL RESEARCH REGISTER
A BTO project
The Register has helped considerably over the past 30 years in encouraging and guiding research, and in the co-ordination of projects. There are currently almost 500 projects in the card index file through which the Register operates.

The owl species currently receiving most attention are Barn and Tawny. As to raptors, the most popular subjects are Kestrel, Buzzard, Sparrowhawk, Hobby and Peregrine, with researchers showing increasing interest in Red Kite, and fewer large in-depth studies of Goshawk, Osprey and harriers.

Contributing is a simple process and involves all raptor enthusiasts, whether it is to describe an amateur activity or professional study. The nature of research on record varies widely — from local pellet analyses to captive breeding and rehabilitation programmes to national surveys of Peregrine, Buzzard and Golden Eagle. Birdwatchers in both Britain and abroad are encouraged to write for photocopies of cards relevant to the species or nature of their work. The effectiveness of the Register depends upon those running projects (however big or small) ensuring that their work is included.
Contact: David Glue, BTO.

RED KITE RE-INTRODUCTION PROJECT
An English Nature/SNH/RSPB project supported by Forest Enterprise, Yorkshire Water and authorities in Germany and Spain
The project involves the translocation of birds from Spain, Germany and the expanding Chilterns population for release at sites in England and Scotland.

Records of any wing-tagged Red Kites in England should be reported to Natural Engand, Northminster House, Peterborough, PEI IUA (tel 01733 455 281). Scottish records should be sent to the RSPB's North Scotland Regional Office, Etive House, Beechwood Park, Inverness, IV2 3BW (tel 01463 715 000).

Sightings are of particular value if the letter/number code (or colour) of wing tags can be seen or if the bird is seen flying low over (or into) woodland. Records should include an exact location, preferably with a six figure grid reference.

RETRAPPING ADULTS FOR SURVIVAL (RAS) SCHEME
Scheme is funded by a partnership between BTO, JNCC, The National Parks & Wildlife Service (Ireland) and ringers themselves.
The RAS scheme started in 1998 and gathers information on recaptures of adult birds. Projects are chosen and run by volunteer ringers and focus on species of conservation concern that are monitored relatively poorly by CES and general ringing activity. Collection of standardised capture/recapture data allows the BTO to monitor survival rates in adult birds. Detailed information about survival helps us to understand population changes as part of the BTO's Integrated Population Monitoring. Ringers themselves choose a target species and aim to catch all the breeding adults within that area on an annual basis. Results are updated annually and published on-line as part of the BirdTrends Report (www.bto.org/birdtrends).
Contact: Greg Conway, BTO, e-mail: ras@bto.org, www.bto.org/ras

RINGING SCHEME
Scheme is funded by a partnership between BTO, JNCC, The National Parks & Wildlife Service (Ireland) and ringers themselves.
Marking birds with individually numbered metal rings allows us to study survival, productivity and movements of British and Irish birds. Nearly 2,500 trained and licensed ringers operate in Britain and Ireland, marking around 800,000 birds annually.

Training to ring, and use mist nets takes at least a year, but more often two or more years depending on the aptitude of the trainee and the amount of ringing they do. A restricted permit can usually be obtained more quickly. Anyone can contribute to the scheme by reporting any ringed or colour-ringed birds they see or find. Reports can be submitted online at www.ring.ac or direct to BTO HQ. Anyone finding a ringed bird should note the ring number, species, when and where found and, if possible, what happened to it. If the bird is dead, it may also be possible to remove the ring, which should be kept in case there is a query. Anyone reporting a ringed bird will be sent details of where and when the bird was originally ringed. More info: www.bto.org/ringing/
'Demog Blog' for up to date news and stories: http://btoringing.blogspot.com/
Contact: Jacquie Clark, BTO

SWIFT CONSERVATION
Endorsed by the BTO and the RSPB,
Swift Conservation works to protect and restore the UK's fast-diminishing Swift population, a once-numerous species that because of changes in building technology and design is facing increasing difficulties in finding places to breed. Practical information on Swift conservation is provided to owners, architects, builders and others via a web site, by e-mail and in person. Swift Conservation also supports Swift

populations through a network of "Swift Champions" who survey their localities for Swift colonies and work to preserve and enhance them. The help of interested bird watchers with this work is always welcome.

Swift Conservation runs a lectures, talks and training programme for bird clubs, local government and building professionals. Please contact them if you are interested in this or any aspect of their work.
Contacts: Edward Mayer: phone 020 7794 2098
e-mail: mail@swift-conservation.org
web site: www.swift-conservation.org/

TOOTH & CLAW

An independent project aimed at improving knowledge about Britain's predators and promoting discussion on the issues that surround them.

Tooth & Claw explores some of the complex issues surrounding our relationship with wild predators and questions how we really feel and why.

Through the web site, Tooth & Claw provides a meeting place between anecdotal input and scientific research and encourages constructive and imaginative dialogue on predator issues.

A series of case studies led by powerful imagery will provide insightful interviews and personal accounts of our lives alongside the likes of eagles and foxes with a glimpse into the future and the return of creatures we have not known for centuries.
Contact: Peter Cairns, Northshots, Ballintean, Glenfeshie, Kingussie, Scotland, PH21 1NX. (44) (0)1540 651 352;
e-mail: peter@toothandclaw.org.uk
www.toothandclaw.org.uk

WATERWAYS BREEDING BIRD SURVEY

A BTO project, supported by the Environment Agency
WBBS uses transect methods like those of the Breeding Bird Survey to record bird populations along randomly chosen stretches of river and canal throughout the UK. Just two survey visits are needed during April-June. WBBS began in 1998 and has now taken over from the Waterways Bird Survey as the main monitoring scheme for birds in this habitat.
Contact: BTO Regional Representative (see County Directory) to enquire if any local stretches require coverage, otherwise John Marchant at BTO HQ; e-mail: john.marchant@bto.org

WETLAND BIRD SURVEY (Webs)

A joint scheme of BTO, WWT, RSPB & JNCC.
The Wetland Bird Survey (WeBS) is the monitoring scheme for non-breeding waterbirds in the UK.

The principal aims are:
1. to determine the population sizes of waterbirds
2. to determine trends in numbers and distribution
3. to identify important sites for waterbirds

WeBS data are used to designate important waterbird sites and protect them against adverse development, for research into the causes of declines, for establishing conservation priorities and strategies and to formulate management plans for wetland sites and waterbirds.

Monthly, synchronised Core Counts are made at as many wetland sites as possible. Low Tide Counts are made on about 20 estuaries each winter to identify important feeding areas. Counts can take from a few minutes up to a few hours depending on the size of the site and are relatively straightforward. The 3,000 participants receive an annual newsletter and a comprehensive annual report. New counters are always welcome.
Contacts: General Webs Enquiries, Heidi Mellan, WeBS Office, BTO. E-mail webs@bto.org
www.bto.org/webs

INTERNATIONAL DIRECTORY

David Cromack

Despite its reputation as a symbol of good fortune, White Storks in Europe have been declining as a result of agricultural intensification, but reintroduction schemes have helped the bird to resume greeding in Holland, Sweden and Switzerland.

BirdLife
INTERNATIONAL

The BirdLife Partnership
BirdLife is a Partnership of non-governmental
organisations (NGOs) with a special focus on
conservation and birds. Each NGO Partner represents
a unique geographic territory/country.

The BirdLife Network explained
Partners: Membership-based NGOs who represent
BirdLife in their own territory. Vote holders and key
implementing bodies for BirdLife's Strategy and
Regional Programmes in their own territories.

Partners Designate: Membership-based NGOs who
represent BirdLife in their own territory, in a transition
stage to becoming full Partners. Non-vote holders.

Affiliates: Usually NGOs, but also individuals,
foundations or governmental institutions when
appropriate. Act as a BirdLife contact with the aim
of developing into, or recruiting, a BirdLife Partner in
their territory.

Secretariat: The co-ordinating and servicing body of
BirdLife International.

SECRETARIAT ADDRESSES

BirdLife Global Office
BirdLife International
Wellbrook Court, Girton Road
Cambridge CB3 0NA
United Kingdom
Tel. +44 1 223 277 318
Fax +44 1 223 277 200
E-mail: Birdlife@birdlife.org.uk
www.birdlife.org

Birdlife Africa Regional Office
c/o ICIPE Campus
Kasarani Road, off Thika Road
Nairobi, Kenya
Postal Address
PO Box 3502
00100 GPO
Nairobi, Kenya
Tel: +254 020 806 8314
Fax: +254 020 806 8315
E-mail: birdlife-africa@birdlife.org
www.birdlife.org/regional/africa/
partnership

**BirdLife Americas Regional
Office**
Birdlife International
Juan de Dios Martinez N35-76 y
Av Portugal
Quito, Ecuador

Postal address
BirdLife International
Casilla 17-17-717
Quito, Equador
Tel. +593 (2) 2464 768
Fax +593 (2) 2469 838
E-mail: americas @birdlife.org
www.birdlife.org/regional/americas/
partnership

BirdLife Asia Regional Office
TM Suidobashi Building
4F, Misaki-cho 2-14-6
Chiyoda-ku
Tokyo 101-0061, Japan
Tel.+81 (3) 5213 0461
Fax.+81 (3) 5213 0422
E-mail: info@birdlife-asia.org
www.birdlife.org/regional/asia/
partnership

BirdLife Europe
Avenue de la Toison d'Or 67
(2nd floor), B-1060 Brussels
Belgium
Tel. +32 2280 08 30
Fax +32 2230 38 02
E-mail: europe@birdlife.org
www.birdlife.org/regional/europe/
partnership

**BirdLife Middle East Regional
Office**
BirdLife International Middle East
Division
P. O. Box 2295
Amman 11953
Jordan
Postal address
Amman
Khalda
Salameh El-Ma'aaytah Street
Building No 6. Jordan
Tel: +962 (6) 564-8173
Fax: +962 (6) 564-8172
E-mail: me@birdlife.org
www.birdlife.org/regional/
middle_east/partnership

BirdLife Pacific Regional Office
10 MacGregor Road
Suva, Fuji
Postal address
GPO Box 18332
Suva, Fuji
Tel: +679 331 3492
Fax: +679 331 9658
E-mail: don@birdlifepacific.org.fj

AFRICA

PARTNERS

Bukina Faso
La Fondation NATURAMA 01 B.P. 6133, Ouagadougou
01, Burkina Faso; e-mail: naturama@fasonet.bf
www.naturama.bf

Ethiopia
Ethiopian Wildlife and Natural History Society, PO Box
13303, Addis Ababa, Pub: *Agazen; Ethiopian Wildl. and
Nat. Hist. News. (& Annual Report); Ethiopian Wildl.*

and *Nat. Hist. Soc. Quarterly News (WATCH); Walia
(WATCH) (Ethiopia);* www.ewnhs.org.et
e-mail: ewnhs@ethionet.et

Ghana
Ghana Wildlife Society, PO Box 13252, Accra, Pub:
Bongo News; NKO (The Parrots);
e-mail: ghanawild@4u.co.gh -
www.ghanawildlifesociety.org

Kenya
Nature Kenya, PO Box 44486, 00100 GPO. Nairobi. Pub:
*Bulletin of the EANHS; Journal of East African Natural;
Kenya Birds;* e-mail: office@naturekenya.org
www.naturekenya.org

INTERNATIONAL ORGANISATIONS

Seychelles
Nature Seychelles, Roche Caiman, Box 1310, Victoria, Mahe, Seychelles. Pub: *Zwazo - a BirdLife Seychelles Newsletter;* e-mail: nature@seychelles.net www.natureseychelles.org.

Sierra Leone
Conservation Society of Sierra Leone, PO Box 1292, Freetown. Pub: *Rockfowl Link, The.* e-mail: cssl_03@yahoo.com http://conservationsl.org

South Africa
BirdLife South Africa, PO Box 515, Randburg, Johannesburg 2125, South Africa, Pub: *Newsletter of BirdLife South Africa; Ostrich;* e-mail: secretary@birdlife.org.za www.birdlife.org.za

Tanzania
Wildlife Conservation Society of Tanzania, PO Box 70919, Dar es Salaam, Pub: *Miombo.* e-mail: wcst@africaonline.co.tz www.wcst@arusha.org

Tunisia
Association Les Amis des Oiseaux, Bureau des Projets, Ariana Centre – Bureau C 208/209, 2080 Ariana, Tunis. Pub: *Feuille de Liaison de l'AAO; Houbara, l'.* e-mail: aao@topnet.tn - www.aao.org.tn

Uganda
Nature Uganda, The EANHS, PO Box 27034, Kampala. Pub: *Naturalist - A Newsletter of the East Africa Nat. His. Soc;* e-mail: nature@natureuganda.org www.natureuganda.org/

Zimbabwe
BirdLife Zimbabwe, P O Box RV 100, Runiville, Harare, Zimbabwe. Pub: *Babbler (WATCH) (Zimbabwe); Honeyguide;* e-mail: birds@zol.co.zw www.birdlifezimbabwe.co.zw/

PARTNERS DESIGNATE

Botswana
Birdlife Botswana, PO Box 26691, Game City, Gaborone, Botswana
e-mail: blb@birdlifebotswana.org.bw www.birdlifebotswana.org.bw

Burundi
Association Burundaise pour la Protection des Oiseaux, P O Box 7069, Bujumbura, Burundi; e-mail: aboconservation.org http://aboconservation.org/

Nigeria
Nigerian Conservation Foundation, PO Box 74638, Victoria Island, Lagos. Pub: *NCF Matters/News/ Newsletter; Nigerian Conservation Foundation Annual Report;* e-mail: info@ncf-nigeria.org www.ncfnigeria.org

AFFILIATES

Cameroon
Cameroon Biodiversity Conservation Society (CBCS), PO Box 3055, Messa, Yaoundé; e-mail: cbcs_cam@yahoo.fr

Egypt
Nature Conservation Egypt, 10 Managem wa Mahager str, Mohandeseen, Giza.
e-mail: halabarakat2002@yahoo.com www.ncegypt.org

Ivory Coast
Cote d'Ivoire (SOS-FORETS), 22 BP 918 Abidjan 22. E-mail: sosforets@hotmail.com

Liberia
Society for Conservation of Nature in Liberia, SCNL, Monrovia Zoo, Lakpazee, PO Box 2628, Monrovia. E-mail: scnlliberia@yahoo.com - www.scnlib.net

Madagascar
Asity Madagascar, Lot IIN 184 PH Ter Analamahitsy – 101 Antananarivio, Madagascar BP 1074. E-mail: zicoma@birdlife-mada.org http://asitymadagascar.org

Malawi
Wildlife & Environmental Socity of Malawi, Private Bag 578, Limbe. E-mail: wesm-hq@africa-online.net www.wildlifemalawi.org

Rwanda
Association pour la Conservation de la Nature au Rwanda, P O Box 4290, Kigali, e-mail: conserverwanda@yahoo.fr www.acnrwanda.org/contact.php

Zambia
Zambian Ornithological Society, Box 33944, Lusaka 10101, Pub: *Zambian Ornithological Society Newsletter;* e-mail: zos@zamnet.zm www.wattledcrane.com

AMERICAS

PARTNERS

Argentina
Aves Argentina (AOP), Matheu 1246/8, C1249AAB, Buenos Aires. Pub: *Hornero; Naturaleza & Conservacion; Nuestras Aves; Vuelo de Pajaro;* e-mail: info@avesargentinas.org.ar www.avesargentinas.org.ar

Belize
The Belize Audubon Society, PO Box 1001, 12 Fort Street, Belize City. Pub: *Belize Audubon Society Newsletter;* e-mail: base@btl.net www.belizeaudubon.org

Bolivia
Asociacion Armonia, Avenidad Lomas de Arena 400, Casilla 3566, Santa Cruz. Pub: *Aves en Bolivia;* e-mail: armonia@armonia-bo.org www.armonia-bo.org

Canada
Bird Studies Canada, PO Box/160, Port Rowan, Ontario N0E 1M0. Pub: *Bird Studies Canada - Annual Report; Birdwatch Canada;* e-mail: generalinfo@bsc-eoc.org www.bsc-eoc.org

Canada
Nature Canada, 1 Nicholas Street, Suite 606, Ottawa, Ontario, K1N 7B7. Pub: *Grass 'n Roots; IBA News Canada; Nature Canada; Nature Matters; Nature Watch News (CNF);* e-mail: info@naturecanada.ca www.naturecanada.ca

INTERNATIONAL ORGANISATIONS

Ecuador
Aves & Conservación (Corporación Ornitológica del Ecuador, Pasaje Joaquin Tinajero E3-05 y Jorge Drom, Casilla 17-17-906, Quito.
e-mail: aves_direccion@avesconservacion.org
www.avesconservaccion.org

Falkland Islands
Falklands Conservation, PO Box 26, Stanley, Falklands or UK Office, 14 East Hatley, sandy, Bedfordshire SG19 3JA. UK. Pub: *Falklands Conservation.*
e-mail: info@falklandsconservation.com
www.falklandsconservation.com

Panama
Panama Audubon Society, Apartado 0843-03076, Balboa, Ancon. Pub: *Toucan;*
e-mail: info@panamaaudubon.org
www.panamaaudubon.org

United States
Audubon Society, 225 Varick Street, 7th Floor New York, NY, 10004. Pub: *American Birds; Audubon (USA); Audubon Field Notes; Audubon Bird Conservation Newsletter;* www.audubon.org
e-mail: international@audubon.org

PARTNER DESIGNATE

Paraguay
Guyra Paraguay, Gaetano Martino 215 esq. Tte. Ross, Asunción. Pub: *Boletin Jara Kuera;*
e-mail: guyra@guyra.org.py
www.guyra.org.py/

AFFILIATES

Bahamas
Bahamas National Trust, PO Box 4105, Nassau. Pub: *Bahamas Naturalist; Currents; Grand Bahama Update.*
e-mail: bnt@bnt.bs - www.bnt.bs

Chile
Comite Nacional Pro defensa de la Flora y Fauna (CODEFF), Ernesto Reyes 035, Providencia, Santiago 21. Pub: *Boletin Chileno de Ornitologia; Boletin Informativo (WATCH) (Chile).*
e-mail: administra@codeff.cl - www.codeff.cl

Cuba
Centro Nacional de Áreas Protegidas (CNAP). Calle 18 a, No 1441, e/ 41 y 47, Playa, Ciudad Habana, Cuba.
e-mail: cnap@snap.cu www.snap.co.cu/

Dominican Republic
Grupo Jaragua (GJI), Calle El Vergel No 36 Ensanche, El Vergel, Santo Domingo. E-mail: jaragua@tricom.net
www.grupjaragua.org.do

El Salvador
SalvaNATURA, 33 Avenida Sur #640, Colonia Flor Blanca, San Salvador. e-mail: info@salvanatura.org
www.salvanatura.org

Mexico
Pronatura, Aspergulas 22 (antes Pino), Colonia San Clemente, CP 01740; www.pronatura.org.mx
e-mail: pronatura@pronatura.org.mx

Suriname
Foundation for Nature Preservation in Suriname, Cornelis Jongbawstraat 14, PO Box 12252, Paramaribo
e-mail: research@stinasu.sr www.stinasu.sr

Uruguay
Aves Uruguay (GUPECA), Casilla de Correo 6955, Correo Central, Montevideo. Pub: *Achara.*
e-mail: info@avesuruguay.org.uy
www.avesuruguay.org.uy/

ASIA

PARTNERS

India
Bombay Natural History Society, Hornbill House, Shaheed Bhagat Singh Road, Mumbai-400 023. Pub: *Buceros; Hornbill; Journal of the Bombay Natural History Society.* www.bnhs.org
e-mail: bnhs@bom4.vsnl.net.in

Japan
Wild Bird Society of Japan (WBSJ), Maruw Bldg, 3-9-23, Nishi-Gotanda, Shinagawa-ku, Tokyo 141-0031, Japan. Pub: *Strix; Wild Birds; Wing.*
e-mail: hogo@wbsj.org - www.wbsj.org

Malaysia
Malaysian Nature Society, PO Box 10750, Kuala Lumpur 50724. Pub: *Enggang; Suara Enggang; Malayan Nature Journal; Malaysian Naturalist.*
e-mail: mns@mns.org.my - www.mns.my

Philippines
Haribon Foundation, 2/F, Santos and Sons Building, 973 Aurora Blvd, Cubao, Quezon CIty 1109. Pub: *Haribon Foundation Annual Report; Haring Ibon; Philippine Biodiversity.*
e-mail: act@haribon.org.ph - www.haribon.org.ph

Singapore
Nature Society (Singapore), 510 Geylang Road, #02-05, The Sunflower, 398466. Pub: *Nature News; Nature Watch (Singapore);* e-mail: nss@nss.org.sg
www.nss.org.sg

Taiwan
Chinese Wild Bird Federation (CWBF), 1F, No. 3, Lane 36 Jing-Long St., 116 Taipei, Taiwan. Pub: *Yuhina Post;*
e-mail: mail@bird.org.tw - www.bird.org.tw

Thailand
Bird Conservation Society of Thailand, 221 moo 2, Soi Ngamwongwan 2, Tambol Bangkhen, Ampur Meung, Nontaburi 11000. Pub: *Bird Conservation Society of Thailand.*
e-mail: bcst@bcst.or.th www.bcst.or.th

PARTNERS DESIGNATE

Hong Kong
The Hong Kong Birdwatching Society, 14/F Ruby Commercial Building, 480 Nathan Road, Kowloon, Hong Kong, People's Republic of China. Pub: *Hong Kong Bird Report;* e-mail: hkbws@hkbws.org.uk
www.hkbws.org.hk

Nepal
Bird Conservation Nepal, P.O.Box 12465, Kathmandu, Nepal. Pub: *Bird Conservation Nepal (Danphe); Ibisbill;*
e-mail: bcn@mail.com.np - www.birdlifenepal.org

INTERNATIONAL ORGANISATIONS

AFFILIATES

Indonesia
Burung Indonesia (Perhimpunan Pelestari Burung dan Habitatnya), Jl. Dadali 32, Bogor 16161, PO. Box 310/ Boo, Bogor 16003, Indonesia; e-mail: birdlife@burung.org - www.burung.org

Kazakhstan
Association for the Conservation of Biodiversity of Kazakhstan (ACBK), Off. 203, 40 Orbita-1, Almaty 050043, Kazakhstan. E-mail: office@acbk.kz www.acbk.kz

Kyrgyzstan
NABS Public Association. www.wildlife.kg

Sri Lanka
Field Ornithology Group of Sri Lanka, Dept of Zoology, University of Colombo, Colombo 03. Pub: *Malkoha - Newsletter of the Field Ornithology Group of Sri Lanka.* e-mail: fogsl@slt.lk - www.fogsl.net

Uzbekistan
Uzbekistan Society for the Protection of Birds (UzSPB), Off.89, Institte of Zoology of Uzbek Academy of sciences, A. Niyazov str.1, Tashkent 100095. E-mial: roman.kashkarov@iba.uz - www.uzspb.uz

UNAFFILIATED COUNTRIES

Cambodia
BirdLife International Cambodia Programme, #9 Street 29, Tonie Basac, Chamkarmon, Phnom Penh. e-mail: admin@birdlifecambodia.org www.birdlifeindochina.org

Laos
BirdLife International in Indochina, No 4 Lane 209, Doi Can, Ba Dinh, Hanoi, Vietnam. e-mail: birdlife@birdlife.netnam.vn

Pakistan
Ornitholgical Society of Pakistan PO Box 73, 109/D, Dera Ghazi Khan, 32200 Pakistan. e-mail: osp@mul.paknet.com.pk

Vietnam
BirdLife International in Indochina, PO Box 89 – 6 Dinh Le, Hanoi, Vietnam. e-mail: birdlife@birdlife.org.vn

EUROPE

PARTNERS

Austria
BirdLife Austria, Museumplatz 1/10/8, AT-1070 Wien. Pub: *Egretta; Vogelschutz in Osterreich.* e-mail: office@birdlife.at www.birdlife.at/

Belarus
BirdLife Belarus (APB), PO Box 306, Minsk, 220050 Belarus. Pub: *Subbuteo - The Belarusian Ornithological Bulletin.* e-mail: apb@tut.by - www.ptushki.org

Belgium
BirdLife Belgium (Natuurpunt-Natagora), Natuurpunt, Michiel Coxiestraat 11N 2800 Mechelen, Belgium.

e-mail: wim.vandenbossche@natuurpunt.be www.natuurreservaten.be

Bulgaria
Bulgarian Society for the Protection of Birds (BSPB), PO Box 50, Yavorov Complex, Block 71, vh.4, ap 1, BG-1111, Sofia, Bulgaria. Pub: *Neophron (& UK);* e-mail: bspb_hq@bspb.org www.bspb.org

Czech Republic
Czech Society for Ornithology (CSO), Na Belidle 252/34, 150 00 Prague 5. Pub: *Ptaci Svet; Sylvia; Zpravy Ceske Spolecnosti Ornitologicke.* e-mail: cso@birdlife.cz - www.birdlife.cz

Denmark
Dansk Ornitologisk Forening (DOF), Vesterbrogade 138-140, DK-1620, Copenhagen V, Denmark. Pub: *DAFIF - Dafifs Nyhedsbrev; Dansk Ornitologisk Forenings Tidsskrift; Fugle og Natur;* e-mail: dof@dof.dk - www.dof.dk

Estonia
Estonian Ornithological Society (EOU), PO Box 227, Vesti Str. 4, EE-50002 Tartu, Estonia. Pub: *Hirundo Eesti Ornitoogiauhing;* e-mail: eoy@eoy.ee www.eoy.ee

Finland
BirdLife FINLAND, Annankatu 29 A 16, FI 00101, Helsinki. Pub: *Linnuston-Suojelu; Linnut; Tiira;* e-mail: office@birdlife.fi www.birdlife.fi

France
(also covers New Calendonia, Wallis & Futuna Islands)
Ligue pour la Protection des Oiseaux (LPO), Fonderies Royale, 8-10 rue de Docteur Pujos, B.P. 90263, 17305 Rochefort Cedex. Pub: *Lettre Internationale; Ligue Francaise Pour La Protection des Oiseaux; Oiseau, L' (LPO); Outarde infos.* e-mail: lpo@lpo.fr - www.lpo.fr/

Germany
Naturschutzbund Deutschland (NABU), Charitestr. 3, D-10117, Berlin. Pub: *Naturschutz Heute (NABU) Naturschutzbund Deutschland.* e-mail: nabu@nabu.de - www.nabu.de

Gibraltar
Gibraltar Ornithological and Nat. History Society, Gibraltar Natural History Field Centre, Jew's Gate, Upper Rock Nature Reserve, PO Box 843, GI. Pub: *Alectoris; Gibraltar Nature News.* e-mail: gohns@gibnet.gi - www.gonhs.org

Greece
Hellenic Ornithological Society (HOS), Vas. Irakleiou 24, GR-10682 Athens, Greece. Pub: *HOS Newsletter.* e-mail: info@ornithologiki.gr www.ornithologiki.gr

Hungary
Hungarian Orn. and Nature Cons. Society (MME), Kolto u. 21, 1121 Budapest. Pub: *Madartani Tajekoztato; Madartavlat; Ornis Hungarica; Tuzok.* e-mail: mme@mme.hu www.mme.hu

Ireland
BirdWatch Ireland, Unit 20, Block D, Bullford Business

INTERNATIONAL ORGANISATIONS

Campus, Kilcoole, Co Wicklow, Eire. Pub: *Irish Birds*; *Wings (IWC Birdwatch Ireland)*; e-mail: info@birdwatchireland.org www.birdwatchireland.ie

Israel
Society for the Protection of Nature in Israel (SPNI), Hanagev 2 St, Tel-Aviv 66186. Pub: *SPNI News*. e-mail: ioc@netvision.net.il www.birds.org.il

Italy
Lega Italiana Protezione Uccelli (LIPU), Via Trento 49, 43100, Parma. Pub: *Ali Giovani; Ali Notizie*. e-mail: info@lipu.org - www.lipu.it

Latvia
Latvijas Ornitologijas Biedriba (LOB), Kalnciema iela 27-18, Riga LV-1046. Pub: *Putni Daba*. e-mail: putni@lob.lv - www.lob.lv

Luxembourg
Letzebuerger Natur-a Vulleschutzliga (LNVL), Kraizhaff, 5 Route de Luxembourg, L-1899 Kockelscheuer. Pub: *Regulus (WATCH); Regulus Info (& Annual Report) (WATCH); Regulus Wissenschaftliche Berichte (WATCH)*; e-mail: birgit.jacoby@luxnatur.lu www.luxnatur.lu

Malta
BirdLife Malta, 57 /28, Triq Abate Rigord, Ta' Xbiex, XBX 1120, Malta. Pub: *Bird Talk (WATCH) (Malta); Bird's Eye View (WATCH) (Malta); Il-Merill*; e-mail: office@ birdlifemalta.org - www.birdlifemalta.org

Netherlands
Vogelbescherming Nederland (VBN), Boulevard 12, 3707, BM Zeist. Pub: *Vogelniews; Vogels*. e-mail: info@vogelbescherming.nl www.vogelbescherming.nl/

Norway
Norsk Ornitologisk Forening (NOF), Sandgata 30 B, N-7012 Trondheim, Norway. Pub: *Fuglearet; Fuglefauna; Var; Ringmerkaren*; e-mail: nof@birdlife.no - www.birdlife.no

Poland
Ogólnopolskie Towarzystwo Ochrony Ptaków (OTOP), ul.Odrowaza 24, 05-270 Marki k. Warsaw, Poland. Pub: *Ptaki; Ptasie Ostoje*; e-mail: office@otop.most.org.pl - www.otop.org.pl/

Portugal
Sociedade Portuguesa para o Estuda das, Aves (SPEA), Avenida da Liberdade, 105-2° Esq, 1250-140, Lisbon. Pub: *Pardela*; e-mail: spea@spea.pt - www.spea.pt

Romania
Romanian Ornithological Society (SOR), Bd. M Kogalniceanu nr 49, sc. A, ap 8, 0150108 Sector 5, Bucharest. Pub: *Alcedo; Buletin AIA; Buletin de Informare Societatea Ornitologica Romana; Milvus (Romania)*; e-mail: office@sor.ro www.sor.ro/

Slovakia
Slovak Ornithological Society (SOS), Mlynske Nivy 41, 821 09 Bratislava, Slovakia. Pub: *Spravodaj SOVS; Vtacie Spravy*; e-mail: vtaky@vtaky.sk www.birdlife.sk

Slovenia
BirdLife Slovenia (DOPPS), Trzaska 2, PO Box 2990, SI-

1000 Ljubljana, Slovenia. Pub: *Acrocephalus; Svet Ptic*; e-mail: dopps@dopps.si - www.ptice.org

Spain
Sociedad Espanola de Ornitologia (SEO), Melquiades Biencinto 34, E-28053, Madrid. Pub: *Ardeola; Areas Importantes para las Aves*. e-mail: seo@seo.org - www.seo.org

Sweden
Sveriges Ornitologiska Forening (SOF), Stenhusa Gard, SE-380 62 Morbylanga. Pub: *Fagelvarld; var; Ornis Svecica*; e-mail: info@sofnet.org www.sofnet.org

Switzerland
SVS/BirdLife Switzerland, Wiedingstrasse 78, PO Box, CH-8036, Zurich, Switzerland. Pub: *Oiwvos Ornis; Ornis Junior; Ornithologische Beobachter; Der Ornithos; Steinadler*. e-mail: svs@birdlife.ch - www.birdlife.ch

Turkey
Doga Dernegi (DD), PK: 640 06445, Yenisehir, Ankara, Turkey. Pub: *Kelaynak; Kuscu Bulteni*. e-mail: doga@dogadernegi.org www.dogadernegi.org

Ukraine
Ukrainian Union for Bird Conservation (UTOP), PO Box 33, Kiev, 1103, UA. Pub: *Life of Birds*. e-mail: uspb@birdlife.org.ua www.birdlife.org.ua

United Kingdom
Royal Society for the Protection of Birds, The Lodge, Sandy, Bedfordshire, SG19 2DL; e-mail: info@rspb.org.uk www.rspb.org.uk

PARTNERS DESIGNATE

Azerbaijan
Azerbaijan Ornithological Society (AOS), Mukhtarov str. 13, apt 16, AZ1001 Baku. e-mail: info@aos.az http://aos.az/eng/index.php

Georgia
Georgian Centre for the Conservation of Wildlife, Nature House (2nd Floor), Didi Digomi, 0131, Tbilisi, Georgia; e-mail: office@gccw.org - www.gccw.org/

Iceland
Icelandic Society for the Protection of Birds (ISPB), Fuglaverndarfélag Islands, Skulatuni 6, , 105 Reykjavik, Simi 5620477. e-mail: fuglavernd@fuglavernd.is www.fuglavernd.is

AFFILIATES

Andorra
Associacio per a la Defensa de la Natura (AND), Apartado de Correus Espanyols No 96, Andorra La Vella, Principat d'Andorra. Pub: *Aiguerola*; e-mail: adn@andorra.ad - www.adn-andorra.org/

Armenia
Armenian Society for the Protection of Birds (ASPB), Garaegin Njdeh 27/2, 10 Yerevan, 0026, Armenia. E-mail: armbirds@yahoo.com - www.aspbirds.org

INTERNATIONAL ORGANISATIONS

Cyprus
BirdLife Cyprus, PO Box 28076, 2090 Lefkosia, Cyprus.
e-mail: birdlifecyprus@birdlifecyprus.org.cy
www.birdlifecyprus.org

Faroe Islands
Føroya Fuglafrøðifelag (Faroese Orginithological Society)
(FOS), Postssmoga 1230, FR-110 Torshavn, Faroe
Islands; e-mail: doreteb@ngs.fo

Liechtenstein
Botanish-Zoologische Gesellschaft (ZG), Im Bretscha 22,
FL-9494 Schaan, Liechtenstein.
e-mail: bzg@bzg.li - www.bzg.li

Lithuania
Lietuvos Ornitologu Draugija (LOD), Naugarduko St. 47-
3, LT-2006, Vilnius, Lithuania. Pub: *Baltasis Gandras;*
e-mail: lod@birdlife.lt - www.birdlife.lt

MIDDLE EAST

PARTNERS

Jordan
Royal Society of the Conservation of Nature, PO Box
6354, Jubeiha-Abu-Nusseir Circle, Amman 11183. Pub:
Al Reem; e-mail: adminrscn@rscn.org.jo
www.rscn.org.jo

Lebanon
Society for the Protection of Nature in Lebanon, Awad
Bldg, 6th Floor, Abdel Aziz Street, P.O.Box: 11-5665,
Beirut, Lebanon; e-mail: spnlorg@cyberia.net.lb
www.spnlb.org

Palestinian Wildlife Territories
Palestine Wildlife Society (PWLS), Beit Sahour, PO Box
89, Palestine. Pub: *Palestine Wildlife Society - Annual
Report.*
e-mail: pwls@wildlife-pal.org www.wildlife-pal.org

AFFILIATES

Bahrain
Dr Saeed A. Mohamed, PO Box 1858, Manama, Bahrain.
e-mail: saeed@alreem.com http://bahrainwildlife.com

Iraq
Nature Iraq, House 25, Street 27, Qtr 104 Ashti,
Sulaimani, Kurdistan, Iraq. e-mail: info@natureiraq.org
www.natureiraq.org

Kuwait
Kuwait Environment Protection Society, PO Box 1896,
Safat 13019, Kuwait; e-mail: rasamhory@hotmail.com
www.keps.org.kw

Qatar
Friends of the Environment Centre, PO Box 1822, Doha,
Qatar. E-mail: cefdoha@qatar.net.qa
http:// my qatar.org

Saudi Arabia
Saudi Wildlife Commission (SWC), PO Box 61681, Riyadh
11575. Pub: *Phoenix; The.*
e-mail: ncwcd@zajil.net www.ncwcd.gov.sa/

Syria
Syrian Society ofr the Conservation of Wildlife (SSCW),
PO Box 9853, Damascus, Syria.
E-mail: sscw.syria@gmail.com
www.sscw.syria.org

Yemen
Yemen Society for the Protection of Wildlife (YSPW), 29
Alger Street, PO Box 19759, Sana'a, Yemen.
e-mail: wildlife.yemen@y.net.ye

PARTNER

Australia
**(also covers Christmas Island, Cocos Islands,
Norfolk Island, Heard & Mcdonald Islands,
Antarctica)**
Birds Australia, Suite 2-05, 60 Leicester Street, Carlton,
VIC 3053, Australia. Pub: *Australia Garcilla; Birds
Australia Annual Report; Eclectus; Emu; Wingspan*
(WATCH) (Australia); from wingspan@birdsaustralia.
com.au; e-mail: mail@birdsaustralia.com.au
www.birdsaustralia.com.au

French Polynesia
Société d'Ornithologie de Polynésie 'Manu', B.P. 7023,
98719 Taravao, Tahiti, French Polynesia;
e-mail: sop@manu.pf
www.manu.pf

New Zealand
(also covers Niue and Tokelau)
Forest & Bird, Level 1, 90 Ghunzee Street, PO Box 631,
Wellington 6140. Pub: *Forest & Bird; Forest & Bird
Annual Report; Forest & Bird Conservation News.*
e-mail: office@forestandbird.org.nz
www.forestandbird.org.nz/

Palau
Palau Conservation Society, PO Box 1811, Koror,
PW96940, Republic of Palau. Pub: *Ngerel a Biib;*
e-mail: pcs@palaunet.com
www.palauconservation.org

PACIFIC

AFFILIATES

Cook Islands
Te Ipukarea Society (TIS), PO Box 649, Rarotonga, Cook
Islands; e-mail: 2tis@oyster.net.ck

Samoa
O le Si'osi'omaga Society Incorporated (OLSSI), P O Box
2282, Apia, Western Samoa;
e-mail: ngo_siosiomaga@samoa.ws

UNAFFILIATED ORGANISATIONS

Fiji
Dr Dick Watling, c/o Environment Consultants Fiji, P O
Box 2041, Government Buildings, Suva, Fiji.
e-mail: watling@is.com.fj www.environmentfiji.com

SPECIAL INTEREST ORGANISATIONS

AFRICAN BIRD CLUB.
c/o Birdlife International as below.

e-mail (general): contact@
africanbirdclub.org
e-mail (membership and sales):
membership@africanbirdclub.org
www.africanbirdclub.org
Pub: *Bulletin of the African Bird Club.*

BIRDLIFE INTERNATIONAL.
Wellbrook Court, Girton Road, Cambridge, CB3
ONA, +44 (0)1223 277 318; (Fax) +44 (0)1223
277 200; www.birdlife.org
e-mail: birdlife@birdlife.org
Pub: *World Birdwatch.*

EAST AFRICA NATURAL HISTORY SOCIETY
see Kenya in preceding list.

EURING (European Union for Bird Ringing).
Euring Data Bank, c/o BTO, The Nunnery,
Thetford, Norfolk IP24 2PU. 01842 750 050.
www.euring.org

FAUNA AND FLORA INTERNATIONAL.
Jupiter House, 4th Floor, Station Road, Cambridge,
CB1 2JD. Call on +44 (0)1223 571 000; (Fax) +44
(0)1223 461 481. www.fauna-flora.org
e-mail: info@fauna-flora.org
Pub: *Fauna & Flora News; Oryx.*

LIPU-UK
**(the Italian League for the Protection of
Birds).**
David Lingard, Fernwood,
Doddington Road, Whisby,
Lincs, LN6 9BX, +44
(0)1522 689 030,
e-mail: david@lipu-uk.org
www.lipu-uk.org

Pub: *The Hoopoe,*
annually, *Ali Notizie,* quarterley.

NEOTROPICAL BIRD CLUB.
(Central and South America and the Caribbean)
c/o The Lodge, Sandy,
Bedfordshire, SG19 2DL.
Pub: *Cotinga.*
email: secretary@
neotropicalbirdclub.org
www.neotropicalbirdclub.org

ORIENTAL BIRD CLUB.
P.O.Box 324, Bedford, MK42 0WG
Pub: *The Forktail; BirdingASIA.*
email: mail@orientalbirdclub.org
www.orientalbirdclub.org

**ORNITHOLOGICAL SOCIETY OF THE MIDDLE
EAST (OSME).**
c/o The Lodge, Sandy, Beds, SG19 2DL.
Pub: *Sandgrouse.* e-mail: secretary@osme.org
www.osme.org

**TRAFFIC International (formerly Wildlife
Trade Monitoring Unit).**
219a Huntingdon Road, Cambridge, CB3 0DL,
+44 (0)1223 277 427; (Fax) +44 (0)1223 277 237.
Pub: *TRAFFIC Bulletin.*
e-mail: traffic@traffic.org
www.traffic.org

WEST AFRICAN ORNITHOLOGICAL SOCIETY.
R E Sharland, 1 Fisher's Heron, East Mills, Hants,
SP6 2JR. Pub: *Malimbus.*
http://malimbus.free.fr

WETLANDS INTERNATIONAL.
PO Box 471, 6700 AL Wageningen, Netherlands,
+31 317 485 774; (Fax) +31 317 486 770,
Pub: *Wetlands.*
e-mail: post@wetlands.org
www.wetlands.org

WORLD OWL TRUST.
The World Owl Centre,
Muncaster Castle,
Ravenglass, Cumbria, CA18
1RQ, +44 (0)1229 717393;
www.owls.org

**WORLD PHEASANT
ASSOCIATION.**
7-9 Shaftesbury St, Fordingbridge, Hants SP6 1JF.
01425 657 129; (Fax) 01425 658 053. Pub: *WPA
News.* e-mail: office@pheasant.org.uk
www.pheasant.org.uk

WORLD WIDE FUND FOR NATURE.
Panda House, Weyside Park, Godalming
United Kingdom. +44 1483 426 444;
(Fax) +44 1483 426 409,
e-mail: supporterrelations@wwf.org.uk
www.panda.org

QUICK REFERENCE SECTION

Bill Coster

While it is perfectly OK to photograph British Ospreys in the act of flying or fishing, a Schedule 1 licence is needed to take images at or near the nest. For a complete list of protected species see page 332.

TIDE TABLES: USEFUL INFORMATION

BRITISH SUMMER TIME

In 2012 BST applies from 01:00 on March 25 to 01:00 on October 28.
Note that all the times in the following tables are GMT.

During British Summer Time one hour should be added.

Shetland 42, 43
Orkney 44, 45

Predictions are given for the times of high water at Dover throughout the year.

The times of tides at the locations shown here may be obtained by adding or subtracting their 'tidal difference' as shown opposite (subtractions are indicated by a minus sign).

Tidal predictions for Dover have been computed by the Proudman Oceanographic Laboratory. Copyright reserved.

Map showing locations for which tidal differences are given on facing page.

TIDE TABLES 2012

Example 1
To calculate the time of first high water at Girvan on February 18
1. Look up the time at Dover (08 11)* = 8:11 am
2. Add the tidal difference for Girvan = 0.54
3. Therefore the time of high water at Girvan = 9.05 am

Example 2
To calculate the time of second high water at Blakeney on June 30
1. Look up the time at Dover (19 42) = 19:42 pm
2. Add 1 hour for British Summer Time (20 42) = 20:42 pm
3. Subtract the tidal difference for Blakeney = - 4.07
4. Therefore the time of second high water at Blakeney = 16:35 pm

*All Dover times are shown on the 24-hour clock.
Following the time of each high water the height of the tide is given, in metres.
(Tables beyond April 2013 are not available at the time of going to press.)

TIDAL DIFFERENCES

1	Dover	See pp 338-341		23	Morecambe	0	20
2	Dungeness	-0	12	24	Silloth	0	51
3	Selsey Bill	0	09	25	Girvan	0	54
4	Swanage (lst H.W.Springs)	-2	36	26	Lossiemouth	0	48
5	Portland	-4	23	27	Fraserburgh	1	20
6	Exmouth (Approaches)	-4	48	28	Aberdeen	2	30
7	Salcombe	-5	23	29	Montrose	3	30
8	Newlyn (Penzance)	5	59	30	Dunbar	3	42
9	Padstow	-5	47	31	Holy Island	3	58
10	Bideford	-5	17	32	Sunderland	4	38
11	Bridgwater	-4	23	33	Whitby	5	12
12	Sharpness Dock	-3	19	34	Bridlington	5	53
13	Cardiff (Penarth)	-4	16	35	Grimsby	-5	20
14	Swansea	-4	52	36	Skegness	-5	00
15	Skomer Island	-5	00	37	Blakeney	-4	07
16	Fishguard	-3	48	38	Gorleston	-2	08
17	Barmouth	-2	45	39	Aldeburgh	-0	13
18	Bardsey Island	-3	07	40	Bradwell Waterside	1	11
19	Caernarvon	-1	07	41	Herne Bay	1	28
20	Amlwch	-0	22	42	Sullom Voe	-1	34
21	Connahs Quay	0	20	43	Lerwick	0	01
22	Hilbre Island			44	Kirkwall	-0	26
	(Hoylake/West Kirby)	-0	05	45	Widewall Bay	-1	30

NB. Care should be taken when making calculations at the beginning and end of British Summer Time. See worked examples above.

TIDE TABLES 2012

Time Zone: GMT

Tidal Predictions : HIGH WATERS 2012

Datum of Predictions = Chart Datum : 3.67 metres below Ordnance Datum (Newlyn)

British Summer Time Dates for 2012 : 25th March to 28th October (data not adjusted)

Units: METRES

DOVER — January

Date	Morning time	m	Afternoon time	m
1 Su	03:45	5.96	16:21	5.49
2 M	04:41	5.65	17:27	5.27
3 Tu	05:49	5.41	18:39	5.20
4 W	07:02	5.35	19:48	5.31
5 Th	08:06	5.46	20:45	5.54
6 F	09:00	5.67	21:30	5.81
7 Sa	09:42	5.89	22:09	6.06
8 Su	10:19	6.10	22:44	6.29
9 M	10:54	6.29	23:19	6.48
10 Tu	11:30	6.45	23:57	6.63
11 W	##:##		12:08	6.56
12 Th	00:36	6.72	12:48	6.58
13 F	01:15	6.73	13:30	6.52
14 Sa	01:56	6.66	14:13	6.39
15 Su	02:39	6.55	15:00	6.22
16 M	03:27	6.38	15:56	6.01
17 Tu	04:25	6.16	17:00	5.79
18 W	05:33	5.93	18:14	5.64
19 Th	06:51	5.82	19:36	5.67
20 F	08:09	5.90	20:51	5.90
21 Sa	09:18	6.11	21:50	6.20
22 Su	10:14	6.33	22:38	6.46
23 M	11:00	6.49	23:19	6.64
24 Tu	11:42	6.56	23:58	6.74
25 W	##:##		12:19	6.56
26 Th	00:35	6.77	12:55	6.49
27 F	01:10	6.73	13:31	6.37
28 Sa	01:46	6.61	14:06	6.20
29 Su	02:21	6.40	14:43	5.96
30 M	02:59	6.11	15:24	5.67
31 Tu	03:41	5.75	16:14	5.34

DOVER — February

Date	Morning time	m	Afternoon time	m
1 W	04:36	5.37	17:23	5.08
2 Th	05:55	5.11	18:50	5.03
3 F	07:21	5.11	20:05	5.25
4 Sa	08:27	5.38	21:00	5.59
5 Su	09:15	5.71	21:42	5.94
6 M	09:54	6.03	22:20	6.26
7 Tu	10:31	6.32	22:57	6.54
8 W	11:09	6.56	23:34	6.77
9 Th	11:48	6.73	##:##	
10 F	00:14	6.91	12:29	6.78
11 Sa	00:54	6.95	13:11	6.74
12 Su	01:35	6.89	13:54	6.60
13 M	02:16	6.73	14:39	6.38
14 Tu	03:04	6.48	15:32	6.09
15 W	04:01	6.14	16:35	5.75
16 Th	05:12	5.77	17:54	5.48
17 F	06:39	5.55	19:28	5.48
18 Sa	08:11	5.66	20:47	5.76
19 Su	09:19	5.94	21:42	6.10
20 M	10:10	6.19	22:24	6.38
21 Tu	10:50	6.37	23:02	6.58
22 W	11:25	6.48	23:37	6.71
23 Th	11:58	6.53	##:##	
24 F	00:12	6.76	12:32	6.51
25 Sa	00:45	6.73	13:03	6.43
26 Su	01:16	6.61	13:33	6.29
27 M	01:45	6.42	14:03	6.09
28 Tu	02:13	6.16	14:34	5.84
29 W	02:47	5.83	15:14	5.52

DOVER — March

Date	Morning time	m	Afternoon time	m
1 Th	03:33	5.44	16:15	5.18
2 F	04:48	5.07	17:44	4.97
3 Sa	06:28	4.98	19:17	5.11
4 Su	07:48	5.24	20:22	5.48
5 M	08:43	5.63	21:10	5.90
6 Tu	09:26	6.03	21:51	6.29
7 W	10:04	6.38	22:29	6.62
8 Th	10:43	6.66	23:08	6.88
9 F	11:24	6.84	23:48	7.04
10 Sa	##:##		12:06	6.91
11 Su	00:30	7.07	12:50	6.86
12 M	01:12	6.98	13:35	6.70
13 Tu	01:57	6.77	14:22	6.45
14 W	02:47	6.45	15:15	6.12
15 Th	03:46	6.03	16:18	5.73
16 F	04:59	5.62	17:39	5.45
17 Sa	06:36	5.42	19:16	5.45
18 Su	08:06	5.58	20:30	5.73
19 M	09:09	5.86	21:23	6.05
20 Tu	09:54	6.10	22:03	6.31
21 W	10:30	6.28	22:39	6.49
22 Th	11:02	6.39	23:13	6.61
23 F	11:34	6.46	23:47	6.65
24 Sa	##:##		12:06	6.48
25 Su	00:18	6.62	12:36	6.42
26 M	00:47	6.50	13:03	6.31
27 Tu	01:12	6.33	13:29	6.15
28 W	01:36	6.13	13:58	5.96
29 Th	02:08	5.88	14:36	5.70
30 F	02:52	5.55	15:31	5.39
31 Sa	04:02	5.19	16:55	5.14

DOVER — April

Date	Morning time	m	Afternoon time	m
1 Su	05:39	5.06	18:27	5.18
2 M	07:04	5.27	19:39	5.51
3 Tu	08:05	5.66	20:33	5.93
4 W	08:52	6.07	21:17	6.33
5 Th	09:34	6.43	21:58	6.67
6 F	10:16	6.70	22:39	6.92
7 Sa	10:59	6.88	23:22	7.06
8 Su	11:44	6.93	##:##	
9 M	00:07	7.07	12:32	6.87
10 Tu	00:54	6.94	13:21	6.71
11 W	01:44	6.69	14:10	6.47
12 Th	02:36	6.36	15:03	6.16
13 F	03:36	5.96	16:03	5.82
14 Sa	04:48	5.59	17:18	5.54
15 Su	06:20	5.43	18:47	5.52
16 M	07:42	5.56	19:58	5.72
17 Tu	08:40	5.78	20:51	5.97
18 W	09:25	5.98	21:33	6.19
19 Th	10:02	6.15	22:11	6.34
20 F	10:36	6.27	22:46	6.44
21 Sa	11:09	6.36	23:21	6.47
22 Su	11:42	6.39	23:53	6.44
23 M	##:##		12:13	6.37
24 Tu	00:21	6.35	12:41	6.29
25 W	00:46	6.22	13:08	6.18
26 Th	01:13	6.08	13:39	6.04
27 F	01:47	5.90	14:17	5.85
28 Sa	02:32	5.67	15:10	5.63
29 Su	03:37	5.42	16:21	5.45
30 M	05:00	5.31	17:40	5.45

National Oceanography Centre (www.noc.ac.uk)

TIDE TABLES 2012

Time Zone: GMT
Units: METRES

Tidal Predictions : HIGH WATERS 2012

Datum of Predictions = Chart Datum : 3.67 metres below Ordnance Datum (Newlyn)

British Summer Time Dates for 2012 : 25th March to 28th October (data not adjusted)

DOVER — May

Day	Morning time	m	Afternoon time	m
1 Tu	06:18	5.44	18:52	5.66
2 W	07:23	5.74	19:51	6.00
3 Th	08:16	6.09	20:41	6.36
4 F	09:03	6.41	21:27	6.66
5 Sa	09:50	6.65	22:13	6.87
6 Su	10:38	6.80	23:00	6.97
7 M	11:27	6.86	23:51	6.95
8 Tu	##:##	##:##	12:19	6.82
9 W	00:43	6.82	13:10	6.70
10 Th	01:36	6.60	13:59	6.52
11 F	02:27	6.31	14:48	6.27
12 Sa	03:21	5.98	15:43	6.00
13 Su	04:25	5.68	16:47	5.75
14 M	05:42	5.50	18:02	5.63
15 Tu	06:57	5.51	19:12	5.69
16 W	07:57	5.63	20:10	5.83
17 Th	08:47	5.80	20:59	5.99
18 F	09:30	5.97	21:41	6.12
19 Sa	10:08	6.11	22:21	6.22
20 Su	10:45	6.22	22:57	6.26
21 M	11:19	6.29	23:30	6.27
22 Tu	11:52	6.32	##:##	##:##
23 W	00:01	6.24	12:24	6.30
24 Th	00:31	6.18	12:57	6.26
25 F	01:03	6.10	13:30	6.17
26 Sa	01:39	5.99	14:09	6.06
27 Su	02:23	5.86	14:57	5.93
28 M	03:18	5.72	15:54	5.82
29 Tu	04:24	5.64	16:59	5.79
30 W	05:34	5.67	18:06	5.87
31 Th	06:40	5.82	19:09	6.06

DOVER — June

Day	Morning time	m	Afternoon time	m
1 F	07:41	6.04	20:07	6.30
2 Sa	08:37	6.28	21:02	6.53
3 Su	09:31	6.49	21:54	6.69
4 M	10:24	6.65	22:48	6.78
5 Tu	11:18	6.75	23:42	6.79
6 W	##:##	##:##	12:10	6.78
7 Th	00:35	6.70	12:58	6.73
8 F	01:24	6.54	13:43	6.61
9 Sa	02:11	6.33	14:28	6.44
10 Su	02:59	6.08	15:15	6.23
11 M	03:52	5.82	16:09	5.98
12 Tu	04:54	5.59	17:12	5.75
13 W	06:02	5.46	18:21	5.62
14 Th	07:08	5.46	19:26	5.63
15 F	08:06	5.58	20:23	5.73
16 Sa	08:57	5.75	21:12	5.86
17 Su	09:42	5.93	21:56	5.99
18 M	10:21	6.09	22:34	6.09
19 Tu	10:57	6.22	23:09	6.17
20 W	11:32	6.32	23:42	6.23
21 Th	##:##	##:##	12:06	6.39
22 F	00:15	6.26	12:42	6.42
23 Sa	00:51	6.26	13:19	6.40

DOVER — July

Day	Morning time	m	Afternoon time	m
1 Su	08:20	6.07	20:47	6.29
2 M	09:23	6.30	21:47	6.47
3 Tu	10:20	6.52	22:42	6.60
4 W	11:11	6.68	23:34	6.66
5 Th	11:58	6.77	##:##	##:##
6 F	00:22	6.64	12:41	6.78
7 Sa	01:06	6.54	13:21	6.72
8 Su	01:48	6.39	14:02	6.60
9 M	02:29	6.19	14:44	6.41
10 Tu	03:14	5.96	15:30	6.15
11 W	04:04	5.70	16:22	5.84
12 Th	05:04	5.45	17:26	5.55
13 F	06:14	5.30	18:39	5.39
14 Sa	07:24	5.33	19:47	5.43
15 Su	08:26	5.51	20:45	5.60
16 M	09:16	5.76	21:33	5.81
17 Tu	09:58	6.01	22:11	6.00
18 W	10:34	6.22	22:45	6.17
19 Th	11:08	6.39	23:18	6.32
20 F	11:43	6.54	23:54	6.44
21 Sa	##:##	##:##	12:20	6.64
22 Su	00:32	6.49	12:58	6.67
23 M	01:11	6.47	13:36	6.63
24 Tu	01:51	6.39	14:14	6.54
25 W	02:33	6.26	14:58	6.41
26 Th	03:24	6.10	15:52	6.23
27 F	04:25	5.91	16:57	6.02
28 Sa	05:35	5.74	18:11	5.86
29 Su	06:55	5.70	19:33	5.88
30 M	08:16	5.88	20:47	6.07
31 Tu	09:22	6.18	21:48	6.32

DOVER — August

Day	Morning time	m	Afternoon time	m
1 W	10:15	6.47	22:39	6.51
2 Th	10:59	6.68	23:23	6.61
3 F	11:40	6.81	##:##	##:##
4 Sa	00:04	6.63	12:18	6.85
5 Su	00:42	6.58	12:56	6.81
6 M	01:18	6.47	13:32	6.70
7 Tu	01:55	6.31	14:09	6.51
8 W	02:33	6.09	14:47	6.23
9 Th	03:15	5.81	15:30	5.88
10 F	04:05	5.49	16:26	5.48
11 Sa	05:12	5.21	17:43	5.19
12 Su	06:36	5.12	19:09	5.16
13 M	07:51	5.30	20:16	5.39
14 Tu	08:48	5.62	21:06	5.69
15 W	09:31	5.96	21:45	5.99
16 Th	10:07	6.26	22:18	6.26
17 F	10:41	6.51	22:52	6.48
18 Sa	11:16	6.71	23:28	6.65
19 Su	11:53	6.85	##:##	##:##
20 M	00:06	6.73	12:31	6.90
21 Tu	00:46	6.71	13:09	6.86
22 W	01:27	6.61	13:48	6.73
23 Th	02:10	6.43	14:33	6.52
24 F	03:01	6.19	15:28	6.23
25 Sa	04:03	5.90	16:36	5.89
26 Su	05:17	5.62	18:01	5.65
27 M	06:50	5.56	19:36	5.71
28 Tu	08:16	5.81	20:51	5.99
29 W	09:16	6.17	21:46	6.17
30 Th	10:03	6.47	22:29	6.47
31 F	10:42	6.69	23:06	6.59

National Oceanography Centre (www.noc.ac.uk)

Time Zone: GMT

Units: METRES

Tidal Predictions : HIGH WATERS 2012

Datum of Predictions = Chart Datum : 3.67 metres below Ordnance Datum (Newlyn)

British Summer Time Dates for 2012 : 25th March to 28th October (data not adjusted)

DOVER — September / October

Sep		Morning time	m	Afternoon time	m		Oct		Morning time	m	Afternoon time	m
1	Sa	11:18	6.82	23:40	6.63		1	M	11:27	6.80	23:48	6.62
2	Su	11:53	6.86	##:##	6.83		2	Tu	##:##	#.##	12:00	6.76
3	M	00:15	6.62	12:27	6.83		3	W	00:20	6.57	12:31	6.64
4	Tu	00:48	6.54	13:01	6.71		4	Th	00:50	6.46	13:00	6.45
5	W	01:21	6.40	13:33	6.51		5	F	01:19	6.29	13:27	6.22
6	Th	01:52	6.20	14:03	6.24		6	Sa	01:48	6.07	13:57	5.94
7	F	02:26	5.94	14:38	5.90		7	Su	02:25	5.81	14:38	5.60
8	Sa	03:06	5.62	15:24	5.50		8	M	03:17	5.49	15:44	5.24
9	Su	04:06	5.28	16:39	5.12		9	Tu	04:36	5.22	17:21	5.06
10	M	05:34	5.06	18:20	5.01		10	W	06:07	5.22	18:49	5.23
11	Tu	07:05	5.18	19:39	5.25		11	Th	07:21	5.50	19:50	5.61
12	W	08:10	5.53	20:33	5.64		12	F	08:15	5.91	20:36	6.02
13	Th	08:57	5.94	21:14	6.02		13	Sa	08:57	6.31	21:15	6.40
14	F	09:35	6.30	21:48	6.36		14	Su	09:36	6.66	21:54	6.70
15	Sa	10:10	6.61	22:24	6.63		15	M	10:15	6.93	22:33	6.92
16	Su	10:46	6.86	23:00	6.83		16	Tu	10:55	7.10	23:16	7.02
17	M	11:24	7.02	23:40	6.92		17	W	11:38	7.13	##:##	#.##
18	Tu	##:##	#.##	12:03	7.07		18	Th	00:02	6.99	12:23	7.04
19	W	00:21	6.90	12:43	7.00		19	F	00:49	6.85	13:12	6.82
20	Th	01:05	6.77	13:27	6.82		20	Sa	01:40	6.63	14:05	6.50
21	F	01:51	6.54	14:15	6.53		21	Su	02:35	6.34	15:05	6.13
22	Sa	02:45	6.25	15:14	6.16		22	M	03:34	6.02	16:15	5.77
23	Su	03:48	5.91	16:26	5.77		23	Tu	04:45	5.74	17:45	5.57
24	M	05:04	5.61	18:00	5.55		24	W	06:12	5.66	19:15	5.65
25	Tu	06:42	5.57	19:36	5.68		25	Th	07:32	5.83	20:19	5.88
26	W	08:03	5.84	20:44	5.97		26	F	08:29	6.08	21:07	6.10
27	Th	09:00	6.17	21:33	6.24		27	Sa	09:14	6.31	21:45	6.28
28	F	09:42	6.45	22:11	6.42		28	Su	09:51	6.48	22:18	6.41
29	Sa	10:18	6.64	22:42	6.54		29	M	10:27	6.58	22:51	6.51
30	Su	10:53	6.75	23:15	6.61		30	Tu	11:03	6.63	23:24	6.56
							31	W	11:36	6.60	23:57	6.55

DOVER — November / December

Nov		Morning time	m	Afternoon time	m		Dec		Morning time	m	Afternoon time	m
1	Th	##:##	#.##	12:07	6.51		1	Sa	00:12	6.48	12:19	6.33
2	F	00:28	6.48	12:35	6.37		2	Su	00:42	6.43	12:49	6.23
3	Sa	00:57	6.36	13:03	6.20		3	M	01:15	6.34	13:21	6.11
4	Su	01:27	6.20	13:34	6.00		4	Tu	01:49	6.21	13:59	5.96
5	M	02:03	6.00	14:14	5.75		5	W	02:28	6.06	14:45	5.79
6	Tu	02:48	5.76	15:09	5.48		6	Th	03:18	5.91	15:43	5.64
7	W	03:52	5.54	16:27	5.35		7	F	04:18	5.79	16:53	5.59
8	Th	05:09	5.45	17:49	5.30		8	Sa	05:27	5.79	18:03	5.67
9	F	06:24	5.59	18:57	5.61		9	Su	06:35	5.92	19:09	5.88
10	Sa	07:25	5.90	19:53	5.97		10	M	07:37	6.16	20:08	6.16
11	Su	08:17	6.27	20:40	6.34		11	Tu	08:33	6.43	21:04	6.44
12	M	09:03	6.61	21:26	6.64		12	W	09:27	6.68	21:57	6.68
13	Tu	09:48	6.87	22:12	6.86		13	Th	10:20	6.85	22:50	6.85
14	W	10:33	7.03	22:59	6.98		14	F	11:12	6.92	23:42	6.93
15	Th	11:21	7.07	23:49	6.98		15	Sa	##:##	#.##	12:04	6.89
16	F	##:##	#.##	12:11	6.98		16	Su	00:31	6.93	12:55	6.77
17	Sa	00:40	6.90	13:03	6.78		17	M	01:18	6.85	13:43	6.57
18	Su	01:31	6.73	13:57	6.51		18	Tu	02:03	6.69	14:31	6.32
19	M	02:21	6.50	14:52	6.20		19	W	02:49	6.48	15:21	6.04
20	Tu	03:15	6.24	15:53	5.88		20	Th	03:40	6.21	16:18	5.75
21	W	04:15	5.97	17:06	5.64		21	F	04:39	5.93	17:25	5.53
22	Th	05:27	5.78	18:27	5.57		22	Sa	05:47	5.70	18:38	5.45
23	F	06:42	5.76	19:35	5.67		23	Su	06:59	5.63	19:45	5.52
24	Sa	07:47	5.88	20:29	5.84		24	M	08:03	5.70	20:42	5.71
25	Su	08:39	6.05	21:14	6.03		25	Tu	08:57	5.85	21:30	5.93
26	M	09:24	6.20	21:53	6.20		26	W	09:44	6.01	22:10	6.13
27	Tu	10:04	6.32	22:30	6.34		27	Th	10:24	6.15	22:47	6.29
28	W	10:42	6.39	23:05	6.44		28	F	10:59	6.25	23:21	6.41
29	Th	11:17	6.41	23:39	6.48		29	Sa	11:31	6.31	23:54	6.49
30	F	11:49	6.39	##:##	#.##		30	Su	##:##	#.##	12:03	6.35
							31	M	00:27	6.52	12:35	6.35

National Oceanography Centre (www.noc.ac.uk)

TIDE TABLES 2013

Time Zone: GMT

Tidal Predictions : HIGH WATERS 2013

Datum of Predictions = Chart Datum : 3.67 metres below Ordnance Datum (Newlyn)

British Summer Time Dates for 2013 : 31st March to 27th October (data not adjusted)

Units: METRES

DOVER — January

Day	Morning time	m	Afternoon time	m
1 Tu	01:00	6.51	13:07	6.30
2 W	01:33	6.45	13:42	6.22
3 Th	02:07	6.35	14:21	6.11
4 F	02:48	6.24	15:09	5.97
5 Sa	03:39	6.11	16:09	5.84
6 Su	04:42	5.98	17:18	5.74
7 M	05:52	5.91	18:30	5.75
8 Tu	07:05	5.97	19:45	5.90
9 W	08:15	6.16	20:53	6.17
10 Th	09:18	6.40	21:52	6.47
11 F	10:15	6.63	22:45	6.72
12 Sa	11:07	6.78	23:33	6.89
13 Su	11:56	6.82	##:##	#.##
14 M	00:18	6.96	12:42	6.77
15 Tu	01:00	6.94	13:24	6.64
16 W	01:40	6.83	14:05	6.44
17 Th	02:21	6.64	14:48	6.19
18 F	03:05	6.38	15:35	5.89
19 Sa	03:54	6.03	16:30	5.57
20 Su	04:54	5.65	17:39	5.30
21 M	06:08	5.37	18:57	5.23
22 Tu	07:26	5.34	20:08	5.38
23 W	08:32	5.50	21:04	5.65
24 Th	09:24	5.73	21:49	5.92
25 F	10:05	5.95	22:26	6.16
26 Sa	10:39	6.14	22:59	6.35
27 Su	11:09	6.29	23:31	6.51
28 M	11:41	6.42	##:##	#.##
29 Tu	00:04	6.62	12:14	6.50
30 W	00:38	6.67	12:48	6.51
31 Th	01:11	6.66	13:22	6.46

DOVER — February

Day	Morning time	m	Afternoon time	m
1 F	01:44	6.59	13:59	6.36
2 Sa	02:21	6.48	14:43	6.21
3 Su	03:09	6.31	15:38	6.00
4 M	04:09	6.06	16:45	5.75
5 Tu	05:22	5.82	18:05	5.59
6 W	06:46	5.73	19:33	5.67
7 Th	08:10	5.89	20:50	5.98
8 F	09:18	6.20	21:48	6.34
9 Sa	10:12	6.47	22:36	6.64
10 Su	11:00	6.66	23:19	6.85
11 M	11:43	6.75	##:##	#.##
12 Tu	00:00	6.95	12:23	6.75
13 W	00:38	6.95	13:00	6.66
14 Th	01:15	6.86	13:36	6.51
15 F	01:51	6.69	14:14	6.29
16 Sa	02:29	6.42	14:54	6.01
17 Su	03:11	6.05	15:41	5.65
18 M	04:02	5.61	16:42	5.28
19 Tu	05:14	5.20	18:04	5.05
20 W	06:44	5.05	19:28	5.12
21 Th	08:01	5.21	20:33	5.41
22 F	08:58	5.51	21:21	5.76
23 Sa	09:39	5.81	21:59	6.06
24 Su	10:12	6.07	22:31	6.32
25 M	10:42	6.30	23:03	6.53
26 Tu	11:14	6.49	23:36	6.70
27 W	11:48	6.63	##:##	#.##
28 Th	00:11	6.80	12:24	6.68

DOVER — March

Day	Morning time	m	Afternoon time	m
1 F	00:45	6.81	13:00	6.64
2 Sa	01:21	6.74	13:39	6.52
3 Su	02:00	6.60	14:24	6.33
4 M	02:48	6.35	15:19	6.05
5 Tu	03:51	6.01	16:28	5.72
6 W	05:09	5.68	17:53	5.49
7 Th	06:43	5.56	19:28	5.59
8 F	08:11	5.78	20:41	5.93
9 Sa	09:15	6.10	21:36	6.29
10 Su	10:05	6.37	22:21	6.58
11 M	10:46	6.56	23:00	6.77
12 Tu	11:24	6.65	23:37	6.87
13 W	##:##	#.##	12:00	6.68
14 Th	00:14	6.87	12:35	6.63
15 F	00:48	6.78	13:09	6.51
16 Sa	01:22	6.60	13:42	6.33
17 Su	01:55	6.35	14:18	6.08
18 M	02:30	6.01	14:57	5.76
19 Tu	03:14	5.60	15:49	5.38
20 W	04:18	5.18	17:05	5.07
21 Th	05:51	4.93	18:36	5.02
22 F	07:17	5.05	19:48	5.27
23 Sa	08:18	5.36	20:42	5.64
24 Su	09:02	5.72	21:22	5.99
25 M	09:36	6.04	21:57	6.29
26 Tu	10:09	6.33	22:30	6.55
27 W	10:44	6.56	23:06	6.75
28 Th	11:21	6.73	23:42	6.88
29 F	##:##	#.##	12:00	6.79
30 Sa	00:21	6.89	12:42	6.75
31 Su	01:02	6.80	13:26	6.61

DOVER — April

Day	Morning time	m	Afternoon time	m
1 M	01:47	6.60	14:15	6.38
2 Tu	02:41	6.30	15:13	6.09
3 W	03:47	5.95	16:21	5.77
4 Th	05:05	5.64	17:44	5.57
5 F	06:40	5.68	19:14	5.66
6 Sa	08:01	5.77	20:24	5.95
7 Su	09:00	6.04	21:15	6.24
8 M	09:47	6.26	21:57	6.47
9 Tu	10:25	6.41	22:36	6.62
10 W	11:00	6.52	23:13	6.70
11 Th	11:36	6.56	23:49	6.70
12 F	##:##	#.##	12:11	6.55
13 Sa	00:24	6.61	12:45	6.47
14 Su	00:57	6.45	13:18	6.32
15 M	01:27	6.23	13:50	6.12
16 Tu	01:59	5.96	14:26	5.87
17 W	02:39	5.64	15:12	5.57
18 Th	03:35	5.30	16:15	5.28
19 F	04:54	5.06	17:35	5.15
20 Sa	06:18	5.07	18:51	5.29
21 Su	07:24	5.33	19:51	5.59
22 M	08:15	5.68	20:37	5.95
23 Tu	08:56	6.03	21:17	6.28
24 W	09:34	6.34	21:55	6.56
25 Th	10:14	6.60	22:35	6.78
26 F	10:56	6.77	23:17	6.90
27 Sa	11:40	6.83	##:##	#.##
28 Su	00:03	6.90	12:29	6.80
29 M	00:51	6.79	13:20	6.67
30 Tu	01:45	6.58	14:13	6.47

National Oceanography Centre (www.noc.ac.uk)

SUNRISE AND SUNSET TIMES FOR 2012

Predictions are given for the times of sunrise and sunset on every Saturday throughout the year. For places on the same latitude as the following, add 4 minutes for each degree of longitude west (subtract if east).

These times are in GMT, except between 01:00 on Mar 25 and 01:00 on Oct 28, when the times are in BST (1 hour in advance of GMT).

		London Rise	London Set	Manchester Rise	Manchester Set	Edinburgh Rise	Edinburgh Set
January	1	08 06	16 02	08 25	16 00	08 44	15 49
	8	08 05	16 10	08 23	16 08	08 41	15 58
	15	08 00	16 20	08 18	16 19	08 34	16 10
	22	07 53	16 31	08 10	16 31	08 25	16 24
	29	07 44	16 44	08 00	16 45	08 14	16 38
February	5	07 34	16 56	07 48	16 58	08 01	16 54
	12	07 21	17 09	07 35	17 12	07 46	17 09
	19	07 08	17 22	07 21	17 26	07 30	17 24
	26	06 54	17 35	07 05	17 40	07 13	17 39
March	4	06 39	17 47	06 49	17 53	06 56	17 54
	11	06 23	17 59	06 32	18 06	06 38	18 09
	18	06 07	18 11	06 16	18 19	06 19	18 23
	25	06 51	19 23	06 59	19 32	07 01	19 38
April	1	06 35	19 35	06 42	19 45	06 43	19 52
	8	06 20	19 46	06 25	19 58	06 24	20 06
	15	06 04	19 58	06 09	20 11	06 07	20 20
	22	05 50	20 10	05 53	20 23	05 49	20 35
	29	05 36	20 21	05 38	20 36	05 33	20 49
May	6	05 23	20 33	05 24	20 48	05 18	21 03
	13	05 11	20 44	05 11	21 00	05 03	21 16
	20	05 01	20 54	05 00	21 12	04 51	21 29
	27	04 53	21 03	04 51	21 22	04 41	21 40
June	3	04 48	21 11	04 45	21 30	04 33	21 50
	10	04 44	21 17	04 41	21 37	04 28	21 57
	17	04 43	21 21	04 39	21 41	04 26	22 02
	24	04 44	21 22	04 41	21 42	04 27	22 03

SUNRISE AND SUNSET TIMES

		London Rise	London Set	Manchester Rise	Manchester Set	Edinburgh Rise	Edinburgh Set
July	1	04 48	21 21	04 45	21 41	04 32	22 01
	8	04 54	21 17	04 51	21 37	04 39	21 56
	15	05 02	21 11	04 59	21 30	04 49	21 48
	22	05 10	21 03	05 09	21 21	05 00	21 38
	29	05 20	20 53	05 20	21 10	05 12	21 25
August	5	05 31	20 41	05 32	20 57	05 25	21 11
	12	05 42	20 28	05 44	20 43	05 39	20 56
	19	05 53	20 14	05 56	20 28	05 52	20 39
	26	06 04	19 59	06 08	20 12	06 06	20 22
September	2	06 15	19 44	06 20	19 56	06 20	20 04
	9	06 26	19 28	06 33	19 39	06 33	19 45
	16	06 38	19 12	06 45	19 22	06 47	19 27
	23	06 49	18 56	06 57	19 04	07 01	19 08
	30	07 00	18 40	07 09	18 47	07 14	18 50
October	7	07 12	18 24	07 22	18 30	07 28	18 32
	14	07 23	18 09	07 35	18 14	07 43	18 14
	21	07 36	17 54	07 48	17 58	07 57	17 57
	28	06 48	16 40	07 01	16 44	07 12	16 41
November	4	07 00	16 28	07 15	16 30	07 27	16 25
	11	07 12	16 17	07 28	16 18	07 42	16 12
	18	07 24	16 07	07 41	16 07	07 56	16 00
	25	07 36	16 00	07 53	15 59	08 10	15 50
December	2	07 46	15 54	08 04	15 53	08 22	15 43
	9	07 54	15 52	08 13	15 50	08 32	15 39
	16	08 01	15 52	08 20	15 50	08 39	15 38
	23	08 05	15 55	08 24	15 53	08 43	15 41
	30	08 06	16 01	08 25	15 58	08 44	15 47

SEA AREAS

REVISION OF SEA AREAS

On 4 February 2002, the southern boundary of areas Plymouth and Sole, and the northern boundary of areas Biscay and Finisterre were realigned along the Metarea I/II boundary at 48°27′ North. At the same time, sea area Finisterre was renamed FitzRoy.

Did you know that the FitzRoy shipping area is named after the founder of the Met Office?

THE BIRDWATCHER'S CODE OF CONDUCT

Around three million adults go birdwatching every year in the UK. Following The birdwatchers' code is good practice, common sense and will help everybody to enjoy seeing birds.

This code puts the interests of birds first, and respects other people, whether or not they are interested in birds. It applies whenever you are watching birds in the UK or abroad. Please help everybody to enjoy birdwatching by following the code, leading by example and sensitively challenging the minority of birdwatchers who behave inappropriately.

1. The interests of the birds come first
Birds respond to people in many ways, depending on the species, location and time of year.

If birds are disturbed they may keep away from their nests, leaving chicks hungry or enabling predators to take their eggs or young. During cold weather, or when migrants have just made a long flight, repeatedly disturbing birds can mean they use up vital energy that they need for feeding.

Intentionally or recklessly disturbing some birds at or near their nest is illegal in Britain.

Whether you are particularly interested in photography, bird ringing, sound-recording or birdwatching, remember to always put the interests of the birds first.

- Avoid going too close to birds or disturbing their habitats – if a bird flies away or makes repeated alarm calls, you're too close. If it leaves, you won't get a good view of it anyway.
- Stay on roads and paths where they exist and avoid disturbing habitat used by birds.
- Think about your fieldcraft. You might disturb a bird even if you are not very close, eg a flock of wading birds on the foreshore can be disturbed from a mile away if you stand on the seawall.
- Repeatedly playing a recording of bird song or calls to encourage a bird to respond can divert a territorial bird from other important duties, such as feeding its young. Never use playback to attract a species during its breeding season.

2. Be an ambassador for birdwatching
Respond positively to questions from interested passers-by. They may not be birdwatchers yet, but good views of a bird or a helpful answer may ignite a spark of interest. Your enthusiasm could start lifetime's interest in birds and a greater appreciation of wildlife and its conservation.

Consider using local services, such as pubs, restaurants, petrol stations, and public transport. Raising awareness of the benefits to local communities of trade from visiting birdwatchers may, ultimately, help the birds themselves.

3. Know the Countryside Code, and follow it
Respect the wishes of local residents and landowners and don't enter private land without permission, unless it is open for public access on foot.

Follow the codes on access and the countryside for the place you're walking in. Irresponsible behaviour may cause a land manager to deny access to others (eg for important bird survey work). It may also disturb the bird or give birdwatching bad coverage in the media.

Access to the countryside
Legislation provides access for walkers to open country in Britain, and includes measures to protect wildlife. Note that the rules and codes are different in each part of Britain, so plan ahead and make sure you know what you can do legally.

4. The law
Laws protecting birds and their habitats are the result of hard campaigning by generations of birdwatchers. We must make sure that we don't allow them to fall into disrepute. In England, Scotland and Wales, it is a criminal offence to disturb, intentionally or recklessly, at or near the nest, a species listed on Schedule 1 of the Wildlife & Countryside Act 1981 (see www.rspb.org.uk/policy/wildbirdslaw for a full list). Disturbance could include playback of songs and calls. In Scotland, disturbing Capercaillie and Ruffs at leks is also an offence. It is a criminal offence to intentionally disturb a bird at or near the nest under the Wildlife (Northern Ireland) Order 1985.

The Government can, for particular reasons such as scientific study, issue licences to individuals that permit limited disturbance, including monitoring of nests and ringing. It is a criminal offence to destroy or damage, intentionally or recklessly, a special interest feature of a Site of Special Scientific Interest (SSSI) or to disturb the wildlife for which the site was notified.

If you witness anyone who you suspect may be illegally disturbing or destroying wildlife or habitat, phone the police immediately (ideally, with a six-figure map reference) and report it to the RSPB.

5. Rare birds
Mobile phones, telephone and pager services and the internet mean you can now share your sightings instantly. If you discover a rare bird, please bear the following in mind

- Consider the potential impact of spreading the news and make an effort to inform the landowner (or, on a nature reserve, the warden) first. Think about whether the site can cope with a large number of visitors and whether sensitive species might be at risk, such as breeding terns, flocks of wading birds or rare plants. The county bird recorder or another experienced birdwatcher can often give good advice.
- On private land, always talk to the landowner first. With a little planning, access can often be arranged.
- People coming to see a rare bird can raise money for a local reserve, other wildlife project or charity. Consider organising a voluntary collection at access points to the site.
- Rare breeding birds are at risk from egg-collectors and some birds of prey from persecution. If you discover a rare breeding species that you think is vulnerable, contact the RSPB; it has considerable experience in protecting rare breeding birds. Please also report your sighting to the county bird recorder or the Rare Breeding Birds Panel. (www.rbbp.org.uk). Also, consider telling the landowner – in most cases, this will ensure that the nest is not disturbed accidentally. If you have the opportunity to see a rare bird, enjoy it, but don't let your enthusiasm override common sense.

323

THE BIRDWATCHER'S CODE OF CONDUCT

In addition to the guidelines above:
• park sensibly, follow instructions and consider making a donation if requested
• don't get too close so that you can take a photograph – you'll incur the wrath of everyone else watching if you scare the bird away
• be patient if the viewing is limited, talk quietly and give others a chance to see the bird too
• do not enter private areas without permission
• not everyone likes to see an 'organised flush' and it should never be done in important wildlife habitats or where there are other nesting or roosting birds nearby. A flush should not be organised more frequently than every two hours and not within two hours of sunrise or sunset, so the bird has chance to feed and rest.

6. Make your sightings count
Add to tomorrow's knowledge of birds by sending your sightings to www.birdtrack.net This online recording scheme from the BTO, the RSPB and BirdWatch Ireland

allows you to input and store all of your birdwatching records, which in turn helps to support species and site conservation. With one click, you can also have your records forwarded automatically to the relevant county recorder.

County recorders and local bird clubs are the mainstay of bird recording in the UK. Your records are important for local conservation and help to build the county's ornithological history. For a list of county bird recorders, look in the County Directory of *The Yearbook*, ask at your local library, or visit www.britishbirds.co.uk/countyrecorders

You can also get involved in a UK-wide bird monitoring scheme, such as the Breeding Bird Survey and the Wetland Bird Survey (see www.bto.org for details). If you've been birdwatching abroad, you can give your sightings to the BirdLife International Partner in that country by visiting www.worldbirds.org Your data could be vital in helping to protect sites and species in the country you've visited.

SCHEDULE 1 SPECIES

Under the provisions of the Wildlife and Countryside Act 1981 the following bird species (listed in Schedule 1 - Part I of the Act) are protected by special penalties at all times.

Avocet	Falcon, Gyr	Owl, Barn	Shrike, Red-backed
Bee-eater	Fieldfare	Owl, Snowy	Spoonbill
Bittem	Firecrest	Peregrine	Stilt, Black-winged
Bittern, Little	Garganey	Petrel, Leach's	Stint, Temminck's
Bluethroat	Godwit, Black-tailed	Phalarope, Red-necked	Swan, Bewick's
Brambling	Goshawk	Plover, Kentish	Swan, Whooper
Bunting, Cirl	Grebe, Black-necked	Plover, Little Ringed	Tern, Black
Bunting, Lapland	Grebe, Slavonian	Quail, Common	Tern, Little
Bunting, Snow	Greenshank	Redstart, Black	Tern, Roseate
Buzzard, Honey	Gull, Little	Redwing	Tit, Bearded
Chough	Gull, Mediterranean	Rosefinch, Scarlet	Tit, Crested
Corncrake	Harriers (all species)	Ruff	Treecreeper, Short-toed
Crake, Spotted	Heron, Purple	Sandpiper, Green	Warbler, Cetti's
Crossbills (all species)	Hobby	Sandpiper, Purple	Warbler, Dartford
Stone-curlew	Hoopoe	Sandpiper, Wood	Warbler, Marsh
Divers (all species)	Kingfisher	Scaup	Warbler, Savi's
Dotterel	Kite, Red	Scoter, Common	Whimbrel
Duck, Long-tailed	Merlin	Scoter, Velvet	Woodlark
Eagle, Golden	Oriole, Golden	Serin	Wryneck
Eagle, White-tailed	Osprey	Shorelark	

The following birds and their eggs (listed in Schedule 1 - Part II of the Act) are protected by special penalties during the close season, which is Feb 1 to Aug 31 (Feb 21 to Aug 31 below high water mark), but may be killed outside this period - Goldeneye, Greylag Goose (in Outer Hebrides, Caithness, Sutherland, and Wester Ross only), Pintail.

THE COUNTRYSIDE CODE

Launched on 12 July 2004, this Code for England has been produced through a partnership between the Countryside Agency and Countryside Council for Wales.

The Countryside Code has been revised and re-launched to reflect the introduction of new open access rights (Countryside & Rights of Way Act 2000) and changes in society over the last 20 years.

● Be safe – plan ahead
Follow any signs, even when going out locally, it's best to get the latest information about where and when you can go; for example, your rights to go onto some areas of open land may be restricted while work is carried out, for safety reasons or during breeding seasons. Follow advice and local signs, and be prepared for the unexpected.

● Leave gates and property as you find them
Please respect the working life of the countryside, as our actions can affect people's livelihoods, our heritage, and the safety and welfare of animals and ourselves.

● Protect plants and animals, and take your litter home
We have a responsibility to protect our countryside now and for future generations,

so make sure you don't harm animals, birds, plants, or trees.

● Keep dogs under close control

The countryside is a great place to exercise dogs, but it's every owner's duty to make sure their dog is not a danger or nuisance to farm animals, wildlife or other people.

● Consider other people
Showing consideration and respect for other people makes the countryside a pleasant Environment for everyone – at home, at work and at leisure.

BIRDLINE NUMBERS - National and Regional

Birdline name	To obtain information	To report sightings (hotlines)
National		
Bird Information Service www.birdingworld.co.uk	09068 700 222	
Flightline (Northern Ireland)	028 9146 7408	
Regional		
Northern Ireland	028 9146 7408	
Scotland	09068 700 234	01292 611 994
Wales	09068 700 248	01492 544 588
East Anglia	09068 700 245	07941 333 970
Midlands	09068 700 247	01905 754 154
North East	09068 700 246	07974 358 988
North West	09068 700 249	01492 544 588
South East www.southeastbirdnews.co.uk	09068 700 240	01845 570 444 or 08000 377 240
South West	09068 700 241	0845 4567 938

Charges
At the time of compilation, calls to premium line numbers cost 60p per minute.

INDEX TO RESERVES

INDEX TO RESERVES

QUICK REFERENCE

327

INDEX TO RESERVES